SOLIDWORKS 2016

Intermediate Skills

Multibody Solids, Surfaces & Patches, Lofts & Boundaries, Bottom Up vs. Top Down Assemblies, Sheet Metal & Revolved & Threaded Parts, Drawings & BOMs, Configure Features & Design Tables.

Written by: Sr. Certified SolidWorks Instructor
Paul Tran, CSWE, CSWI

SDC Publications
P.O. Box 1334
Mission, KS 66222
913-262-2664
www.SDCpublications.com
Publisher: Stephen Schroff

ISBN-13: 978-1-63057-016-3
ISBN-10: 1-63057-016-8

Printed and bound in the United States of America.

Acknowledgments

Thanks as always to my wife Vivian and my daughter Lani for always being there and providing support and honest feedback on all the chapters in the textbook.

I would like to give a special thanks to Karla Werner and Rachel Schroff for their editing and corrections. Additionally thanks to Jennifer Douglas for writing the forewords.

I also have to thank SDC Publications and the staff for their continuing encouragement and support for this edition of **SOLIDWORKS 2016 Intermediate Skills**. Thanks also to Zach Werner for putting together such a beautiful cover design.

Finally, I would like to thank you, our readers, for your continued support. It is with your consistent feedback that we were able to create the lessons and exercises in this book with more detailed and useful information.

Preface

Paul Tran and I met professionally 20 years ago.

I have learned through the years that Paul has a unique ability to deeply understand technical concepts, along with a passion to help students learn—I marvel at his ability to combine these talents.

It takes an exceptional person to get students to learn technical skills quickly, especially when these skills are directly tied to career success. Time and time again, when students return to take additional classes, they specifically request Paul for their instructor. That kind of endorsement speaks for itself.

His commitment to help others improve their technical skills runs deep and seems without end as evidenced by this latest book *SOLIDWORKS 2016 Intermediate Skills*. The lessons and exercises in Paul's books are based on the real world projects. The lectures and delivery methods are extremely easy to follow. Literally anyone can learn SOLIDWORKS from his books.

Besides more than the 9,000 engineering professionals that have been trained by Paul, there are nearly 600 schools (high schools, colleges, universities, and other technical institutions) that have adopted Paul's books to teach on the subject of SOLIDWORKS.

Paul's 30 years of experience in the fields of mechanical and manufacturing engineering, along with 20 years teaching and supporting SOLIDWORKS, make him a trusted partner. But beyond all that, Paul has become our friend.

Myself and many others at GoEngineer feel privileged to work with Paul. He's been a mentor for other trainers and aspiring authors, and we could not be more grateful that he's chosen to commit so much of his training time and talent to us—our customers do have the best in the business.

To all of those wanting to take your SOLIDWORKS skills to the next level, you are in good hands!

Jennifer Douglas
Vice President Marketing, GoEngineer

Foreword

I first met Paul Tran when I was busy creating another challenge in my life. I needed to take a vision from one man's mind, understand what the vision looked like, how it was going to work and comprehend the scale of his idea. My challenge was I was missing one very important ingredient, a tool that would create a picture with all the moving parts.

Research led me to discover a great tool, SOLIDWORKS. It claimed to allow one to make 3D components, in picture quality, on a computer, add in all moving parts, assemble it and make it run, all before money was spent on bending steel and buying parts that may not fit together. I needed to design and build a product with thousands of parts, make them all fit and work in harmony with tight tolerances. The possible cost implications of failed experimentation were daunting.

To my good fortune, one company's marketing strategy of selling a product without an instruction manual and requiring one to attend an instructional class to get it, led me to meet a communicator who made it all seem so simple.

Paul Tran has worked with and taught SOLIDWORKS as his profession for 30 years. Paul knows the SOLIDWORKS product and manipulates it like a fine musical instrument. I watched Paul explain the unexplainable to baffled students with great skill and clarity. He taught me how to navigate the intricacies of the product so that I could use it as a communication tool with skilled engineers. ***He teaches the teachers***.

I hired Paul as a design engineering consultant to create the thousands of parts for my company's product. Paul Tran's knowledge and teaching skills have added immeasurable value to my company. When I read through the pages of these manuals, I now have an "instant replay" of his communication skill with the clarity of having him looking over my shoulder - ***continuously***. We can now design, prove and build our product and know it will always work and not fail. Most important of all, Paul Tran helped me turn a blind man's vision into reality and a monument to his dream.

Thanks Paul.

These books will make dreams come true and help visionaries change the world.

Peter J. Douglas

CEO, Cake Energy, LLC

CAKE
A New Movement In Energy

Images courtesy of C.A.K.E. Energy Corp., designed by Paul Tran

Author's Note

SOLIDWORKS 2016 Basic Tools, Intermediate Skills, and Advanced Techniques are comprised of lessons and exercises based on the author's extensive knowledge on this software. Paul has 30 years of experience in the fields of mechanical and manufacturing engineering; 20 years were in teaching and supporting the SOLIDWORKS software and its add-ins. As an active Senior SOLIDWORKS instructor and design engineer, Paul has worked and consulted with hundreds of reputable companies including; IBM, Intel, NASA, US-Navy, Boeing, Disneyland, Medtronic, Terumo, Toyota, Kingston and many more. Today, he has trained nearly 9,000 engineering professionals, and given guidance to nearly half of the number of Certified SOLIDWORKS Professionals and Certified SOLIDWORKS Expert (CSWP & CSWE) in the state of California.

Every lesson and exercise in this book was created based on real world projects. Each of these projects have been broken down and developed into easy and comprehendible steps for the reader. Learn the fundamentals of SOLIDWORKS at your own pace, as you progress from simple to more complex design challenges. Furthermore, at the end of every chapter, there are self test questionnaires to ensure that the reader has gained sufficient knowledge from each section before moving on to more advanced lessons.

Paul believes that the most effective way to learn the "world's most sophisticated software" is to learn it inside and out, create everything from the beginning, and take it step by step. This is what the **SOLIDWORKS 2016 Basic Tools, Intermediate Skills, and Advanced Techniques** manuals are all about.

About the Training Files

The files for this textbook are available for download on the publisher's website at **www.SDCpublications.com/downloads/978-1-63057-016-3**. They are organized by the chapter numbers and the file names that are normally mentioned at the beginning of each chapter or exercise. In the <u>Built Parts folder</u> you will also find copies of the parts, assemblies, and drawings that were created for cross references or reviewing purposes.

It would be best to make a copy of the content to your local hard drive and work from these documents; you can always go back to the original training files location at anytime in the future, if needed.

Who this book is for

This book is for the mid-level user, who is already familiar with the SOLIDWORKS program. It is also a great resource for the more CAD literate individuals who want to expand their knowledge of the different features that SOLIDWORKS 2016 has to offer.

The organization of the book

The chapters in this book are organized in the logical order in which you would learn the SOLIDWORKS 2016 program. Each chapter will guide you through different tasks, from navigating through the user interface, to exploring the toolbars, from some simple 3D modeling to more complex tasks that are common to all SOLIDWORKS releases. There is also a self-test questionnaire at the end of each chapter to ensure that you have gained sufficient knowledge before moving on to the next chapter.

The conventions in this book

This book uses the following conventions to describe the actions you perform when using the keyboard and mouse to work in SOLIDWORKS 2016:

Click: means to press and release the left mouse button. A click of a mouse button is used to select a command or an item on the screen.

Double Click: means to quickly press and release the left mouse button twice. A double mouse click is used to open a program or to show the dimensions of a feature.

Right Click: means to press and release the right mouse button. A right mouse click is used to display a list of commands, a list of shortcuts that is related to the selected item.

Click and Drag: means to position the mouse cursor over an item on the screen, then press and hold down the left mouse button; still holding down the left button, move the mouse to the new destination and release the mouse button. Drag and drop makes it easy to move things around within a SOLIDWORKS document.

Bolded words: indicates the action items that you need to perform.

Italic words: Side notes are tips that give you additional information, or explain special conditions that may occur during the course of the task.

Numbered Steps: indicate that you should follow these steps in order to successfully perform the task.

Icons: indicate the buttons or commands that you need to press.

SOLIDWORKS 2016

SOLIDWORKS 2016 is a program suite, or a collection of engineering programs that can help you design better products faster. SOLIDWORKS 2016 contains different combinations of programs; some of the programs used in this book may not be available in your suites.

Start and exit SOLIDWORKS

SOLIDWORKS allows you to start its program in several ways. You can either double click on its shortcut icon on the desktop, or go to the Start menu and select the following: All Programs / SOLIDWORKS 2016 / SOLIDWORKS, or drag a SOLIDWORKS document and drop it on the SOLIDWORKS shortcut icon.

Before exiting SOLIDWORKS, be sure to save any open documents, and then click File / Exit. You can also click the X button on the top right of your screen to exit the program.

Using the Toolbars

You can use toolbars to select commands in SOLIDWORKS rather than using the drop down menus. Using the toolbars is normally faster. The toolbars come with commonly used commands in SOLIDWORKS, but they can be customized to help you work more efficiently.

To access the toolbars, either right click in an empty spot on the top right of your screen or select View / Toolbars.

To customize the toolbars, select Tools / Customize. When the dialog pops up, click on the Commands tab, select a Category, then drag an icon out of the dialog box and drop it on a toolbar that you want to customize. To remove an icon from a toolbar, drag an icon out of the toolbar and drop it into the dialog box.

Using the task pane

The task pane is normally kept on the right side of your screen. It displays various options like SOLIDWORKS resources, Design Library, File Explorer, Search, View Palette, Appearances and Scenes, Custom Properties, Built-in Libraries, Technical Alerts and News, etc.

The task pane provides quick access to any of the mentioned items by offering the drag and drop function to all of its contents. You can see a large preview of a SOLIDWORKS document before opening it. New documents can be saved in the task pane at anytime, and existing documents can also be edited and re-saved. The task pane can be resized, closed or moved to different locations on your screen if needed.

Table of Contents

Copyright
Disclaimer
Trademarks

Introduction: **SOLIDWORKS 2016 User Interface** **XIX**

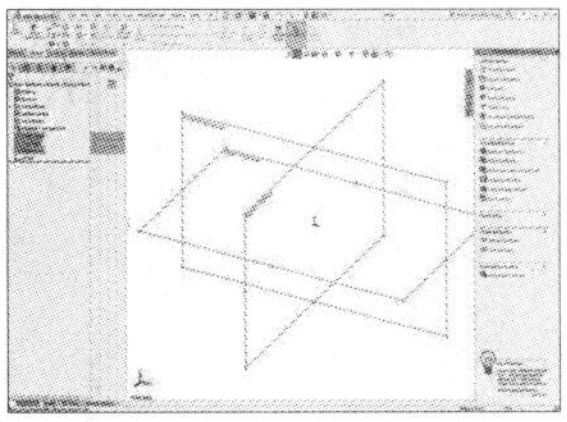

The 3 references planes XX
The toolbars XX
The system feedback symbols XXII
The status bar XXII
2D sketch examples XXIII
3D feature examples XXIV

Chapter 1: **Document Properties** **1-1**

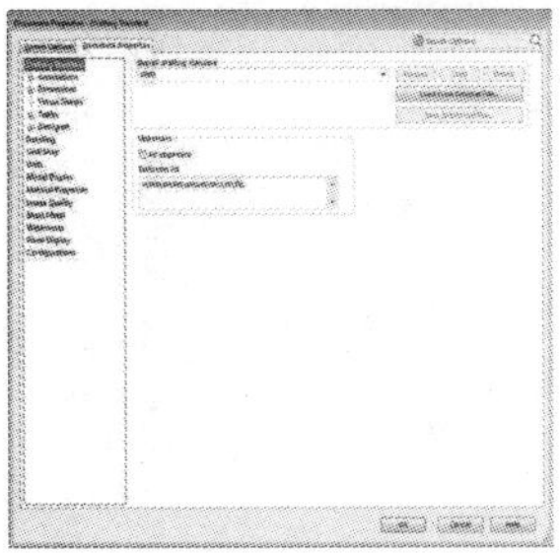

Lesson Overview 1-1
Different standards in the world 1-2
Starting a new part document 1-3
Setting the ANSI drafting standards 1-3
Setting the dimension options 1-4
Setting the virtual sharp options 1-5
Setting the units options 1-5
Setting the image quality options 1-6
Saving the settings as a Part Template 1-6
Customizing Keyboard Shortcuts 1-7
Customizing Tool Buttons 1-12

Chapter 2: **Sketching** **2-1**

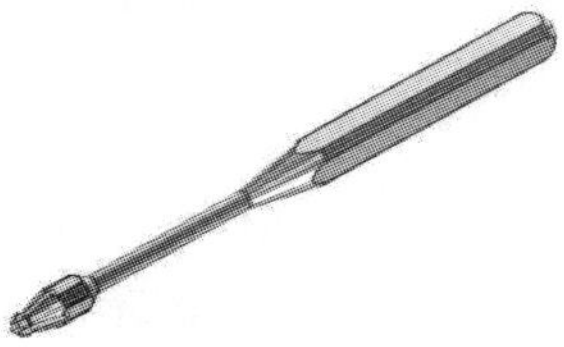

Lesson Overview 2-1
Tools needed 2-2
Starting a new part document 2-3
Changing the system options 2-3
Creating the parent sketch 2-4
Sketching with the line tool 2-5
Adding the smart dimensions 2-6
Revolving the parent sketch 2-7

	Adding the tip detail	2-7
	Revolving the sketch	2-8
	Transitioning from line-to-arc	2-8
	Mirroring in sketch mode	2-8
	Adding dimensions	2-9
	Extruding a cut	2-10
	Using through all type	2-10
	Creating a circular pattern	2-11
	Entering the pattern parameters	2-11
	Adding other cut features	2-12
	Creating another circular pattern	2-13
	Adding constant size fillets	2-14
	Assigning material to the model	2-15
	Calculating the mass of the model	2-16
	Saving your work	2-16
Chapter 3:	**Creating Multibody Parts**	**3-1**
	Lesson overview	3-1
	Tools needed	3-2
	Starting a new part document	3-3
	Sketching the first body profile	3-4
	Starting a new sketch	3-4
	Adding dimensions	3-4
	Sketch a straight slot	3-5
	Extruding the solid body	3-6
	Copying a solid body	3-6
	Creating the second body	3-7
	Patterning a solid body	3-9
	Mirroring the solid bodies	3-10
	Creating the third solid body	3-11
	Patterning a solid body	3-12
	Creating an exploded view	3-13
	Collapsing the view	3-15
Chapter 4:	**Working with Multibody Parts**	**4-1**
	Lesson overview	4-1
	Tools needed	4-2
	Opening a part document	4-3
	Creating an exploded view	4-4
	Selection box	4-5
	Collapsing the solid bodies	4-6

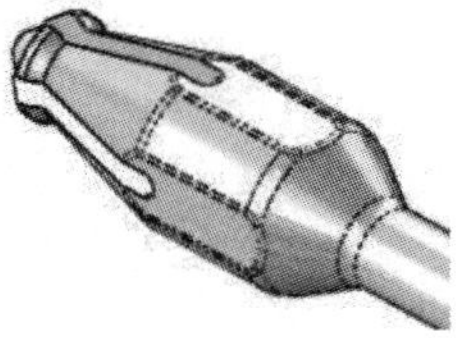
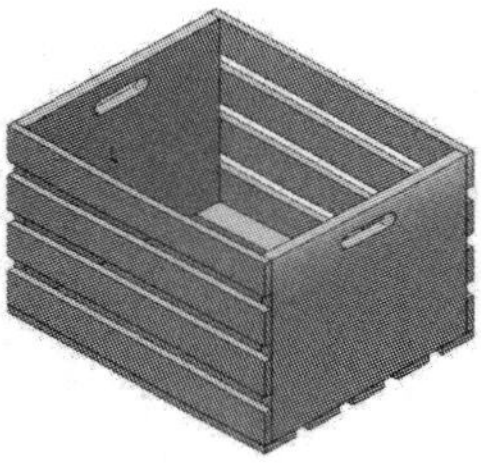

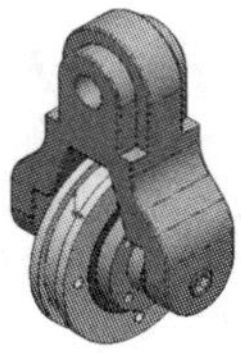

Inserting another part 4-7
Locating part 4-8
Adding a concentric mate 4-8
Adding a coincident mate 4-9
Making a new plane 4-10
Mirroring the solid body 4-11
Editing the exploded view 4-11
Splitting the feature tree 4-12
Insert another part 4-13
Adding more mates 4-14
Editing the exploded view 4-16
Drag with the triad 4-17

Chapter 5: Revolved & Thread Features 5-1
Lesson overview 5-1
Tools needed 5-2
Opening a part document 5-3
Creating a revolved feature 5-3
Adding chamfers 5-4
Creating the mounting holes 5-4
Using the circular sketch pattern 5-5
Creating the cut extrude 5-6
Adding threads 5-7
Entering the thread parameters 5-8
Adding threads to the opposite side 5-9
Creating a zonal section view 5-11

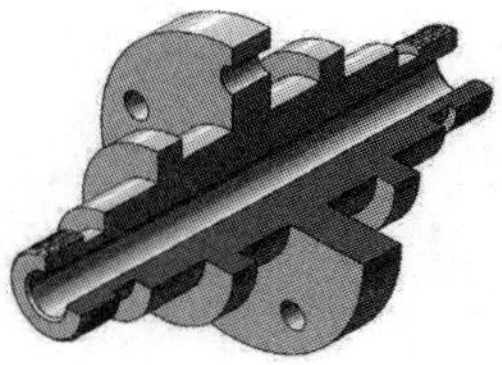

Chapter 6: Flex Bending 6-1
Lesson overview 6-1
Tools needed 6-2
Flex Bending - Part 1 6-3
Creating the 1st flex bending 6-3
Using the triad 6-3
Bending up 45 degrees 6-4
Viewing the flex options 6-4
Creating the 2nd flex bending 6-5
Bending down 45 degrees 6-5
Flex examples 6-6
Flex twisting 6-7
Flex stretching 6-7
Flex tapering 6-8

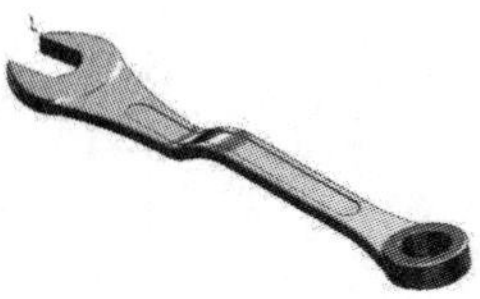

Flex bending 6-8
Flex Bending - Part 2 6-9
Creating a flex bending feature 6-9
Bending at 359.9 degrees 6-9
Creating a linear pattern 6-10
Combining the bodies 6-10

Chapter 7: Sweep with Guide Curves 7-1
Lesson overview 7-1
Tools needed 7-2
Opening a part document 7-3
Creating the main body with sweep 7-3
Selecting the sweep profile 7-3
Selecting the sweep path 7-3
Viewing the sweep sections 7-4
Creating the 1st split line 7-5
Creating a face fillet 7-6
Using the hold line 7-6
Creating the 2nd split line 7-7
Making an offset surface 7-8
Creating a ruled surface 7-8
Knitting the surfaces 7-9
Adding fillets 7-9
Creating a surface cut 7-10
Shelling a solid model 7-11
Adding a revolved neck 7-15
Creating a new plane 7-16
Making a helix-spiral 7-17
Sketching the thread profile 7-18
Sweeping the threads 7-19
Rounding off the ends of threads 7-19

Chapter 8: Lofts and Boundaries 8-1
Lesson overview 8-1
Tools needed 8-2
Opening a part document 8-3
Creating a lofted feature 8-3
Selecting the loft profiles 8-4
Using the selection manager 8-4
Selecting the guide curves 8-4
Previewing the lofted feature 8-4

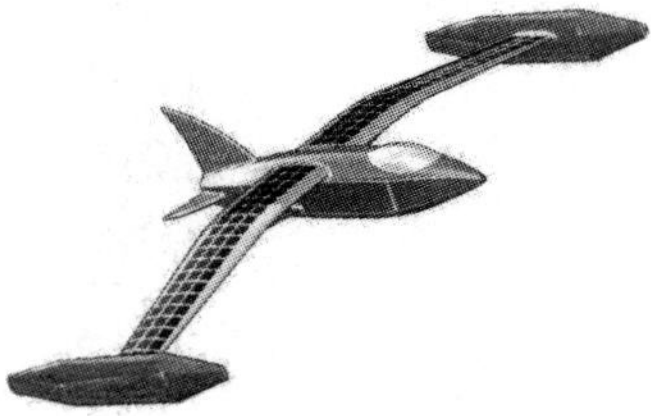

Creating the boundary feature 8-5
    Selecting the direction 1 profiles 8-5
    Selecting the direction 2 profiles 8-5
    Previewing the boundary feature 8-5
Creating the wing with loft 8-6
Creating the wing support with sweep 8-7
Constructing the nose feature 8-8
Loft and boundary comparison 8-10
Creating the horizontal tail fins 8-11
Creating the vertical tail fin 8-12
Constructing the canopy 8-13
Mirroring the solid features 8-17
Adding fillets 8-18
Creating the solar panels 8-21
    Changing color of a feature 8-22
    Changing the edge display 8-23

Chapter 9: **Surfaces & Patches** **9-1**
Lesson overview 9-1
Tools needed 9-2
Opening a part document 9-3
Creating a swept surface 9-3
    Selecting the sweep profile 9-3
    Selecting the sweep path 9-3
Creating an extruded surface 9-4
Creating a standard trimmed surface 9-5
    Using the keep option 9-6
Creating a mutual trimmed surface 9-7
Constructing a lofted surface 9-9
Constructing a boundary surface 9-10
Constructing a filled surface 9-12
Creating a face fillet 9-14
Knitting all surfaces 9-15
Thickening the surface model 9-16
Creating a section view 9-17
Changing the edge display 9-18

Chapter 10: **Configure Features** **10-1**
Lesson overview 10-1
Tools needed 10-2

Opening a part document 10-3
Configuring features 10-3
    Understanding the configuration dialog 10-4
    Adding columns 10-4
    Saving the table 10-5
Adding new configurations 10-5
Viewing configurations 10-6
Renaming the configurations 10-9
Inserting a design table 10-10
    Viewing configurations in MS-Excel 10-11
    Adding a material column 10-11
Viewing new configurations in SOLIDWORKS 10-14

Chapter 11: Assembly Motions & Mates 11-1
Lesson overview 11-1
Tools needed 11-2
Opening an assembly document 11-3
Adding advanced mates 11-3
    Adding a width mate 11-3
    Adding a concentric mate 11-4
    Testing the assembly motions 11-6
Testing the mates 11-4
    Adding a limit-angle mate 11-7
    Adding a parallel mate 11-8
    Adding a gear mate 11-9
Making the sub assembly flexible 11-9
Testing the assembly motions 11-10

Radial Explode 11-11
Lesson overview 11-11
Opening an assembly document 11-11
Creating the 1st pattern driven component pattern 11-12
    Selecting the pattern component 10-12
    Selecting the driving pattern 11-12
Creating the 2nd pattern driven component pattern 11-12
Creating the 1st radial exploded view 11-13
Creating the 2nd radial exploded view 11-13
Changing to the configuration tree 11-14
    Viewing the exploded view 11-14
    Switching between the configurations 11-14

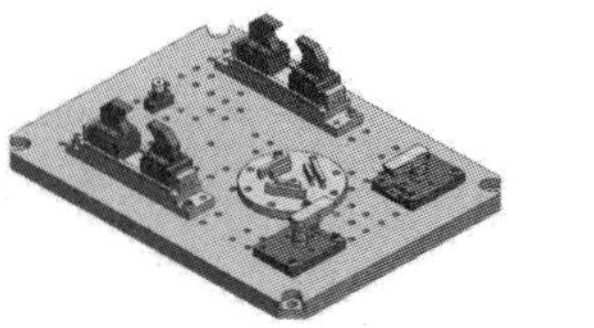

	Collapsing the exploded view	11-14
	Saving the document as a copy	11-14
Chapter 12	**Using Smart-Mates**	**12-1**
	Using Smart-Mates	12-2
	Enabling the selection options	12-3
	Exploring the Smart-Mate options	12-4
	Checking the status of a component	12-9
	Switching configuration	12-9
Chapter 13:	**Top-Down Assembly**	**13-1**
	Lesson overview	13-1
	Tools Needed	13-2
	Opening a part document	13-3
	Making an assembly from part	13-3
	Placing the 1st component	13-4
	Creating a new part	13-4
	Converting the entities	13-5
	Extruding the sketch	13-6
	Adding fillets	13-6
	Shelling the part	13-7
	Hiding the component	13-7
	Adding more features	13-8
	Creating offset entities	13-9
	Showing the component	13-11
	Creating a section view	13-11
	Applying the dimension changes	13-12
	Rebuilding the components	13-13
	Creating an exploded view	13-14
	Playing the animation	13-15
	Looping the animation	13-15
	Changing the display mode	13-16
Chapter 14	**Using the Lip & Groove Option**	**14-1**
	Lesson overview	14-1
	Opening an assembly document	14-4
	Editing the housing	14-4
	Adding the lip & Groove feature	14-5
	Selecting the lip details	14-6
	Selecting the groove details	14-6

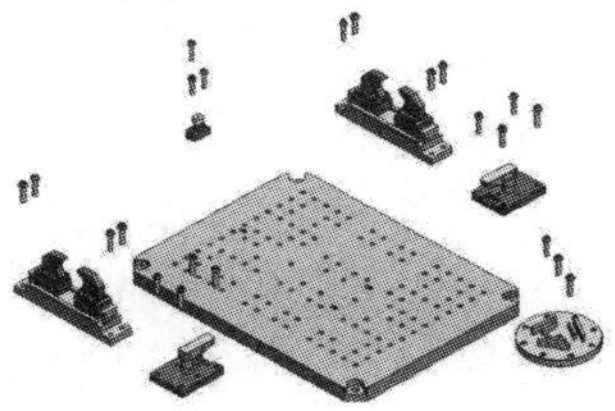

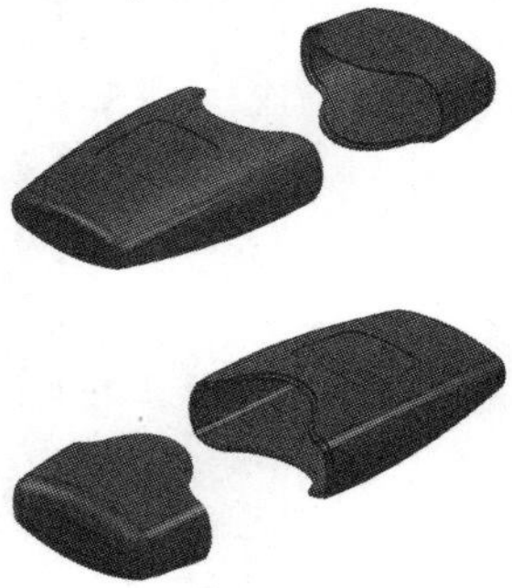

Creating a section view 14-7
Exiting the edit part mode 14-7

Using the Mounting Boss Options **14-8**
Lesson overview 14-8
Editing component 14-9
Adding a mounting boss 14-10
Selecting the mounting reference geometry 14-10
Adding more mounting bosses 14-11
Toggling between Explode & collapse views 14-12
Selecting the mating references 14-13
Creating a section view 14-14

Chapter 15: **Assembly Drawings & BOM** **15-1**
Lesson overview 15-1
Tools needed 15-2
Starting a new drawing 15-3
Selecting the ANSI sheet size 15-3
Setting the type of projection 15-3
Setting the scale 15-3
Switching to IPS unit 15-4
Using the view palette 15-5
Drag & drop from the palette 15-5
Inserting a bill of materials 15-6
Select the BOM parameters 15-6
Placing the BOM 15-7
Modifying the BOM 15-8
Customizing the columns 15-9
Changing the color of the paper 15-10
Adding balloons 15-11
Adding an isometric view 15-12
Changing the display style 15-13
Editing the sheet format 15-13
Filling out the title block information 15-14
Linking notes 15-15
Editing the sheet 15-16
Reference reading GD&T 15-18
Form examples 15-18
Orientation examples 15-19
Profile examples 15-19

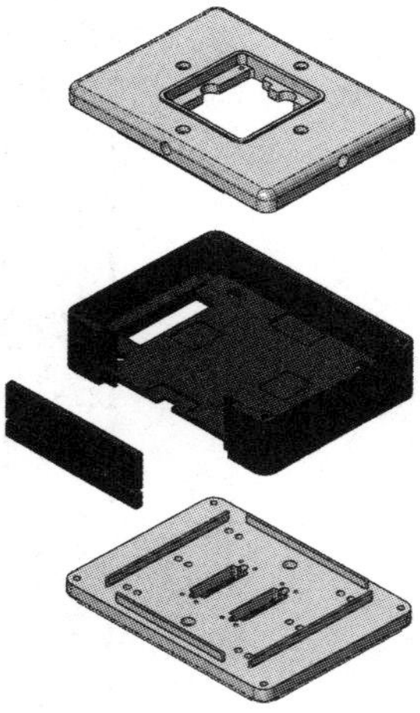

Runout examples 15-20
Location examples 15-20
ASME – Y14.5 Symbols description 15-22
Feature control frames 15-25
MMC maximum material condition 15-26
LMC least material condition 15-26

Chapter 16: **Drawings & Detailing** **16-1**
Lesson overview 16-1
Tools needed 16-2
Making drawing from part 16-3
Selecting the ANSI sheet size 16-3
Creating the drawings views 16-4
Changing the line styles 16-6
Creating a partial section 16-7
Flipping the section direction 16-8
Changing the hatch pattern 16-8
Creating a detail view 16-9
Inserting the model dimensions 16-10
Cleaning up the dimensions 16-11
Adding annotations 16-12
Breaking the view alignments 16-13
Creating a projected view 16-14
Adding the centerline symbols 16-15
Adding datums 16-16
Adding a flatness tolerance 16-18
Adding a perpendicular tolerance 16-19
Copying the control frame 16-20
Modifying the tolerance 16-21
Adding a position tolerance 16-22
Adding a symmetric tolerance 16-23
Adding a bilateral tolerance 16-23
Adding a limit tolerance 16-24
Adding a basic tolerance 16-24
Adding general notes 16-25
Filling out the title block information 16-26
Using the 3D drawing view command 16-28

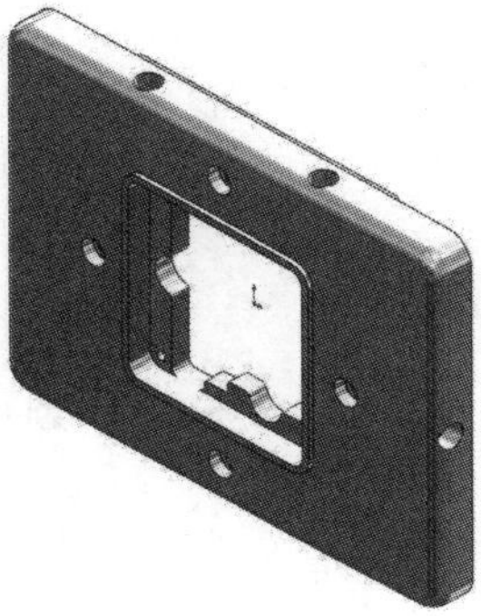

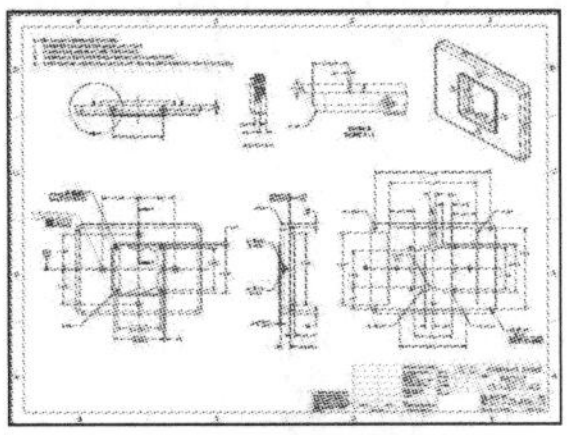

Chapter 17: **Sheet Metal Parts** **17-1**
Lesson overview 17-1
Tools needed 17-2

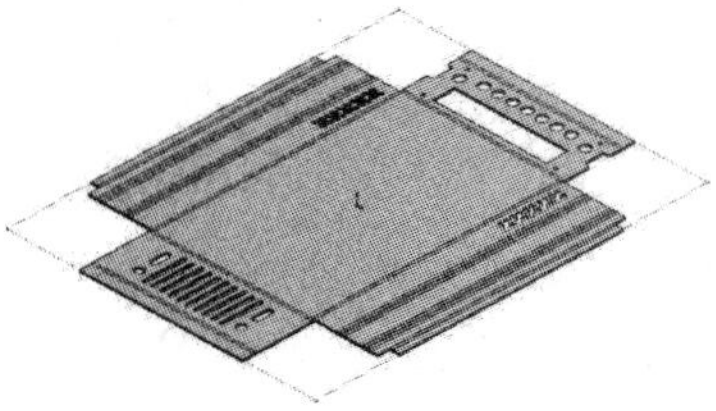

Staring a new part document	17-3
Creating the Base sketch	17-3
Making the base flange	17-4
Entering the sheet metal parameters	17-4
Creating a sheet metal cut feature	17-5
Creating an edge flange	17-6
Entering the edges flange references	17-6
Editing the flange profile	17-7
Copying and pasting a sketch	17-11
Fully defining the sketch	17-12
Creating more cuts	17-13
Adding a library feature cut	17-15
Editing the feature's sketch	17-15
Mirroring the library feature	17-17
Toggling the flat display	17-18
Creating the flat pattern	17-19
Accessing the sheet metal properties	17-20
Viewing the cut list information	17-20

Glossary

Index

SOLIDWORKS 2016 Quick-Guides:

Quick Reference Guide to SOLIDWORKS 2016 Command Icons and Toolbars.

Introduction

SOLIDWORKS User Interface

The SOLIDWORKS 2016 User Interface

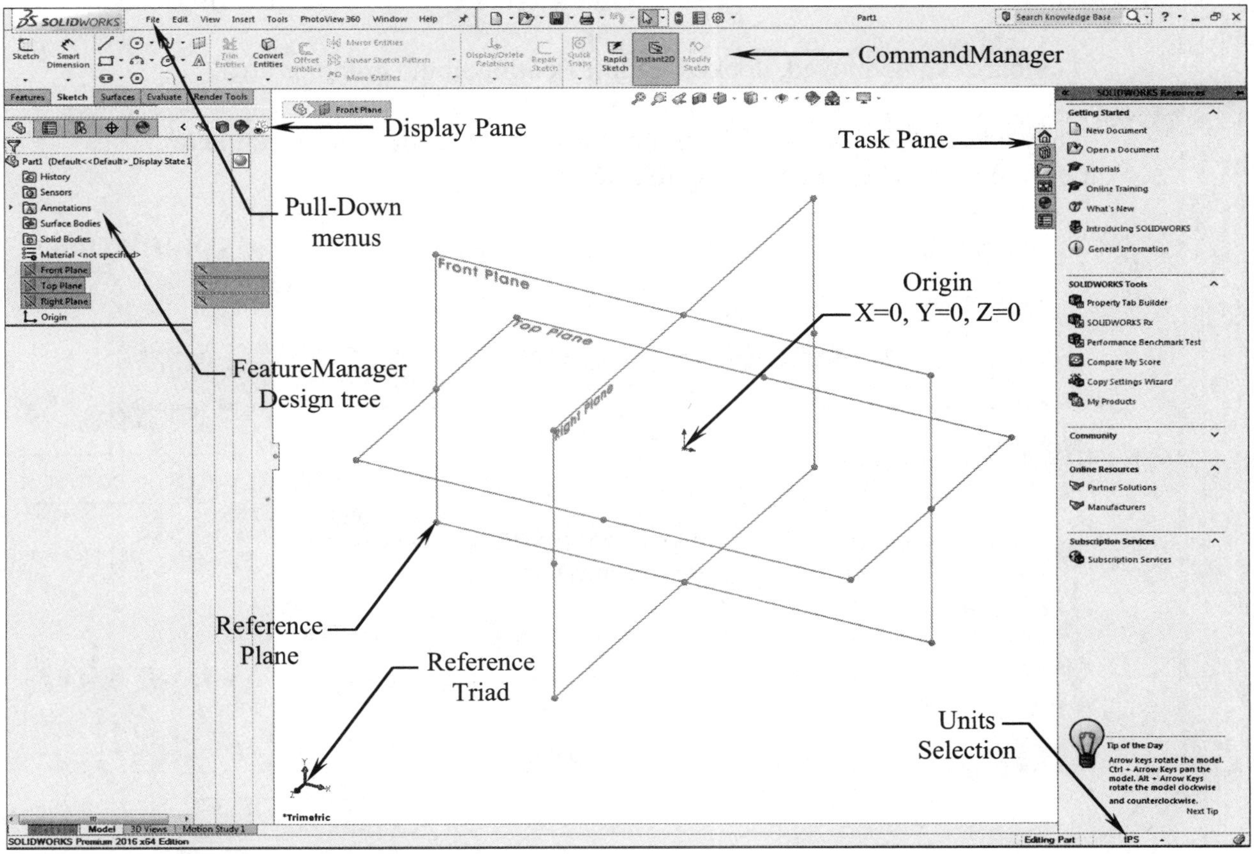

The 3 reference planes:

- The Front, Top and the Right plane are 90° apart. They share the same center point called the Origin.

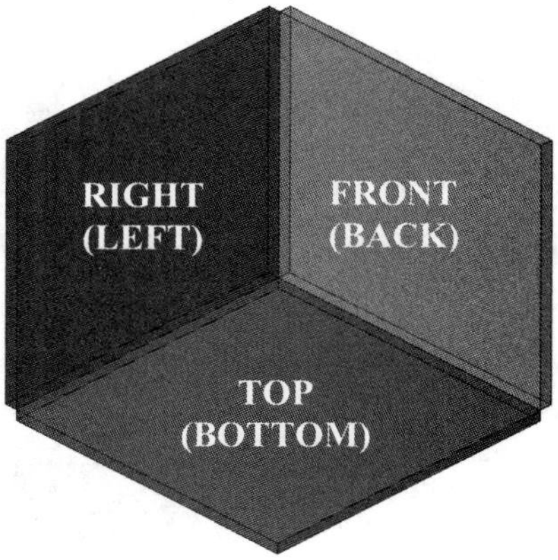

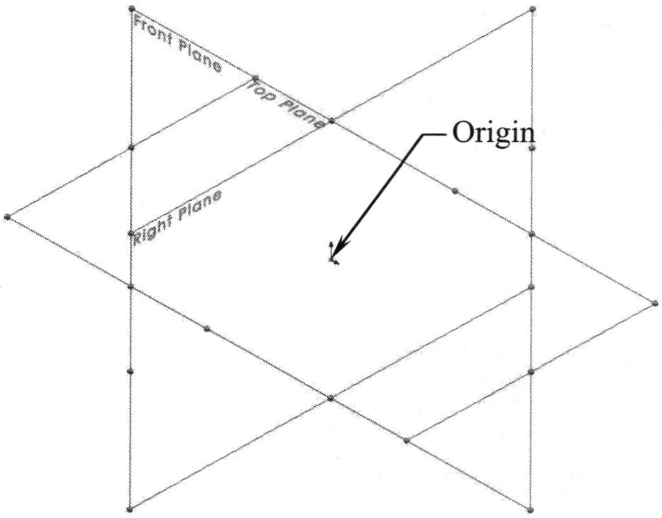

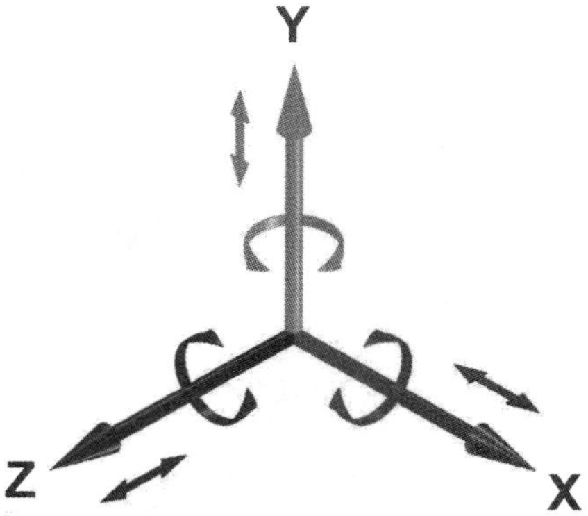

6 Degrees of Freedom

The Toolbars:

- Toolbars can be moved, docked, or left floating in the graphics area.

- They can also be "shaped" from horizontal to vertical, or from single to multiple rows when dragging on their corners.

- The CommandManager is recommended for the newer releases of SOLIDWORKS.

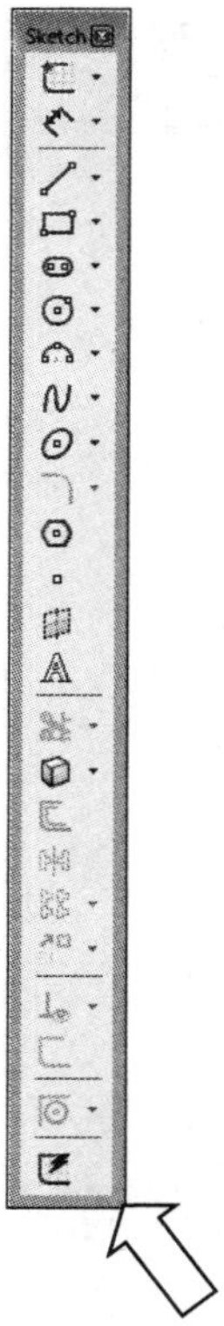

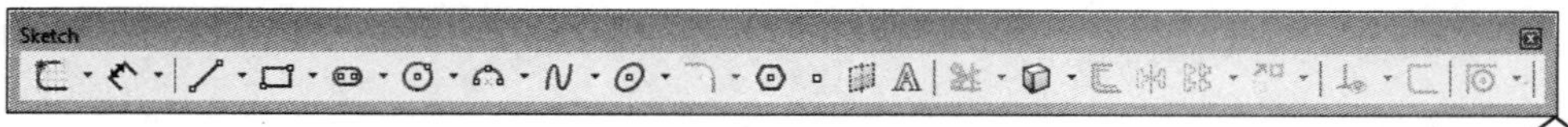

Drag corner

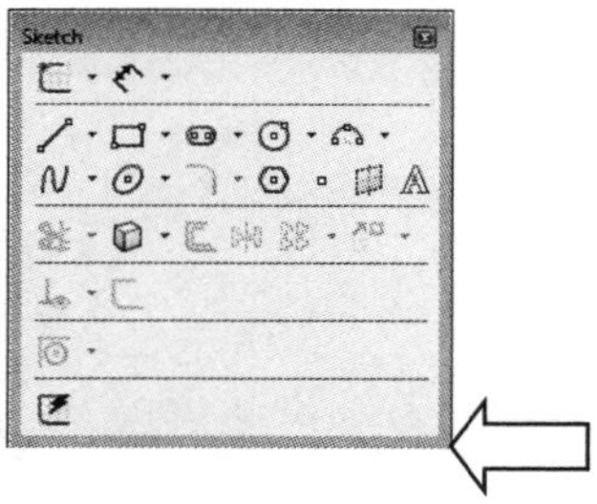

Right click in this area to access the CommandManager

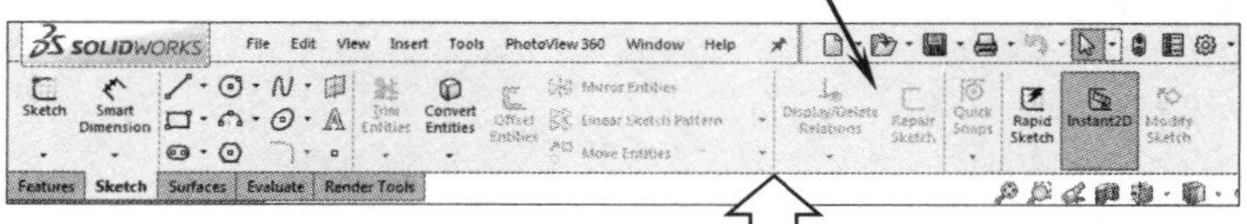

CommandManager

- If the CommandManager is not used, toolbars can be docked or left floating.

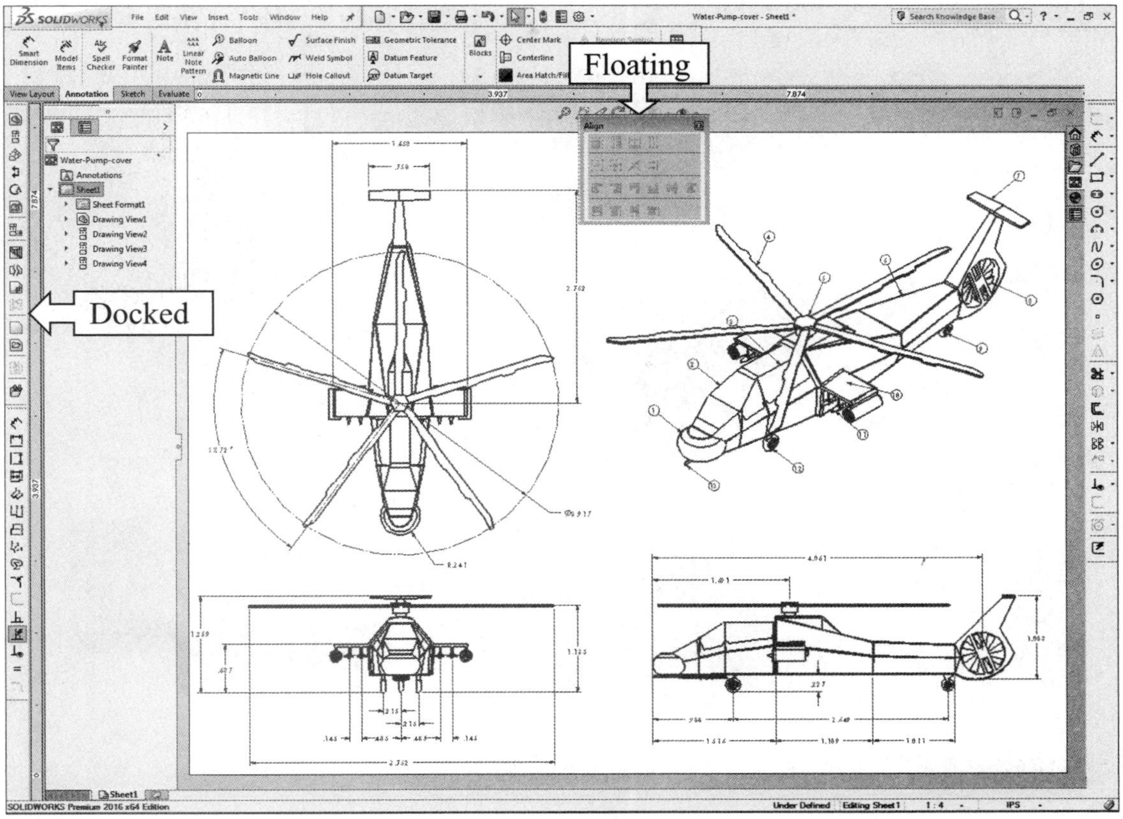

- Toolbars can be toggled on or off by activating or de-activating their check boxes:

- Select **Tools / Customize / Toolbars** tab.

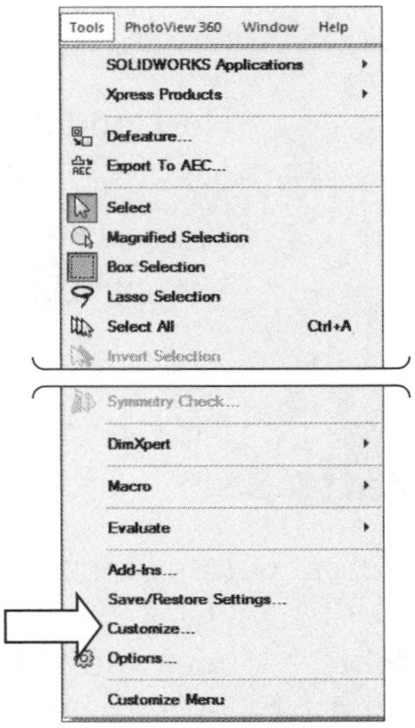

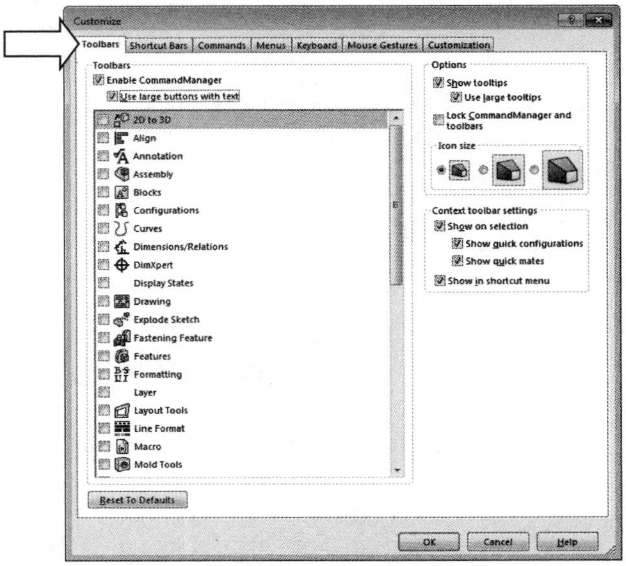

- The icons in the toolbars can be enlarged when its check box is selected

The View ports: You can view or work with SOLIDWORKS model or an assembly using one, two or four view ports.

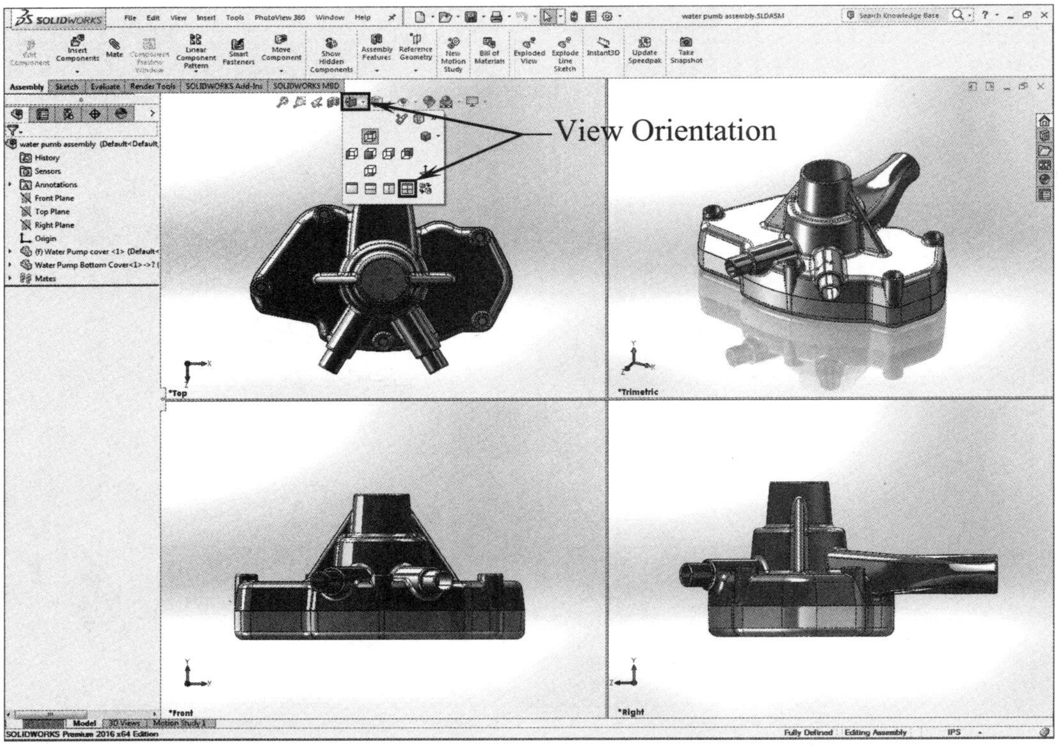

System Feedback symbols (Inference pointers):

 Snap to Vertex (endpoint)

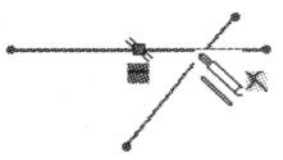 Snap to Intersection

 Snap to Edge (curve)

 Horizontal Line

 Snap to Mid-point

 Vertical Line

The Status Bar: (View / Status Bar)

Displays the status of the sketch entity using different colors to indicate:

Green = Selected
Black = Fully defined
Blue = Under defined
Red = Over defined

2D Sketch examples:

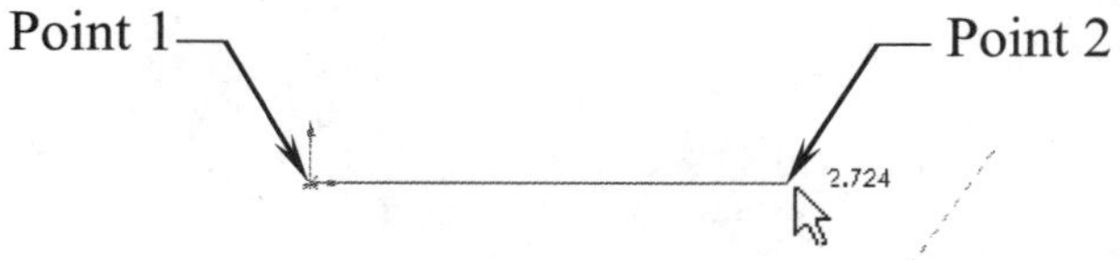

Click-Drag-Release: Single entity.

(Click Point 1, hold the mouse button, drag to point 2 and release).

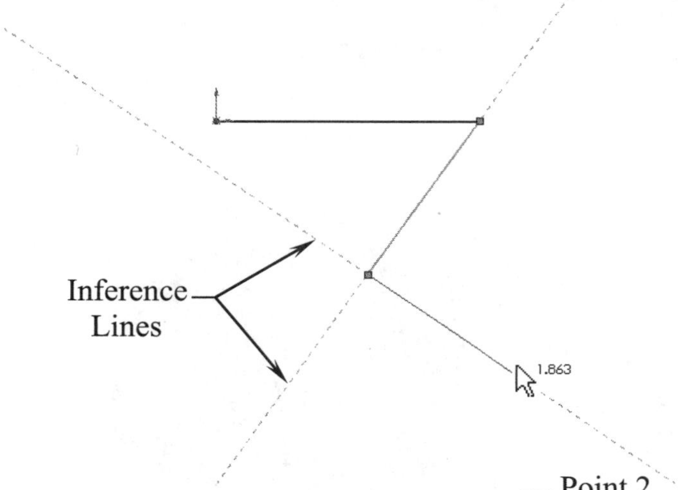

Click-Release: Continuous multiple entities.

(The Inference Lines appear when the sketch entities are Parallel, Perpendicular, or Tangent with each other).

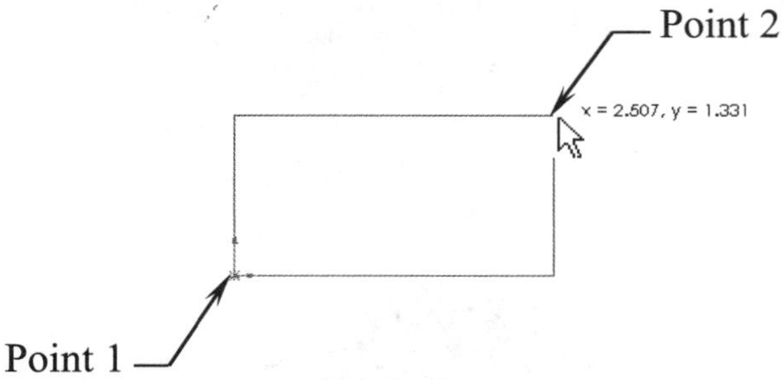

Click-Drag-Release: Single Rectangle

(Click point 1, hold the mouse button, and drag to Point 2 and release).

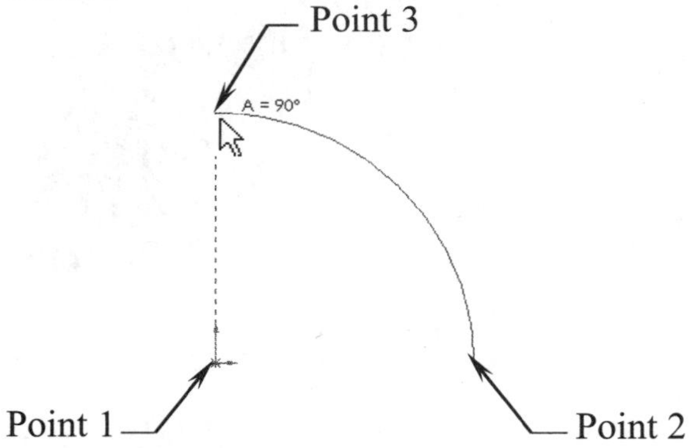

Click-Drag-Release: Single Centerpoint Arc

(Click point 1, hold the mouse button and drag to Point 2, release; then drag to Point 3 and release).

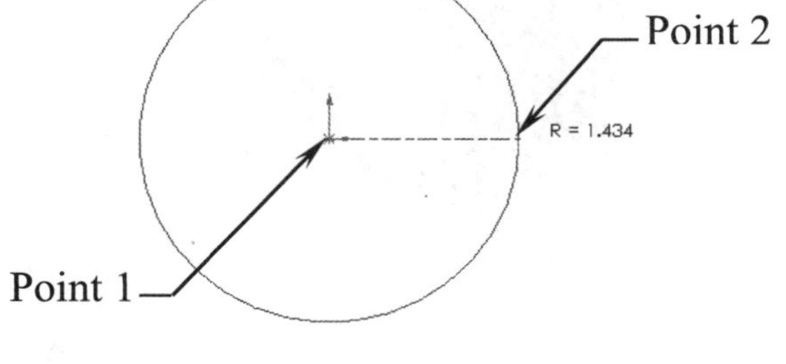

Click-Drag-Release: Single Circle

(Click point 1 [center of circle], hold the mouse button, drag to Point 2 [Radius] and release).

3D Feature examples:

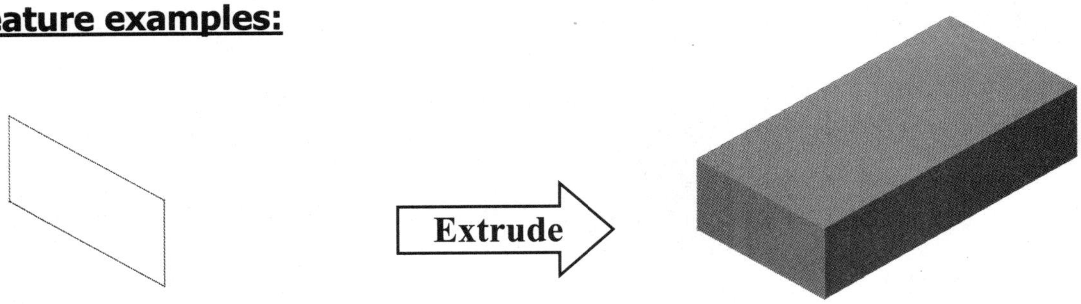

2D sketch 3D feature

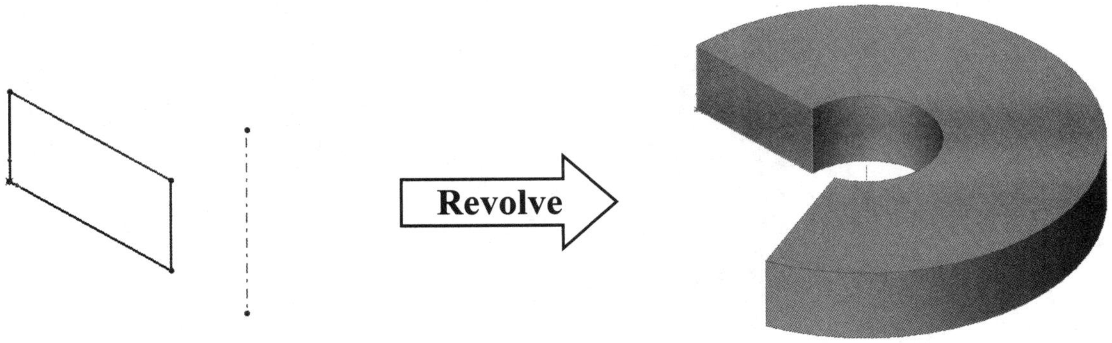

2D sketch 3D feature

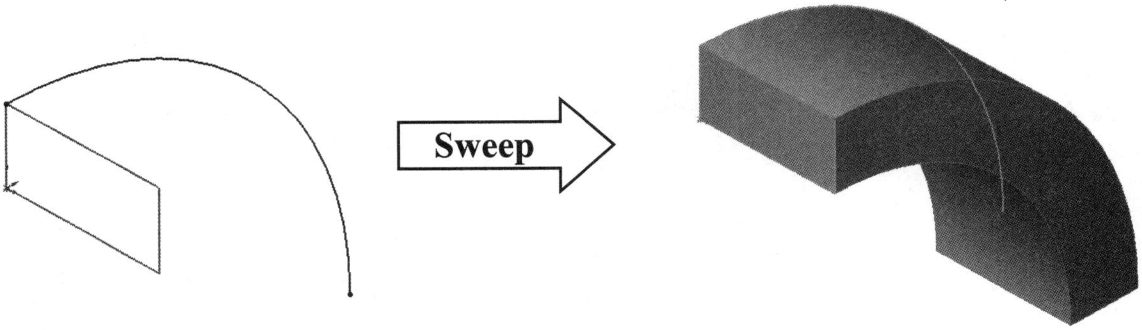

2D sketch 3D feature

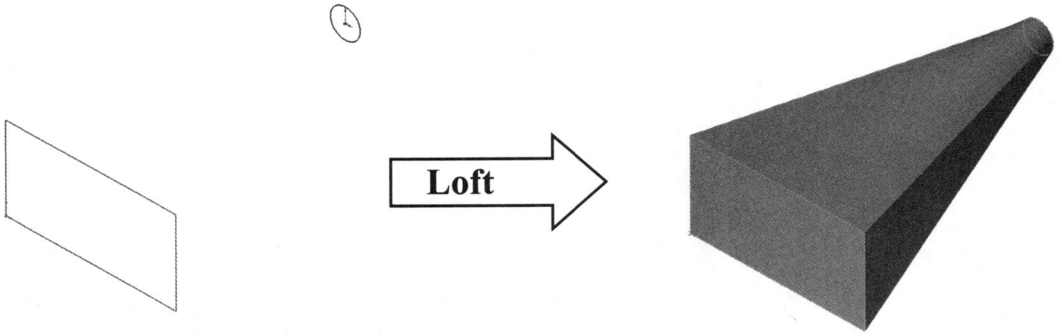

2D sketch 3D feature

Box-Select: Use the Select Pointer to drag a selection box around items.

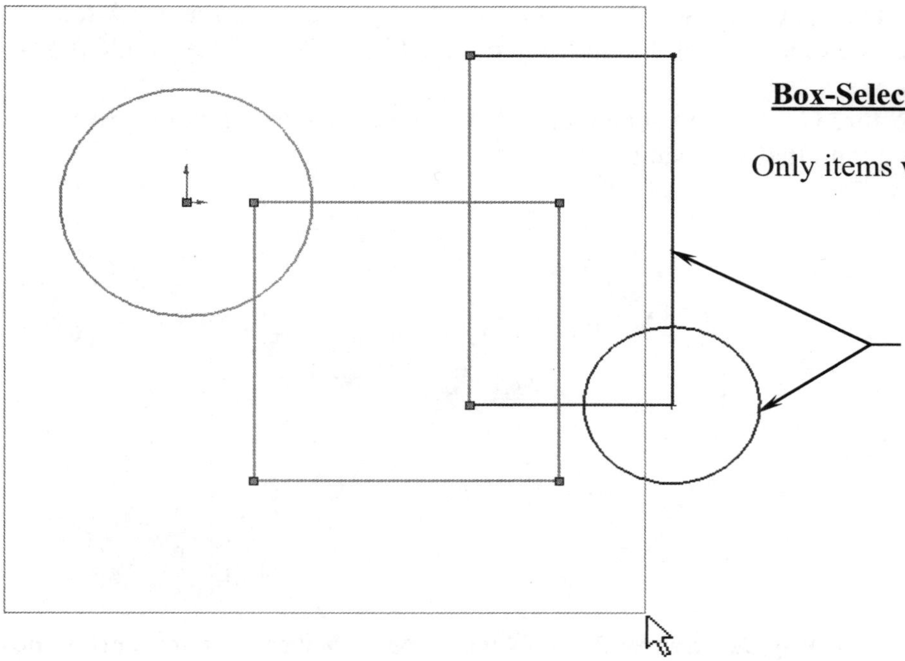

Box-Select from LEFT to RIGHT

Only items within the box are selected.

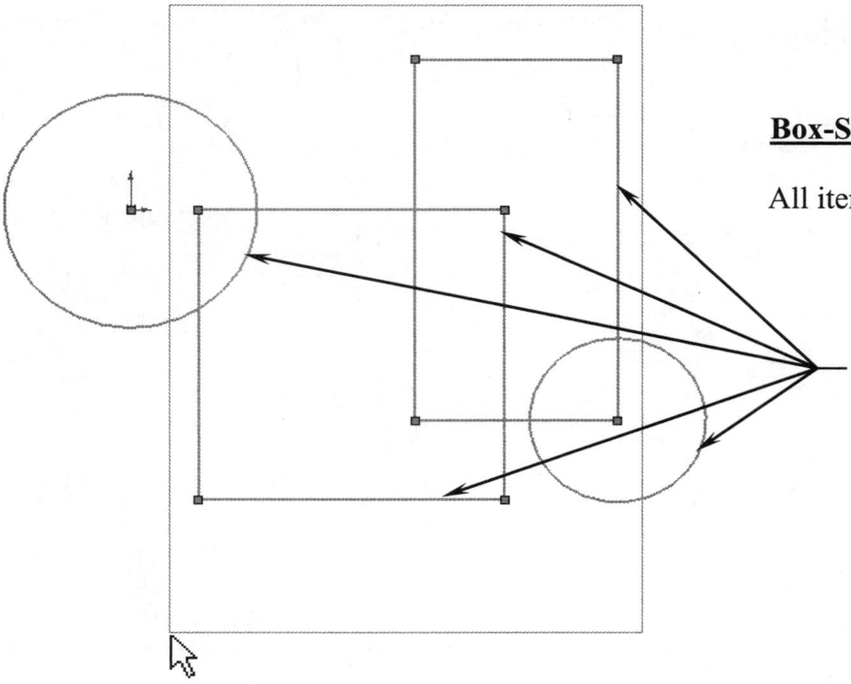

Box-Select from RIGHT to LEFT

All items crossing the box boundary are selected.

The default geometry type selected is as follows:

* Part documents – edges * Assembly documents – components * Drawing documents - sketch entities, dims & annotations. * To select multiple entities, hold down **Ctrl** while selecting after the first selection.

The Mouse Gestures for Sketches, Drawings and Parts

- Similar to a keyboard shortcut, you can use a Mouse Gesture to execute a command. A total of 8 keyboard shortcuts can be independently mapped and stored in the Mouse Gesture Guides.

- To activate the Mouse Gesture Guide, **right-click-and-drag** to see the current eight-gestures, then simply select the command that you want to use.

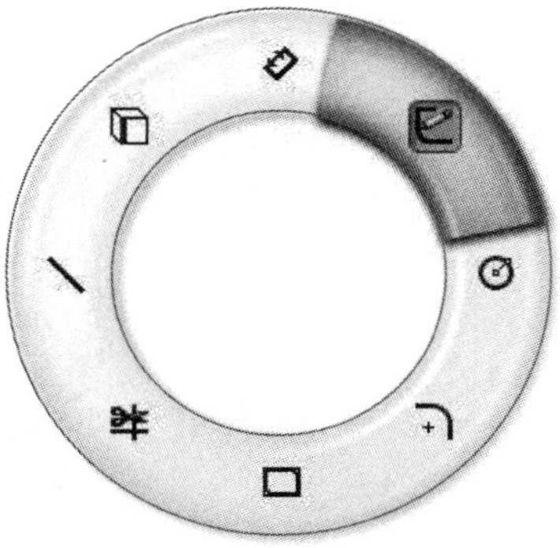

Mouse Gestures for Sketches

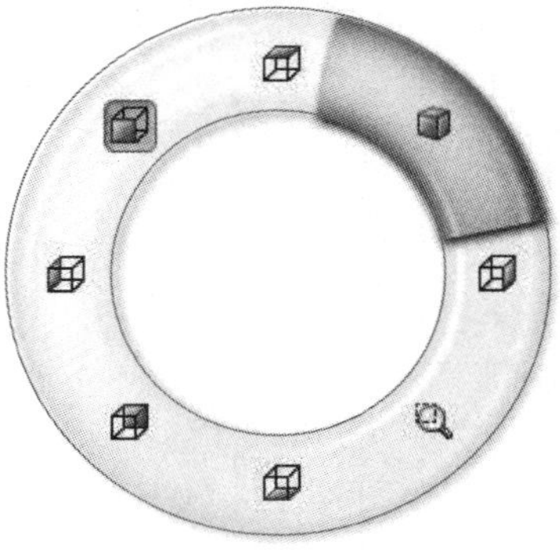

Mouse Gestures for Parts & Assemblies

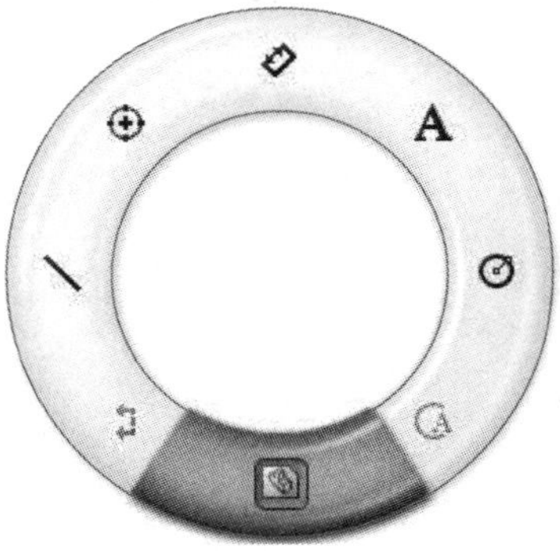

Mouse Gestures for Drawings

- To customize the Mouse Gestures and include your favorite shortcuts, go to:

Tools / Customize.

- From the **Mouse Gestures** tab, select **All Commands** and enable the **Show only commands with Mouse Gestures assigned** check box.

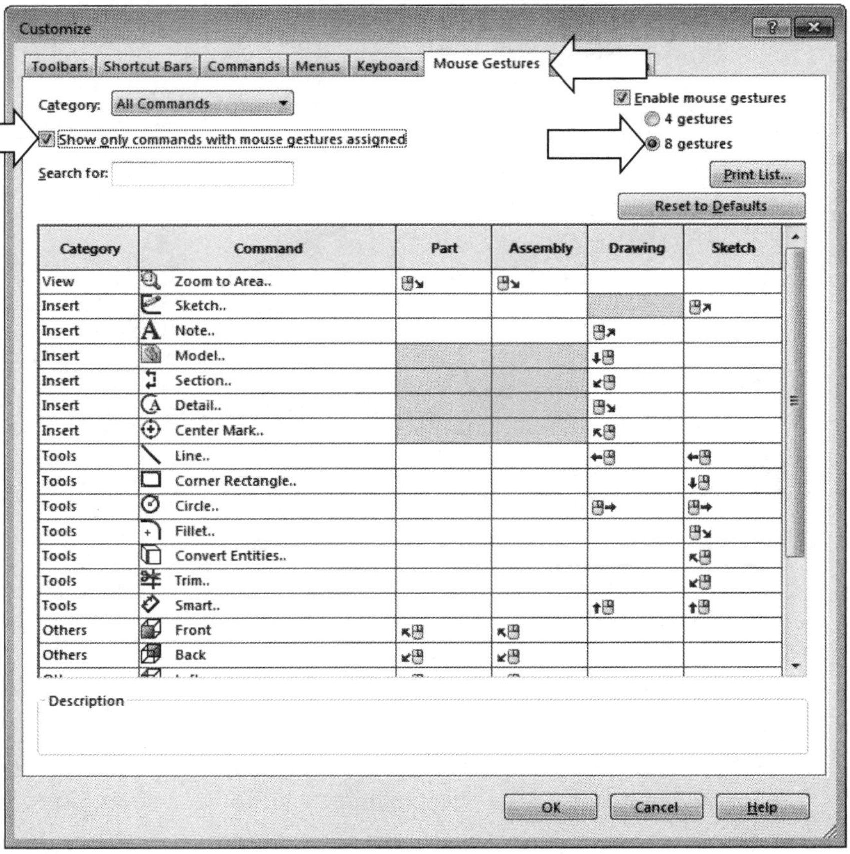

CHAPTER 1

Document Properties

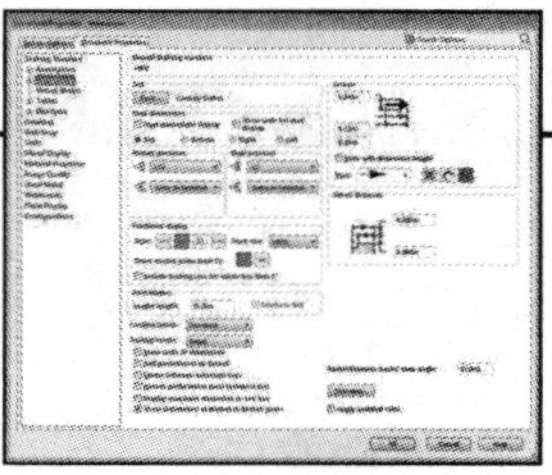

Document Properties - Overview

Setting up the Document Template

In SOLIDWORKS there are two types of settings that allow the user to create their own parameters and use them to create models, assemblies, and drawings.

The first type is called System Options. They are settings that are stored in the registry and are not part of the documents. Therefore, these changes affect all documents, current and future.

The second type is called Document Properties. They are settings that you can preset and save in the templates, all settings affect only the **current document.**

SOLIDWORKS provides templates for parts, assemblies, and drawings. You can create custom templates by opening existing templates, setting options and inserting items, then saving the documents as templates.
Template files have the following extensions:

*** .prtdot (parts)** *** .asmdot (assemblies)** *** .drwdot (drawings)**

The Document Templates are stored in one the following directories:
C:\Program Files\SolidWorks Corp\SolidWorks Data\Templates.
OR
C:\Program Files\SolidWorks Corp\SolidWorks\Lang\English\Tutorial.

You can specify the document-level overall detailing drafting standard such as: dimensions, annotations, view labels, tables available for all document types.

This chapter discusses the parameters that are needed to use throughout the textbook, and they are intended for use with this textbook only; you may need to modify them to ensure full compatibility with your applications.

Setting up the Document Template
Document Properties

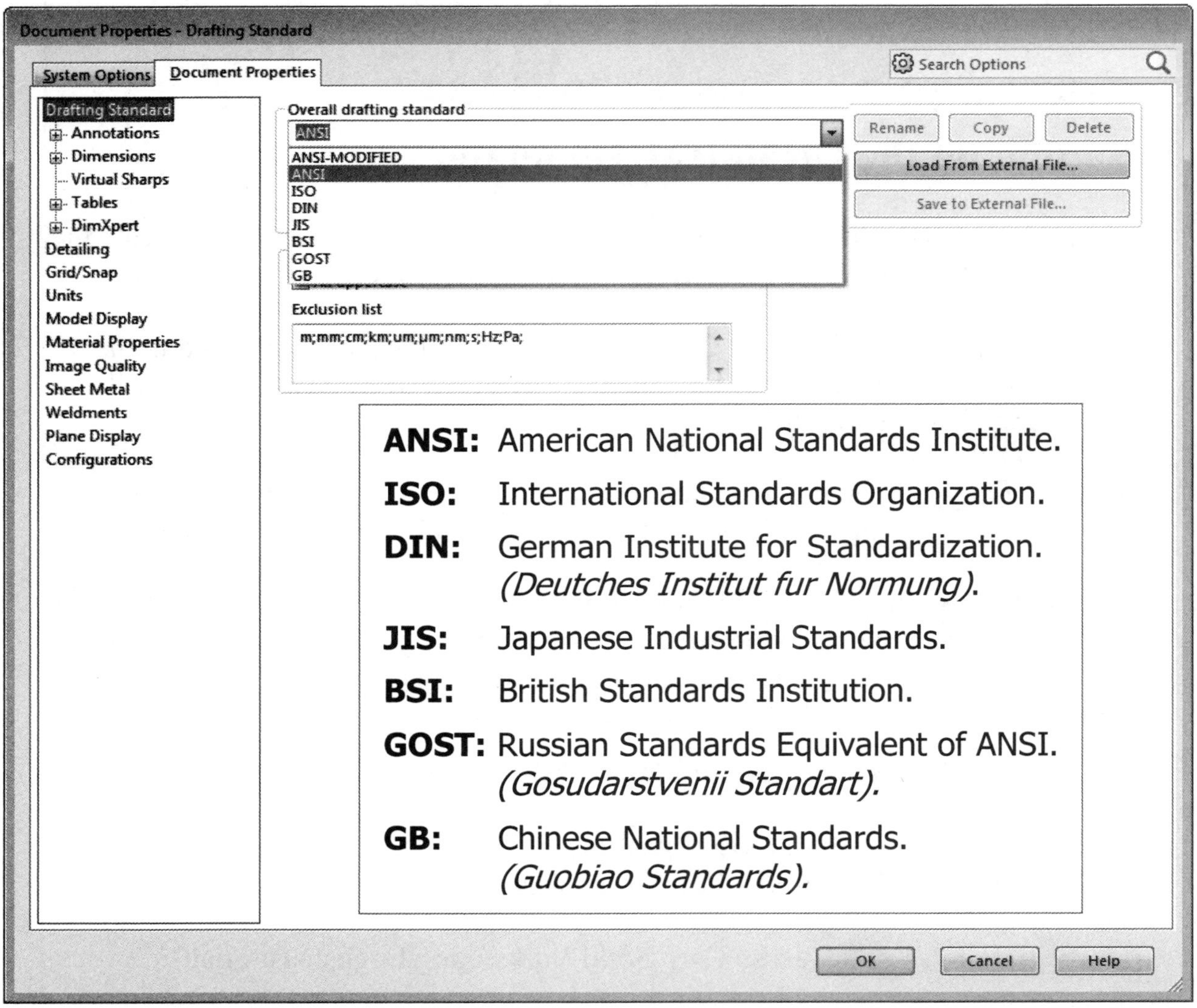

- The settings shown in this chapter are intended for use with this textbook only. The Standards will be set to ANSI and the Units are Inch, Pound, and Second.

1. Starting a new part document:

- Select: **File / New**.

- Select the **Part** template from the New SOLIDWORKS Document Dialog box.

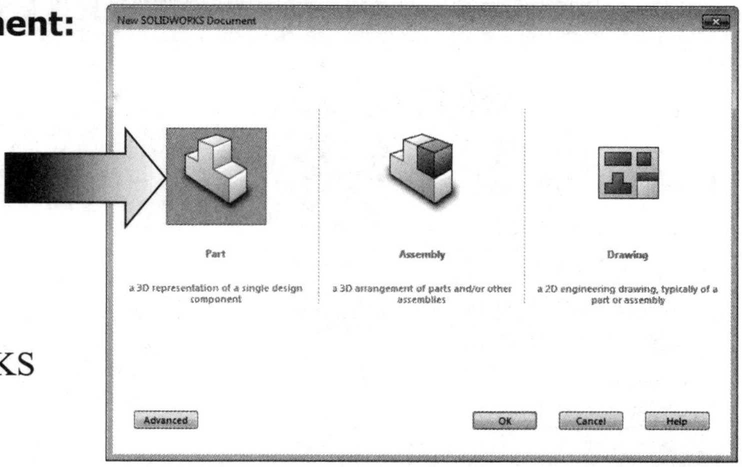

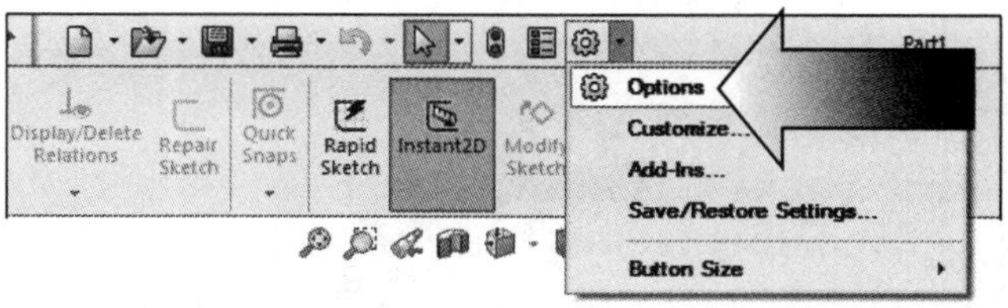

- The document properties apply only to the current document, and the Document Properties tab is available only when a document is open. New documents get their document settings (such as Units, Image Quality, and so on) from the document properties of the template used to create the document. Use the Document Properties tab when you set up document templates.

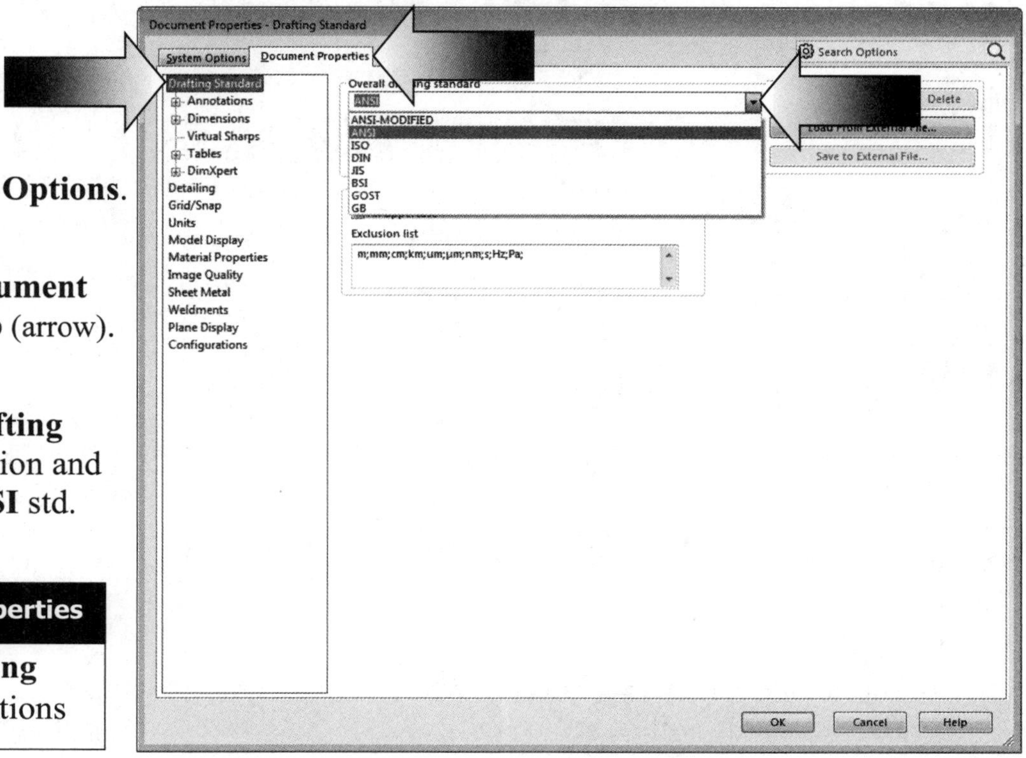

- Select **Tools / Options**.

- Click the **Document Properties** tab (arrow).

- Click the **Drafting Standard** section and select the **ANSI** std.

Document Properties
The **Drafting Standard** options

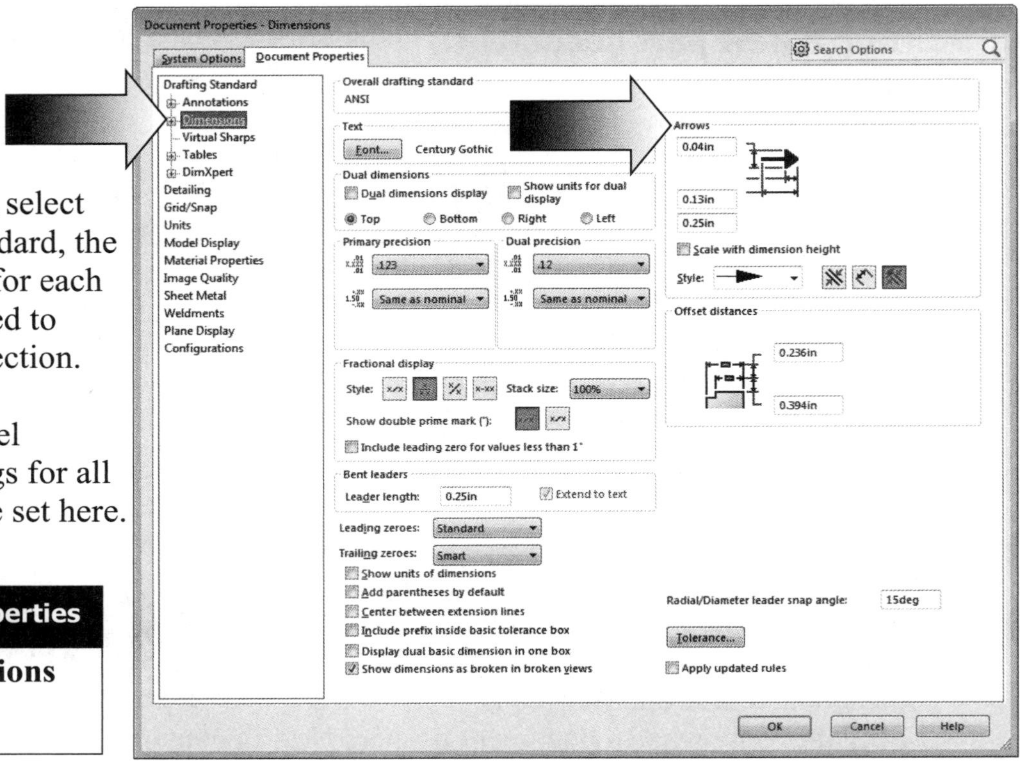

- Each time you select an overall standard, the base standard for each detail is updated to reflect this selection.

- Document-level drafting settings for all dimensions are set here.

Document Properties

The **Dimensions** options

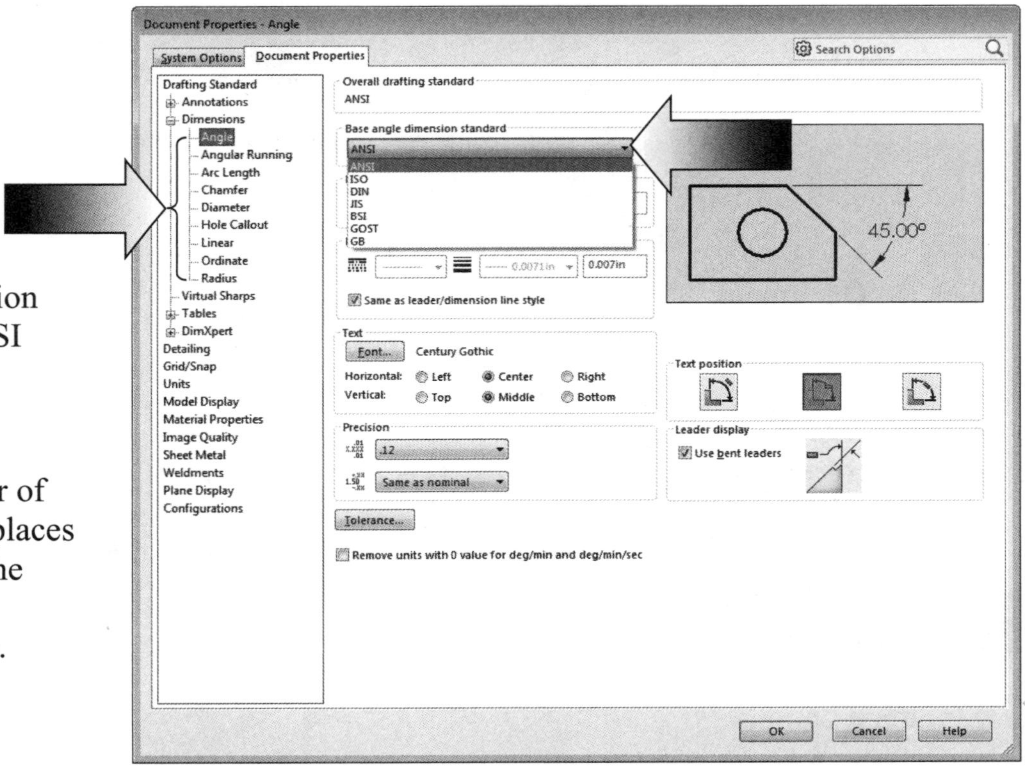

- Set all dimension options to ANSI standards.

- Set the number of decimals to 3 places (for use with the lessons in this textbook only).

- Select the Plus symbol for Virtual Sharp (the intersection between the two entities).

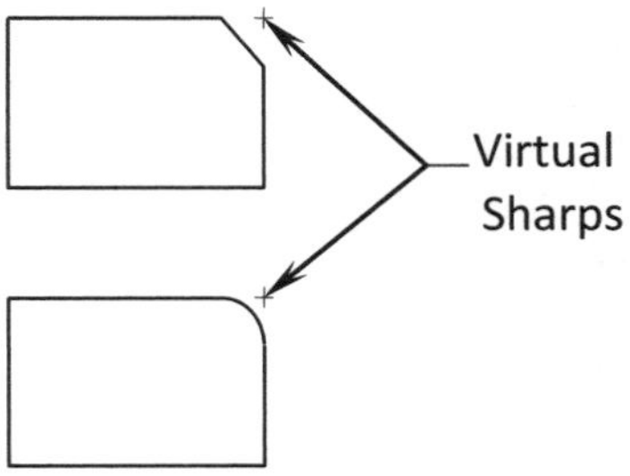

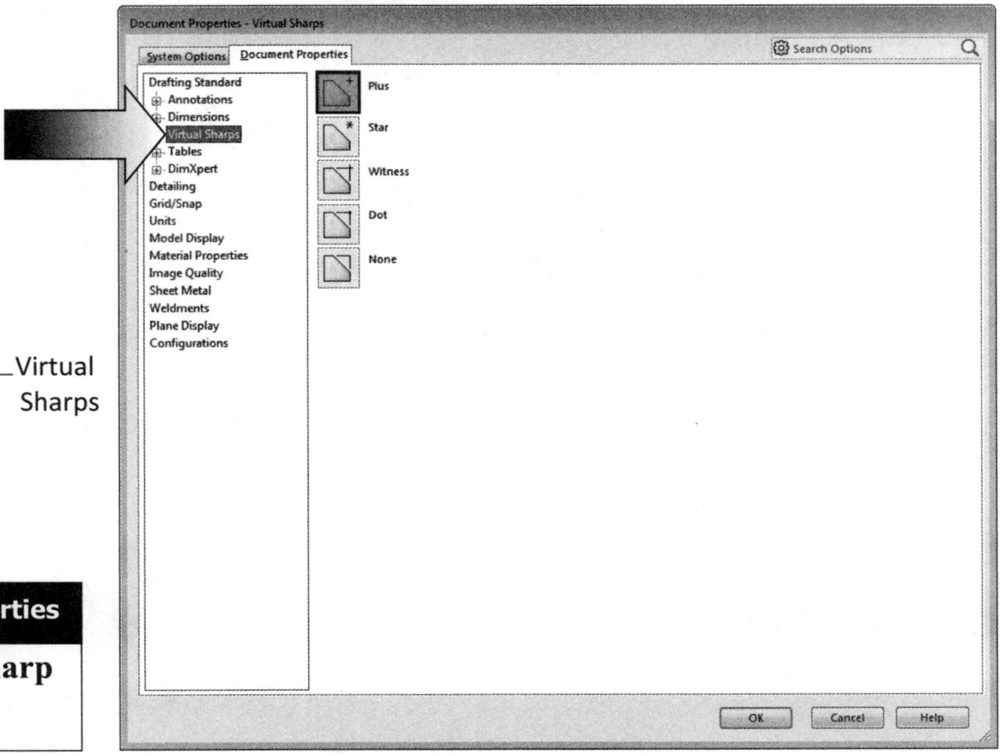

Document Properties

The **Virtual Sharp** options

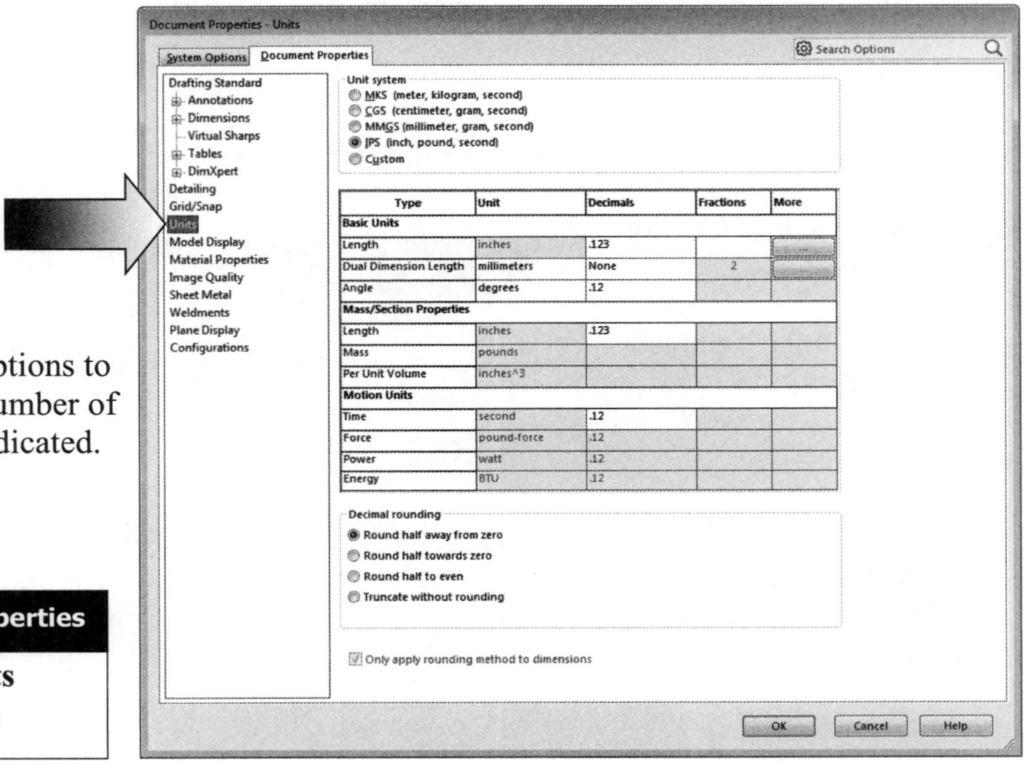

- Set the Unit options to IPS, and the number of decimals as indicated.

Document Properties

The **Units** options

- Set the resolutions for Shaded and Wireframe to approximately half way…

- Depends on the amount of video memory in your system. If this option is set too high it can affect the performance of your computer.

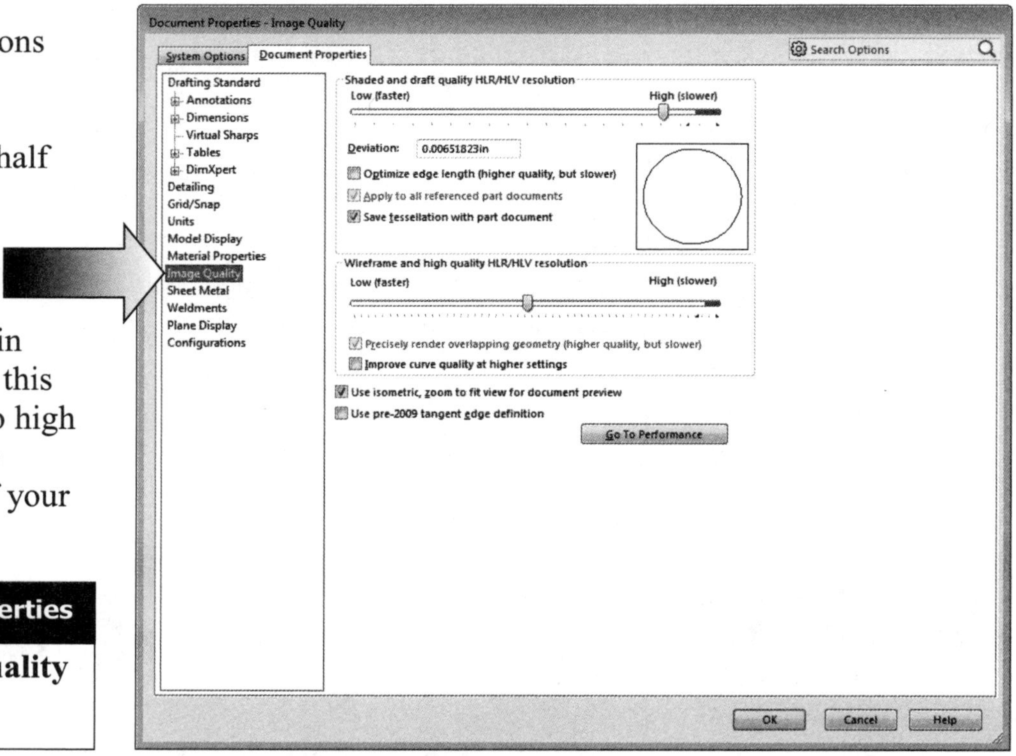

Document Properties
The **Image Quality** options

Saving the settings as a Part Template:

- These settings should be saved as a Document Template for use in future documents.

- Go to **File / Save As.**

- Change the Save-As-Type to: **Part Templates** (*.prtdot - part document template).

- Enter **Part-Inch.prtdot** for the file name.

- Save either in the Templates folder *(C:\Program Files\ Solidworks Corp\ SolidWorks\ Data\ Templates).*

  – or – in the Tutorial folder

  (C:\Program Files\SolidWorks Corp\Solidworks\Lang\English\ Tutorial).

- Click **Save**.

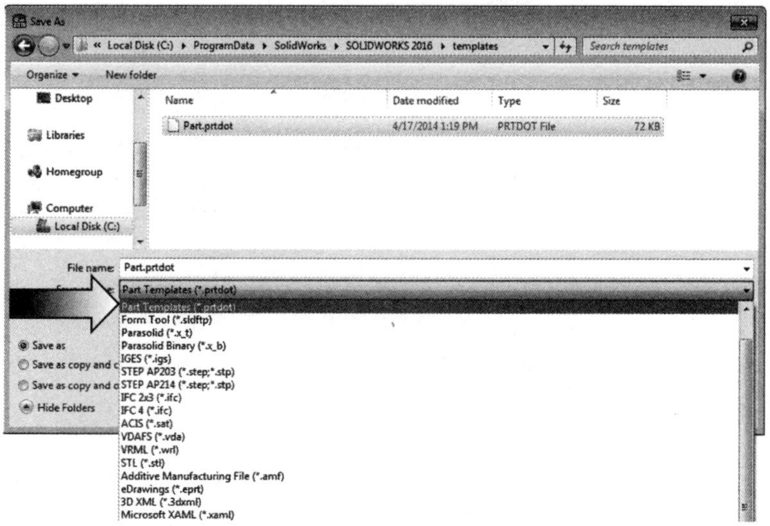

Customizing Keyboard Shortcuts

- You can customize keyboard shortcuts to a command from the Keyboard tab of the Customize dialog box.

- There are many shortcuts available in SOLIDWORKS but you can assign your own shortcut keys to any of your frequently used commands.

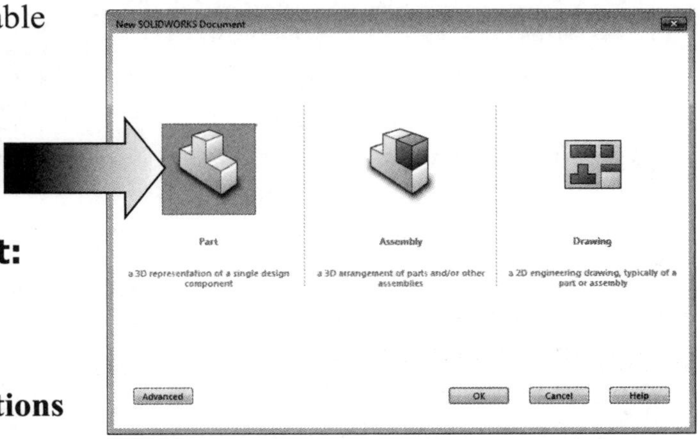

1. Starting a new part document:

- Click **File / New / Part**.

- Select **Customize** from the **Options** drop down menu (arrow).

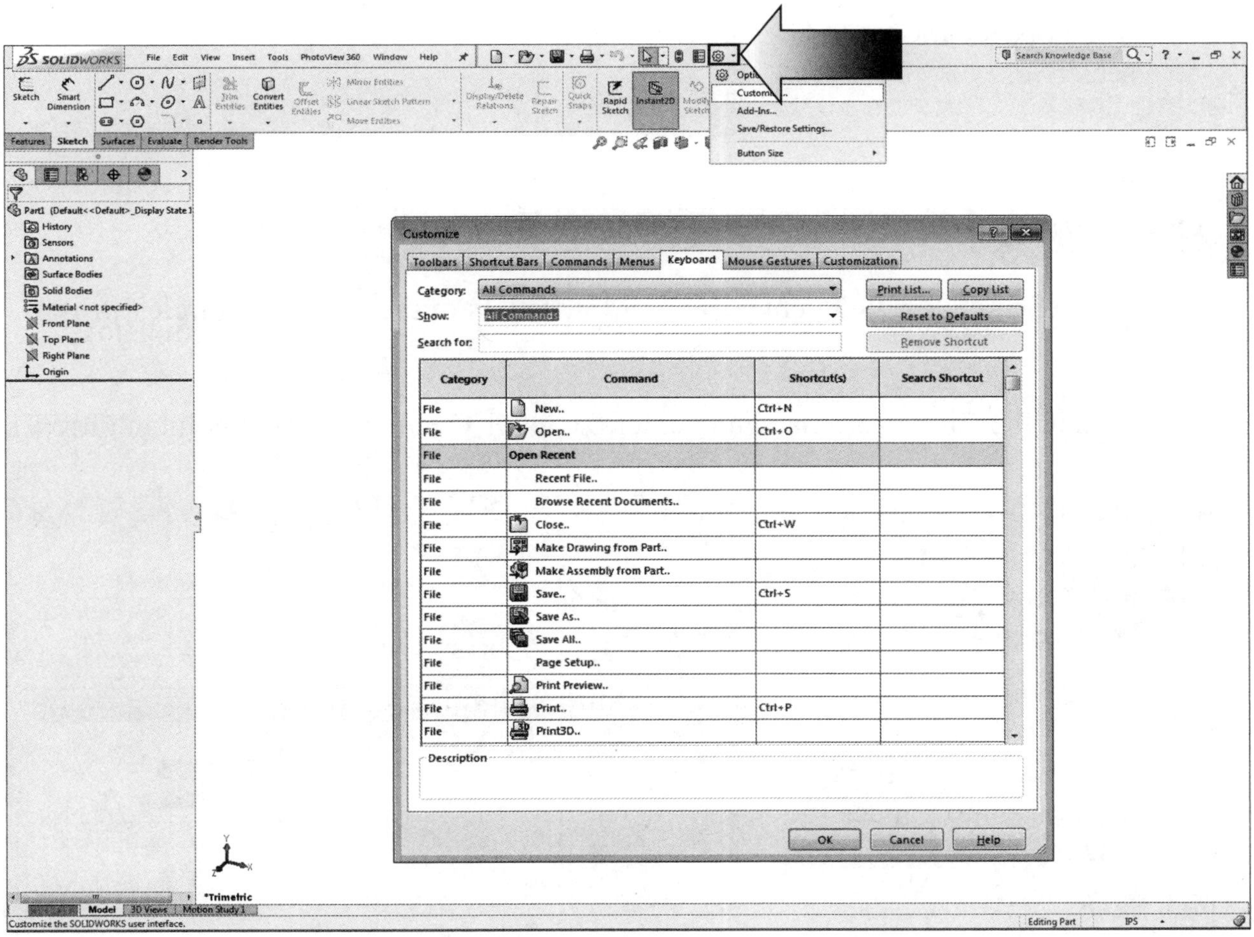

2. Creating a new hotkey:

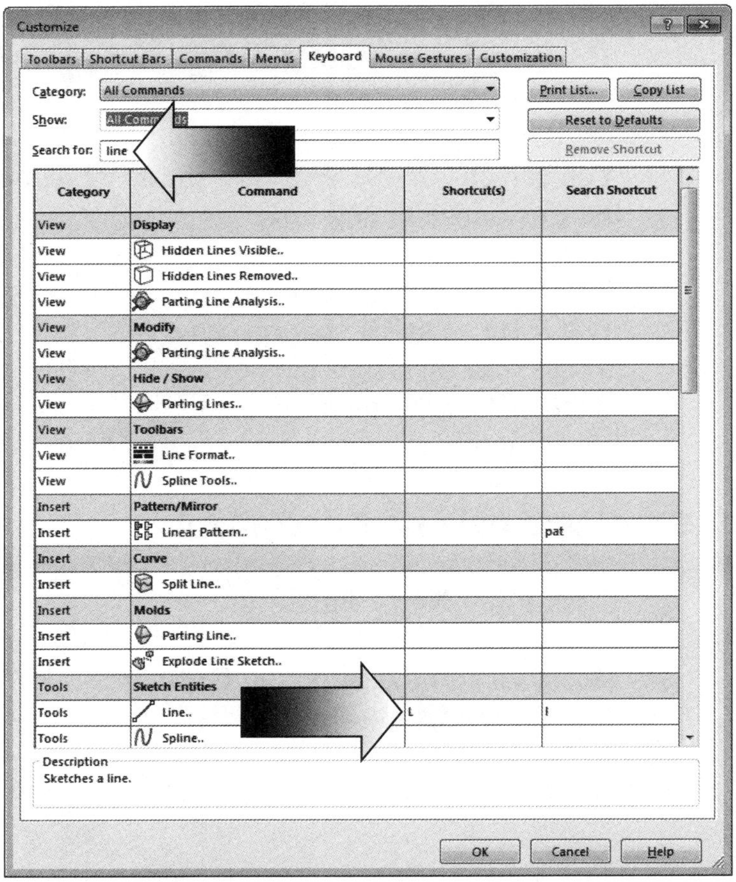

- It is much quicker to search for the command than to scroll through a long list of commands.

- In the Search For field, enter the command name: **line** (arrow).

- Locate the **Line** command and enter the letter **L** under the Shortcut column (arrow).

- The hotkeys are not case sensitive.

3. Overwriting an existing hotkey:

- In the Search For field, enter the first few letters of the command circle (arrow).

- Locate the Circle command and enter the letter **C** in the Shortcut column (arrow).

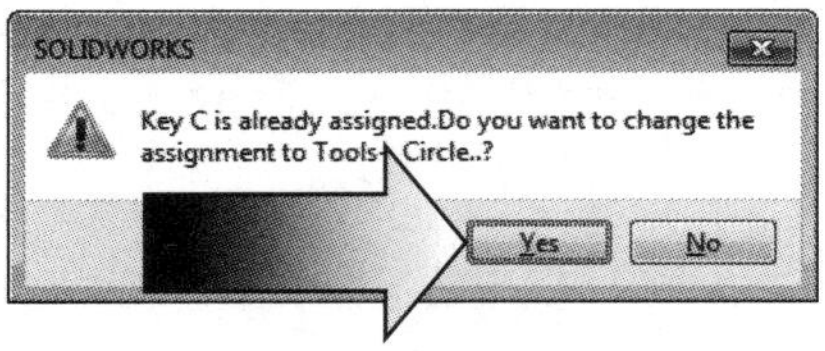

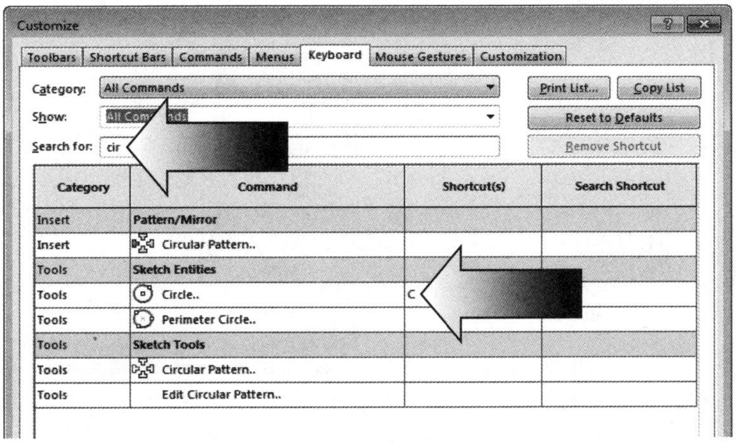

- A message appears asking if you want to replace the existing hotkey with your new one, click **YES**.

4. Adding other hotkeys:

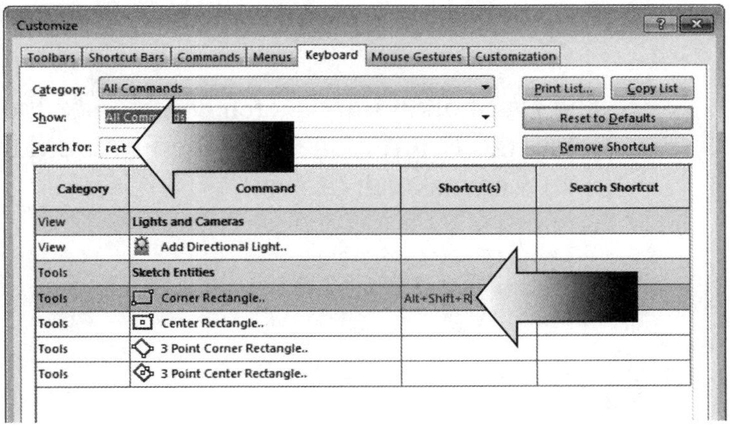

- For practice purposes, we will assign a couple hotkeys to the Rectangle and the Dimension commands.

- Assign the letter **R** to the Rectangle command. If the shortcut shows more than one key (Alt+Shift+R), erase it and press the letter **R** again to reassign it.

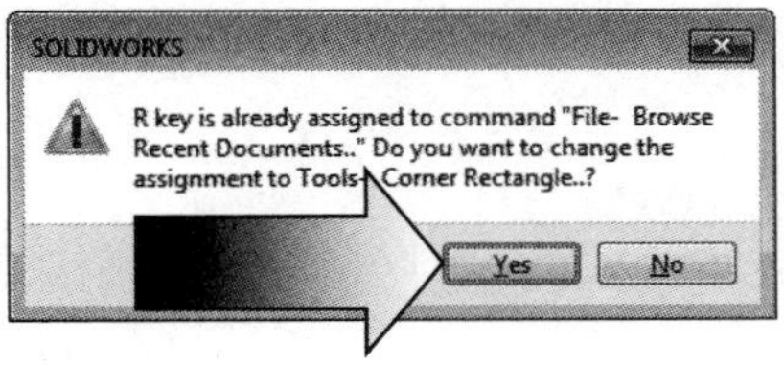

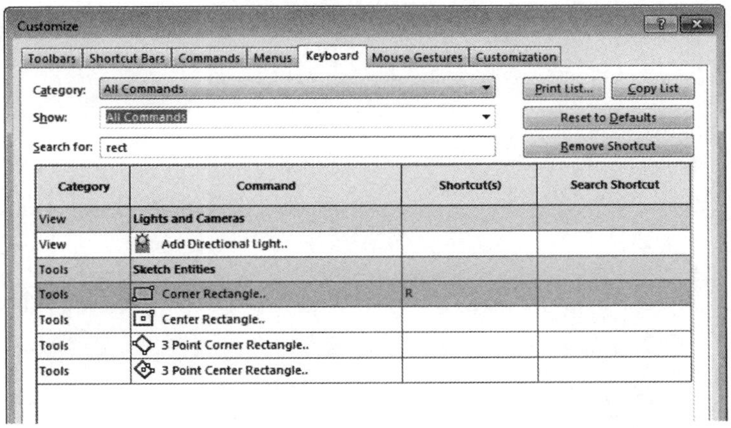

- Click **YES** to overwrite the existing hotkey with your new key.

- Type the word **smart** (for Smart Dimension) in the <u>Search For</u> field.

- Enter the letter **D** as the new hotkey for the Smart Dimension command (arrow).

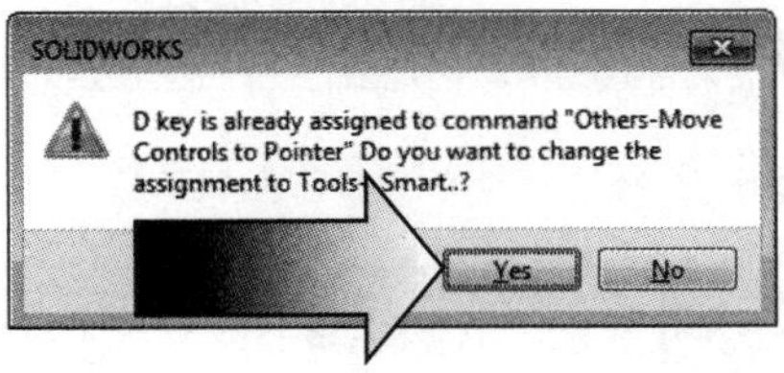

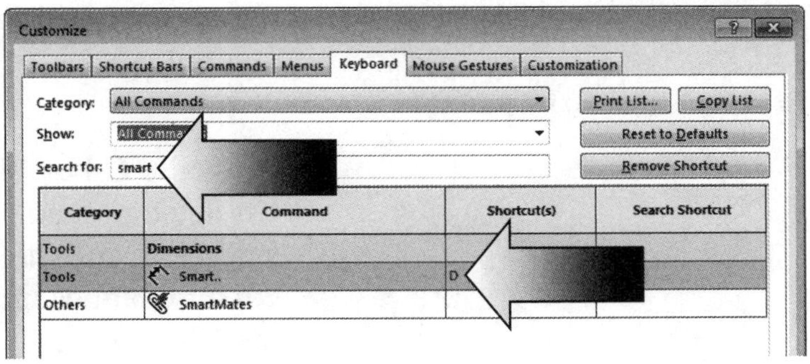

- Click YES to confirm the assignment of the new key.

5. Testing the new hotkeys:

- The four hotkeys are sketch commands: they must be tested in the sketch mode. Select the **<u>Front</u>** plane from the FeatureManager tree and click the **<u>Pencil</u>** icon to open a new sketch (arrow).

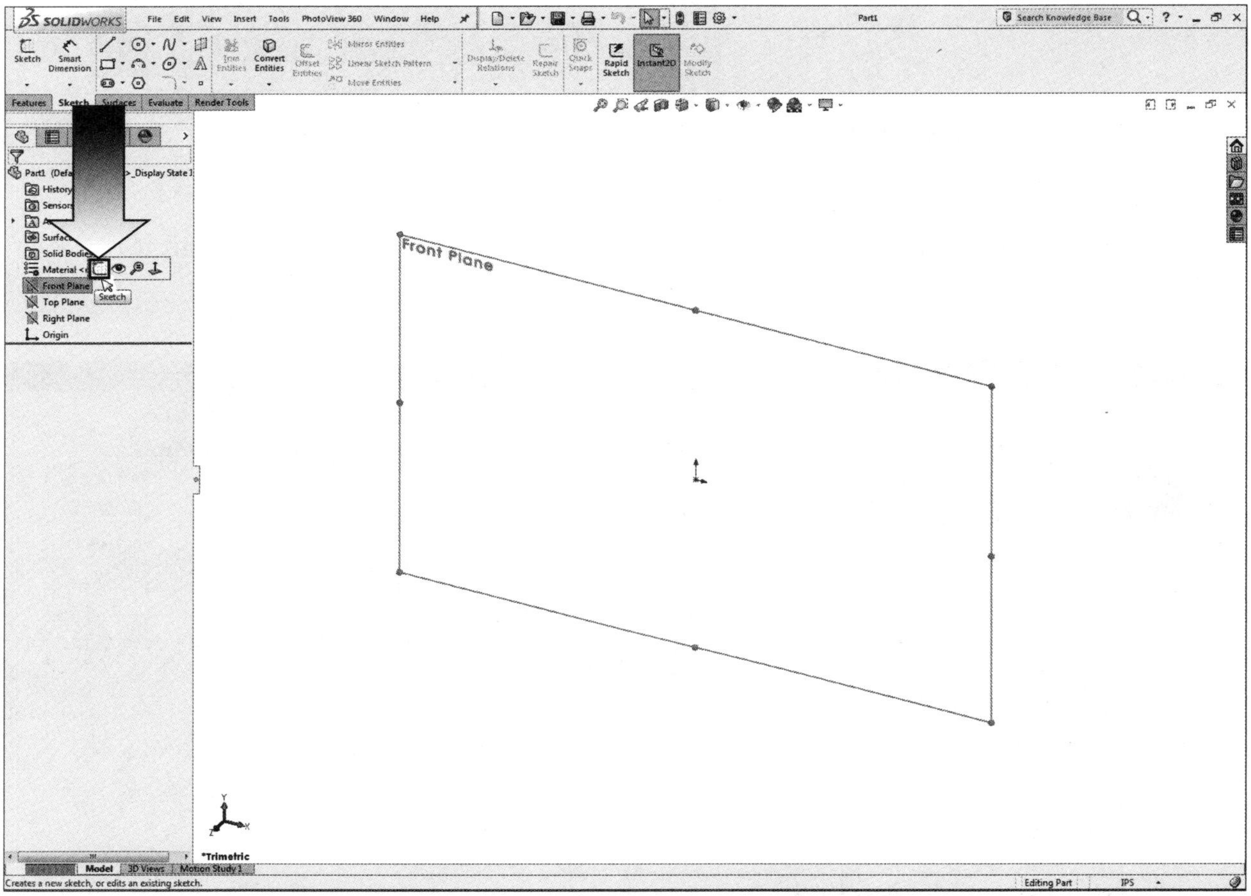

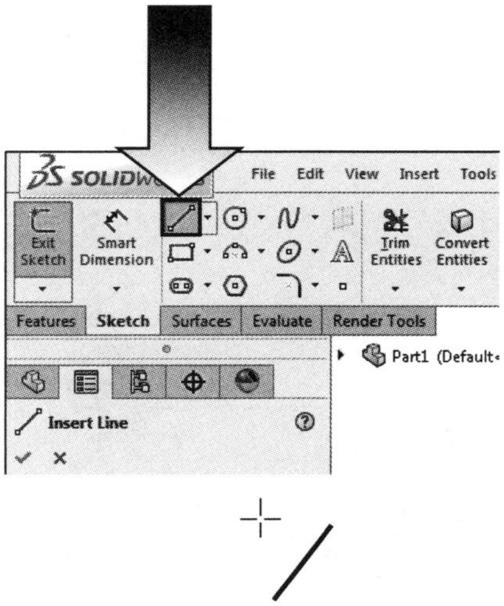

- Press the **L** key, the Line command is activated, and the cursor changes into the Line symbol.

- Press the **C** key, the Circle command is activated, and the cursor changes into the Circle symbol.

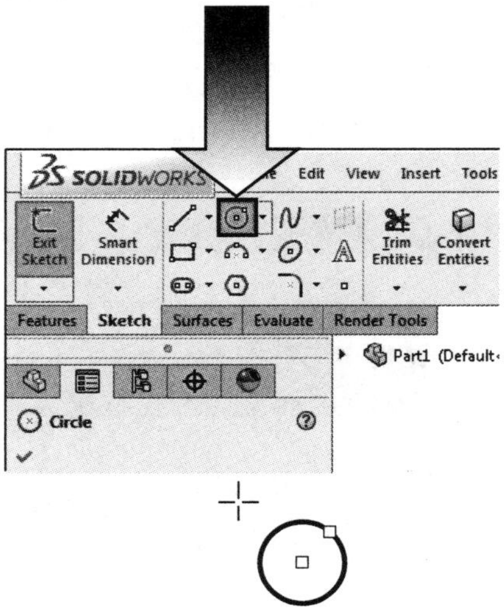

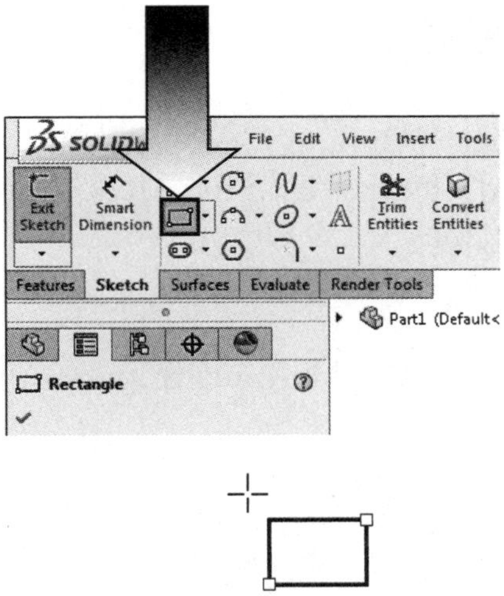

- Press the **R** key, the Rectangle command is activated and the cursor changes into the Rectangle symbol.

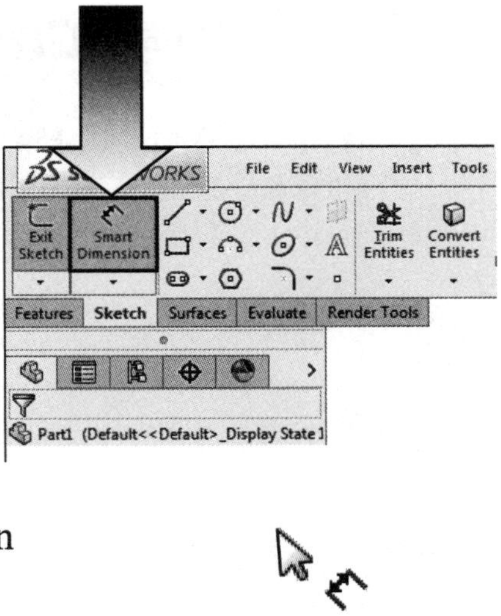

- Press the **D** key, the Dimension command is activated and the cursor changes into the Dimension symbol.

6. Resting the hotkeys back to default (optional):

- The new hotkeys can be reset back to their default commands or simply erased from the Shortcut column.

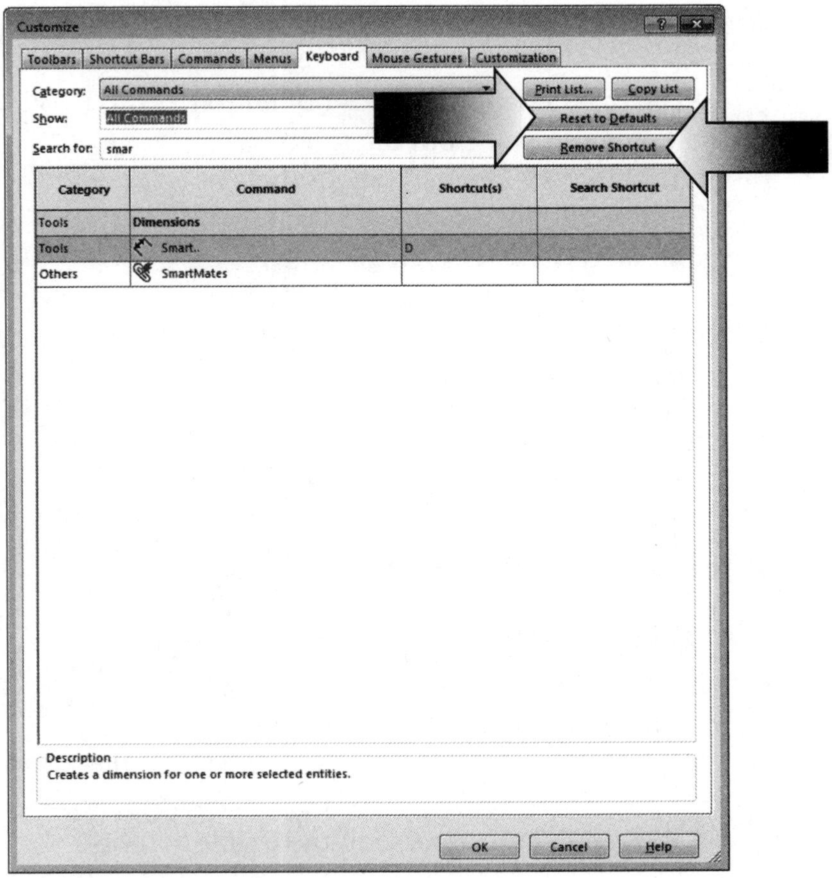

- The list of shortcut keys can be printed from the Keyboard tab of the Customize dialog box.

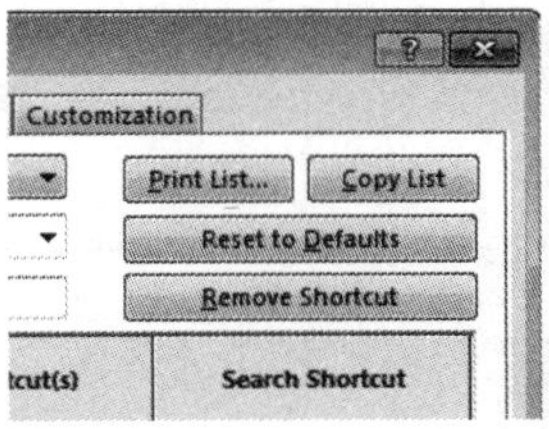

- Click **OK** to exit the dialog box.

Customizing Tool Buttons

- You can add tool buttons to one or more active toolbars from the Keyboard tab of the Customize dialog box, including the CommandManager, and the Menu Bar toolbar. This includes buttons with flyout controls such as View Orientations.

- You can use drag and drop to remove, rearrange, or move tool buttons from one toolbar to another.

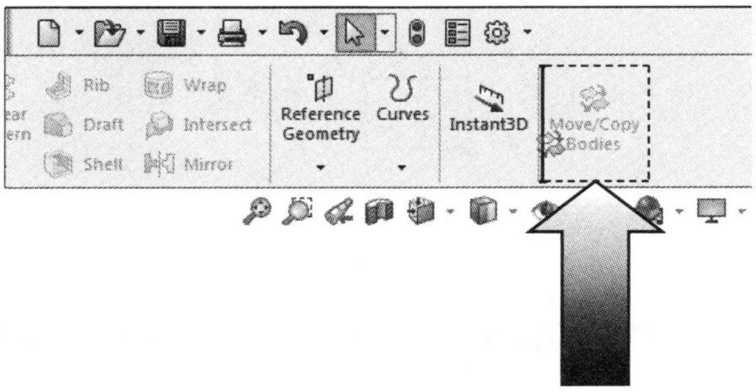

- The first two images on the right show an example of a tool button being dragged from the right side and dropped onto the left side of the same toolbar.

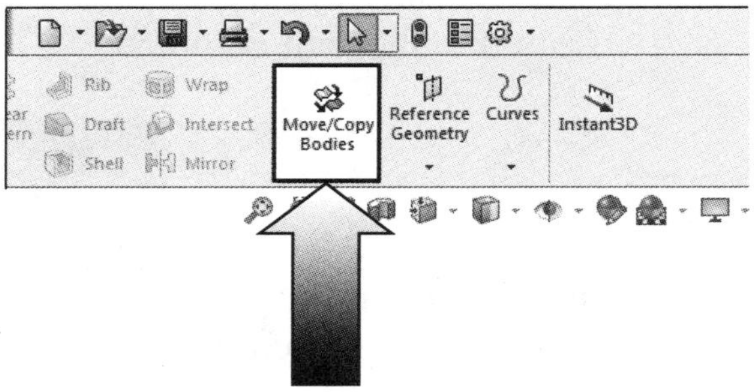

- The third image shows a tool button being removed from the toolbars: Hold the Alt key and drag a tool button into the graphics area. When the mouse cursor changes to a Red Delete indicator, release the mouse button to drop and remove it from the toolbar.

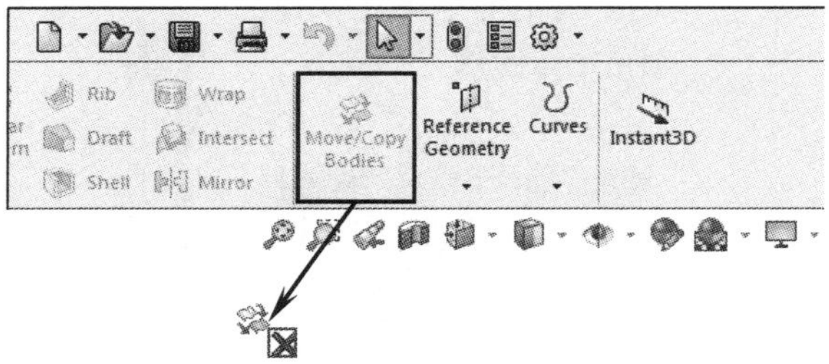

1. Adding tool buttons to toolbars:

- With a document open, click: **Tools / Customize** or right-click in the window border and select Customize.

- Click the **Commands** tab (arrow).

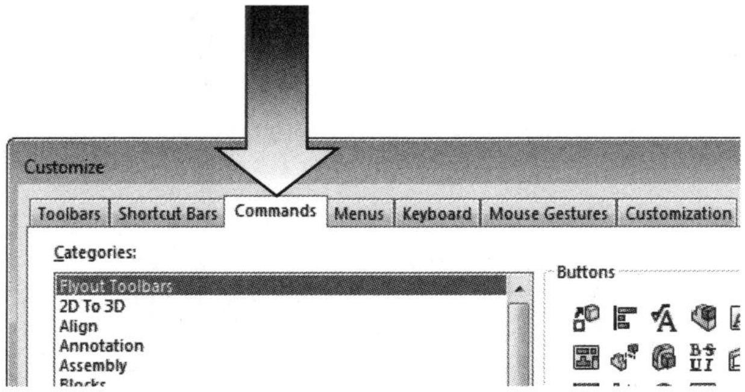

- Click the **Sketch tab** on the upper left side of the screen.

- Select **Sketch** under the Categories section (arrow).

- Locate the **Modify Sketch** command from the Buttons list (arrow).

- **Drag** the Modify Sketch command into the Sketch toolbar as shown below. The new command is added to the toolbar.

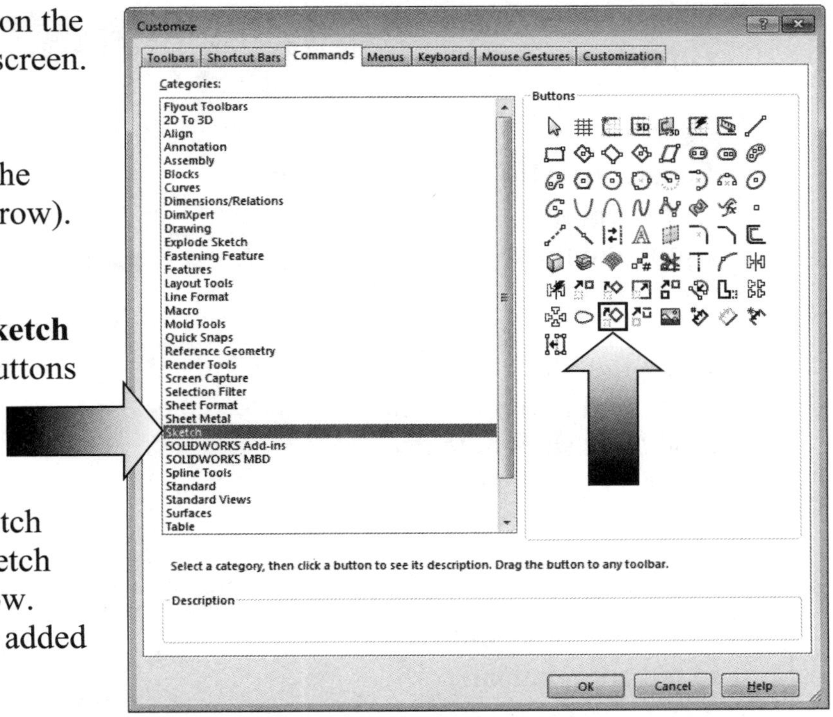

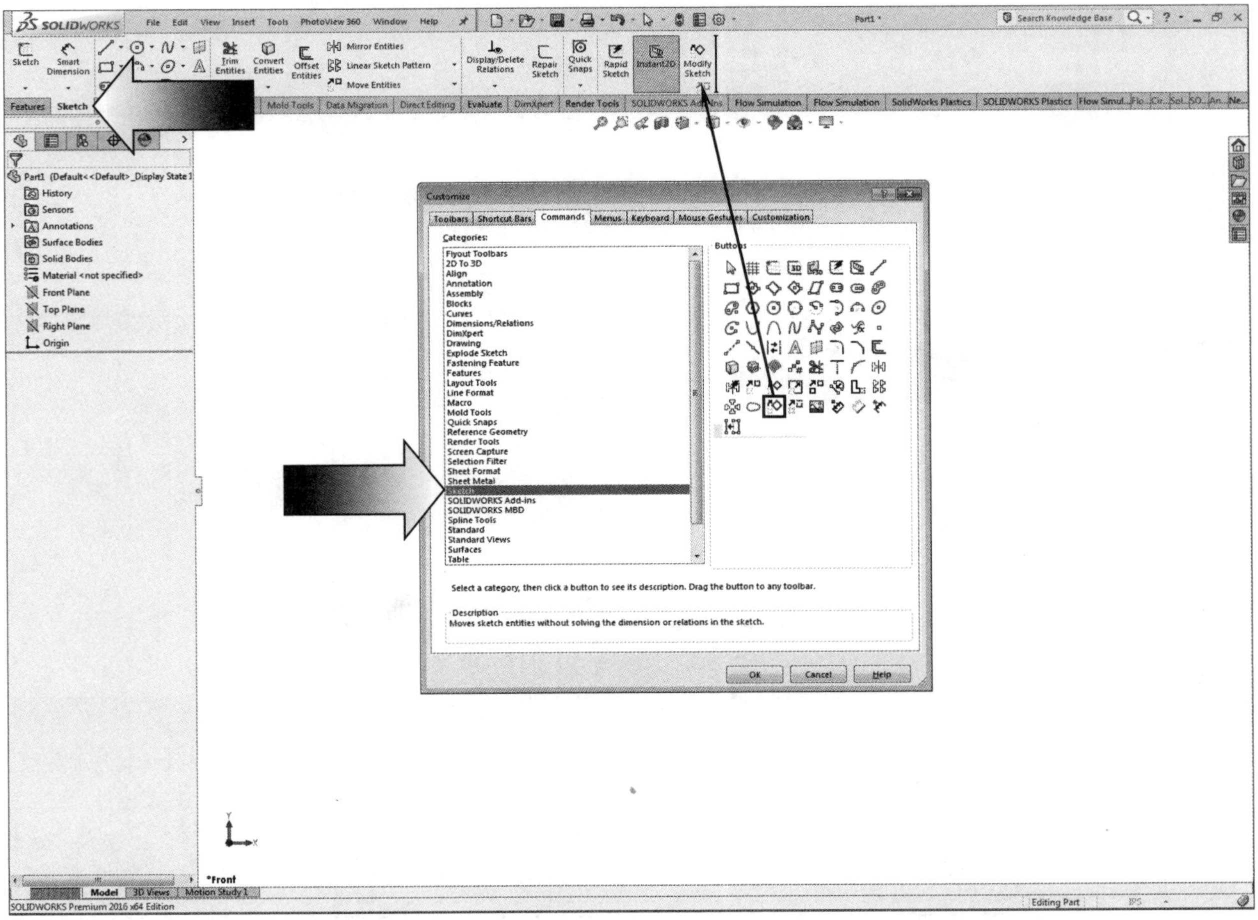

- Change to the **Features tab** (arrow).

- Locate the **Move/ Copy Bodies** command (arrow).

- **Drag** the Move/Copy Bodies command into the Features toolbar as shown below. The new command is added to the toolbar.

- The new commands are saved automatically.

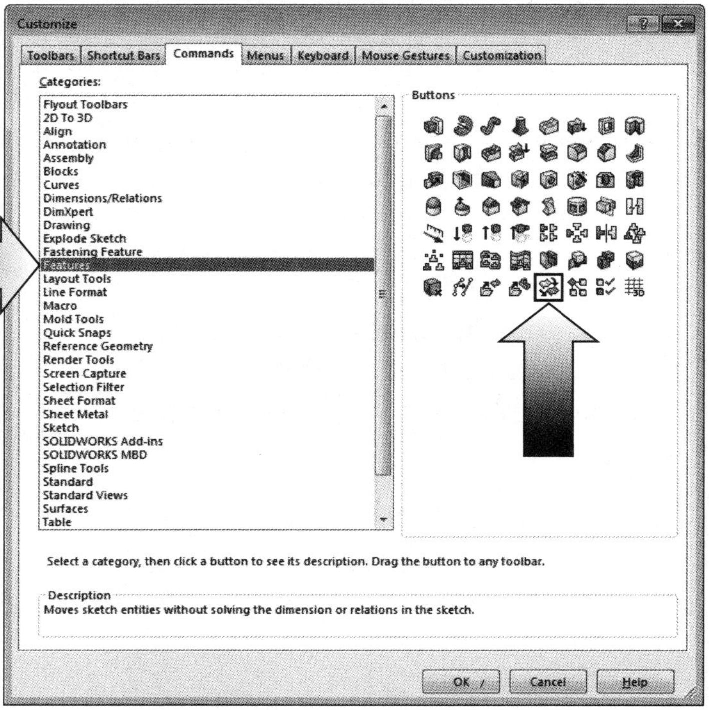

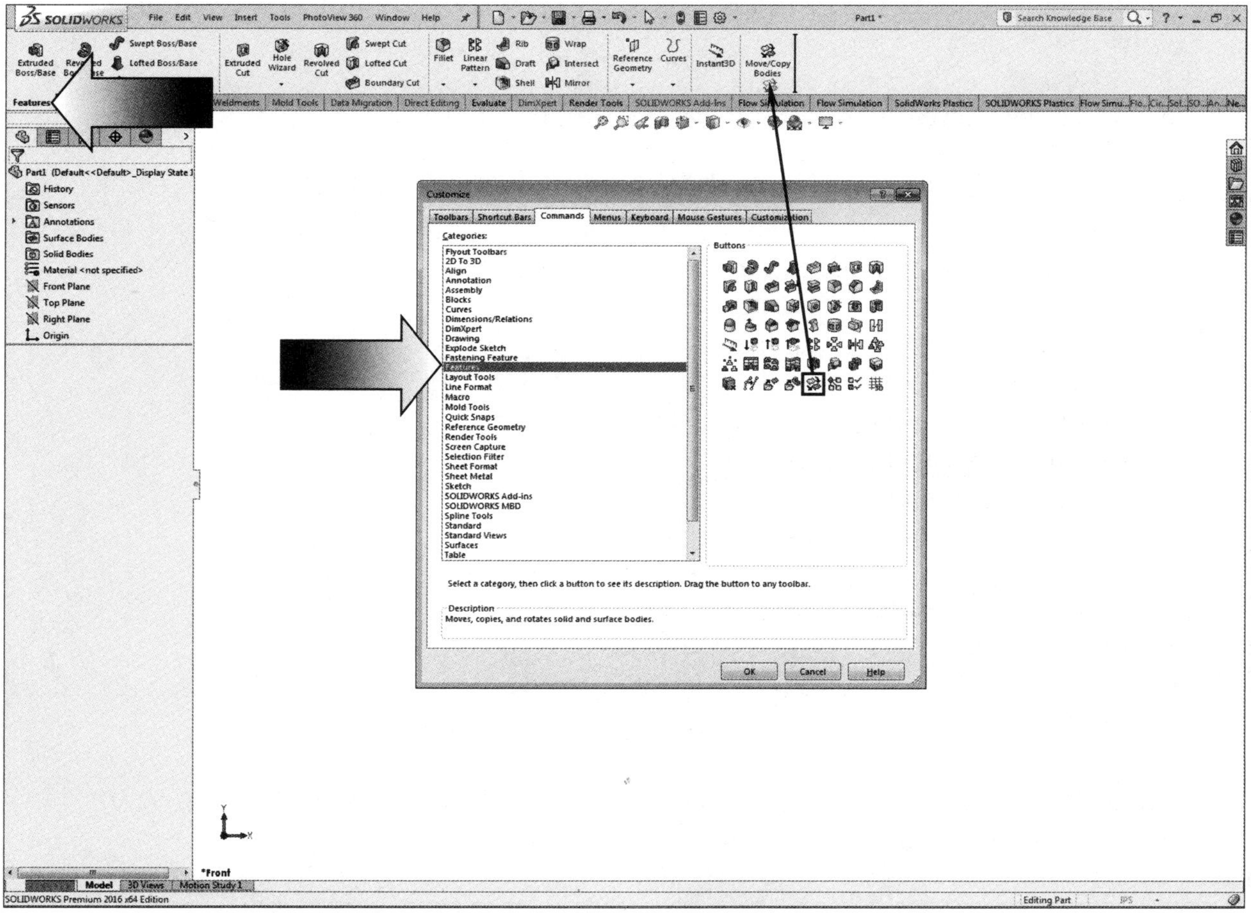

CHAPTER 2

Sketching

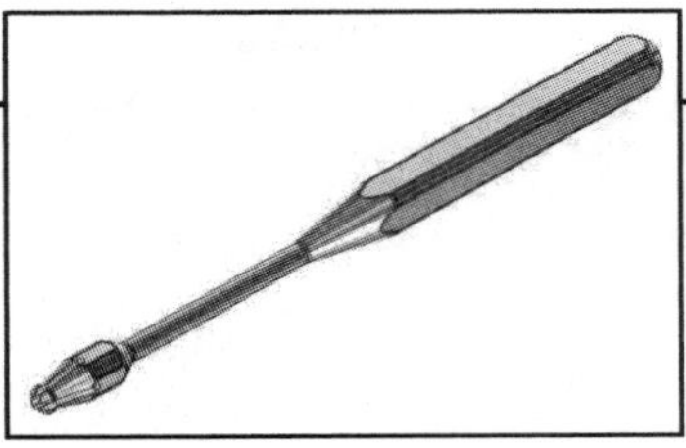

Sketching - Overview
Handle

Most features in SOLIDWORKS start with a sketch. The sketch is the basis for a 3D model. You can create a sketch on any of the default planes (Front Plane, Top Plane, and Right Plane) or a created plane.

There are two modes for sketching in 2D: click-drag or click-click. The click-drag method will create a single entity each time, but the click-click creates multiple, connecting lines.

While sketching the lines you can transition from sketching a line to sketching a tangent arc, and vice versa, without selecting the arc tool. Simply press the A key on the keyboard to switch from a line to a tangent arc – OR - start the line with the first click, move the pointer outward and back to the starting point, then away again.

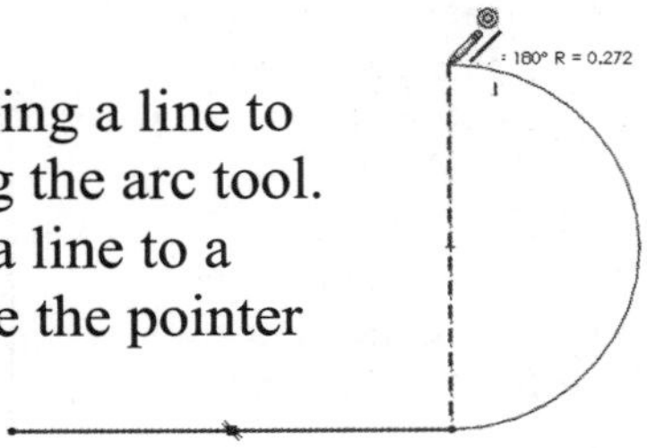

Inferencing lines are dotted lines that appear as you sketch, displaying relations between the pointer and existing sketch entities or model geometry. When your pointer approaches highlighted cues such as midpoints, the inferencing lines guide you relative to existing sketch entities.

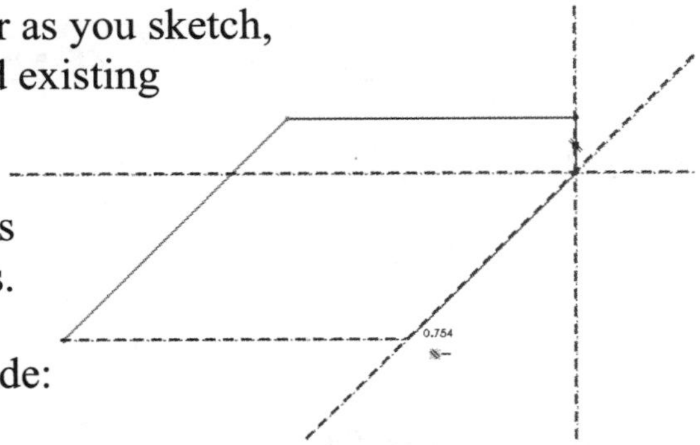

There are 2 types of Snaps in the sketch mode: Sketch Snap and Quick Snap.
Each Sketch Snap allows you to automatically snap to selected entities as you sketch. By default, all Sketch Snaps except Grid are enabled.

Quick Snaps are instantaneous, single operation Sketch Snaps. Sketching any sketch entity (such as a line) from start to finish is a single operation.

Sketching
Handle

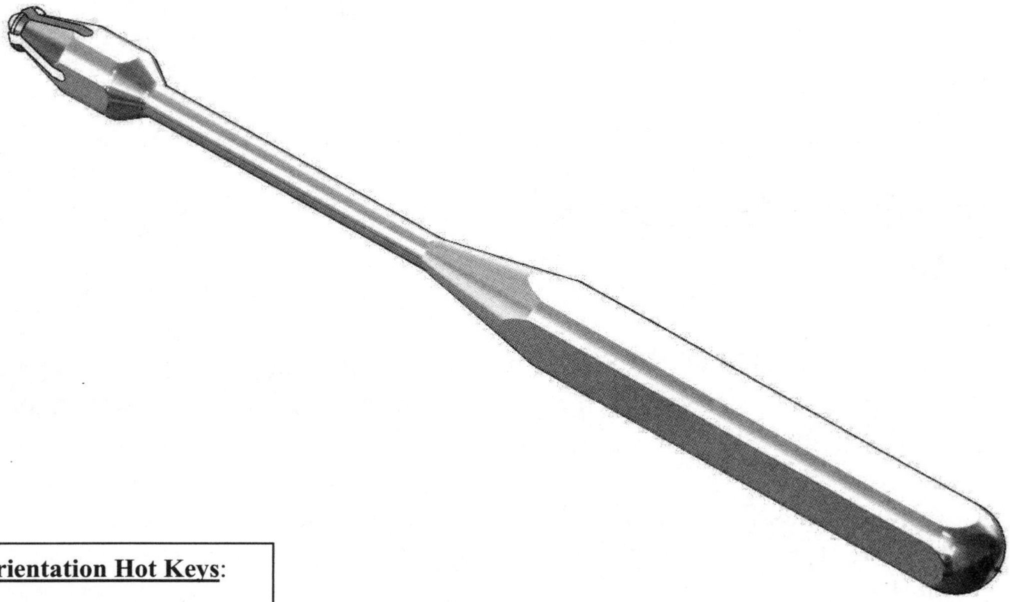

View Orientation Hot Keys:

Ctrl + 1 = Front View
Ctrl + 2 = Back View
Ctrl + 3 = Left View
Ctrl + 4 = Right View
Ctrl + 5 = Top View
Ctrl + 6 = Bottom View
Ctrl + 7 = Isometric View
Ctrl + 8 = Normal To Selection

Dimensioning Standards: **ANSI**

Units: **INCHES** – 3 Decimals

Tools Needed:

Insert Sketch	Line	Circle
Straight Slot	Centerline	Smart Dimension
Extruded Boss	Extruded Cut	Chamfer

1. Starting a new part document:

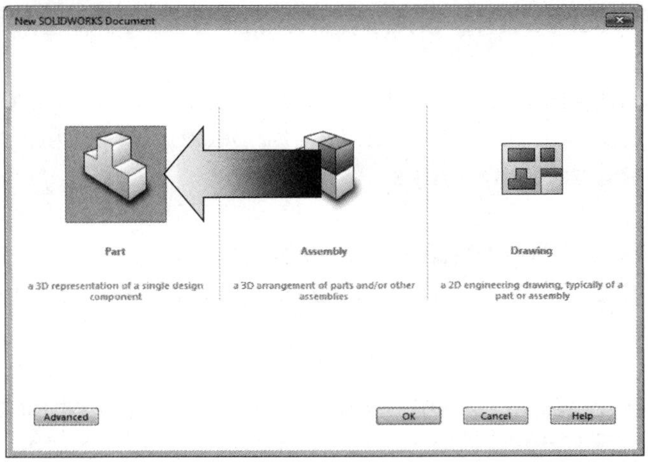

- Select **File / New**.

- The "Novice" dialog box by default displays three template options: **Part, Assembly**, and **Drawing**.

- Select the **Part** template and click **OK** (arrow).

2. Changing the System Options:

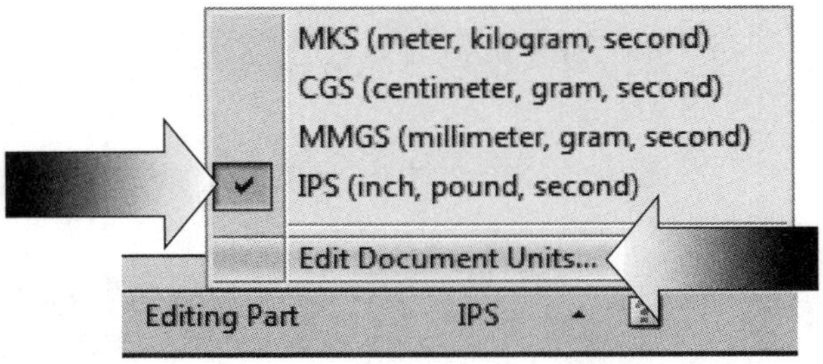

- Click the small arrow at the bottom right corner of the screen and select **IPS** for **Inch, Pound, Second**.

- Select **Tools, Options**.

- Click the **Sketch** option.

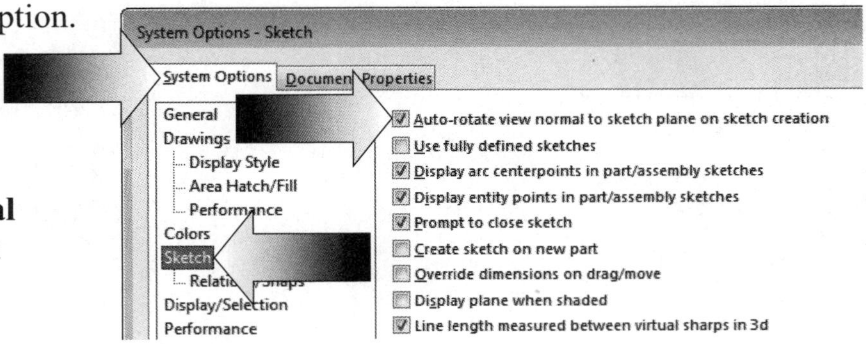

- Enable the check-box for: **Auto-rotate view normal to sketch plane on sketch creation**.

- Switch to the **Document Properties** tab.

- Click the **Drafting Standard** option and select the **ANSI** standard from the list.

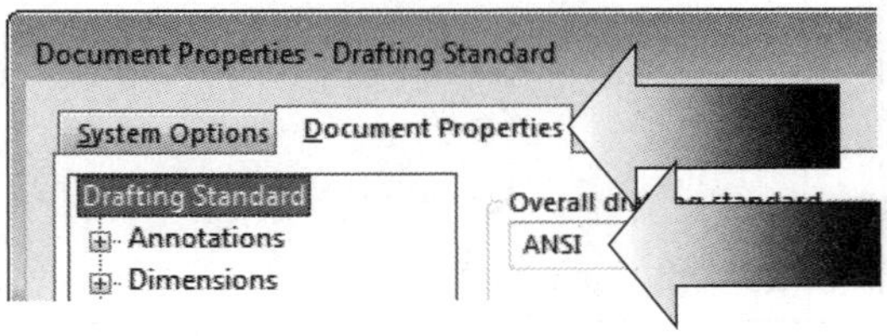

- Click **OK**.

3. Creating the Parent sketch:

Sketching in SOLIDWORKS is the basis for creating features. Features are the basis for creating parts, which can be put together into assemblies. Sketch entities can also be added to drawings.

SOLIDWORKS sketch entities can snap to points (endpoint, midpoints, intersections, etc.) of other sketch entities. With Quick Snaps, you can filter the types of sketch snaps that are available.

Inferencing displays relations by means of dotted inferencing lines, pointer display, and highlighted cues such as endpoints and midpoints.

The sketch status appears in the window status bar. Colors indicate the state of individual sketch entities.

- The 1st sketch in a part document is considered the parent sketch.

- Select the **Front** plane and open a **new sketch** (click the Sketch Pencil).

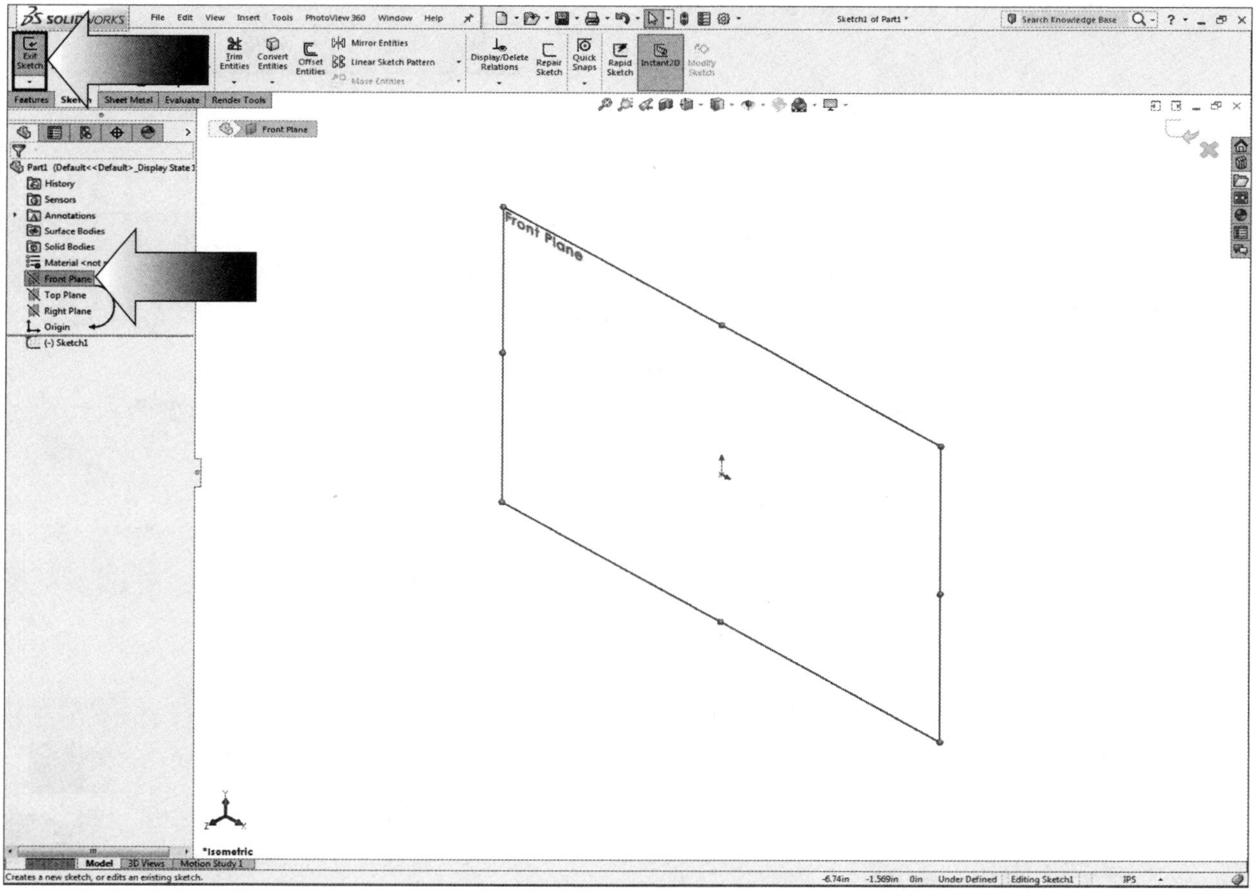

- Select the **Line** command  from the Sketch toolbar.

- Use the **Click-Click** method and start the first line at the Origin, move upward to make a vertical line, and then a horizontal line as indicated.

- Continue with sketching the rest of the lines as shown below.

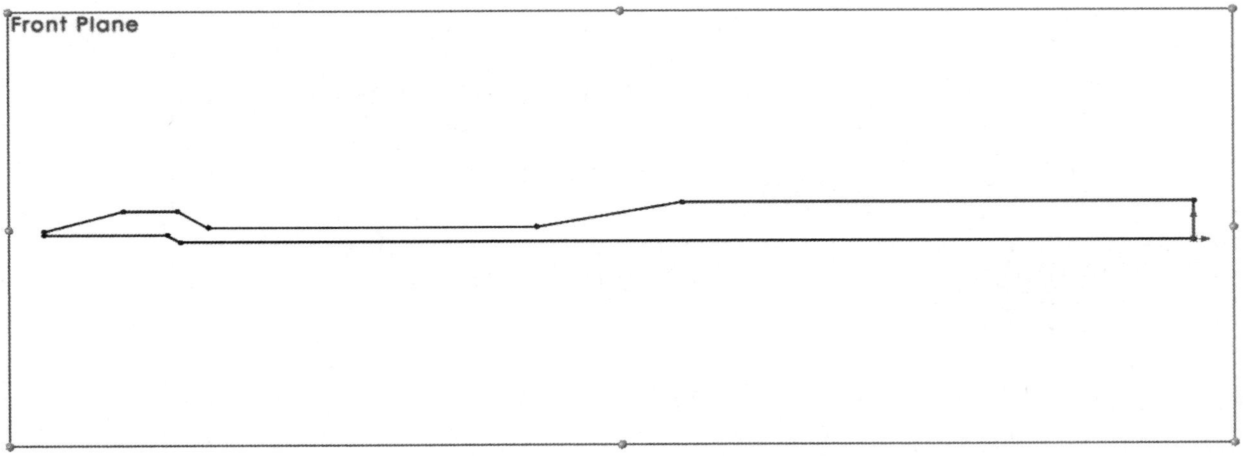

- Select the **Smart Dimension** command , add the dimensions shown 

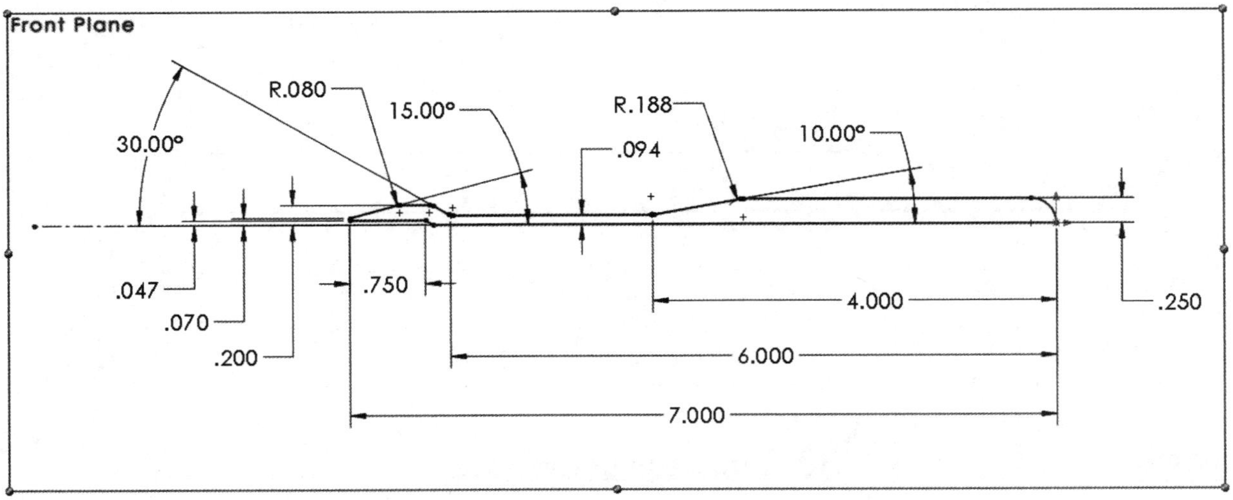

- It is better to add the Sketch Fillets <u>after</u> the sketch is fully defined.

- Add the dimensions to the left end of the sketch as indicated below.

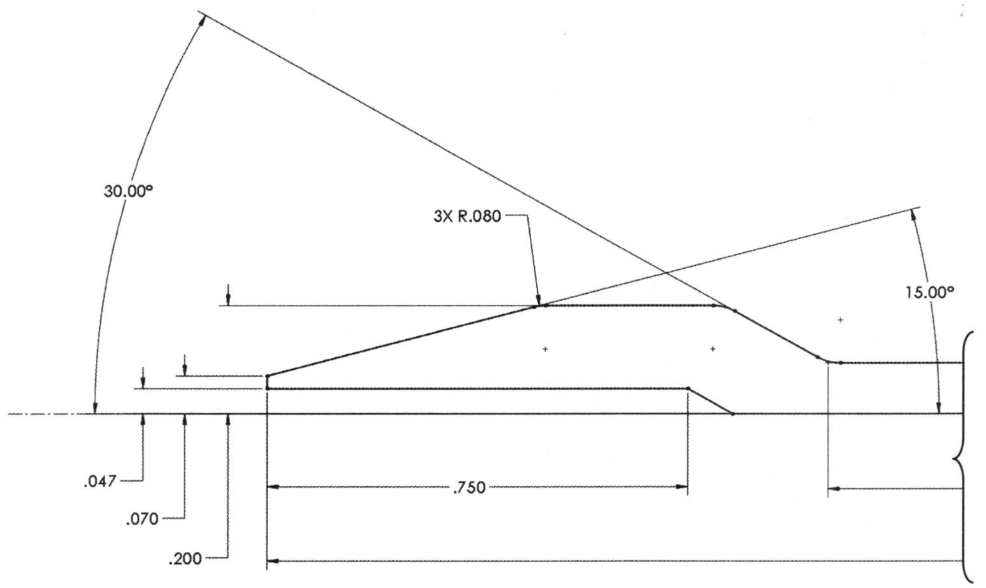

<u>Left end of the sketch</u>

- Add the dimensions to the right end of the sketch as shown.

- The dimension R.250 is a reference dimension and shown in gray color.

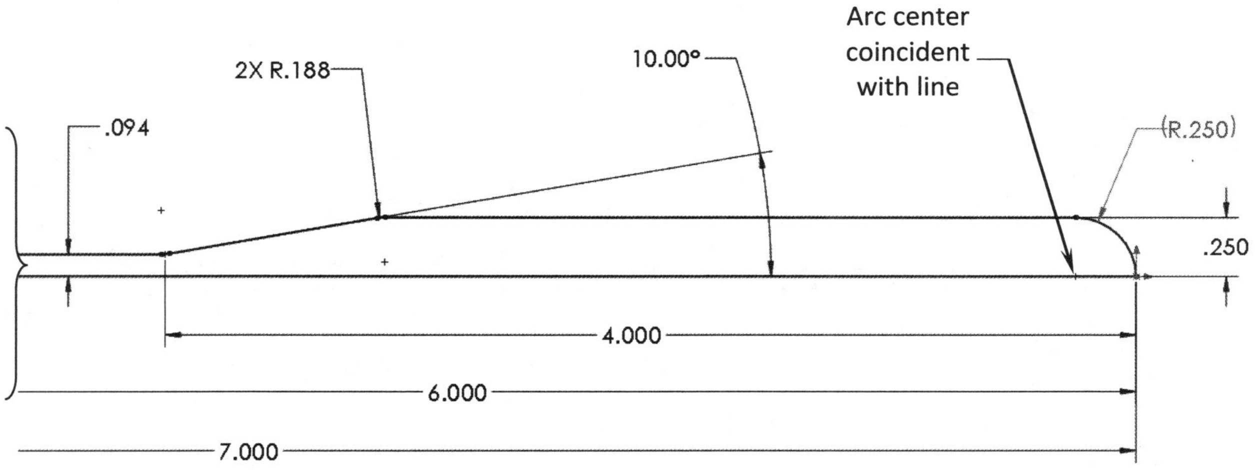

<u>Right end of the sketch</u>

4. Revolving the parent sketch:

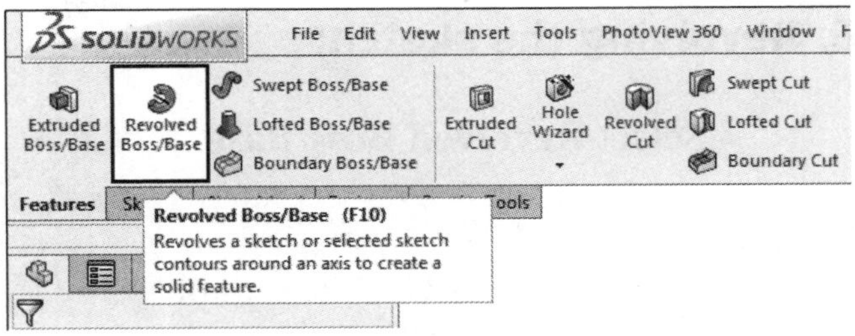

- Switch to the **Features** tool tab.

- Select the revolved **Boss/Base** command.

- Use the default **Blind** type and **360°** angle.

- Click **OK**.

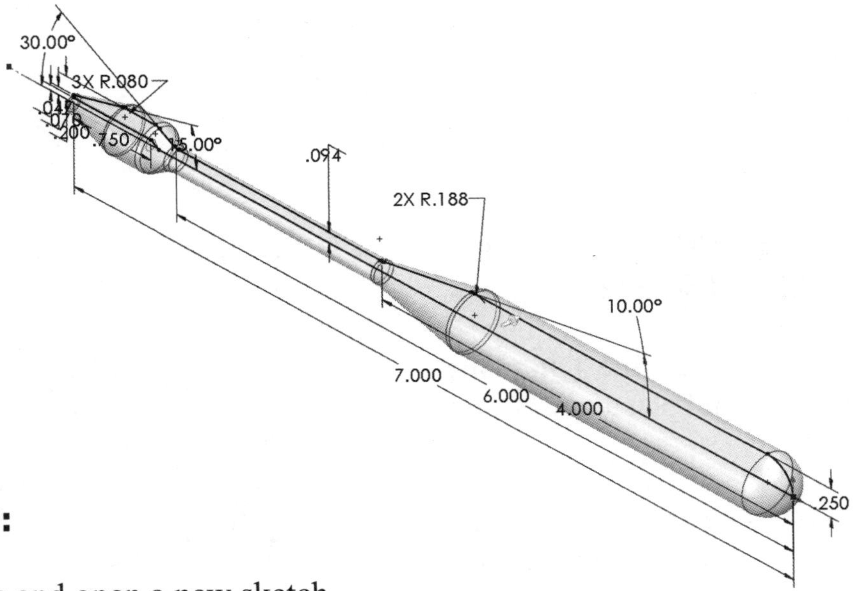

5. Adding the tip detail:

- Select the **Top** plane and open a new sketch.

- Sketch the profile shown on the right.

- Sketch a horizontal centerline to use as the revolve line.

- Add the relations and the dimensions as indicated.

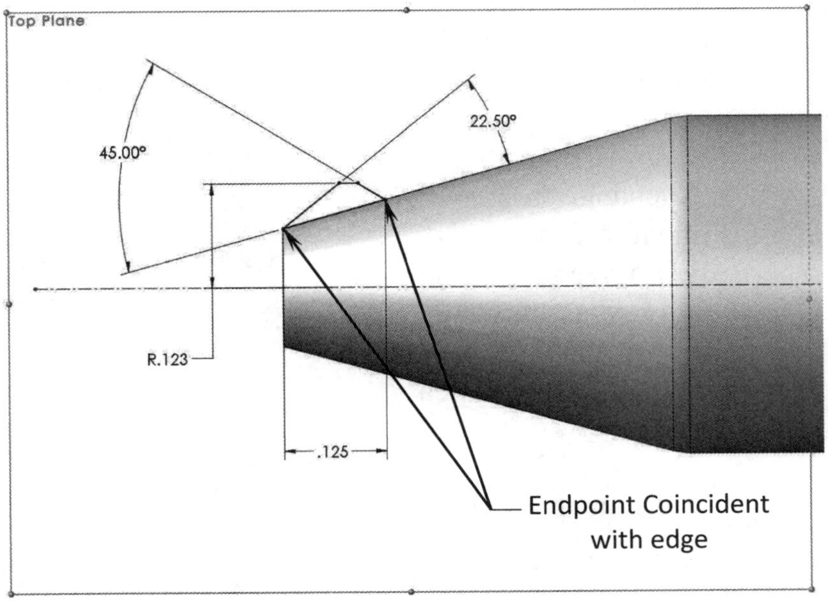

- Be sure to fully define the sketch before revolving it.

6. Revolving the sketch:

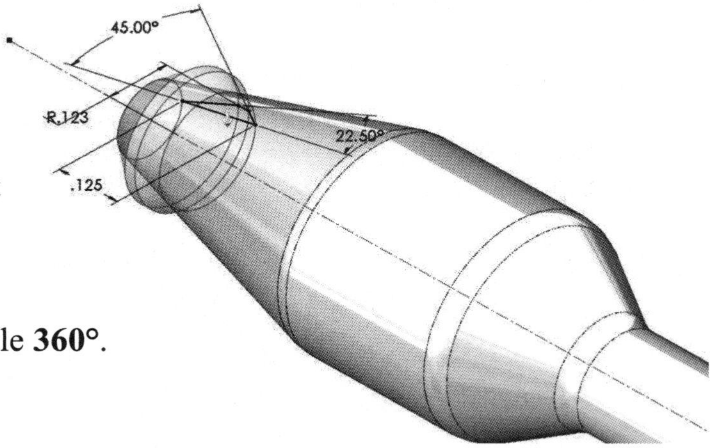

- Select **Revolved Boss/Base**.

- Use the default **Blind** type.

- Revolved Angle **360°**.

- Click **OK**.

7. Transitioning from Line-to-Arc:

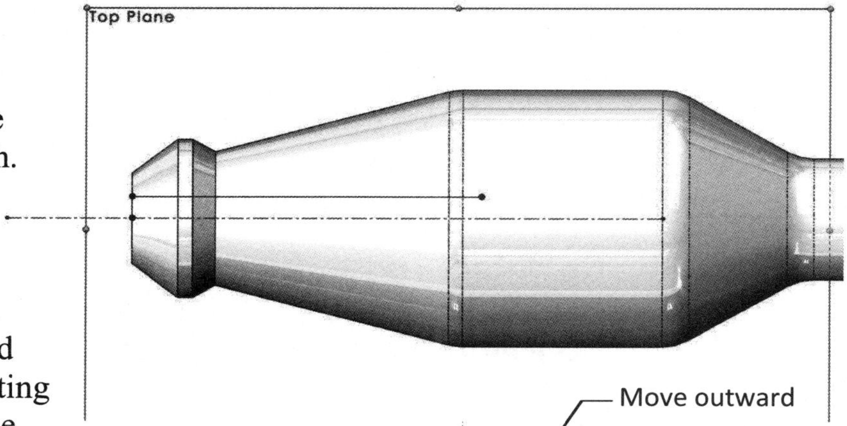

- Select the **Top** plane and pen a new sketch.

- Use the **click-click** method and sketch a short vertical line and a horizontal line starting at the midpoint on the left side.

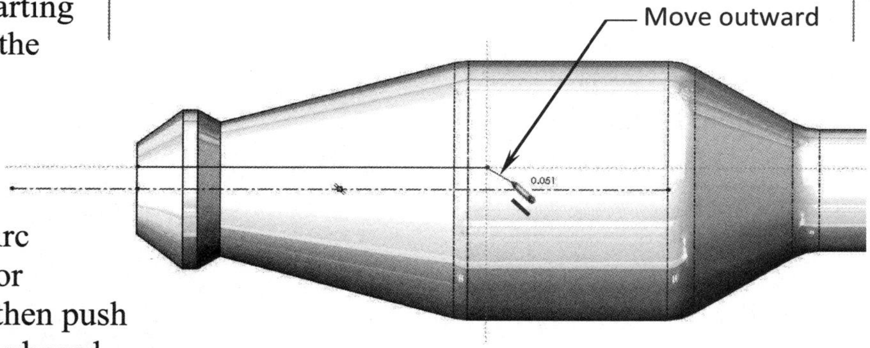

- To change from a line to a Tangent Arc first move the cursor outward as shown then push the **A** key on the keyboard, the tangent arc appears.

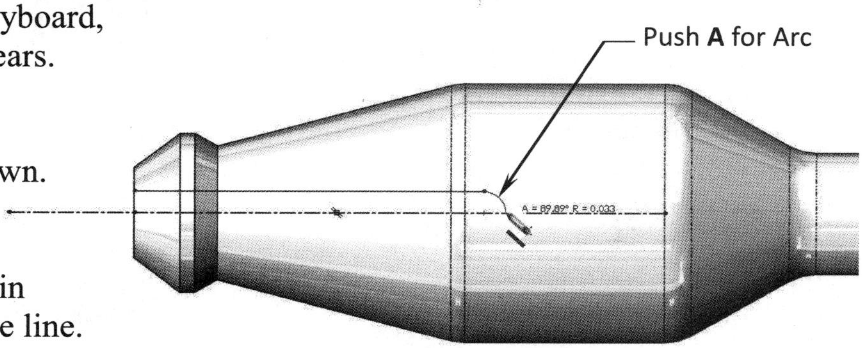

- Make an arc as shown.

- Push the A key again to switch back to the line.

8. Mirroring in sketch mode:

> **Mirror Entities**
>
> Mirrors selected entities about a centerline, a line, or a model edge.
> A Symmetric relation is added to each mirrored entity.

- Push **Esc** to exit the line command.

- Box-Select all sketch entities and click the **Mirror Entities** command.

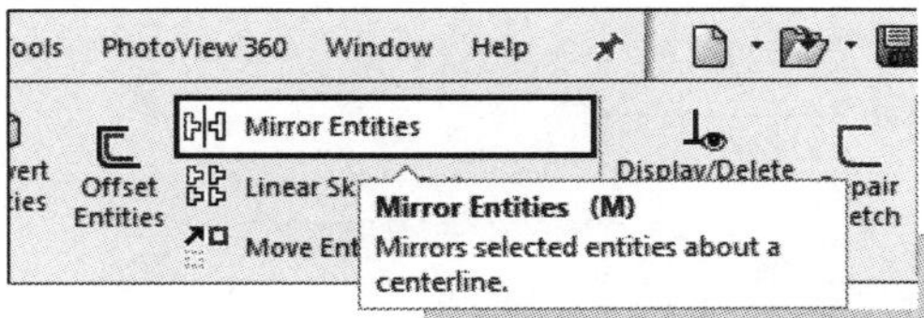

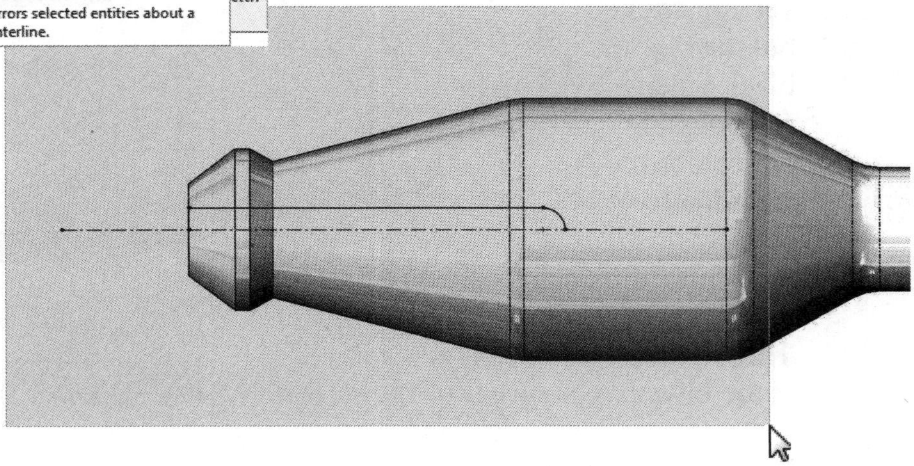

- All selected entities are mirrored about the horizontal centerline.

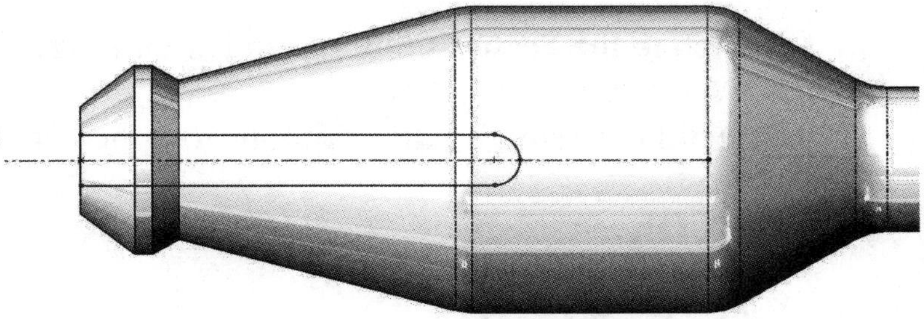

- A **Symmetric** relation is added to each mirrored entity.

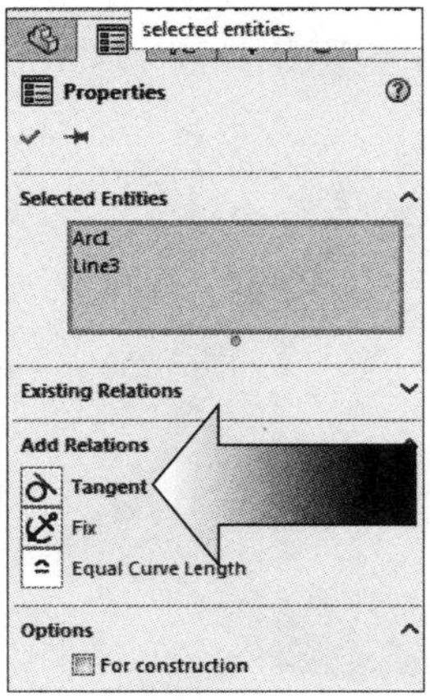

- Hold the **Control** key and select the 2 arcs, click the **Tangent** relation (arrow).

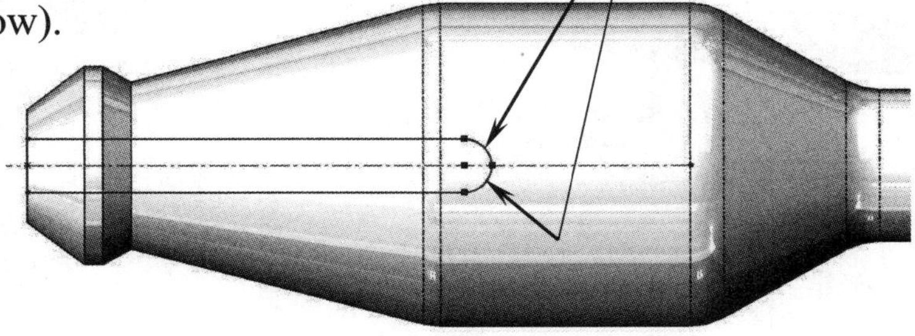

- Click **OK**.

9. Adding dimensions:

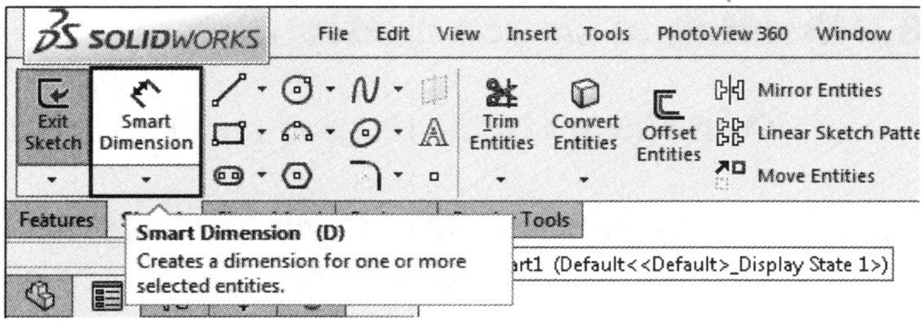

- Use Smart Dimension tool to specify the size and location for each sketch entity.

- The sketch entities appear in blue color when they are not yet constrained, but turn black when relations or dimensions are added.

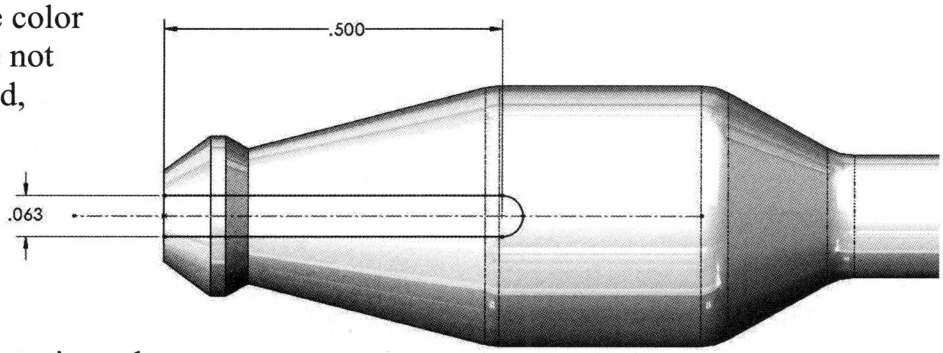

- Add the 2 dimensions shown.

- The Status of the sketch is displayed at the lower right corner of the screen.

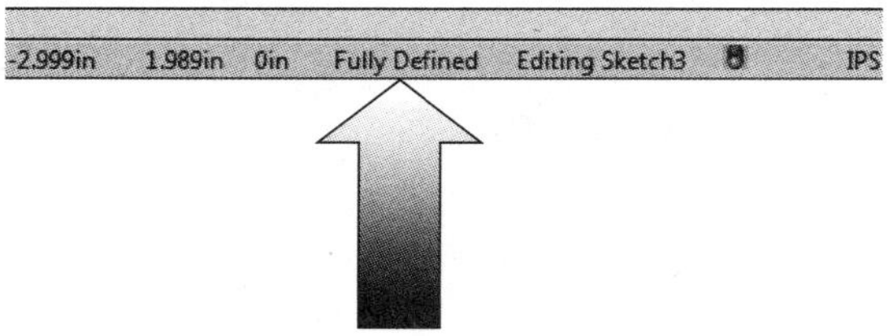

10. Extruding a cut:

- Switch to the Features tool tab and click **Extruded Cut**.

- Select the **Through All** condition from the list and click **Reverse** direction.

- Click **OK**.

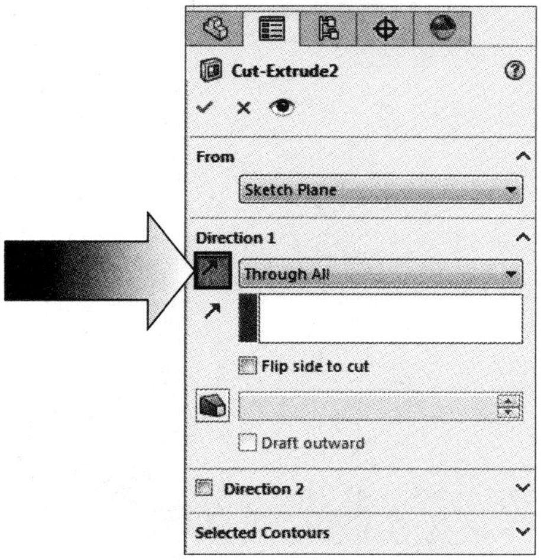

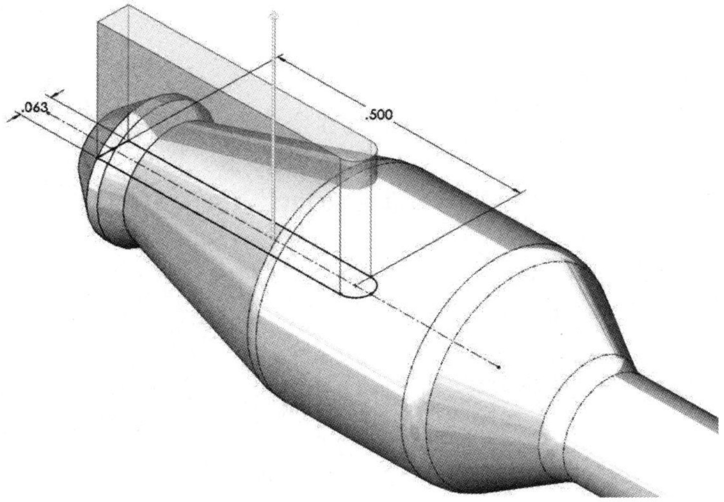

11. Creating a Circular Pattern:

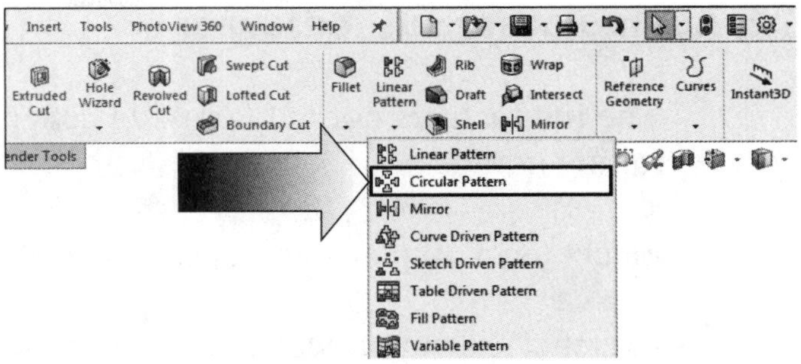

- Circular patterns create multiple instances of one or more features and space them uniformly around an axis.

- Select the **Circular Pattern** command below the Linear Pattern drop down.

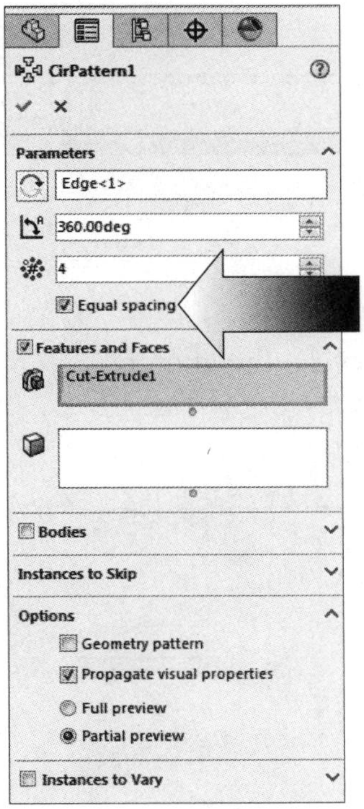

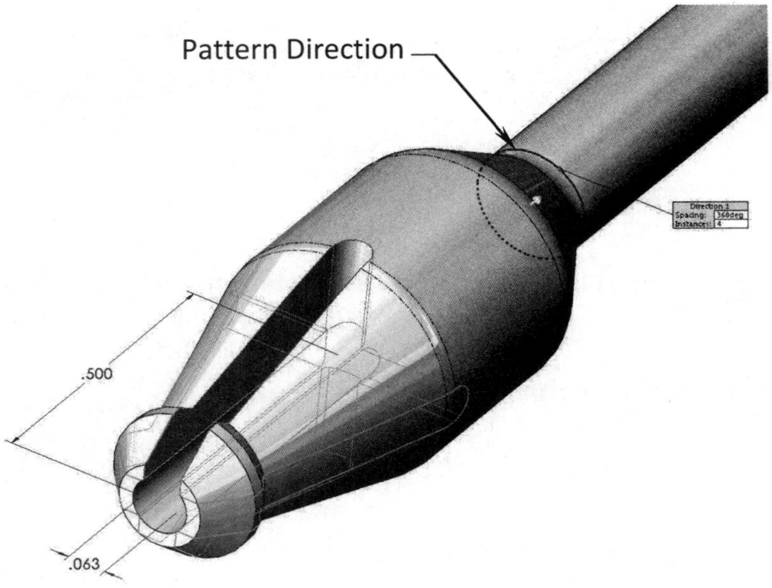

- For Pattern Direction, select one of the **circular edges** in the model.

- Enable the **Equal Spacing** checkbox (arrow).

- Enter **4** for Number of Instances.

- Select the **Cut-Extrude1** either from the Feature tree or from the graphics area. The preview graphics of the 4 instances appears.

- Click **OK**.

12. Adding other cut features:

- The flat features not only provide better grips but also help keep the device from rolling around.

- Select the **Top** plane and open a new sketch.

- Sketch **2 Corner Rectangles** at both ends of the model.

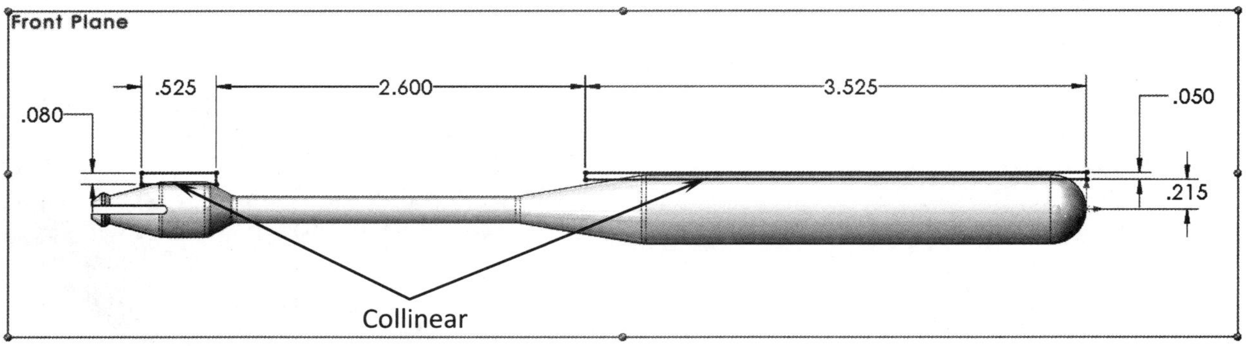

- Add the dimensions and relations shown to fully define the sketch.

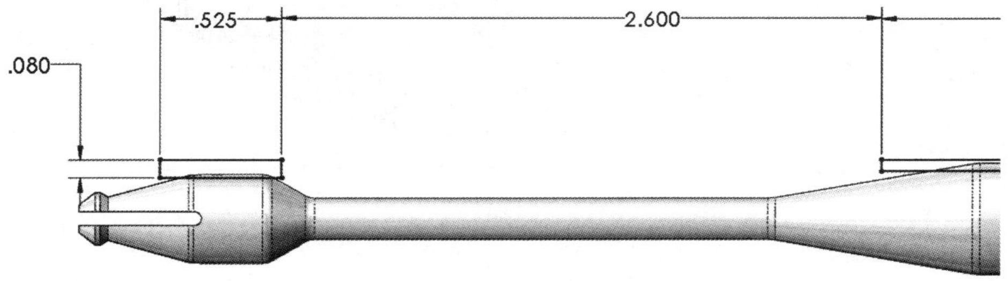

Left end of the sketch

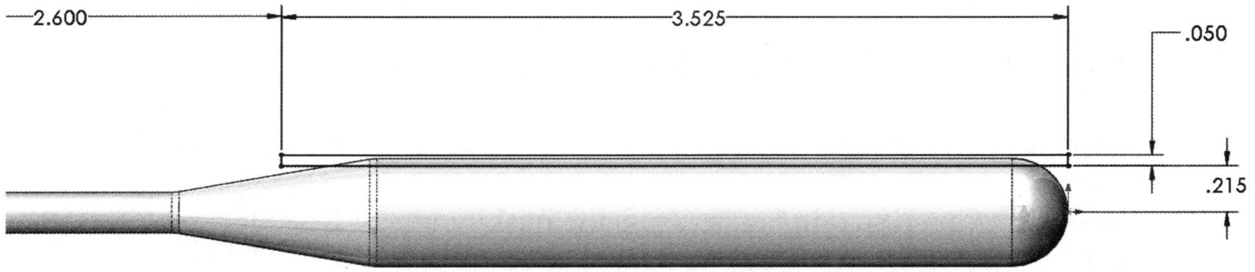

Right end of the sketch

- Switch to the **Features** tool tab and click the **Extruded Cut** command.

- Select the **Through All – Both** from the list to cut through both directions.

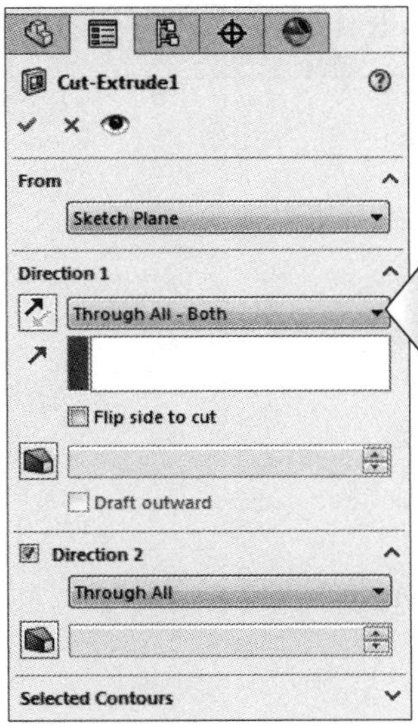

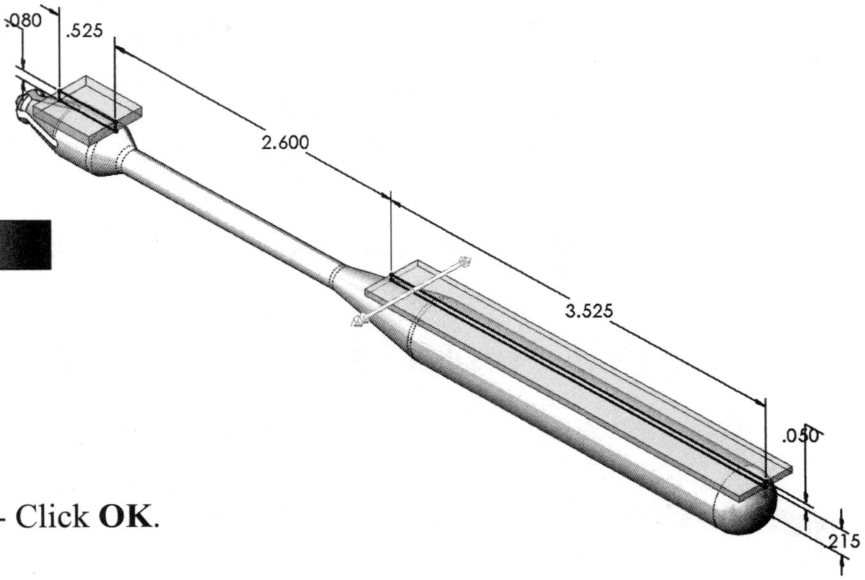

- Click **OK**.

13. Creating another Circular Pattern:

- Select the Circular Pattern command below the Linear Pattern option.

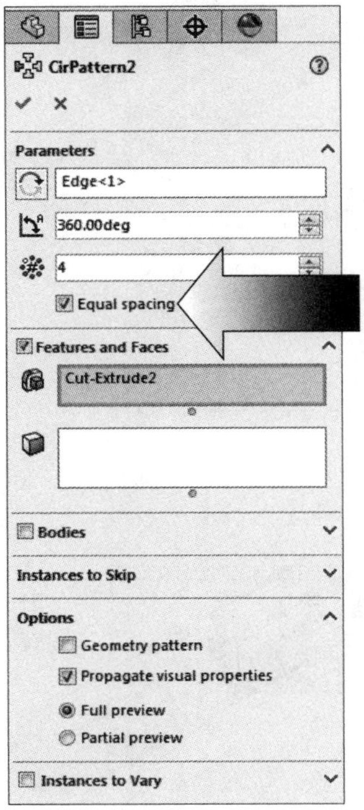

- For Pattern Direction, select one of the **circular edges** of the model.

- Enable the **Equal Spacing** checkbox.

- Enter **4** for Number of Instances.

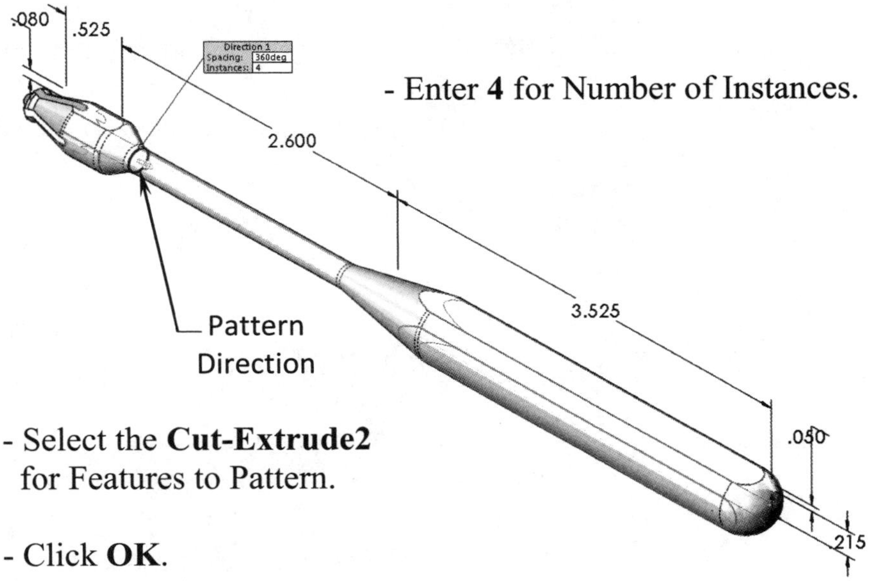

- Select the **Cut-Extrude2** for Features to Pattern.

- Click **OK**.

14. Adding a .032" Constant Size Fillet:

> **Constant Size Fillet**
>
> Creates fillets that have a constant size for the entire length of the fillet.

- Select the **Fillet** command from the Features tool tab.

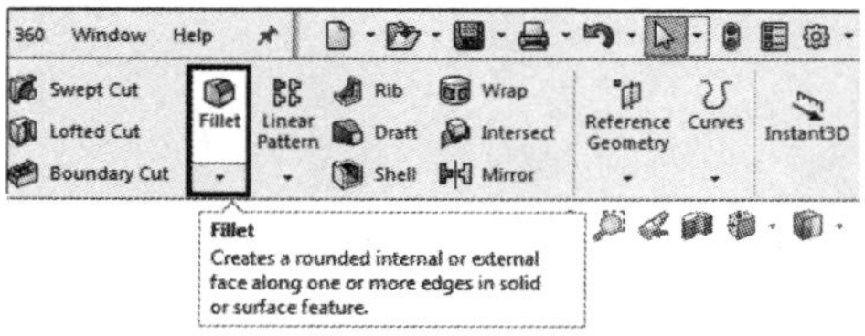

- The **Constant Size Radius** is the default type.

- Select 1 edge for each flat feature, total of **8 edges**.

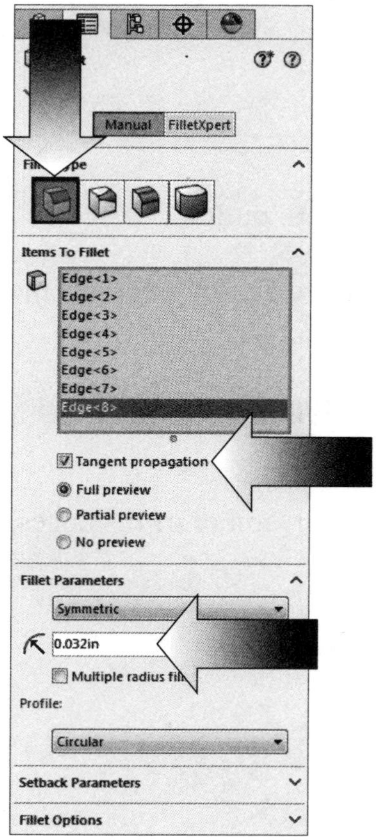

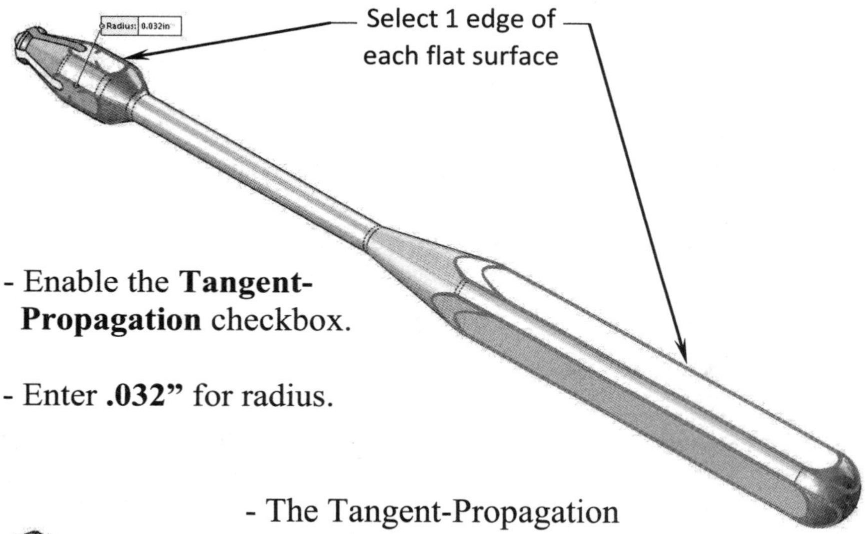

- Enable the **Tangent-Propagation** checkbox.

- Enter **.032"** for radius.

- The Tangent-Propagation extends the fillet to all faces that are tangent to the selected face (arrow).

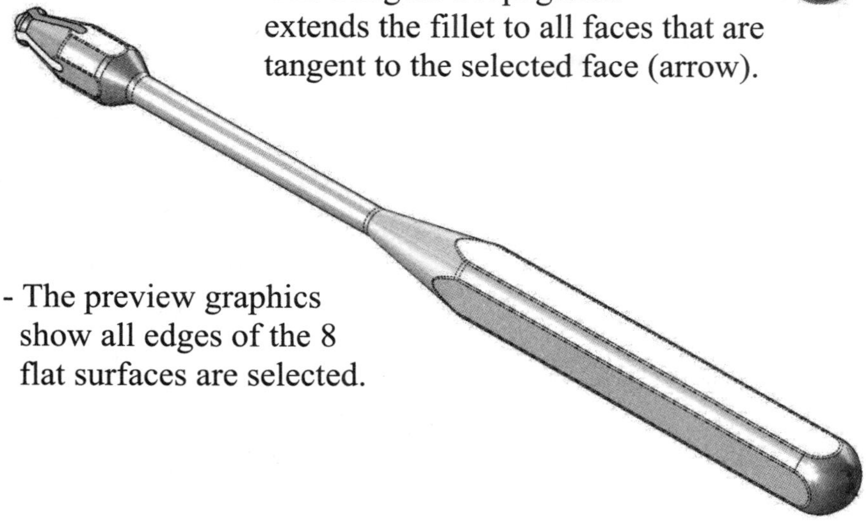

- The preview graphics show all edges of the 8 flat surfaces are selected.

- Click **OK**.

15. Assigning material to the model:

- SOLIDWORKS has two sets of properties, visual and physical (mechanical). The response of a part when loads are applied to it depends on the material assigned.

- Right click **Material** on the FeatureManager tree and select **Edit Material**.

- In the SOLIDWORKS Materials folder, expand the **Steel** sub folder.

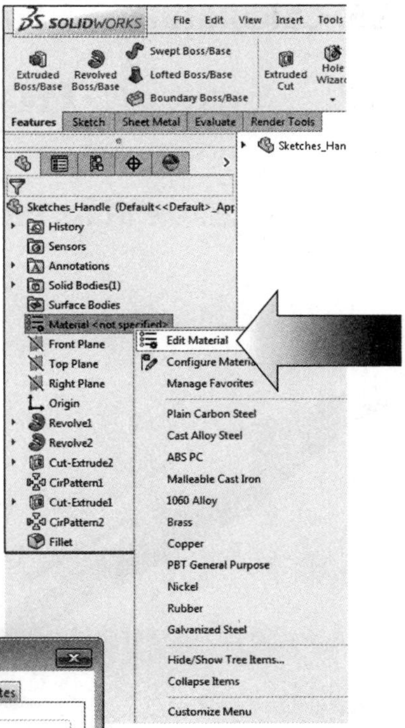

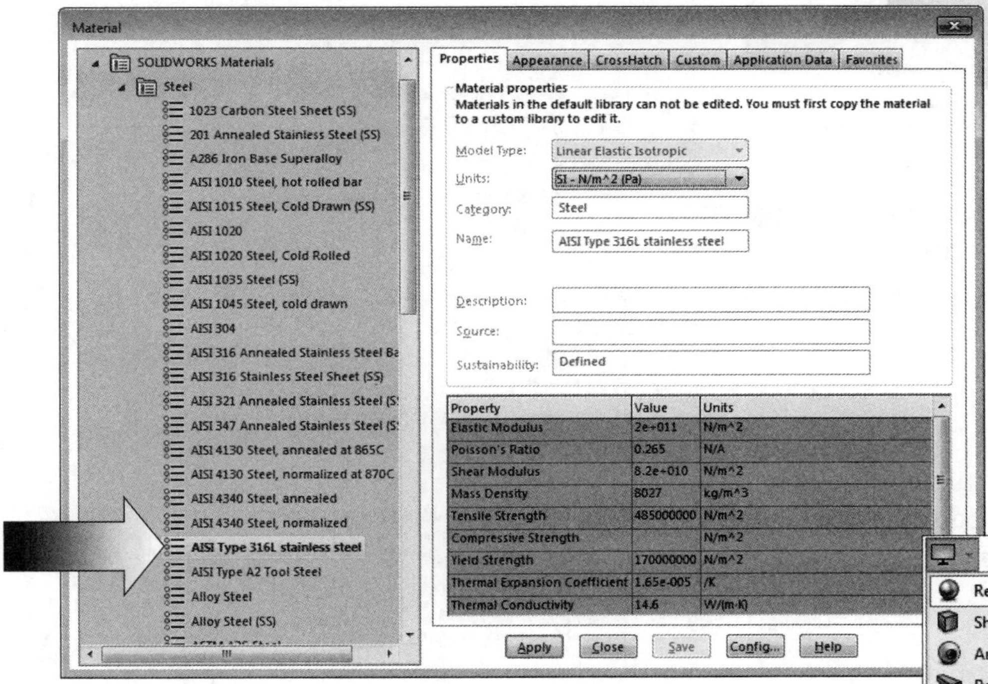

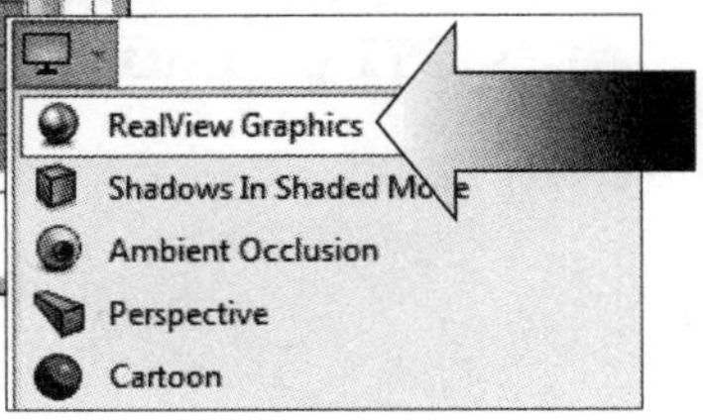

- Select the material **AISI Type 316L Stainless Steel** from the list (arrow).

- Click **Apply** and **Close**.

- Enable the RealView Graphics option to enhance the model display if applicable.

16. Calculating the Mass of the model:

- Switch to the **Evaluate** tab.

- Click the **Mass Properties** command (arrow).

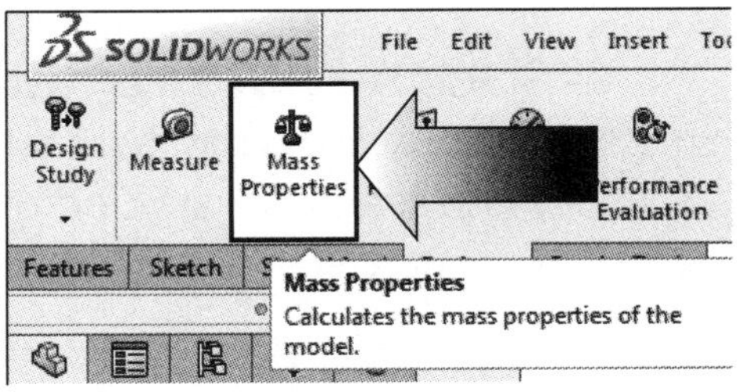

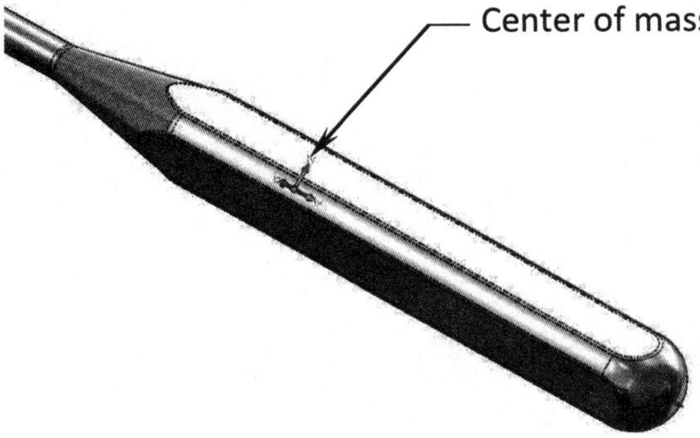

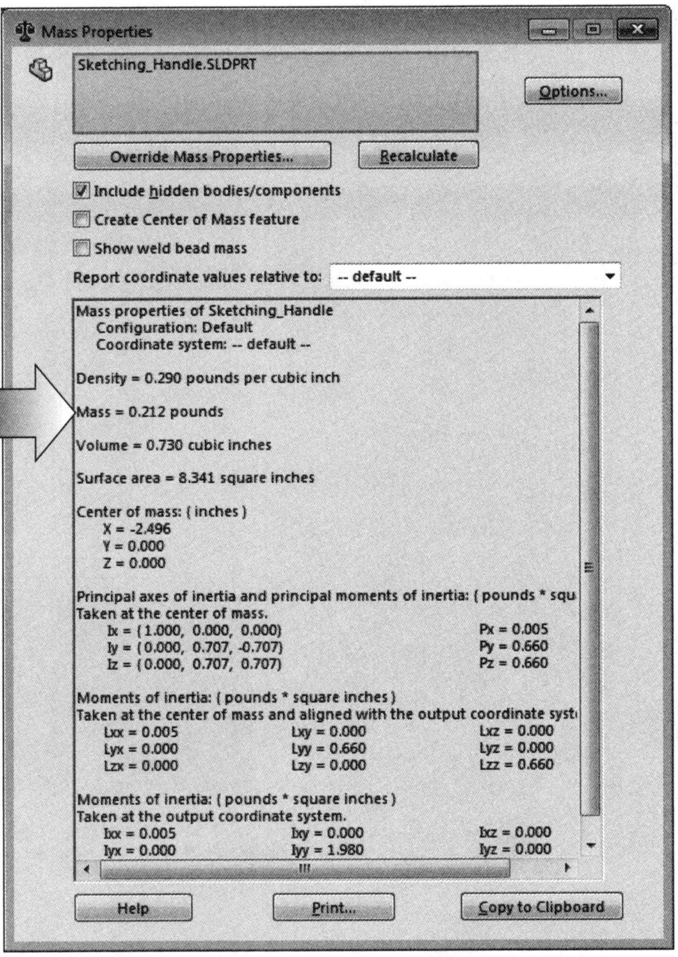

- In the graphics area, a single-colored triad indicates the principal axes and center of mass of the model.

- The mass of the model based on the selected material is: **.212 pounds**.

17. Saving your work:

- Select File / Save As.

- Enter **Sketcing_Hanlde.sldprt** for the name of the part.

- Click **Save**.

CHAPTER 3

Creating Multibody Parts

Creating Multibody Parts
Wooden Crate

Part documents can contain multiple solid bodies.
Multibody parts should not replace the use of assemblies.

A general rule to keep in mind is that one part (multibody or not) should represent one part number in a Bill of Materials. A multibody part consists of multiple solid bodies that are not dynamic. If dynamic motion among bodies is needed it should be done in an assembly instead. Tools such as Move Component, Dynamic Clearance, and Collision Detection are available only with assembly documents.

Multibody solids can be manipulated the same ways you manipulate single solid bodies. For example, you can add and modify features, and change the names and colors of each solid body.

A folder named Solid Bodies appears in the FeatureManager design tree when there are solid bodies in a single part document. The number of solid bodies in the part document is displayed in parentheses next to the Solid Bodies folder. The solid bodies can be organized and managed in the following ways:

- Group bodies into folders in the Solid Bodies folder.
- Select commands to apply to all bodies within a folder.
- List features that belong to each body.

Multiple solid bodies can be created from a single feature with the following commands:

- Extrude boss and cut.
- Surface cut.
- Boss and cut thicken.
- Revolve boss and cut (including thin features).
- Sweep boss and cut (including thin features).
- Cavity.

Wooden Crate
Creating Multibody Parts

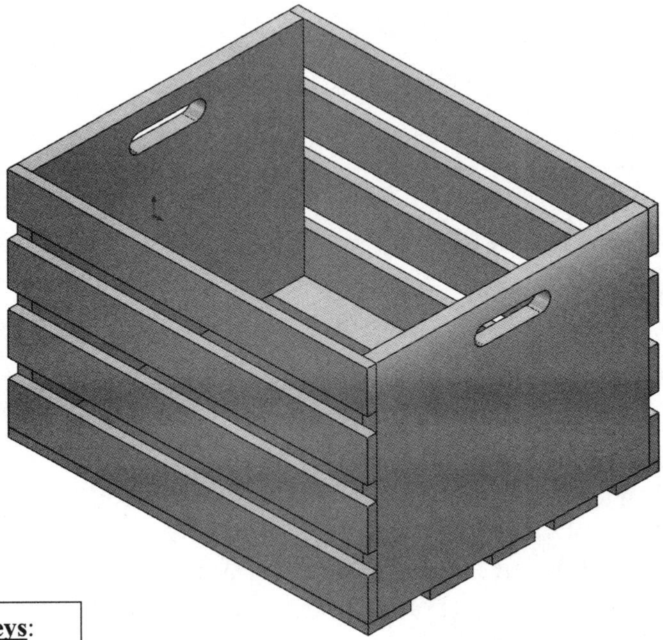

View Orientation Hot Keys:

Ctrl + 1 = Front View
Ctrl + 2 = Back View
Ctrl + 3 = Left View
Ctrl + 4 = Right View
Ctrl + 5 = Top View
Ctrl + 6 = Bottom View
Ctrl + 7 = Isometric View
Ctrl + 8 = Normal To Selection

Dimensioning Standards: **ANSI**

Units: **INCHES** – 3 Decimals

Tools Needed:

Insert Sketch	Center Rectangle	Extruded Boss/Base
Dimension	Add Relations	Linear Pattern
Move/Copy	Exploded View	Mirror

1. Starting a new part document:

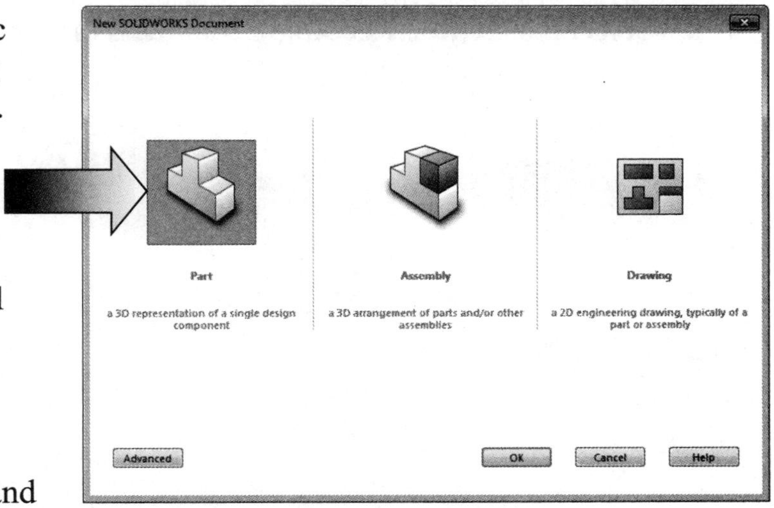

- The Multibody-Parts topic is best learned by creating a new model from scratch. You can see step-by-step how each body gets created and how the bodies get organized and managed as the model is built.

- Select: **File / New / Part.**

- Select the **Part** template and click **OK.**

- Select the **Front** plane from the FeatureManager tree (arrow) and open a new sketch by clicking on the **Pencil** icon (arrow).

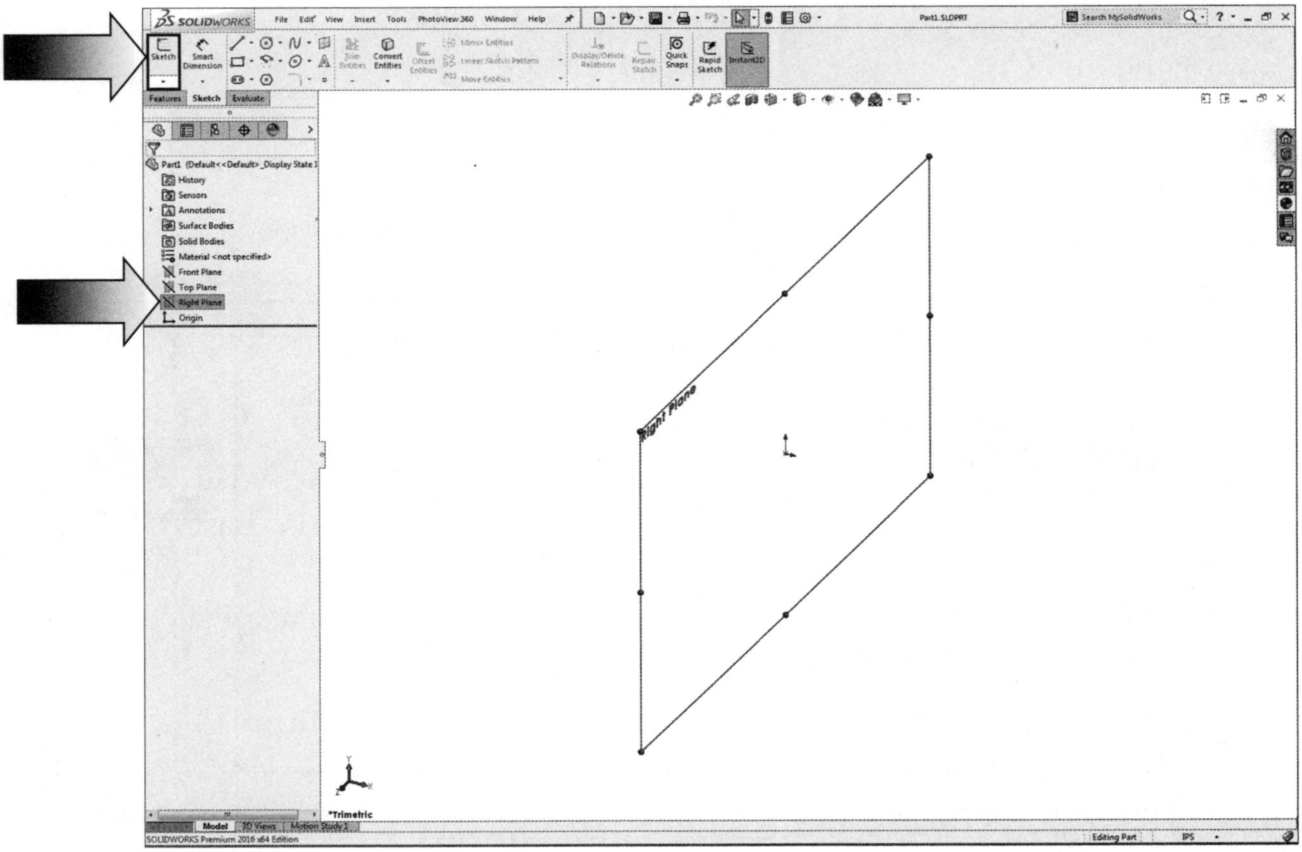

2. Sketching the 1st body profile:

- Select the **Center Rectangle** command (arrow) and sketch a rectangle that is centered on the origin.

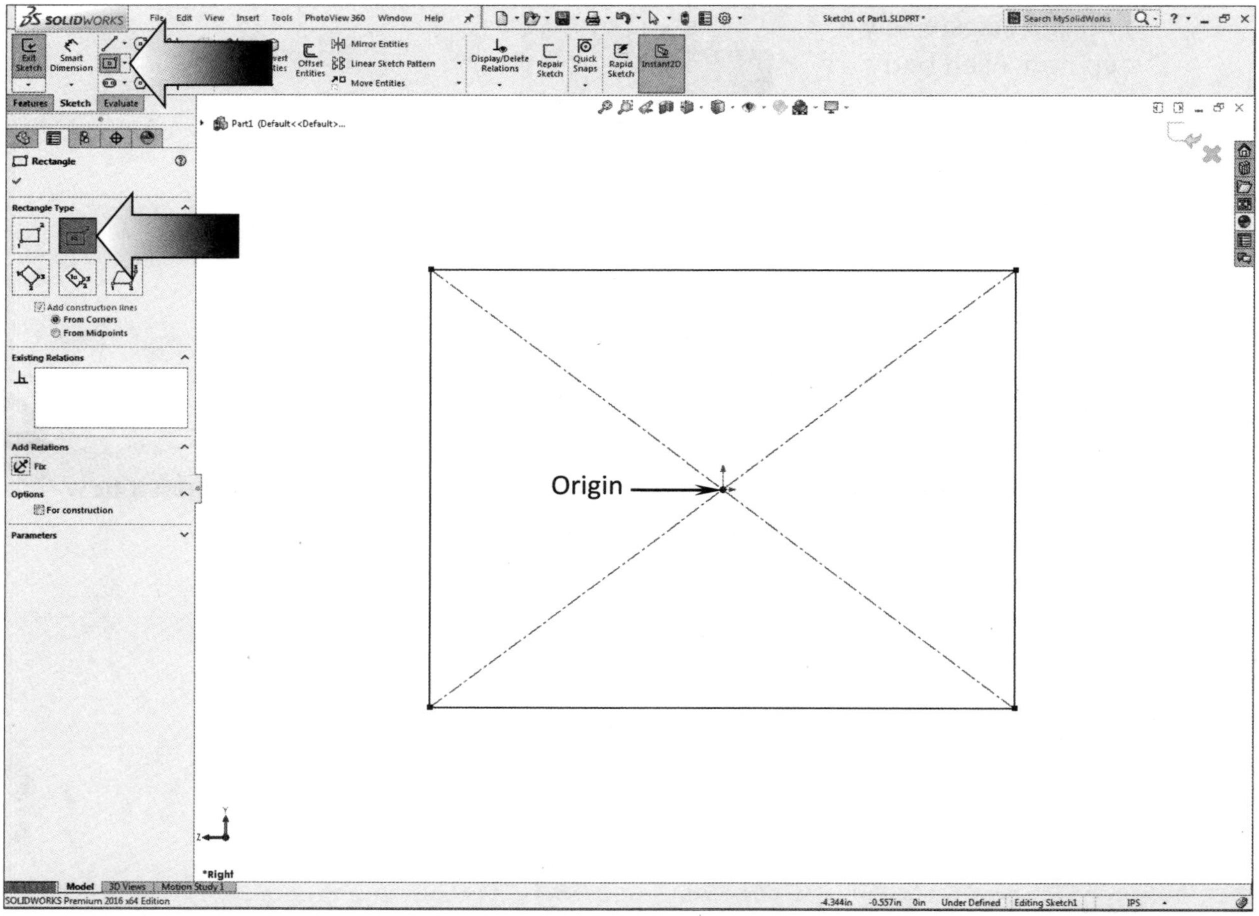

- Add the vertical and the horizontal dimensions shown.

- Vertical dim. = **12.000"**
- Horizontal dim. = **14.250"**

- The sketch should become fully defined at this point.

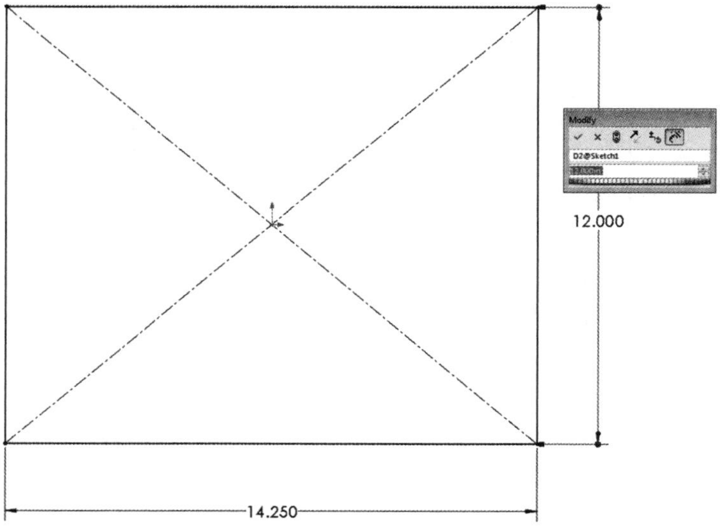

- Click the **Straight-Slot** command, clear the Add Dimensions checkbox (arrows).

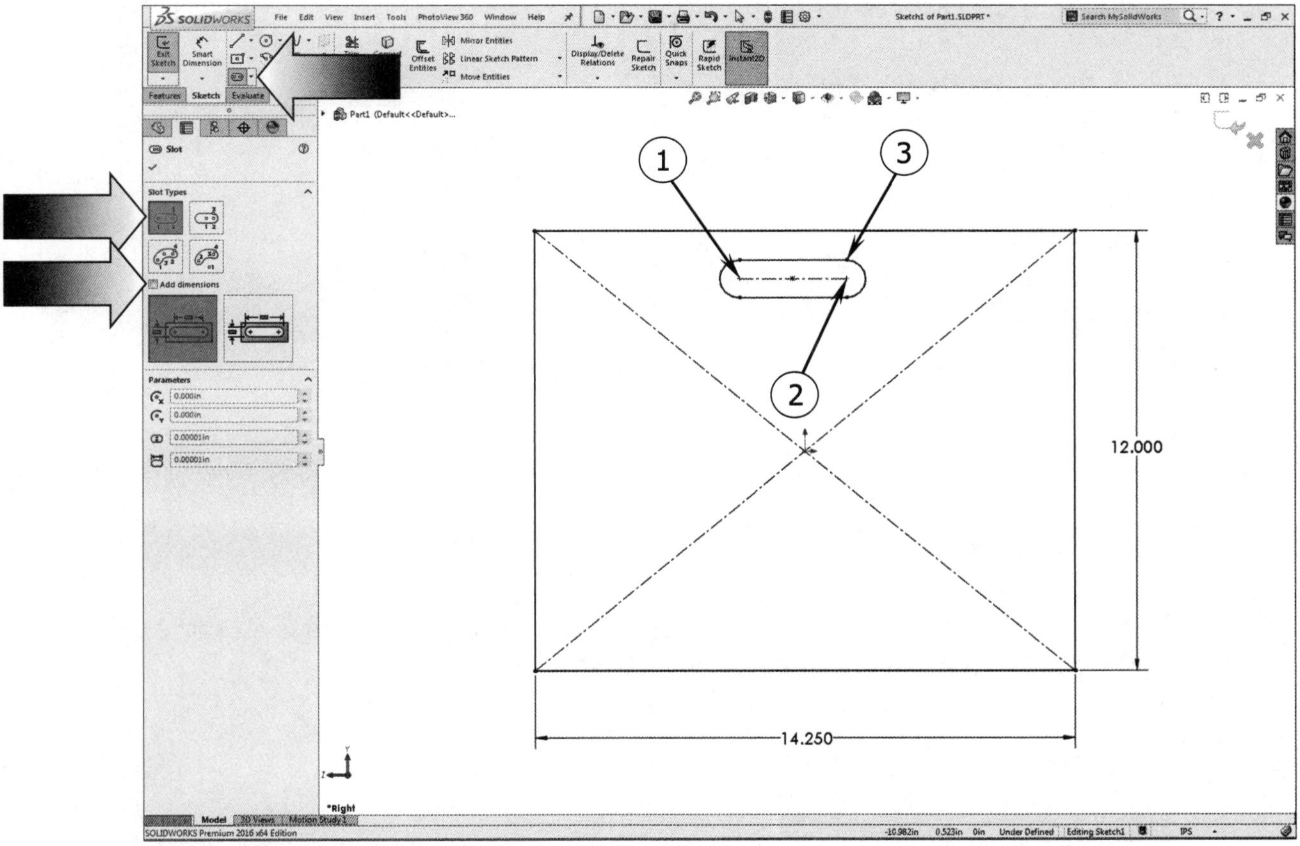

- Sketch the slot by clicking the 3 points in the order noted above.

- Add the 3 dimensions as indicated to position the slot.

- Add the vertical relation to fully define the slot.

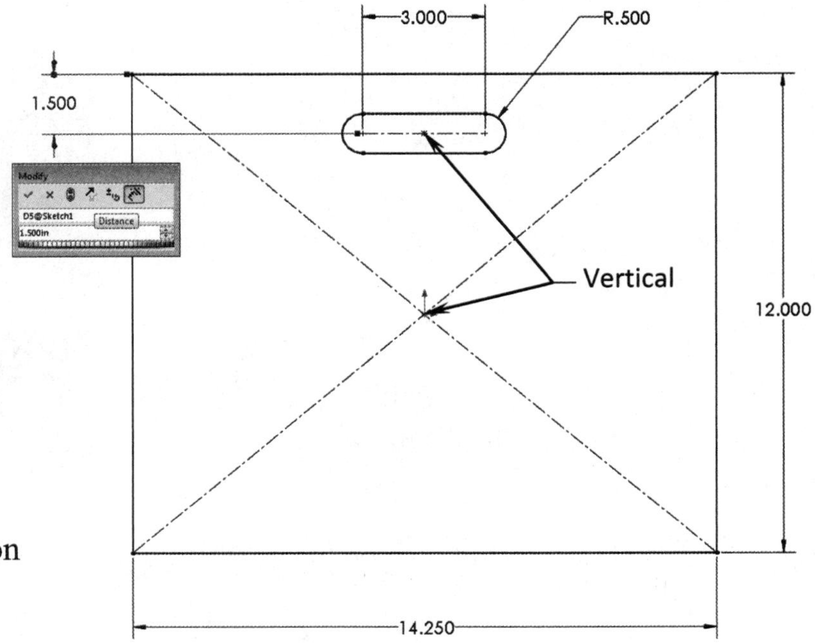

3. Extruding the 1st body:

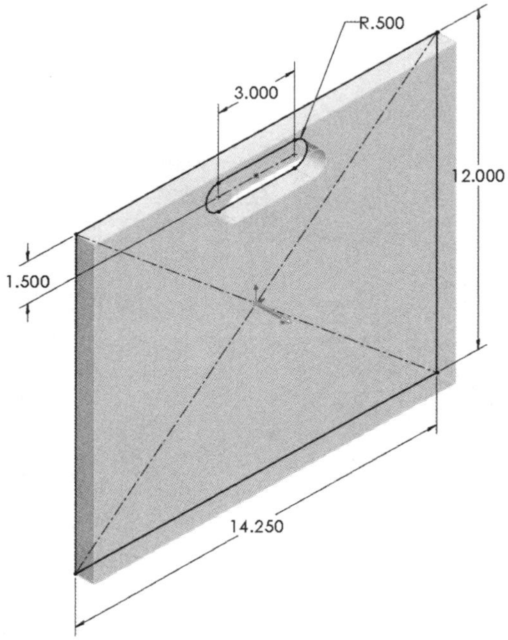

- Switch to the **Features** tool tab.

- Click the **Extruded Boss-Base** command.

- Use the default **Blind** extrude type.

- Enter **.750in** for extrude depth.

- Click **OK**.

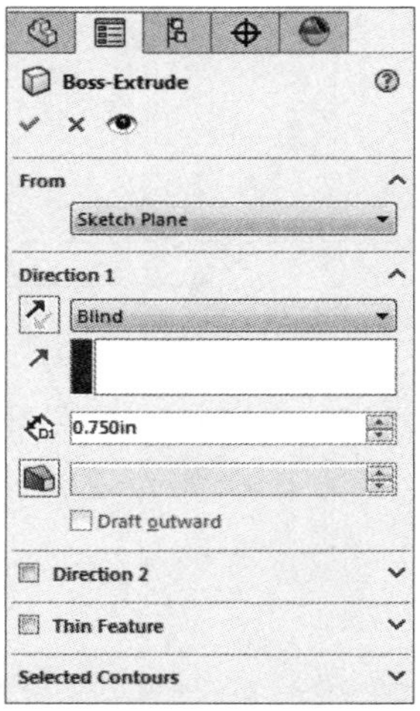

4. Copying the body:

- Since the 2nd body is identical to the first one, it is quicker to make a copy than to recreate it. Select: **Insert / Features / Move/Copy** (arrow).

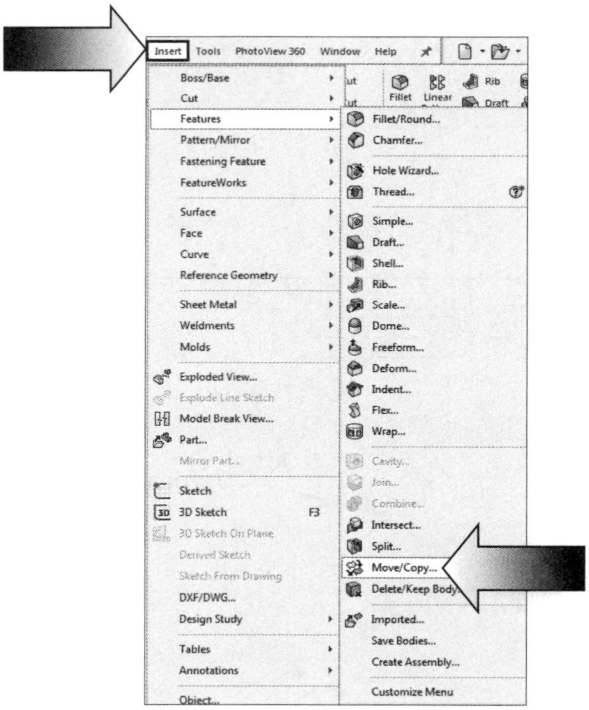

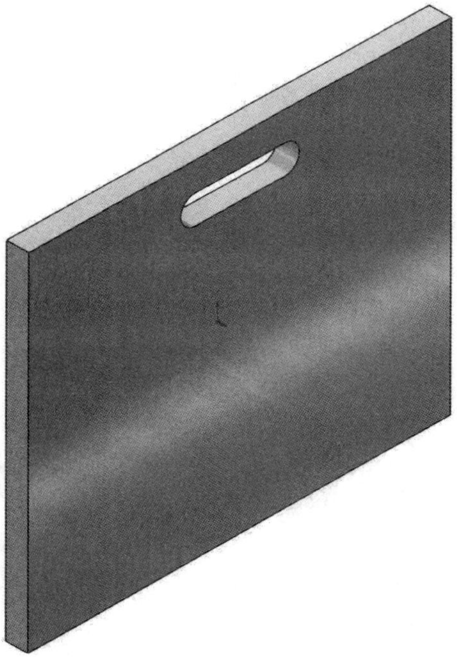

Tip: *Select **Tools / Customize / Commands / Features** and drag/drop the **Move/Copy** command to your Features tool tab.*

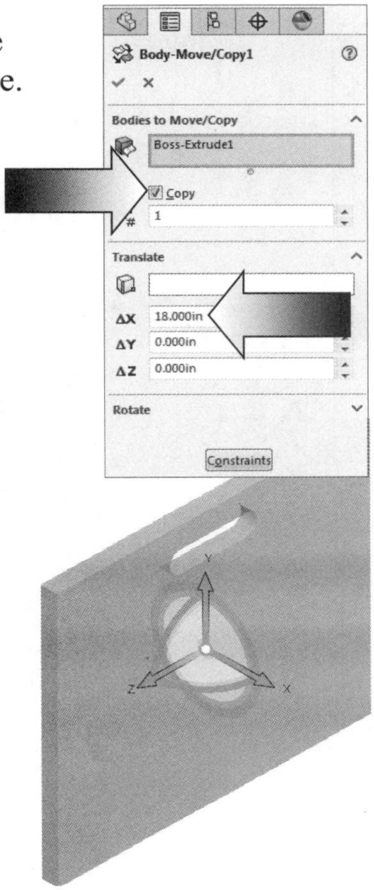

- Click the **Translate/Rotate** button at the bottom of the tree to switch from the Constraints mode to Move mode.

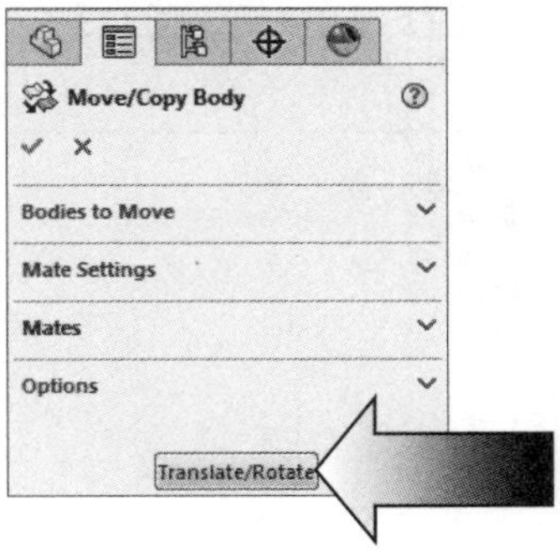

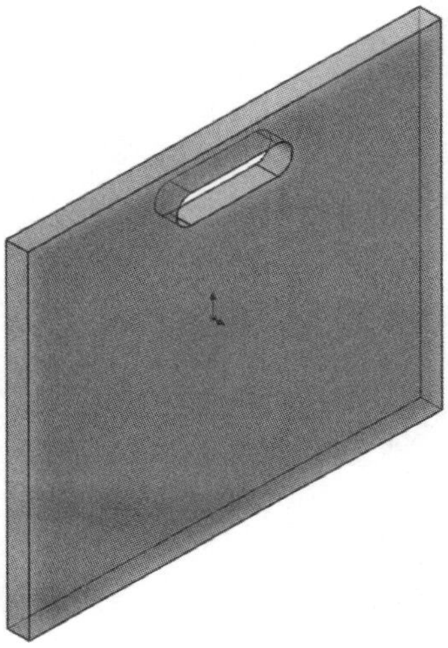

- For Bodies to Move/Copy select the **Boss-Extrude1** either from the graphics or from the Feature tree.

- Enable to **Copy** checkbox (arrow).

- Enter **18.00in**. in the **Delta X** dimension field.

- Click **OK**.

5. Creating the upper plank:

- Only one of the planks will be made. It will then be replicated and mirrored a few times to create the front and rear planks.

- Select the <u>left side face</u> and open a new sketch.

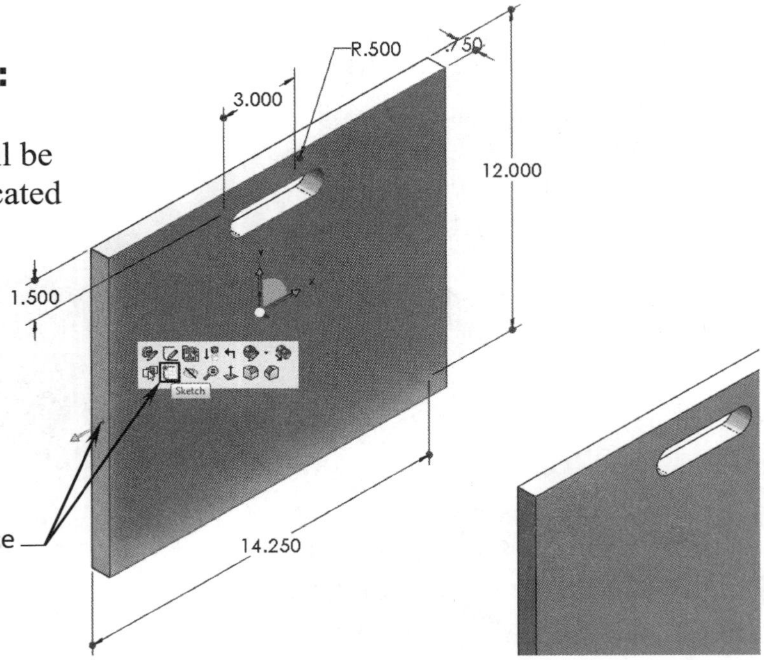

- Change to the front orientation (Ctrl+1).

- Sketch a **Corner Rectangle** from the upper left corner to the outer edge of the 2nd panel.

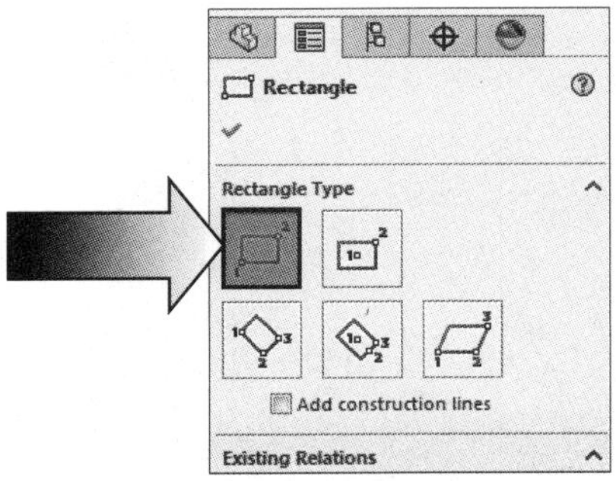

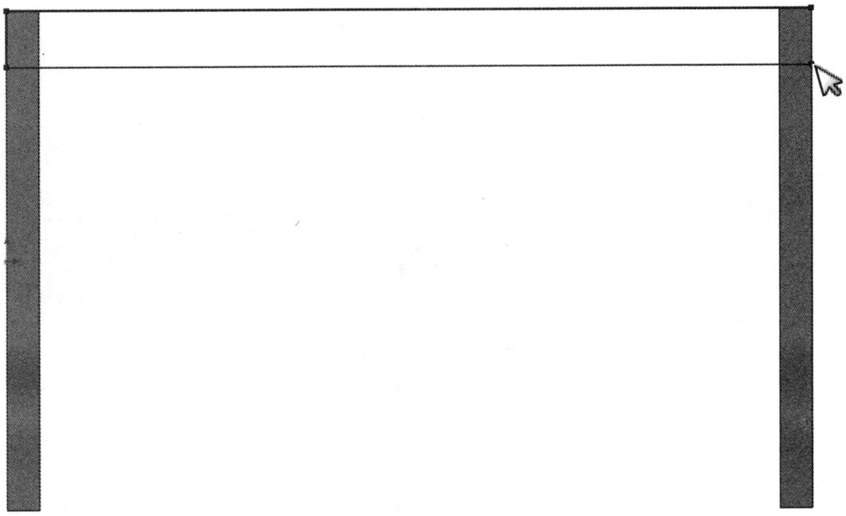

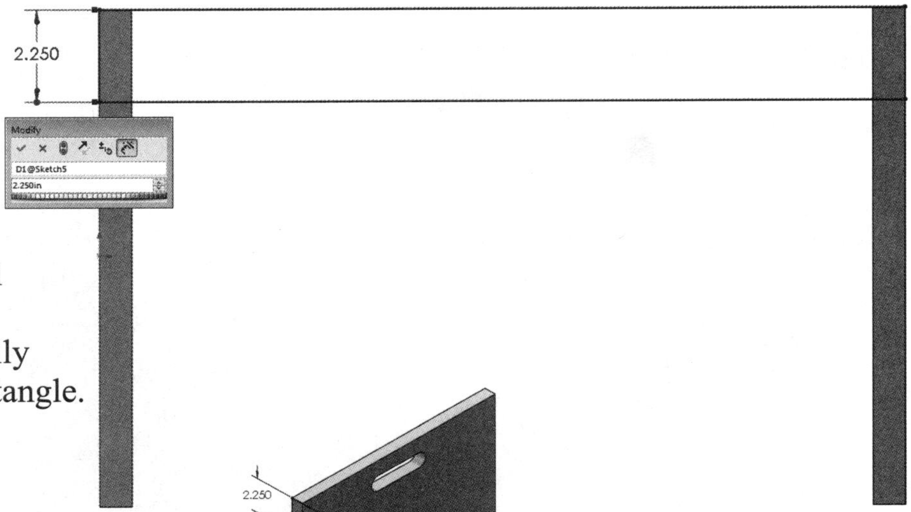

- Add a vertical dimension of **2.250in**. to fully define the rectangle.

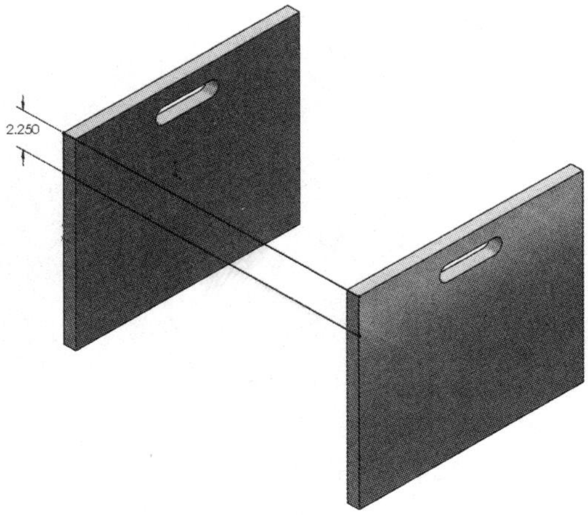

- Change to the Isometric view (Ctrl+7), it will help with seeing the extrude direction more clearly in the next step.

- Switch to the **Features** tool tab and click **Extruded Boss/Base**.

- Use the default **Blind** type, extrude away from the bodies.

- Enter **.500in**. for extrude depth.

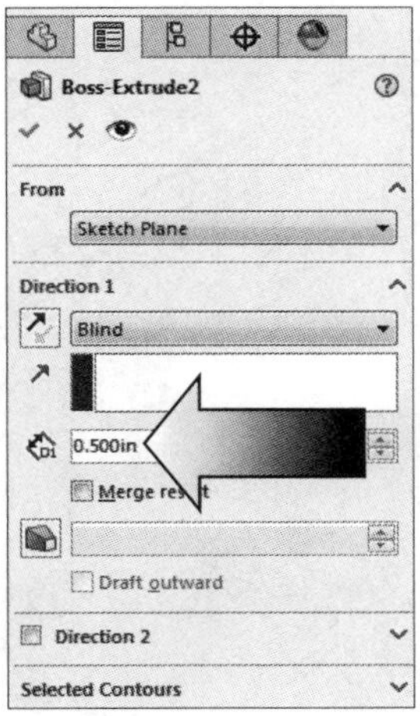

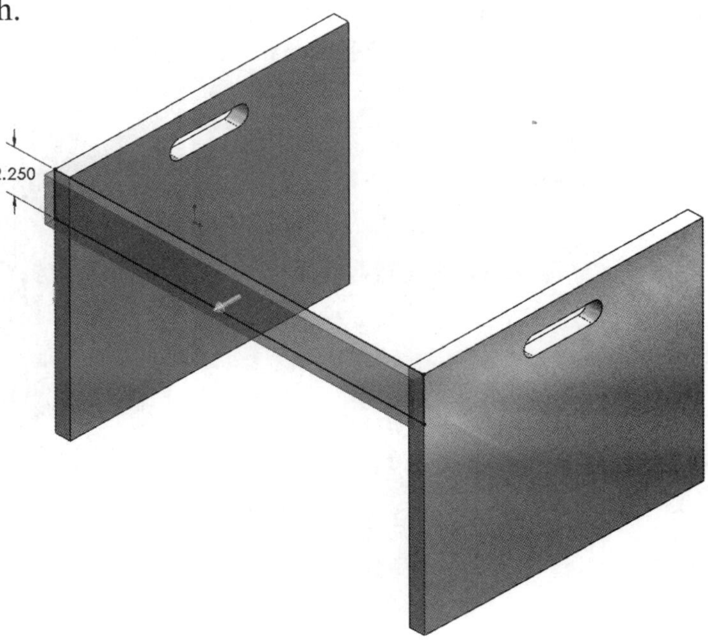

- Click **OK**.

6. Creating the 1st linear pattern:

- Click the **Linear Pattern** command from the Features tool tab.

- Select the <u>**edge**</u> as noted for Pattern Direction.

- Enter **3.25in** for spacing.

- Enter **4** for Number of Instances.

- Expand the **Bodies** section (arrow) and select the plank (**Boss-Extrude2**) for Bodies to Pattern.

- Click **OK**.

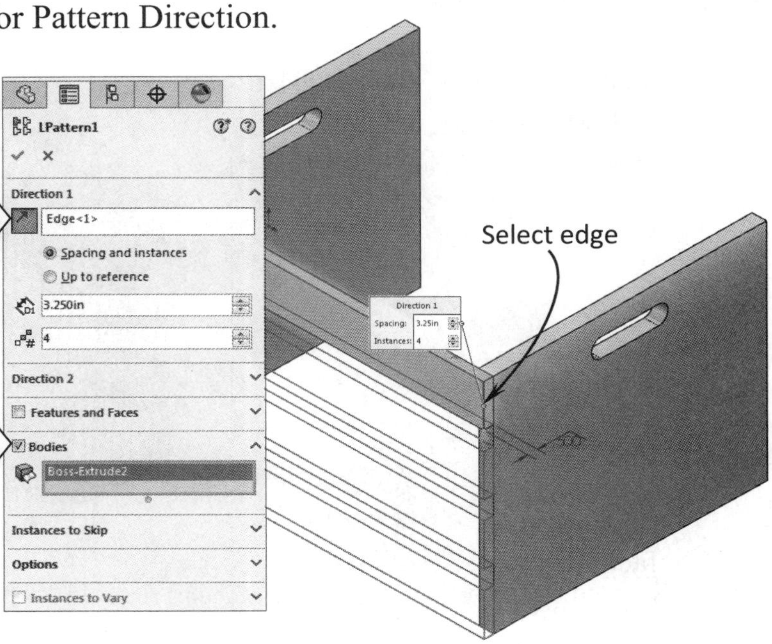

7. Mirroring the planks:

- Click the **Mirror** command from the Features tool tab.

- Select the **Front** plane from the Feature tree for Mirror Face/Plane.

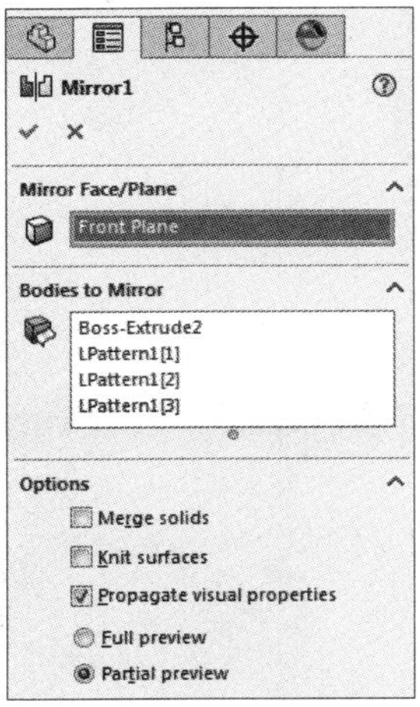

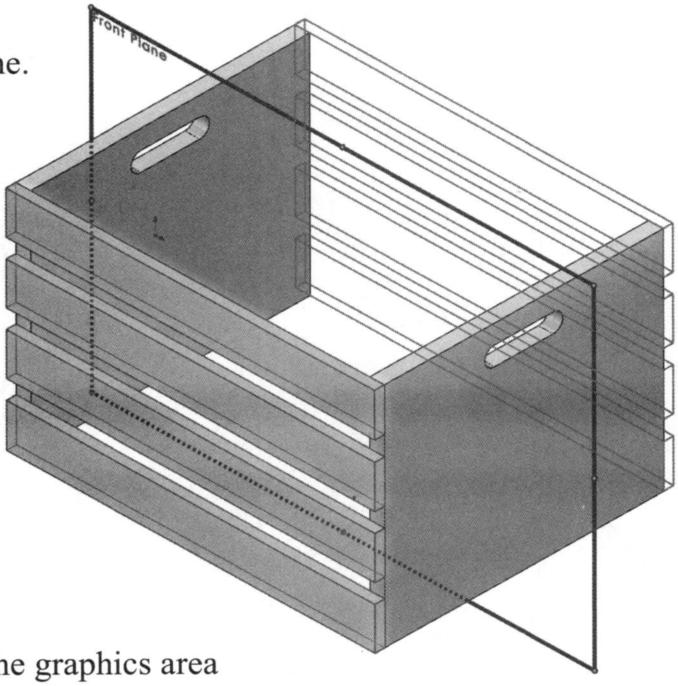

- Select all **4 planks** either from the graphics area or from the Solid Bodies folder.

- Click **OK**.

8. Creating the lower plank:

- There should be a total of **10 Solid bodies** at this point.

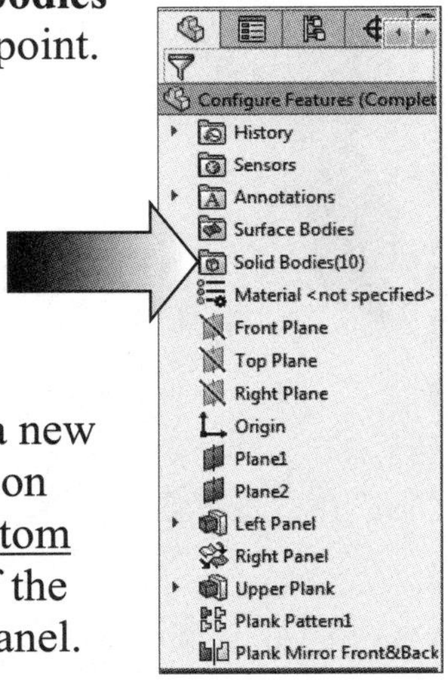

- Open a new sketch on the <u>bottom face</u> of the right panel.

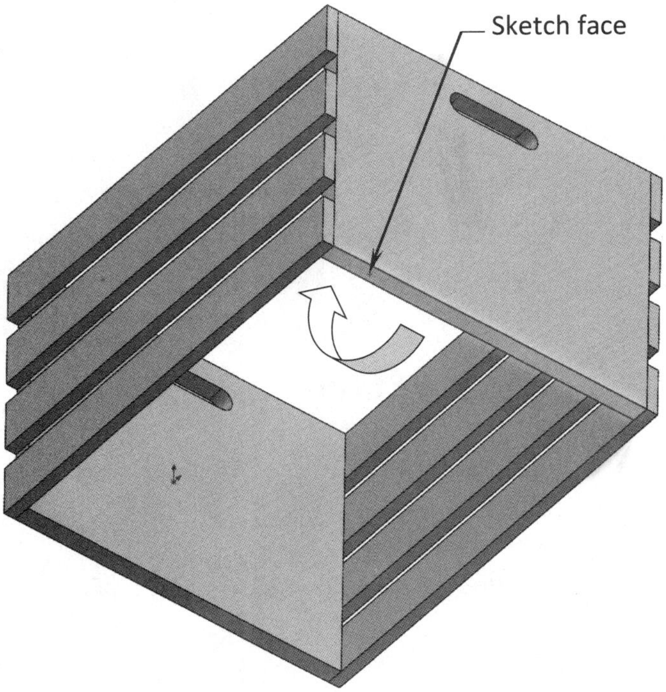

- Change to the bottom orientation (Ctrl+6).

- Sketch a **Corner Rectangle** approximately as shown.

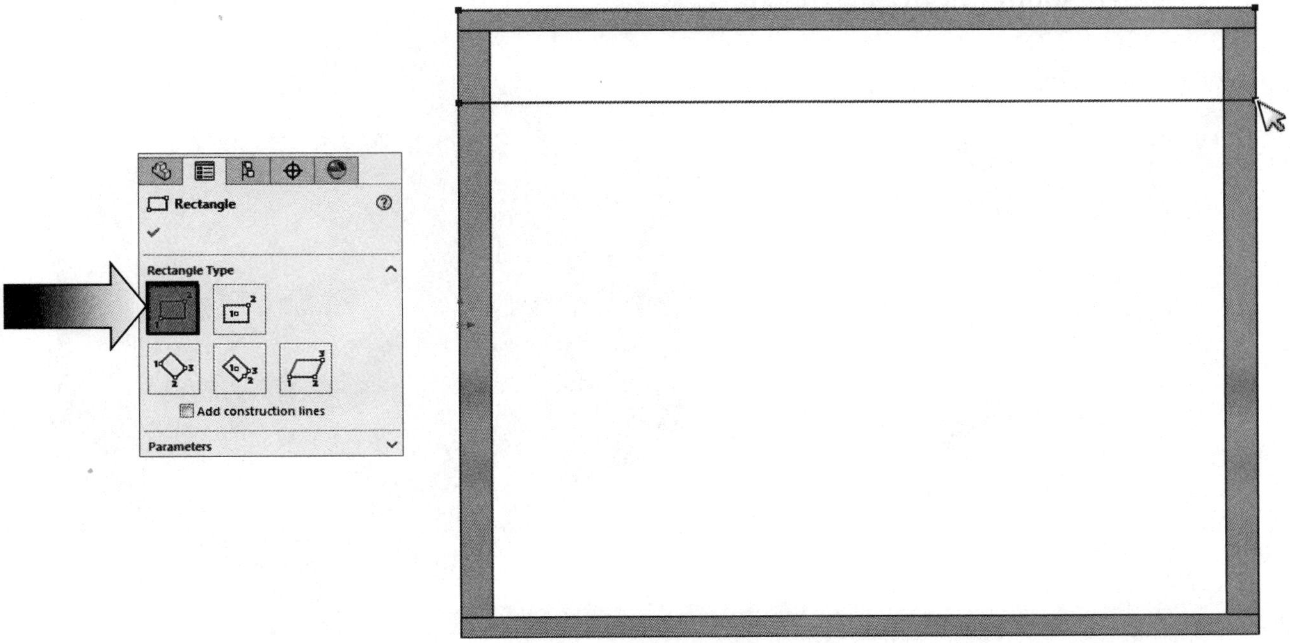

- Add the vertical dimension of **2.250in.** to match the height of the other planks.

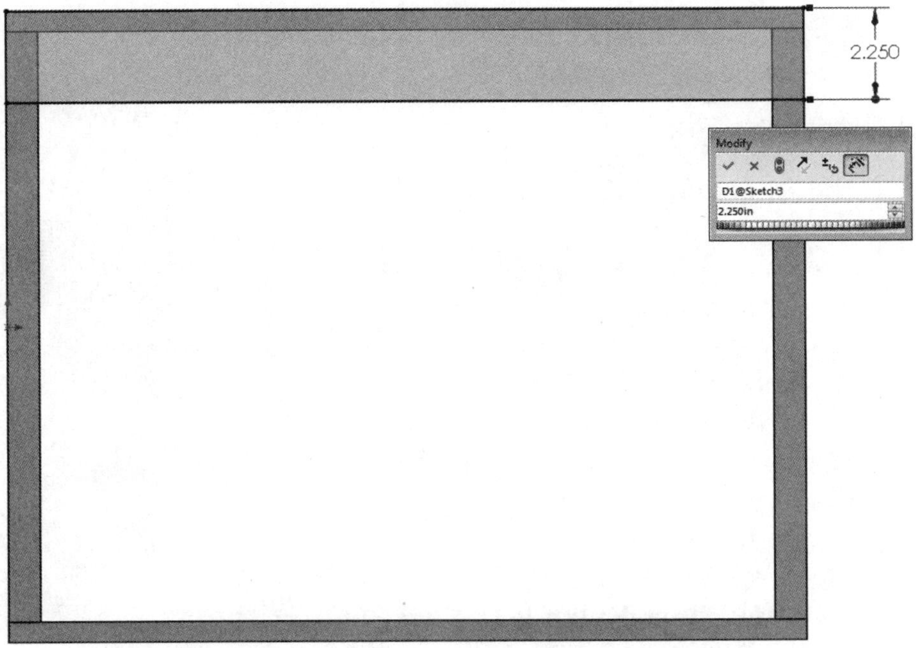

- Change to the Isometric view (Ctrl+7) before extruding the sketch.

- Switch to the **Features** tool tab and click **Extruded Boss/Base**.

- Use the default **Blind** type and extrude away from the bodies.

- Enter **.500in**. for extrude depth.

- Click **OK**.

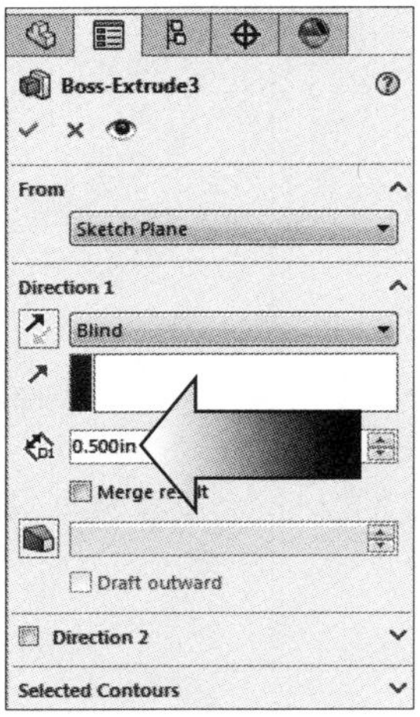

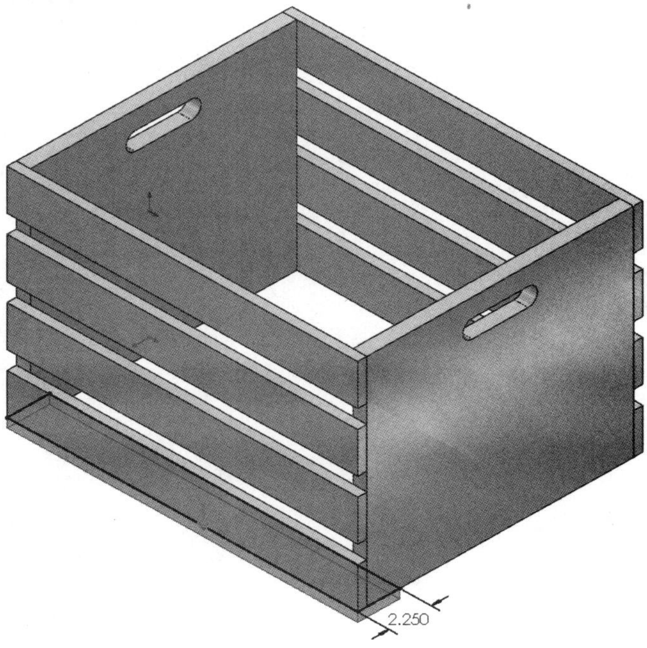

9. Creating the 2nd linear pattern:

- Click the **Linear Pattern** command from the Features tool tab.

- Select the **edge** as noted for pattern direction.

- Enter **3.250in** for Spacing.

- Enter **5** for Number of Instances.

- Expand the **Bodies** section (arrow) and select the plank (**Boss-Extrude3**) for Bodies to Pattern.

- Click **OK**.

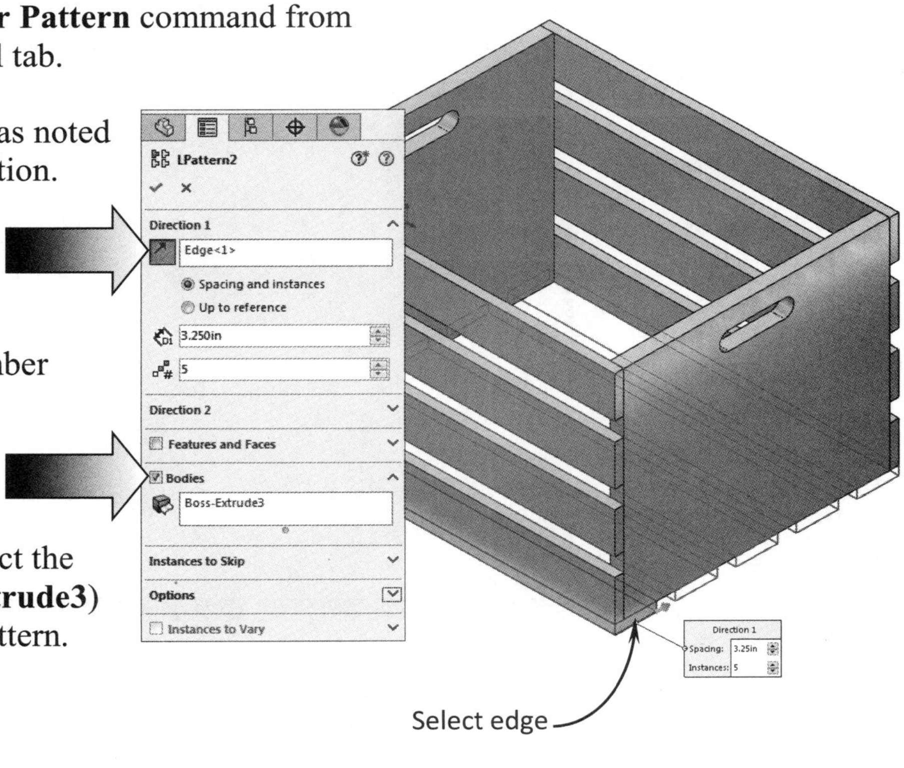

10. Creating an exploded view:

- An exploded view is created by selecting and dragging a triad arm in the graphics area to show the solid bodies spread out, creating one or more explode steps.

- Select **Insert / Exploded View**.

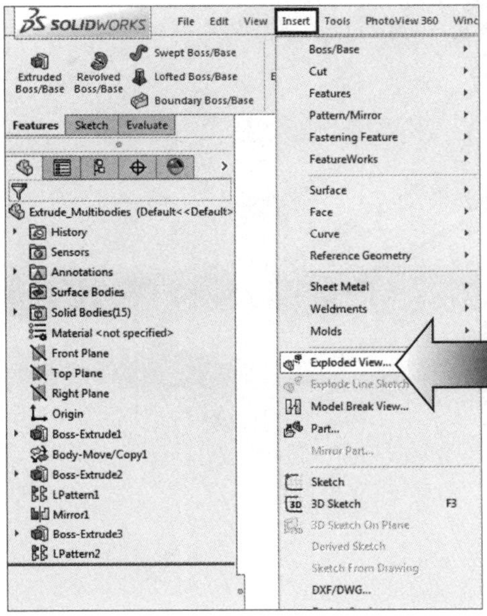

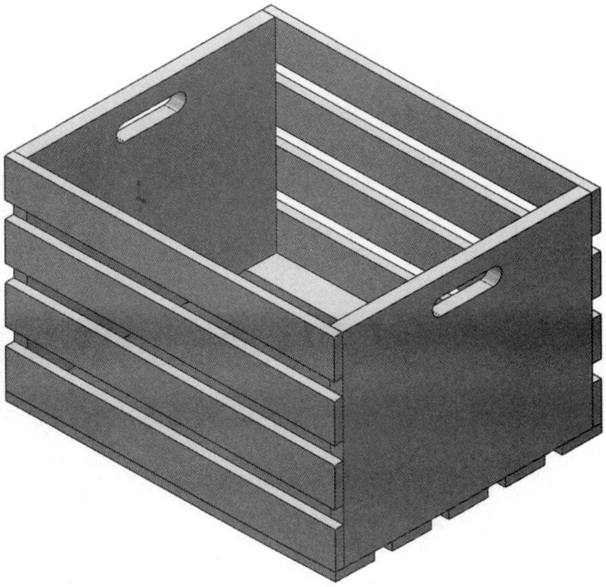

- Select the **4 solid bodies** as indicated.

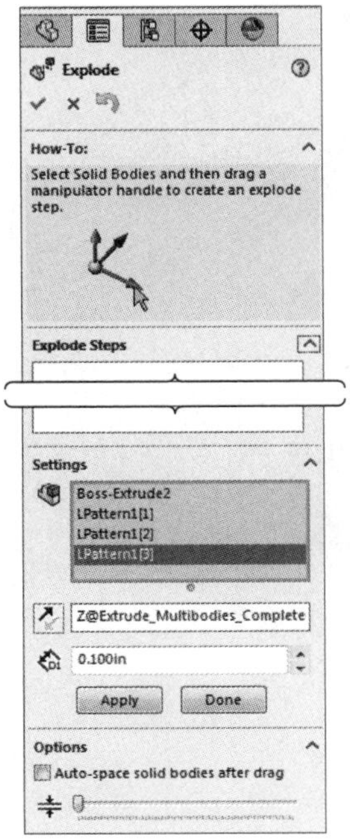

- A triad appears in the graphics area.

- Click the **Z direction** arrow of the triad.

- Clear the Auto-Space checkbox.

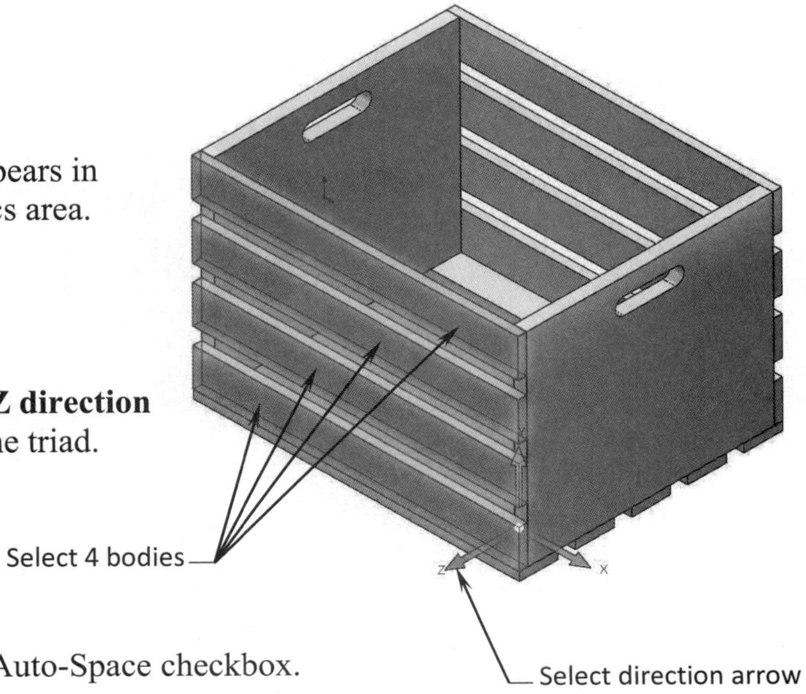

- Enter **15.00in** for Explode Distance.

- Click **Apply** to move the selected bodies.

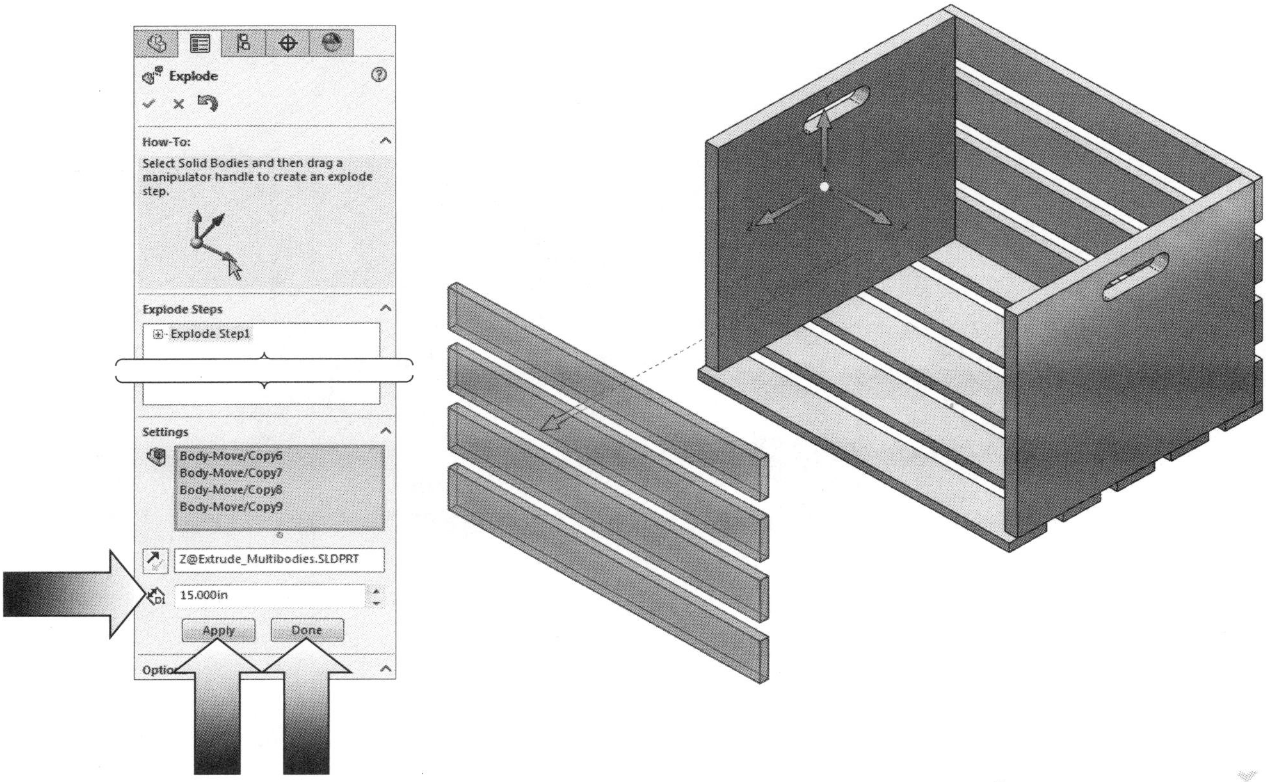

- Click **Done**.

- The 4 bodies are moved 15 inches along the Z direction.

- Repeat the same step and move the other 4 bodies along the opposite direction.

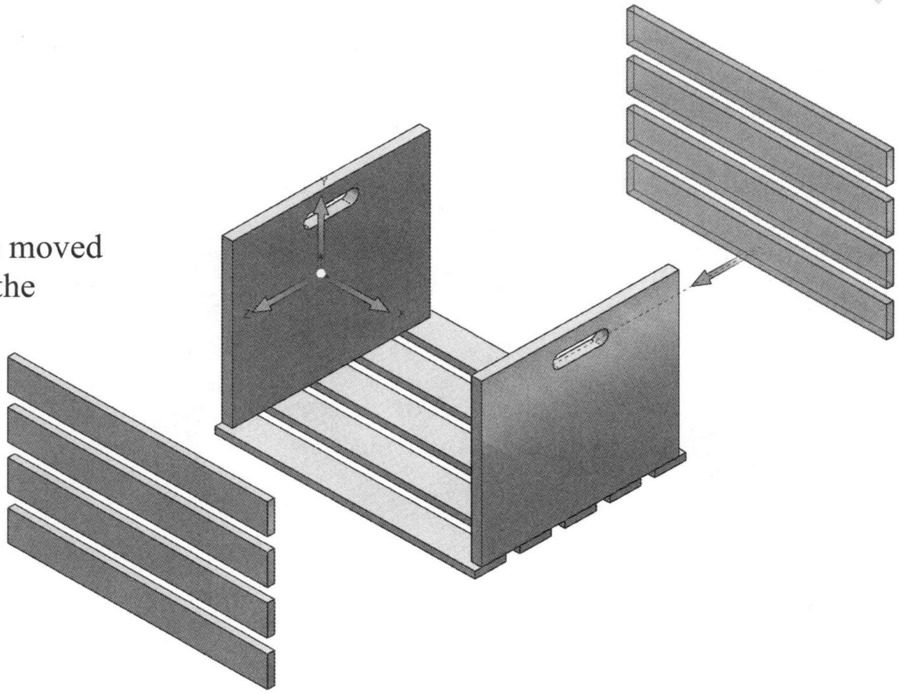

- Create 3 additional steps to explode the left panel, the right panel, and the bottom planks similar to the image shown here.

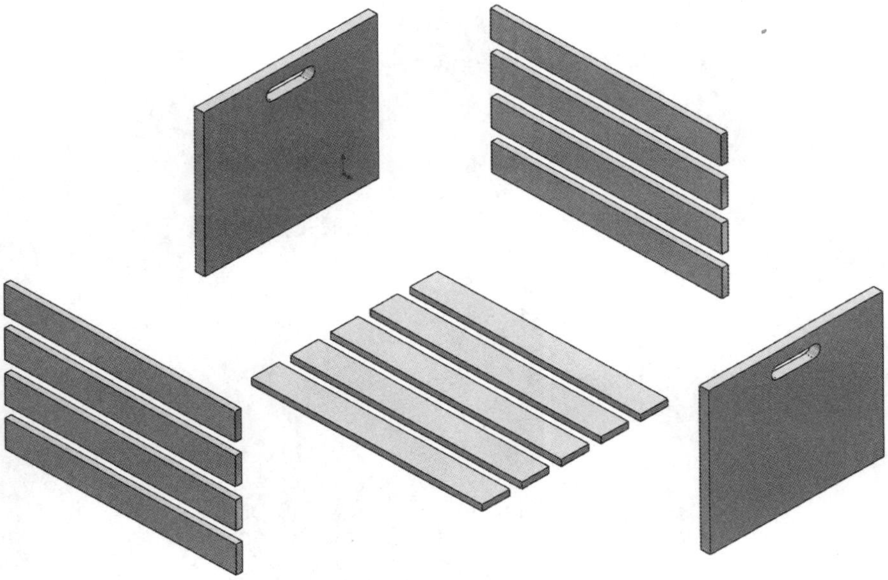

11. Collapsing the view:

- The exploded view can be collapsed, edited, or deleted.

- Change to the ConfigurationManager tree (arrow).

- Expand the Default configuration.

- Right click on ExplView1 and select **Collapse**.

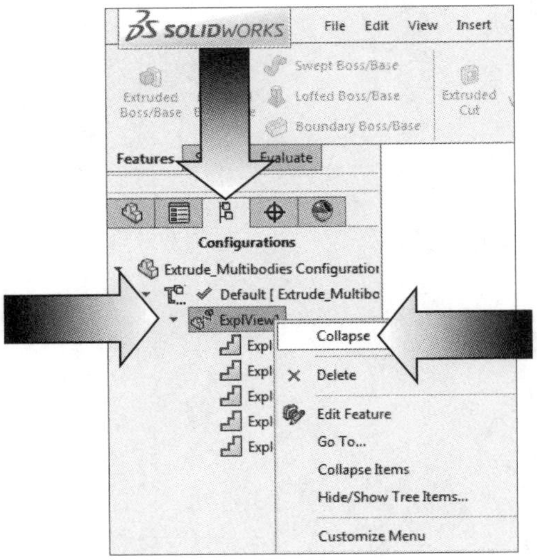

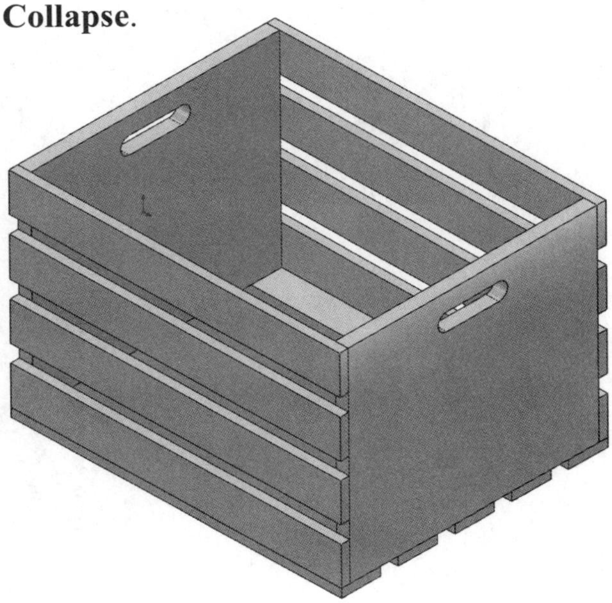

12. Saving your work:

- Select **File / Save As**.

- Enter **Multibody Parts** for the file name

- Click **Save**.

CHAPTER 4

Working with Multibody Parts

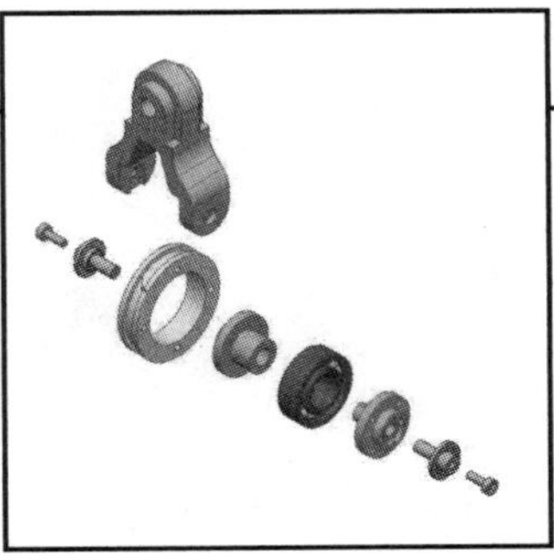

Working with Multibody Parts
Creating Mates & Exploded Views

Use the **Insert Part** command  to insert a base part into another part document.

When you insert a part into another part, it becomes a Multibody Part, and the part you insert becomes a Solid Body.

If the inserted part contains mate references, you can use them to position the inserted part.

There are 3 options available to help locate a solid body: Constraints, Translate, and Rotate. You can move or rotate the body after it is placed in the graphics area. A feature Body-Move/Copy is then added to the FeatureManager design tree.

The inserted body can also be constrained with the mate options. Some of the standard mates are available in the part mode to help position the solid bodies.

An exploded view is created after all solid bodies are positioned. Exploded views are stored in the ConfigurationManager. They can be edited, deleted, or more than one exploded views can be created, if needed.

This chapter will guide you through the use of multibodies parts, where an existing part document with a number of solid bodies is used. Other parts will then get inserted into the same document and constrained with some mates. After all solid bodies are positioned, an exploded view will be created in the same part mode and the Solid Bodies folder is used to help keep track of the number of solid bodies existing in the part document.

Working with Multibody Parts
Creating Mates and Exploded Views

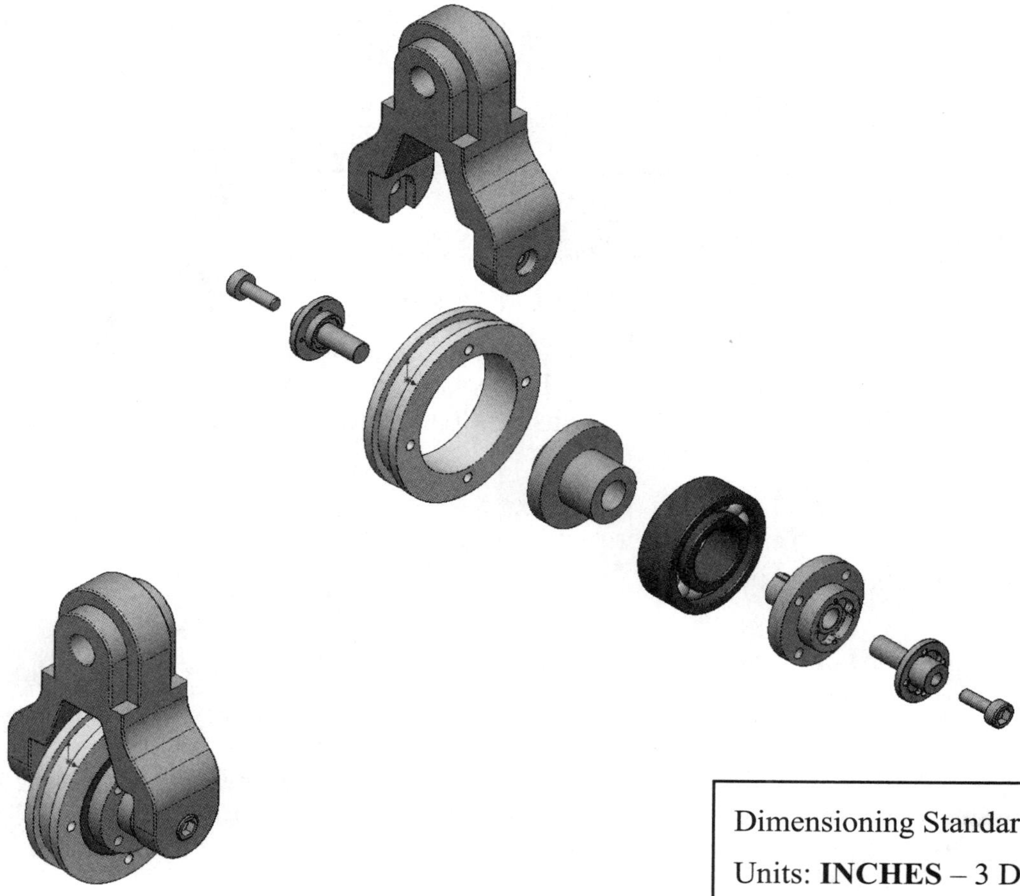

Dimensioning Standards: **ANSI**

Units: **INCHES** – 3 Decimals

Tools Needed:

Insert Part	Locate Part	Plane
Mirror	Exploded View	Mates
Concentric	Coincident	Mate alignment:

1. Opening a part document:

- Go to **File / Open**.

- Browse to the Training Files folder. Locate the part document named: **MultiBodyParts** and open it.

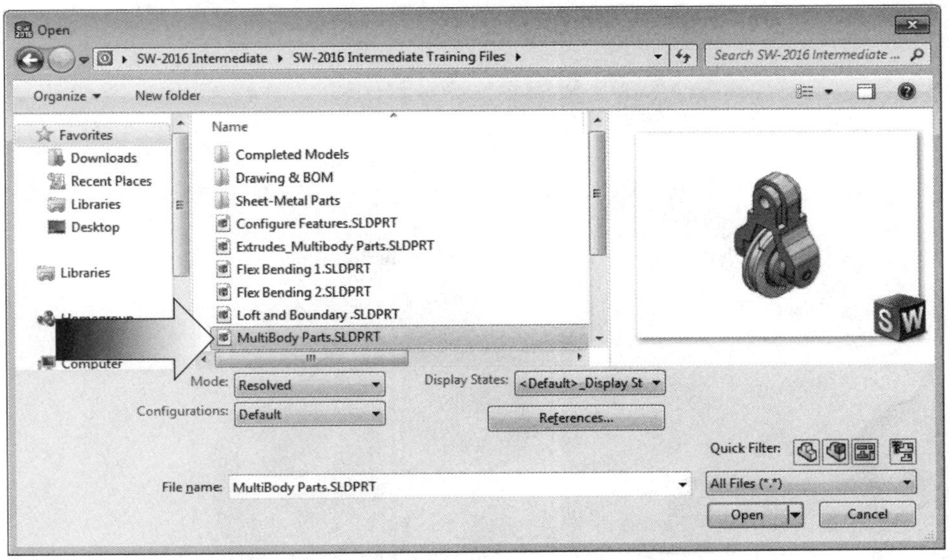

- When opening a non-SOLIDWORKS native document, the program will prompt you with a couple of options such as Import Diagnostics or Feature-Recognition. We will not discuss these options in this chapter but focus on the use of MultiBodies instead.

- If prompted, click **No** to cancel the Import Diagnostics option.

- Click **No** once again to cancel the Feature Recognition options.

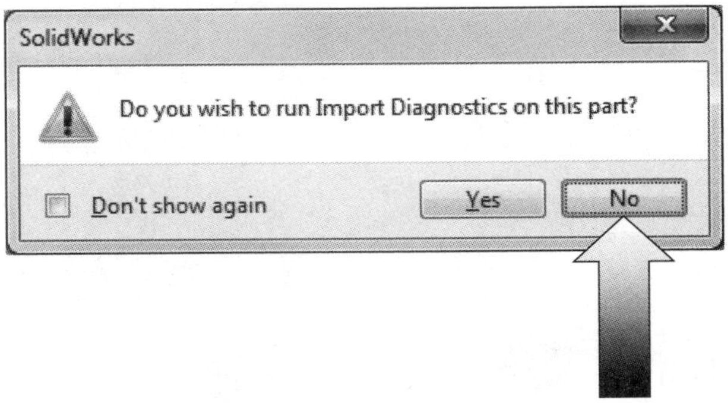

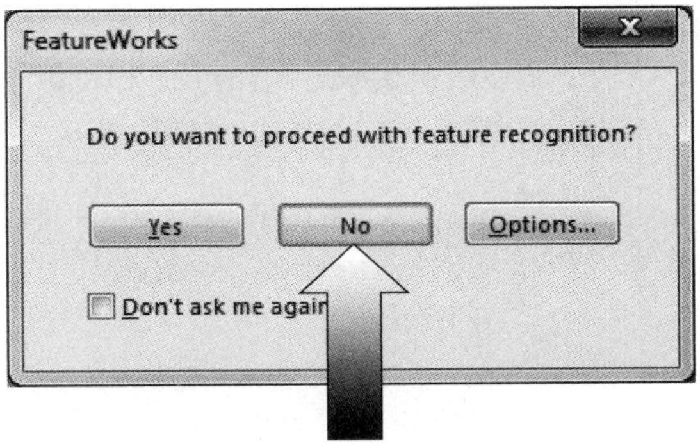

2. Creating an exploded view:

- An exploded view is going to be created so that the collapse / explode stages can be toggled back and forth in the future.

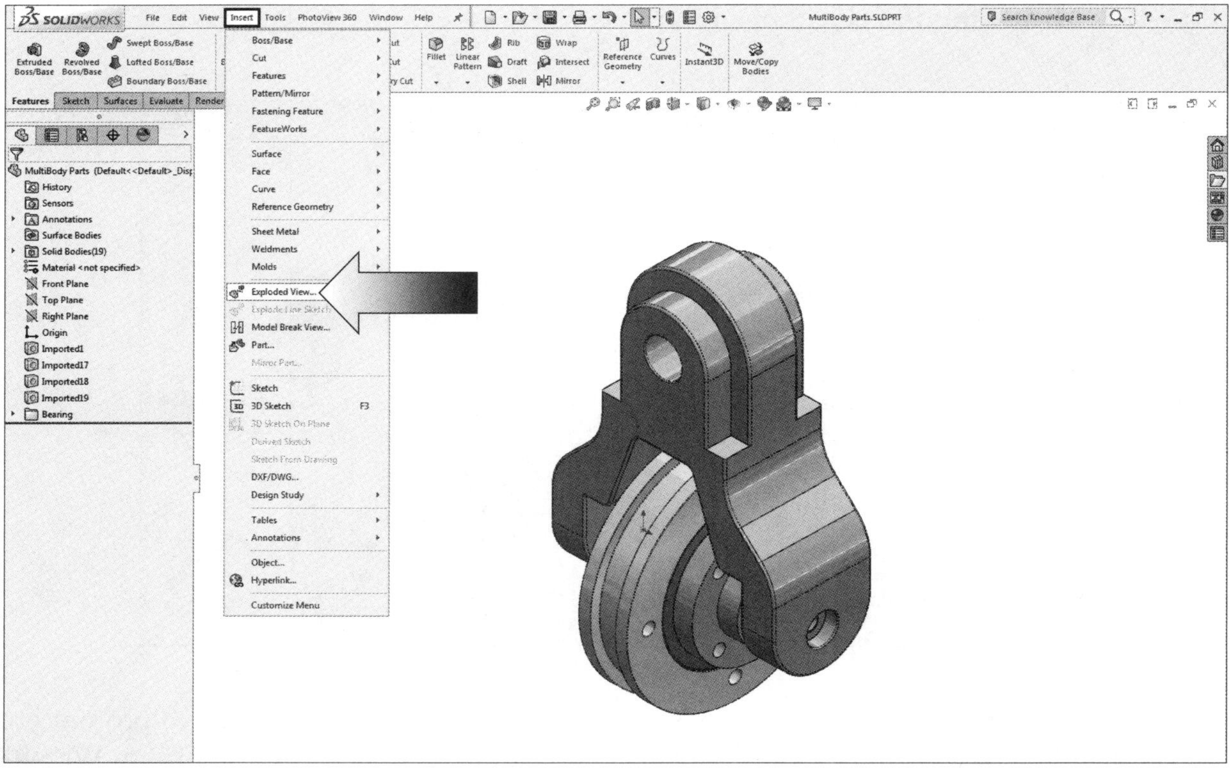

- Select **Insert/ Exploded View**.

- The Exploded dialog appears similar to the one seen in the assembly mode.

- Select the **Imported2** solid body either from the graphics area or from the feature tree.

- Drag the **Vertical** arrow head upward to approximately **10 inches**.

- Right click anywhere in the graphics area and select: **Box Selection**.

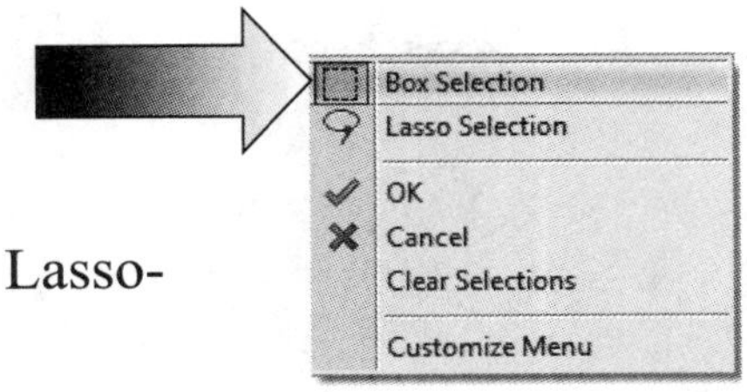

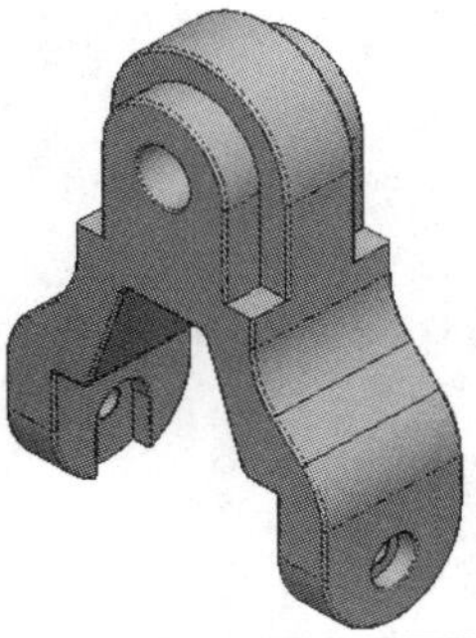

- The default is set to Lasso-Selection.

- Drag a selection-box around the solid bodies as shown. All solid bodies within the selections box are selected.

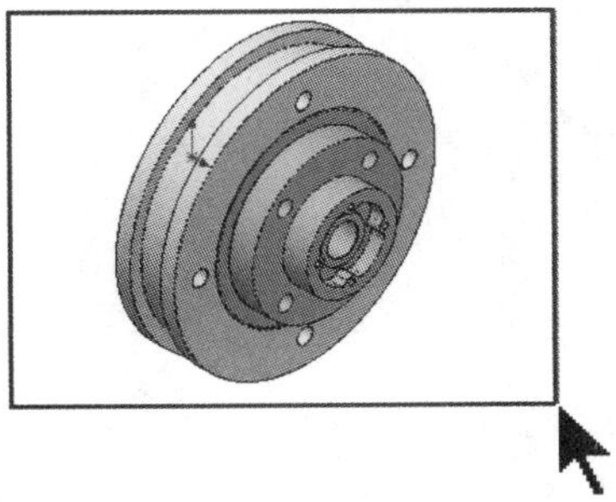

- The outer pulley (Imported1) should not be part of this group, so we are going to unselect it before exploding this group of solid bodies.

- Either hold the Control key and click the Imported1 body to exclude it from the group, or delete it from the list under the Settings section.

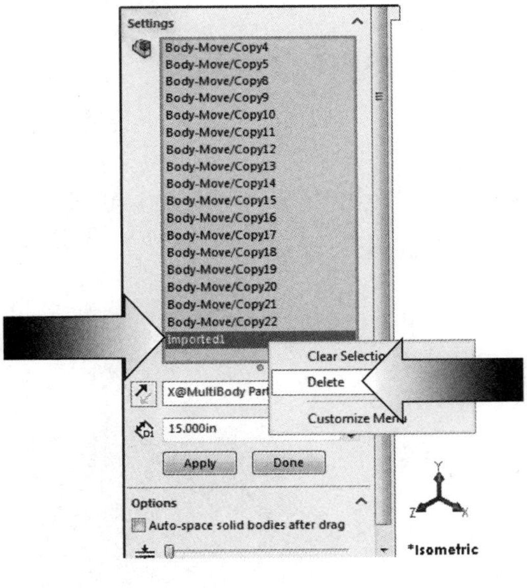

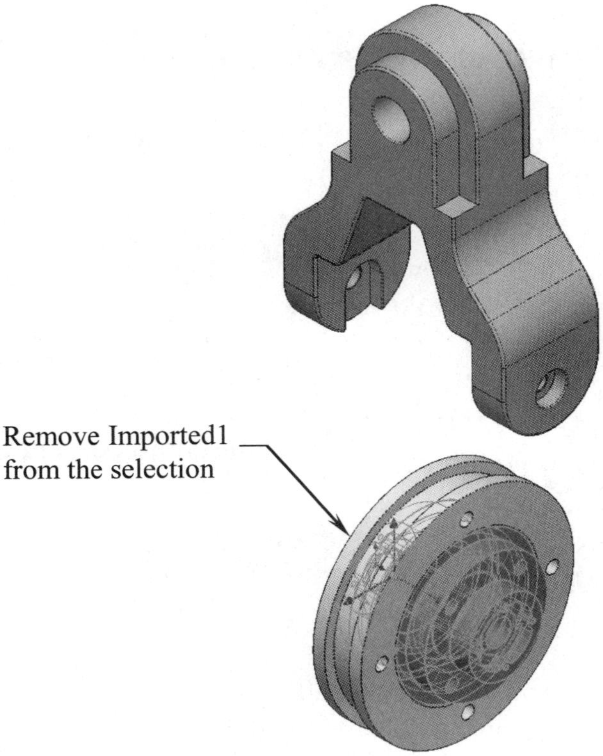

- An alternate method is to select the bodies-to-explode from the Solid Bodies folder, on the FeatureManager tree.

- Explode the solid bodies similar to the image shown below.

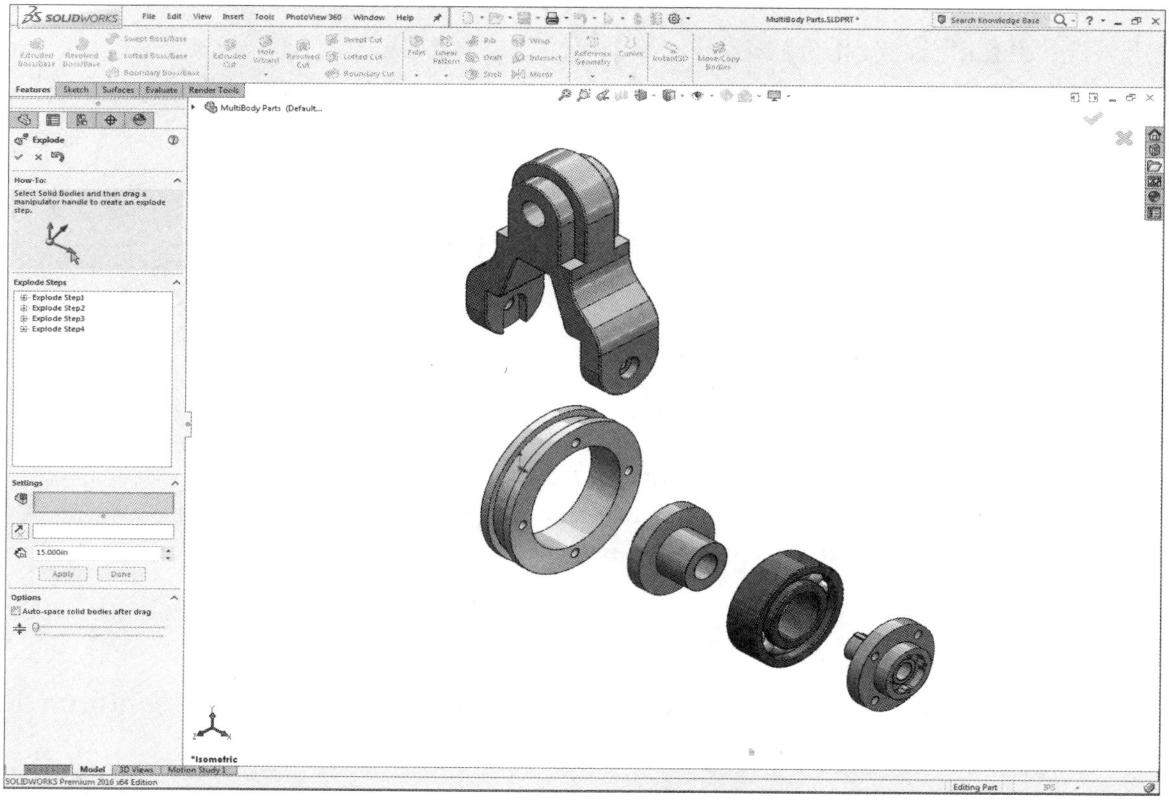

3. Collapsing the solid bodies:

- Switch to the **ConfigurationManager** tree (arrow).

- Expand the Default configuration to see the ExpView1. Right click on ExpView1 and select **Collapse** (arrow).

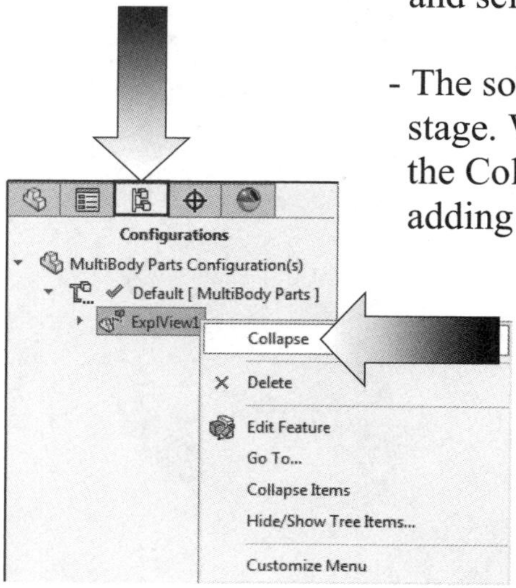

- The solid bodies are collapsed to their initial stage. We'll toggle back and forth between the Collapse and Explode modes while adding more parts in the next few steps.

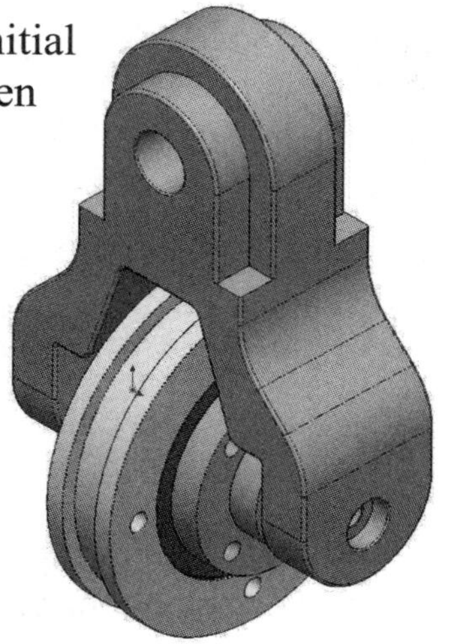

- Switch back to the **FeatureManager** tree by clicking on its tab.

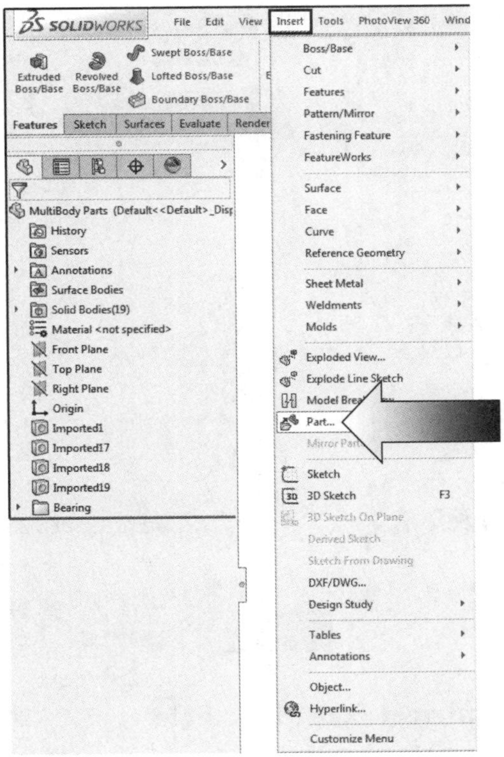

4. Inserting another part:

- Other parts can be inserted into an existing part document. Once inserted they will become Solid Bodies, and the original part becomes a Multibody Part.

- Click **Insert / Part**.

- Select the part document named: **Conn-Rod.sldprt** from the same training files directory and open it.

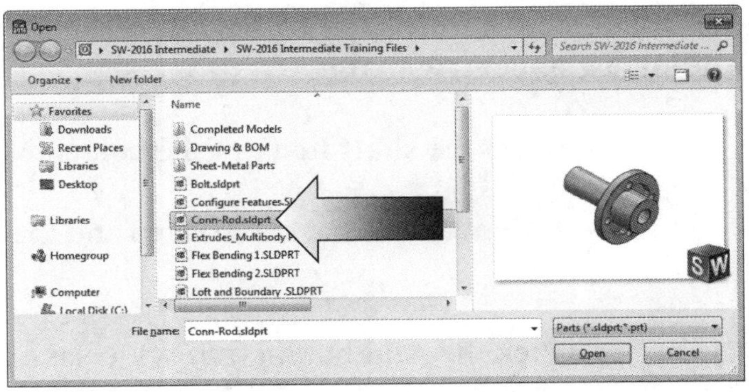

- Place the new part on the right side of the others, approx. as shown below.

- The **Insert Part** dialog box appears.

- Select the following options:

  * **Solid Bodies**

  * **Planes**

  * **Locate Part with Move/ Copy feature**

- Uncheck all other checkboxes.

- Click **OK**.

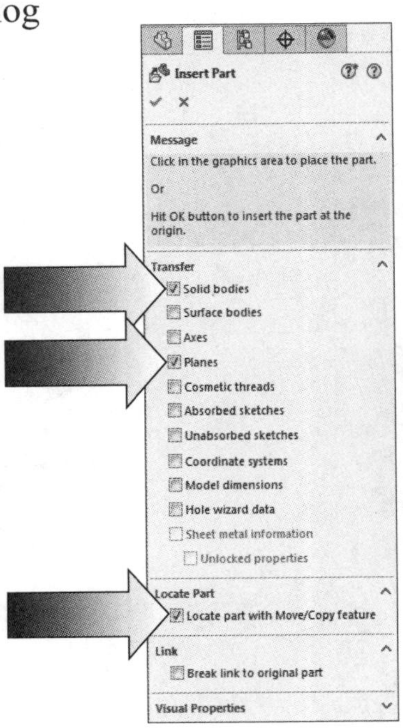

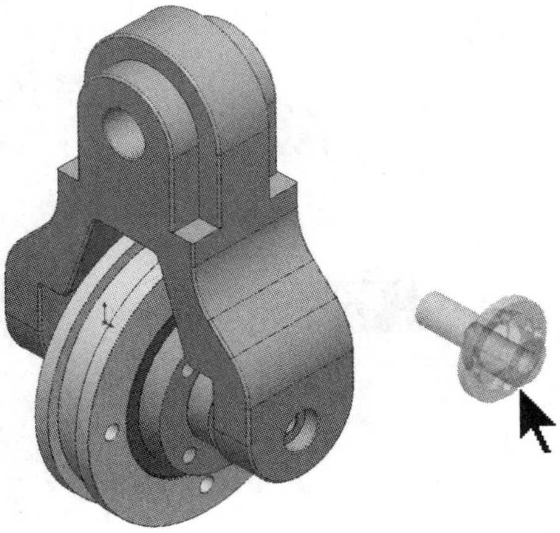

5. Constraining the solid bodies:

- By clicking OK from the previous step the **Locate Part** section is activated.

- Click the **Constraints** button to switch to the Mate Settings mode (arrow).

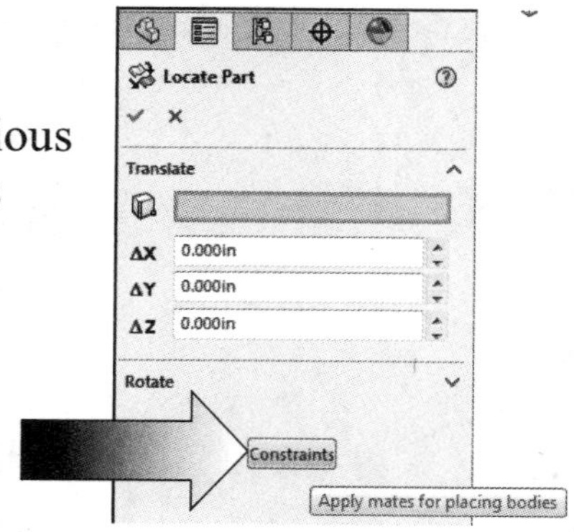

(Click the Translate / Rotate button to change to the Constraints section if it is not visible on the tree.)

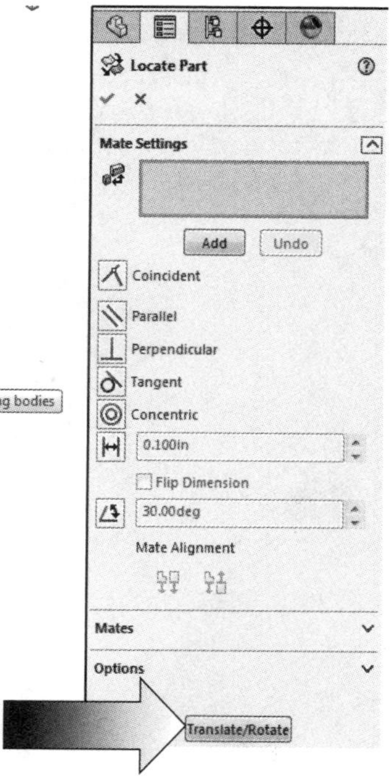

Adding a Concentric mate:

- Select the **shaft body** of the bolt and the **cylindrical face** of the hole.

- A **Concentric** mate is created and the bolt moves to the same center with the hole.

- Click the **Add** button (arrow) to save the mate in its mate group below.

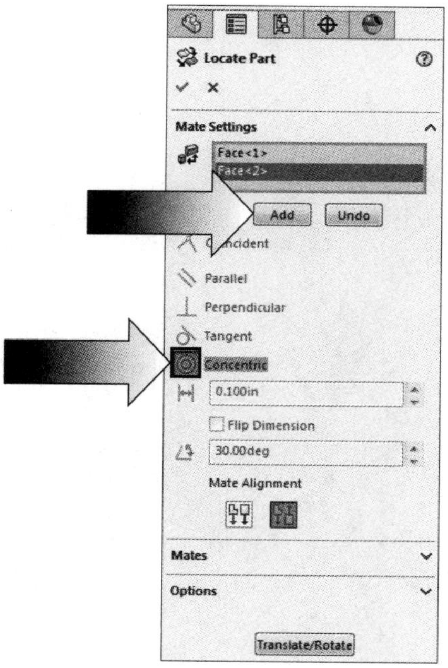

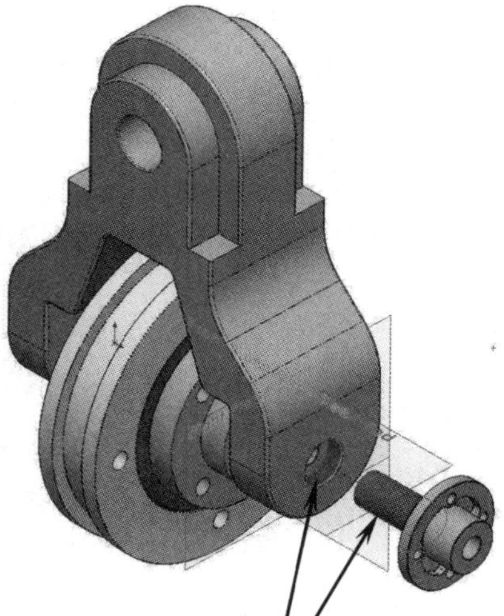

Select the shaft body and the hole

Adding a Coincident mate:

- Select the 1st **planar face** (face1) as indicated.

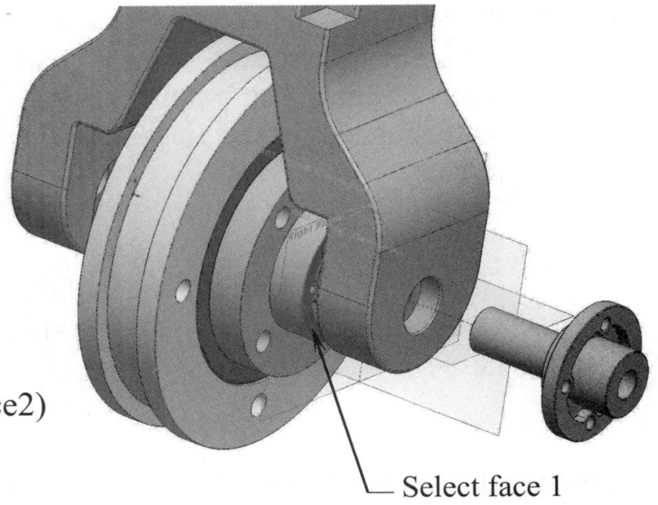

- Select the 2nd **planar face** (face2) as noted.

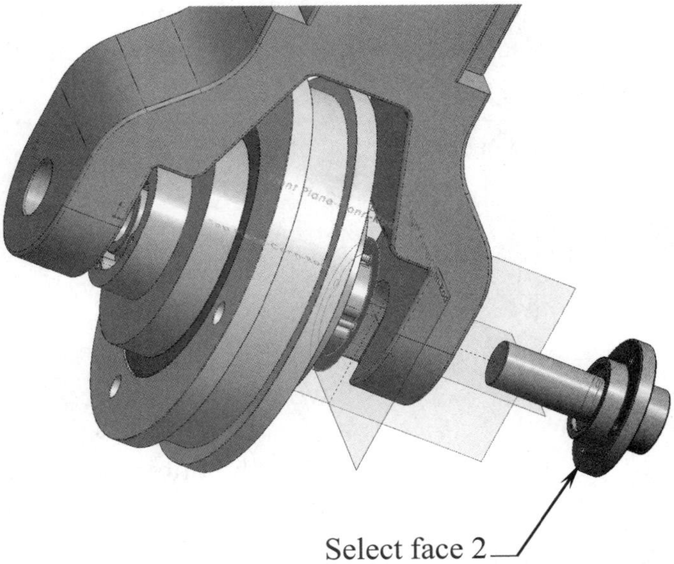

- A **Coincident** mate is created and the 2 selected faces are now coinciding or occupying the same place.

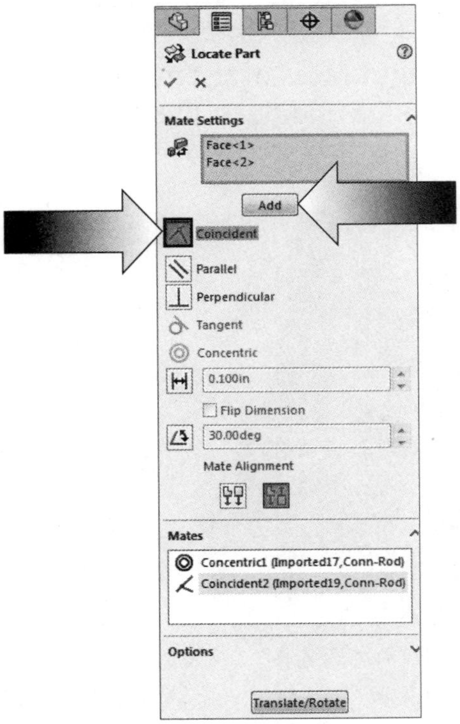

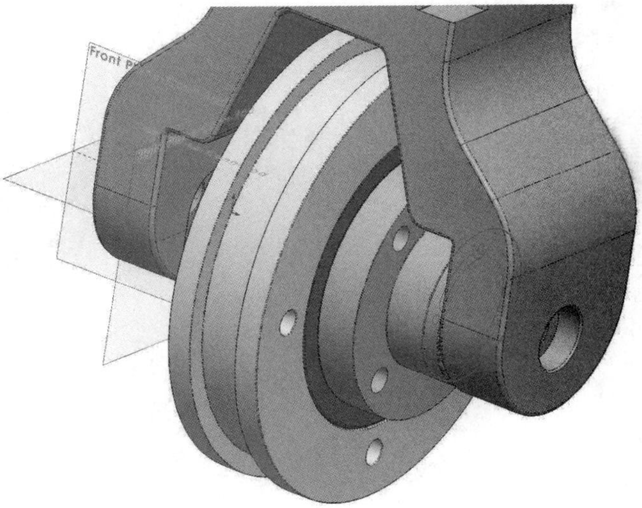

- To help keep the file size smaller, we are going to leave the 3rd degree of freedom open. The last mate is not really needed for the purpose of the lesson.

- Click: **View / Planes** to hide all the planes in the Imported1 solid body (arrow).

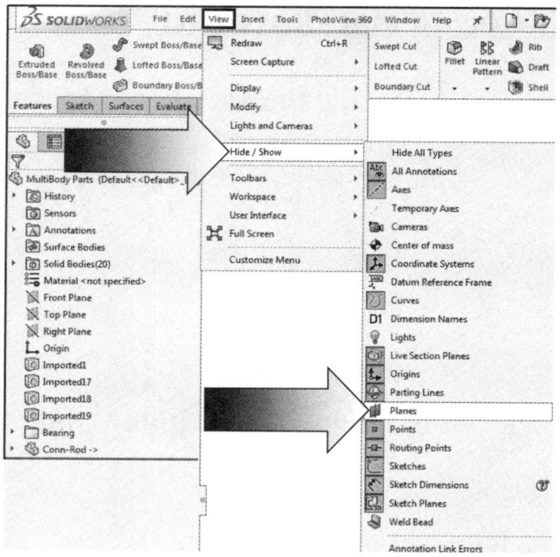

6. Creating a new mirror plane:

- Change to the **Features** tool tab and select the **Plane** command from the Reference Geometry drop down arrow.

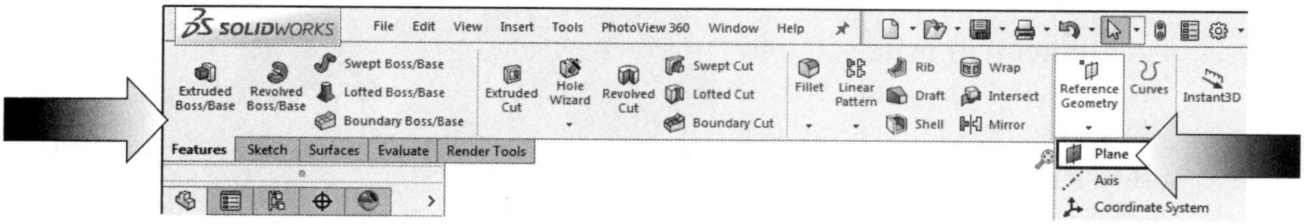

- Two **planar surfaces** are needed to create a Mid Plane.

- Select the outer most **left** and **right** faces of the main housing as noted. A Mid Plane is created in the middle of the 2 selected faces.

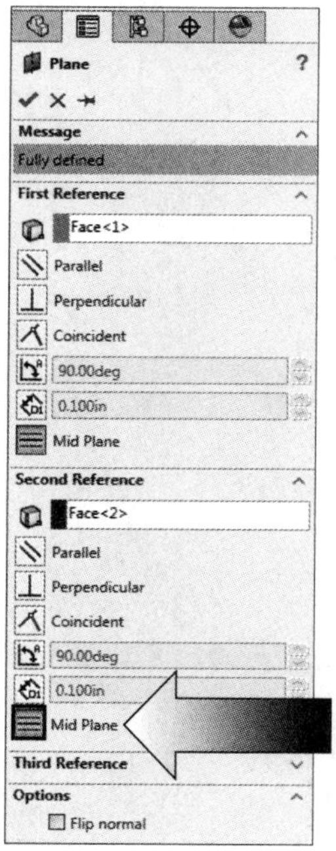

Select face 1
(Left side)

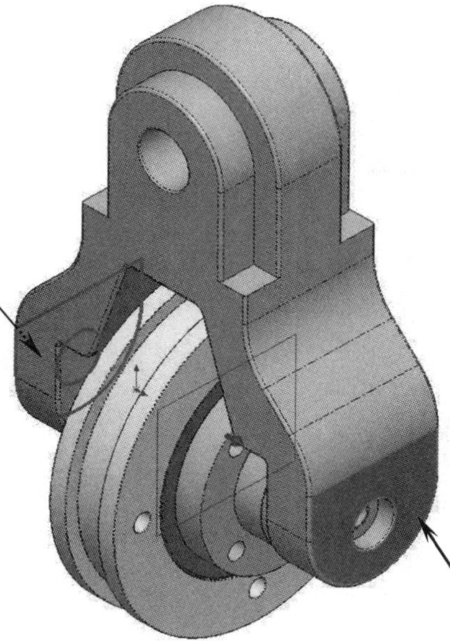

Select face 2
(Right side)

7. Creating a mirror body:

- Click the **Mirror** command from the Features tool tab.

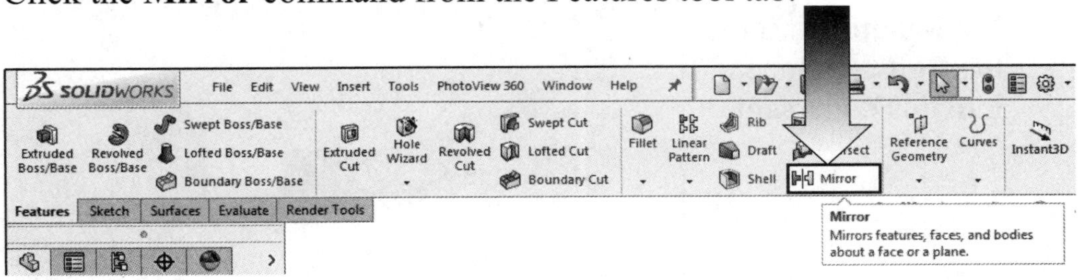

- Select the **new plane** for **Mirror Face / Plane** (arrow).

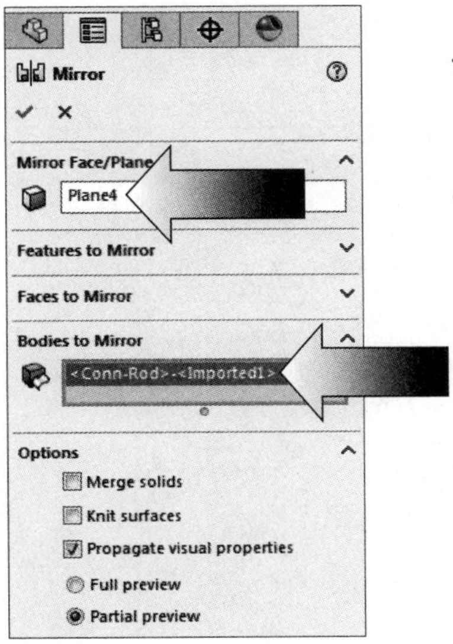

- Expand the **Bodies to Mirror** section.

- Expand the **Solid Bodies folder** from the FeatureManager tree and select the **Conn-Rod** from the list.

- **Clear** the **Merge Solids** checkbox and click **OK**.

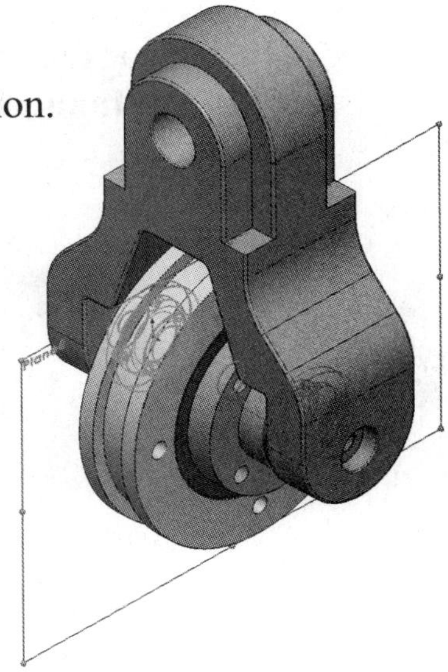

- Switch back to the **Configuration** tree, **Edit** the Exploded view and **move** the solid bodies to the positions approx. as shown.

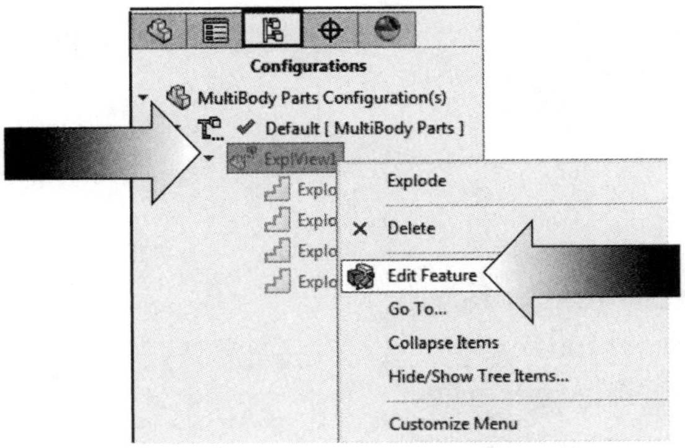

- Right click on ExplView1and select **Collapse**. We will now insert the **Bolt** component into this document.

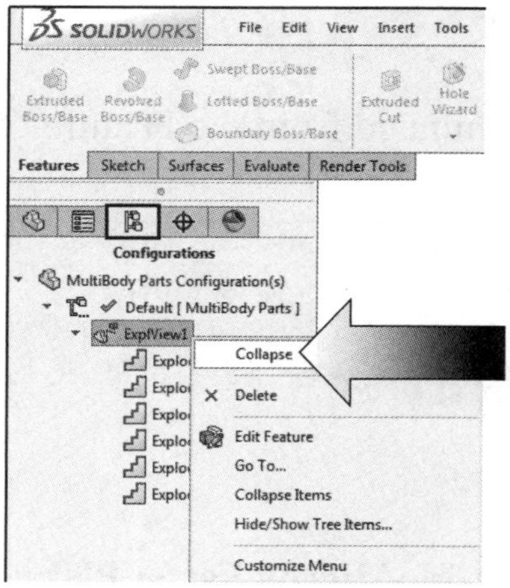

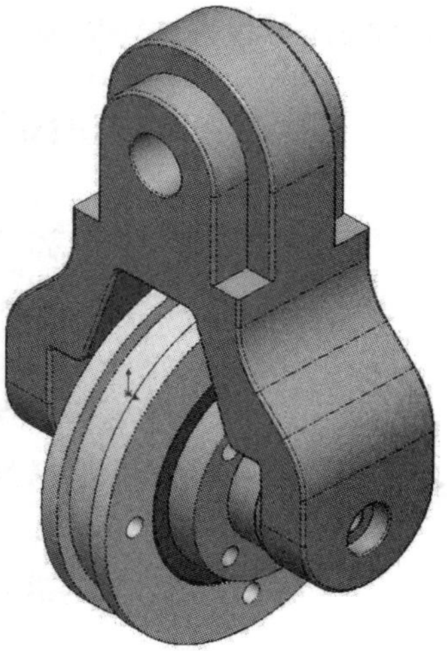

- Switch back to the **FeatureManager** tree (arrow).

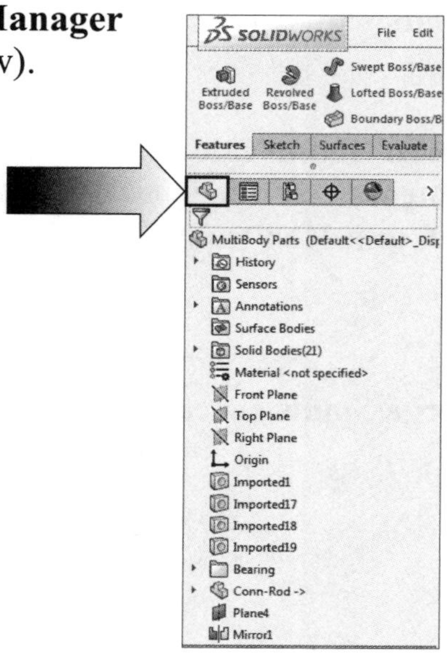

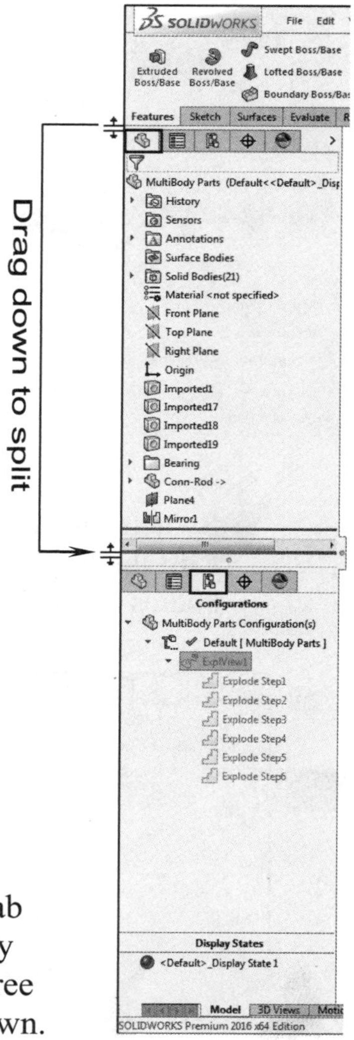

Optional:

- The FeatureManager tree can be split to display any combination of:

  * FeatureManager Design tree
  * PropertyManager tree
  * ConfigurationManager
  * DimXpertManager

- Move the mouse pointer under the FeatureManager tab until it changes to ⇟, drag the split bar down half way to split it into two panes. Show the FeatureManager tree on top and the ConfigurationManager below it as shown.

8. Inserting another part:

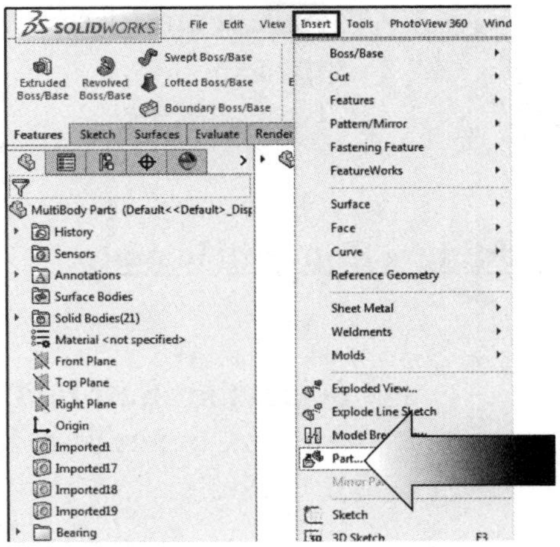

- The Bolt is going to be inserted into the same part document, it will become another solid body, and the part document is called a Multi-Body Part.

- Click **Insert / Part**.

- Select the part **Bolt.sldprt** from the previous training files folder.

- Place the new part on the right side of the main housing.

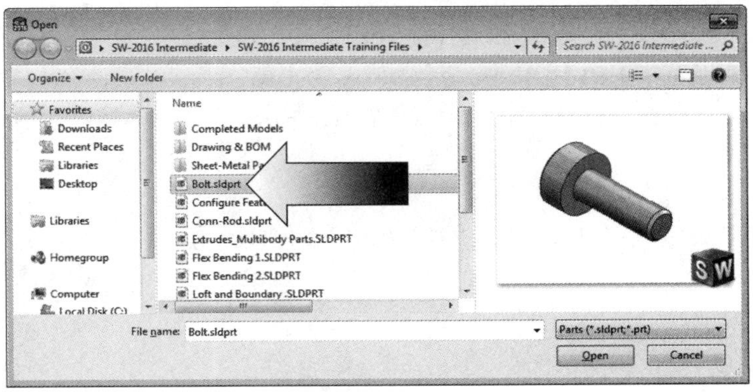

- Click **YES** to change the units of the new part to match the units of the MultiBody part.

- Select the **3 checkboxes** as noted and click **OK**.

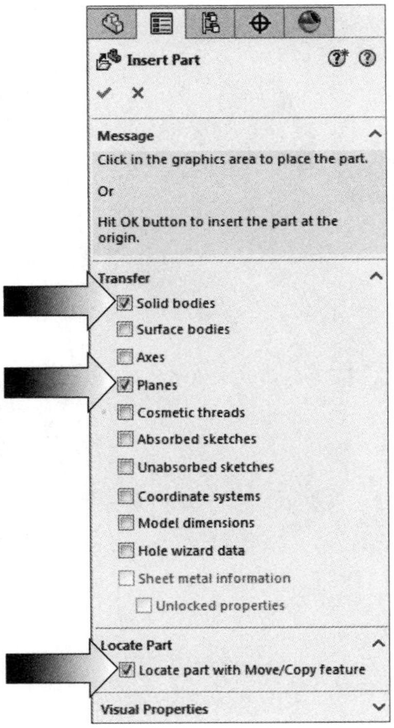

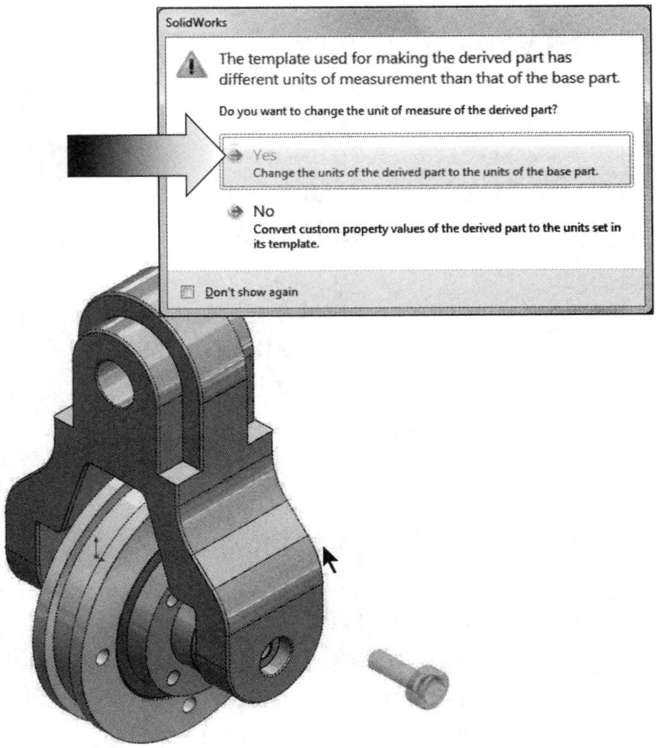

- The **Locate Part** options appear.

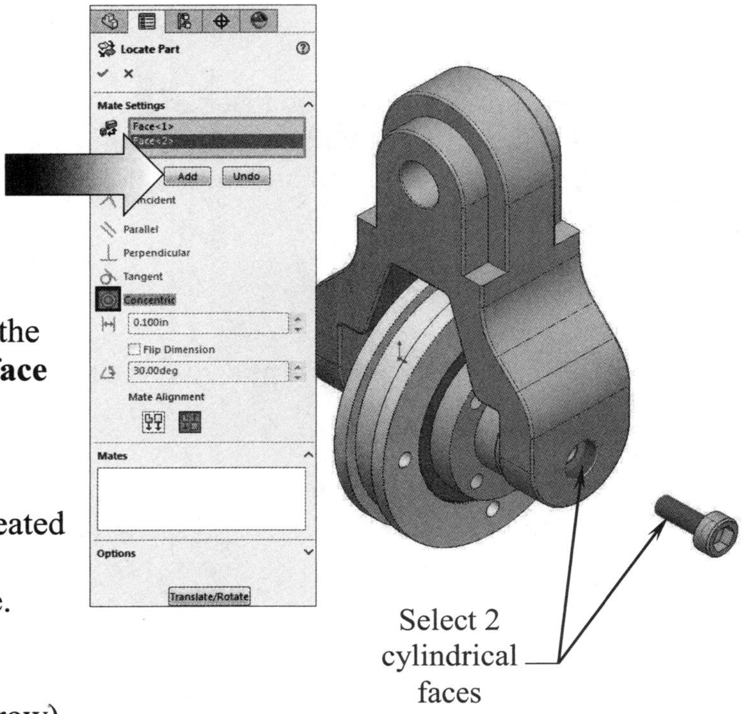

Adding a Concentric mate:

- Select the **shaft body** of the bolt and the **cylindrical face** of the hole.

- A **Concentric** mate is created and the bolt moves to the same center with the hole.

- Click the **Add** button (arrow) to save the mate in its mates group below.

Adding a Coincident mate:

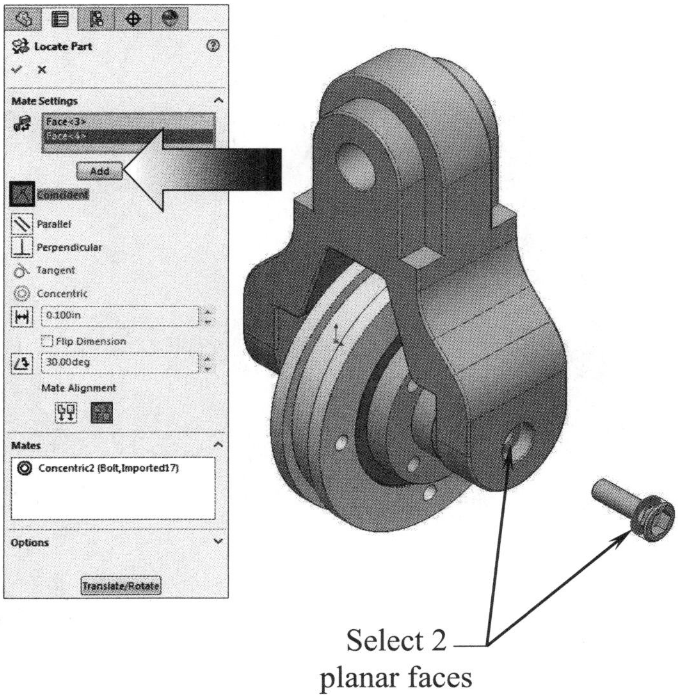

- Select the 2 **planar-faces** as indicated and click the **Add** button.

- A **Coincident** mate is created and the 2 selected faces are now coincident.

- The bolt is mated to the hole and still has 1 degree of freedom left. (It is good practice to add only 2 mates to each fastener to help keep the file size down a little.)

9. Adding another instance of the bolt:

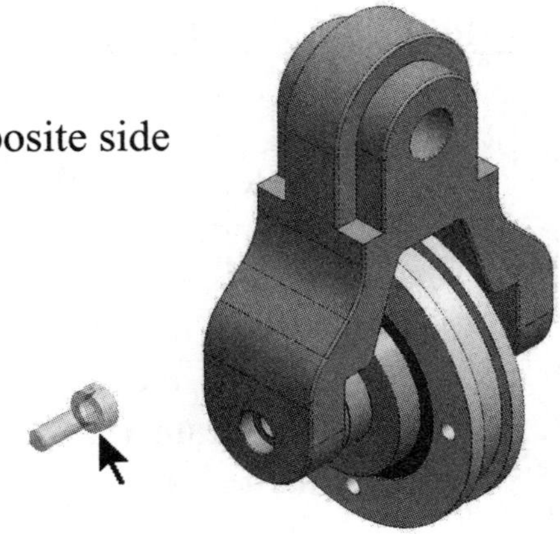

- A second instance of the bolt is needed on the opposite side of the main housing.

- Click **Insert / Part**.

- Select the part **Bolt.sldprt** once again from the previous directory.

- Rotate the view and place the new part on the left side of the main housing.

<u>**Adding a Concentric mate:**</u>

- Select the body of the bolt and the side hole of the main housing to add a **Concentric** mate.

- Click the **Anti-Aligned** button to flip the bolt 180 degrees (arrow), and then click the **Add** button to save the new mate in its Mates group.

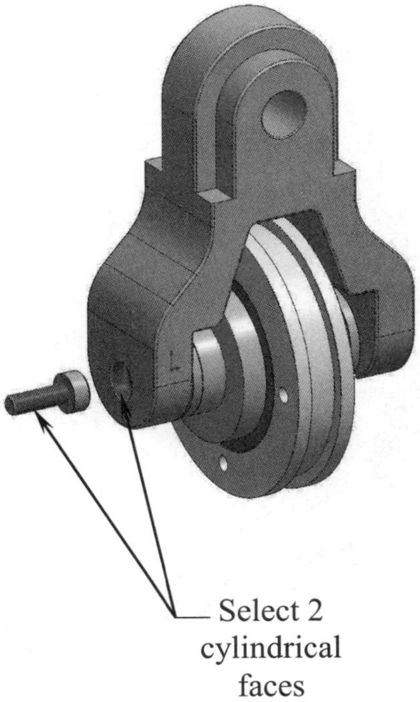

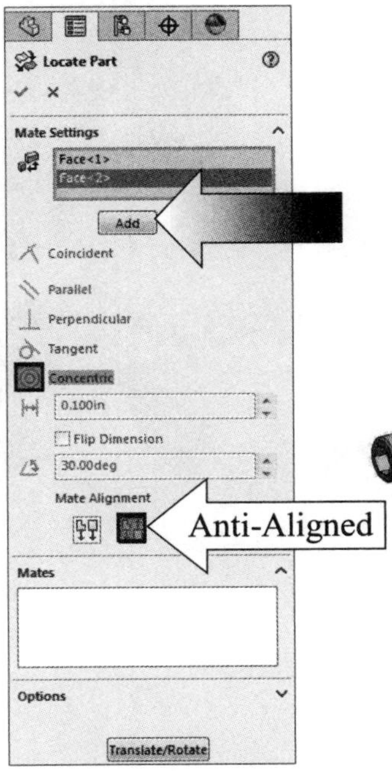

Adding a Coincident mate:

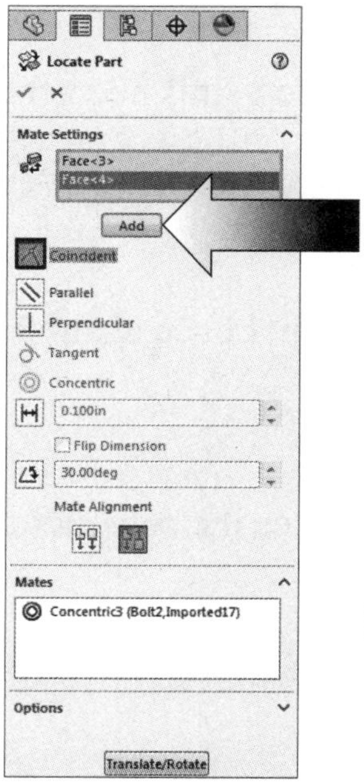

- Select the 2 **planar faces** as indicated.

- The 2 selected faces are constrained to share the same location.

- Click the **Add** button to save the new mate.

- Click **OK** to exit the Locate Part mode.

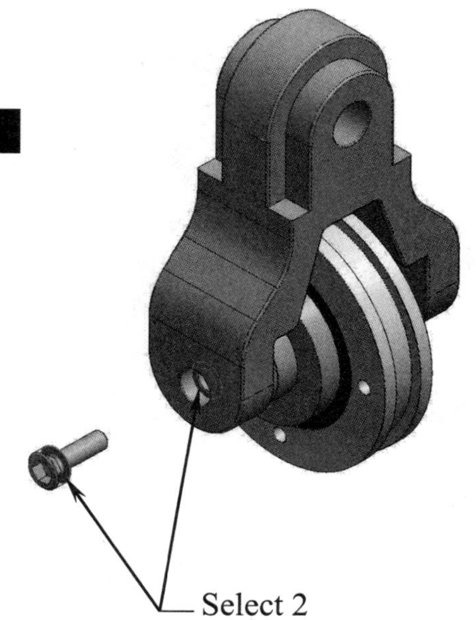

Select 2 planar faces

10. Editing the exploded view:

- Switch to the ConfigurationManager.

- Expand the Default configuration. Right click the **ExpView1** and select **Edit Feature** (arrow).

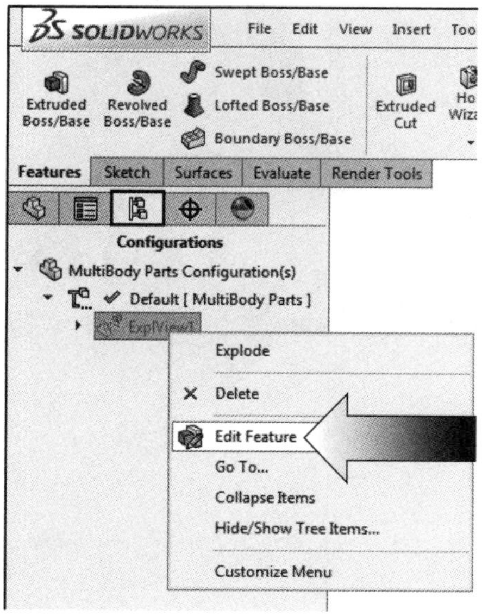

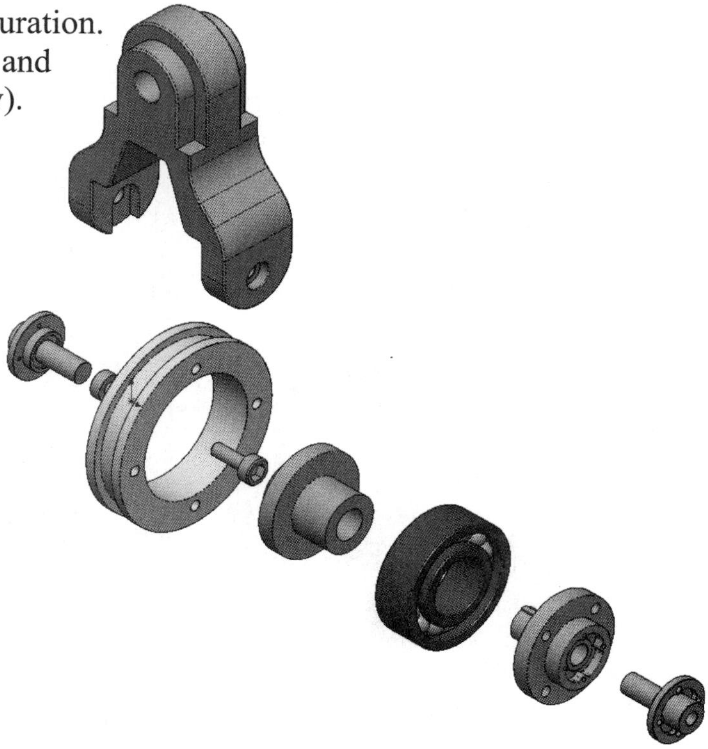

- Select the **Bolt** on the right.

- Drag the head of the **horizontal arrow** to move the bolt along the X direction.

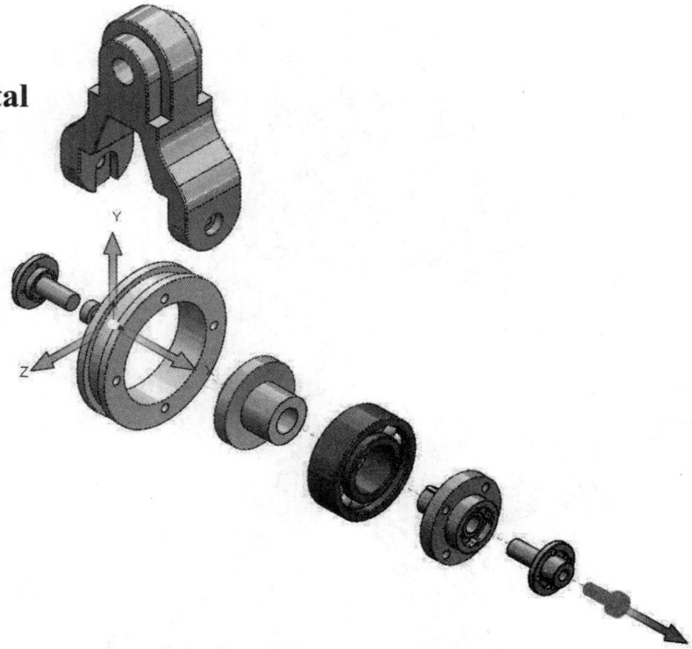

NOTE: *Enter a dimension* if a precise distance is preferred.*

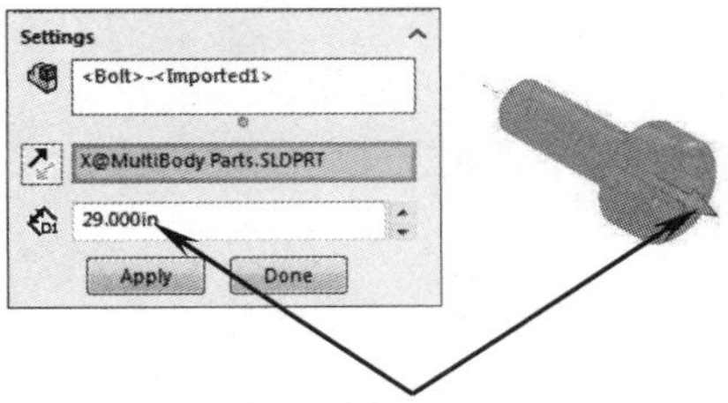

** If distance is used: Select a direction arrow (red), enter a dimension then click Apply and Done.*

- Select the bolt on the left.

- Drag the head of the **horizontal arrow** to the left to move the bolt along the -X direction.

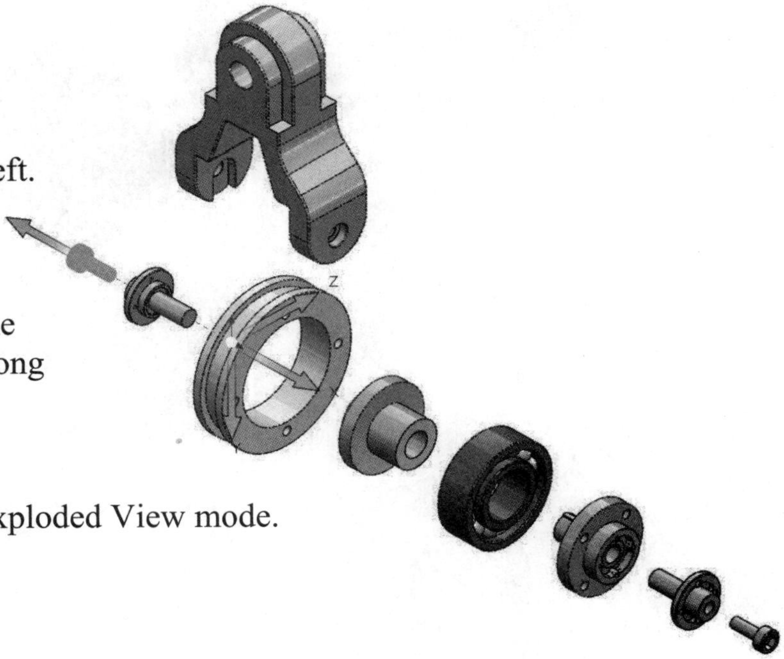

- Click **OK** to exit the exploded View mode.

11. Saving your work:

- Click **File / Save As**.

- Enter: **MultiBody Parts** for the name of the file.

- Click **Save**.

- Close all documents.

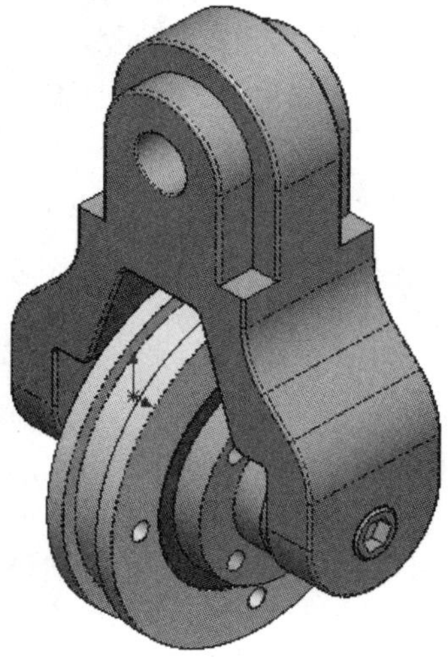

CHAPTER 5

Revolved & Thread Features

Revolved & Thread Features
Cylinder

The revolve command adds or removes material by revolving one or more profiles around a centerline. The revolve feature can be a boss/base, revolved cut, or a revolved surface. The revolve feature can be a solid, a thin feature, or a surface.

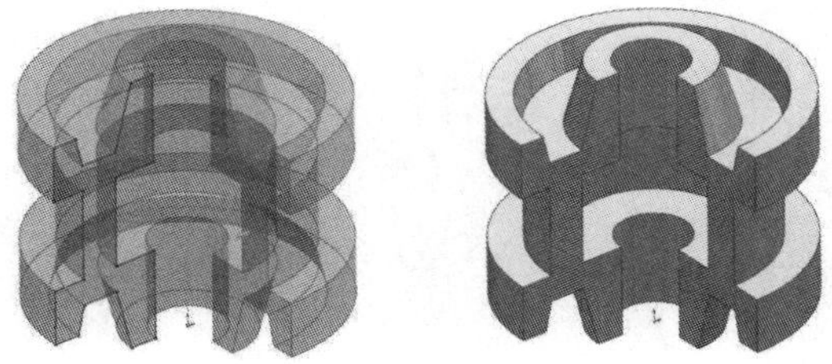

Solid Feature

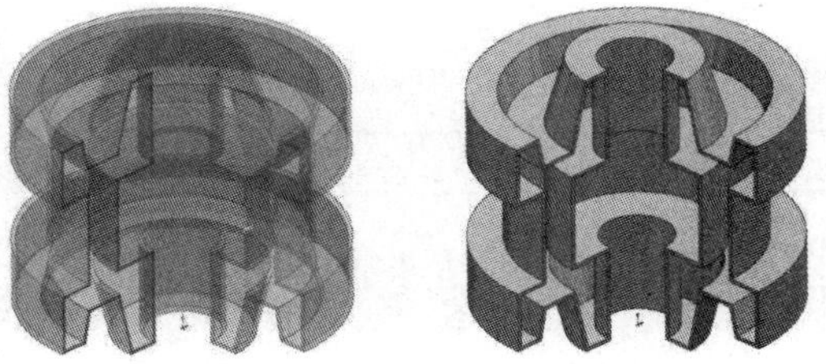

Thin Feature

The sketch for a thin or surface revolved feature can contain multiple open or closed intersecting profiles. The profile sketch must be a 2D sketch; 3D sketches are not supported for profiles. The Axis of Revolution can be a 3D sketch.

Profiles cannot cross the centerline. If the sketch contains more than one centerline, select the centerline you want to use as the axis of revolution. For revolved surfaces and revolved thin features only, the sketch cannot lie on the centerline.

When you dimension a revolve feature inside the centerline, you produce a radius dimension for the revolve feature.
When you dimension across the centerline, you produce a diameter dimension for the revolve feature.

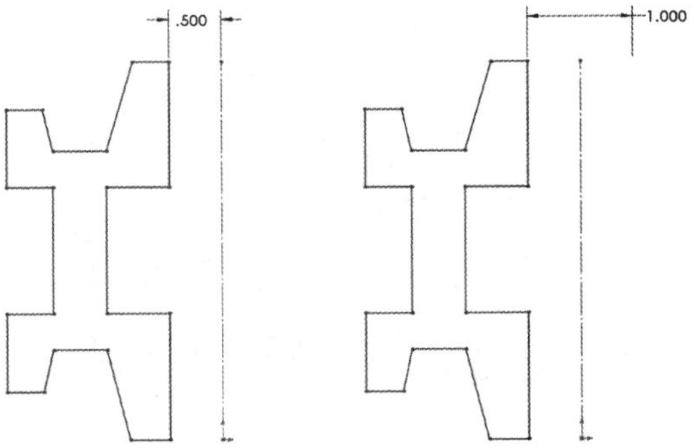

Cylinder
Revolved & Thread Features

View Orientation Hot Keys:

Ctrl + 1 = Front View
Ctrl + 2 = Back View
Ctrl + 3 = Left View
Ctrl + 4 = Right View
Ctrl + 5 = Top View
Ctrl + 6 = Bottom View
Ctrl + 7 = Isometric View
Ctrl + 8 = Normal To Selection

Dimensioning Standards: **ANSI**

Units: **INCHES** – 3 Decimals

Tools Needed:

Insert Sketch	Circle	Circular Sketch Pattern
Dimension	Geometric Relation	Chamfer
Revolved Boss/Base	Thread	Section View

1. Opening a part document:

- Select **File / Open**.

- Locate the part document named: **Revolved Features** and open it.

- The sketch has been fully dimensioned to help focus on the revolved features.

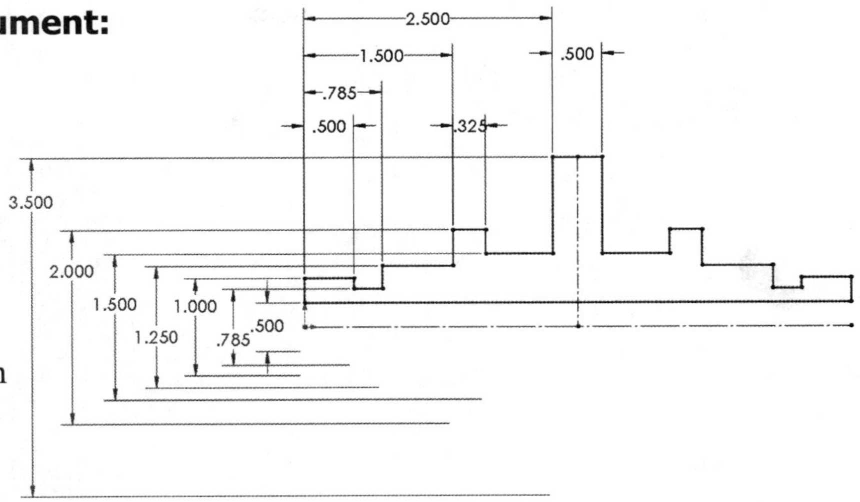

2. Creating a revolved feature:

- Switch to the **Features** tool tab.

- Click the **Revolved Boss/Base** command.

- Select the **horizontal centerline** as noted for the Axis of Revolution.

- Use the default **Blind** condition.

- Keep the revolve angle at **360°**.

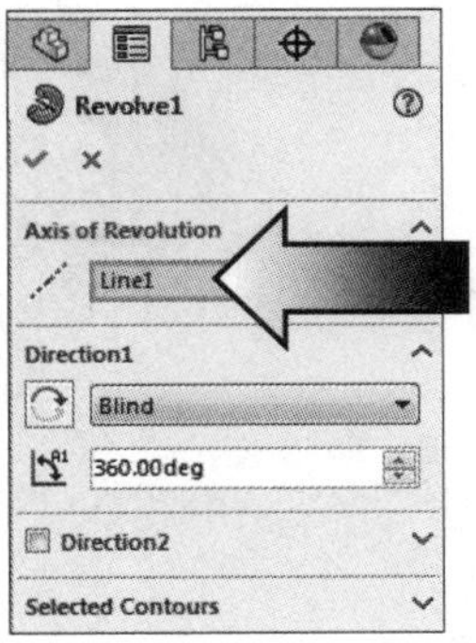

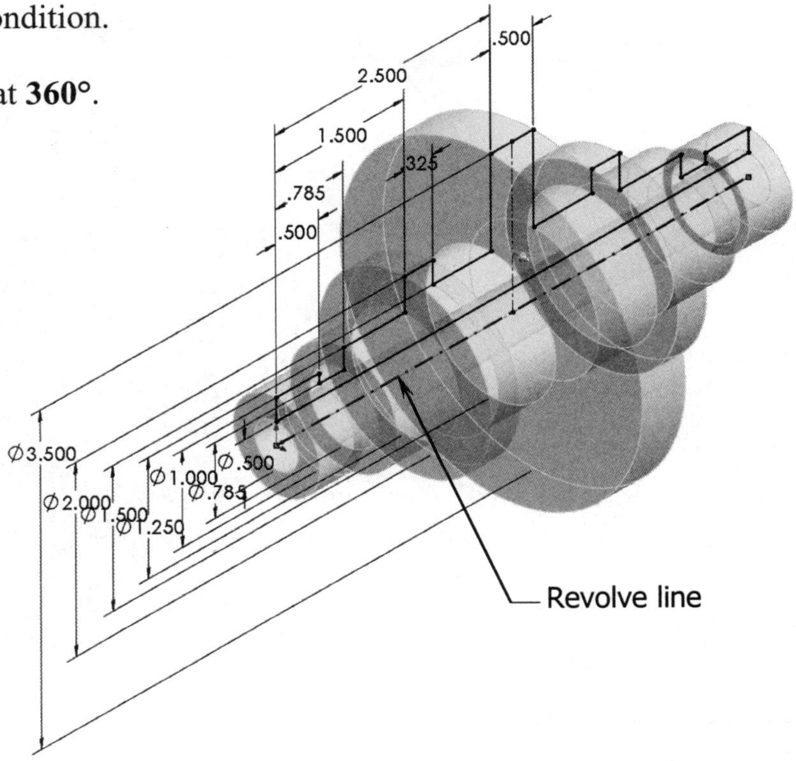

- Click **OK**.

3. Adding chamfers:

- Select the **Chamfer** command under the Fillet drop down arrow.

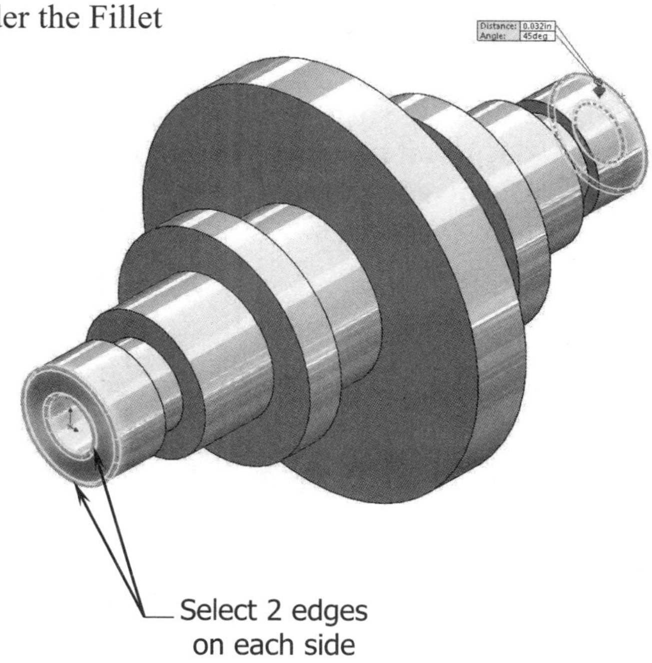

- Enter **.032in** for the depth of chamfer.

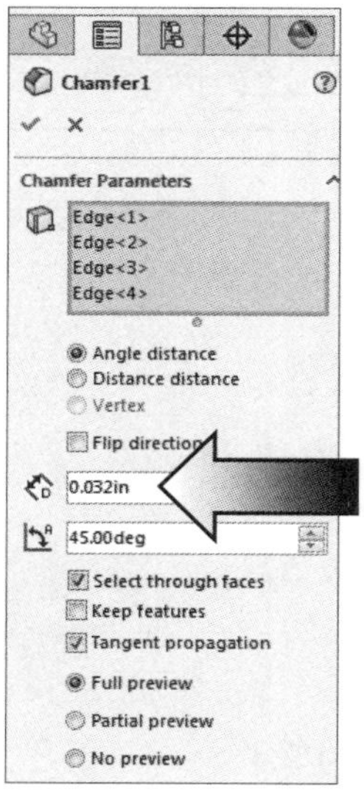

- Keep the default angle **45.00 deg**.

- Select the **4 edges** as noted.

- Click **OK**.

4. Creating the mounting holes:

- Select the <u>face</u> as indicated and open a new sketch.

- Sketch the large circle (Bolt-Circle*) and change it to construction geometry (click the For Construction checkbox on the Feature-Manager tree).

- Sketch the small circle whose center is coincident with the construction circle.

- Add the dimensions and relations indicated.

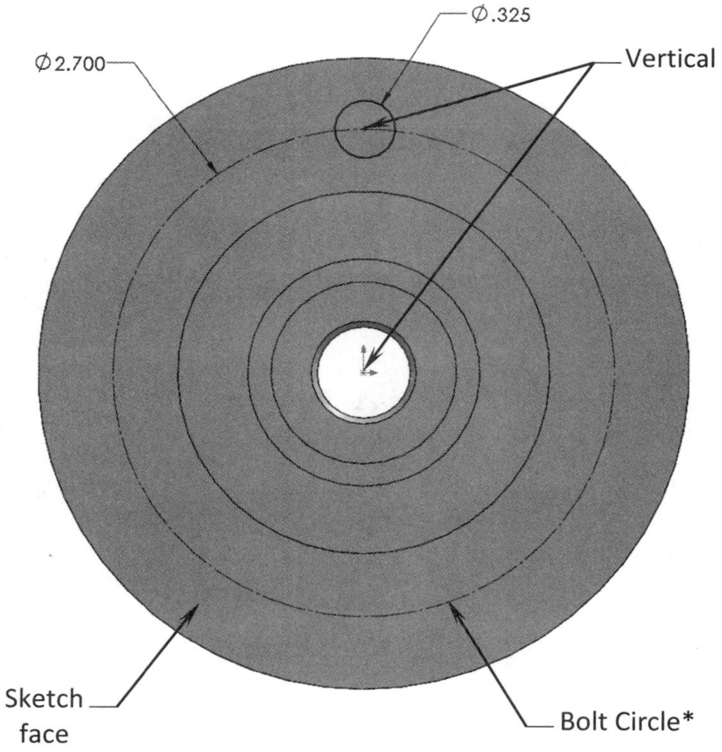

- Click the small circle to highlight it.

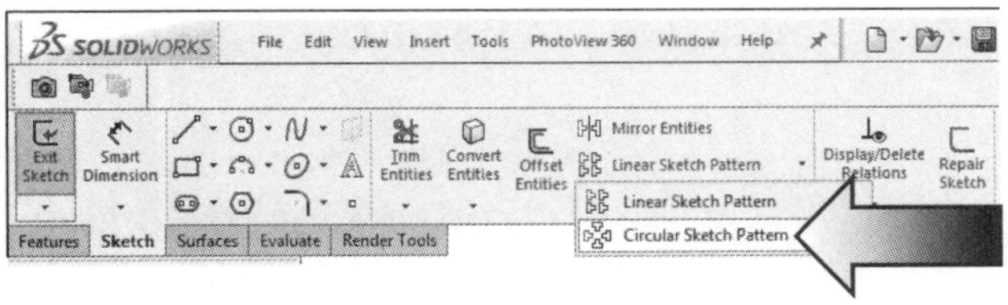

- Expand the Linear Sketch Pattern and select the **Circular- Sketch- Pattern** command (arrow).

- Enter **72deg** for spacing.

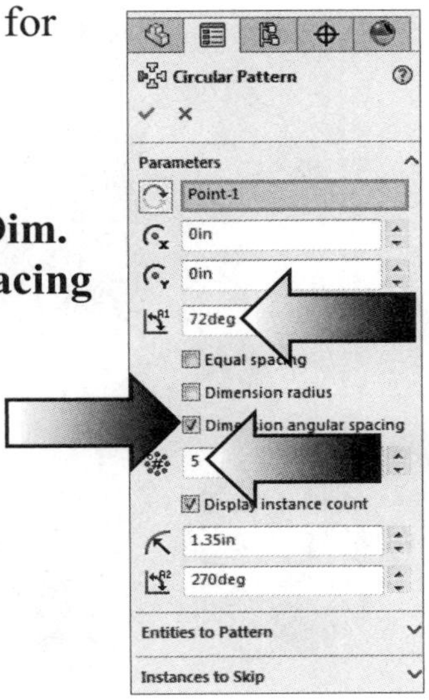

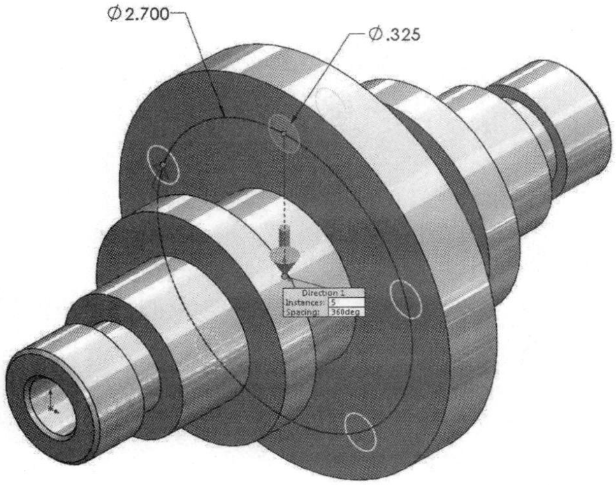

- Enable the **Dim. Angular Spacing** checkbox.

- Enter **5** for Number of Instances.

- Click **OK**.

- The circle is replicated 5 times but their centers are not yet constrained to the construction circle.

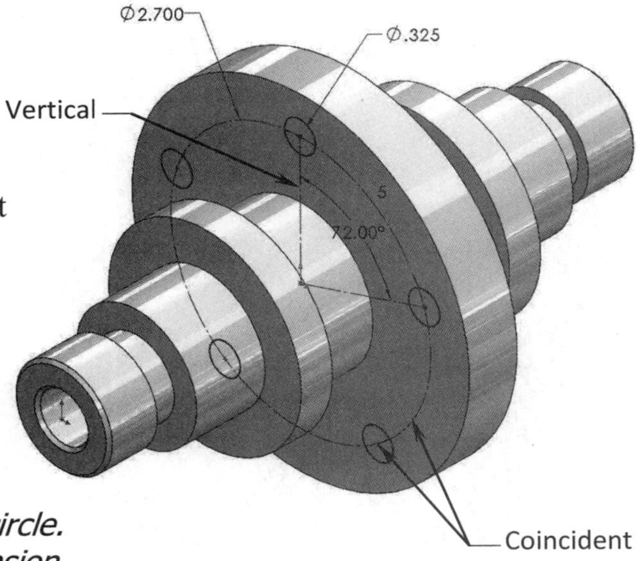

- Add the Vertical and the Coincident relations as shown to fully define the sketch.

* ***Bolt Circle:*** *A theoretical circle on which the centerpoints of bolt holes lie when the bolt holes are positioned as equally spaced in a circle. It is often treated as a basic dimension, when true position for the centers is specified using GD&T.*

- Switch to the **Features** tool tab.

- Click the **Extruded Cut** command.

- Select the **Up-To-Next** condition for Direction 1.

> **Up To Next**
>
> Extends the feature from the sketch plane to the next surface that intercepts the entire profile.

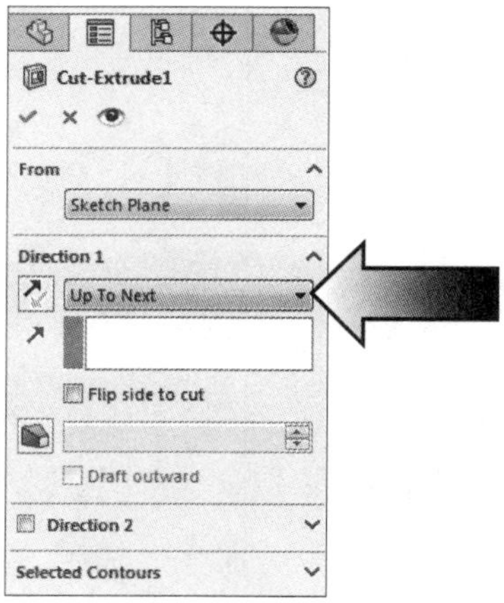

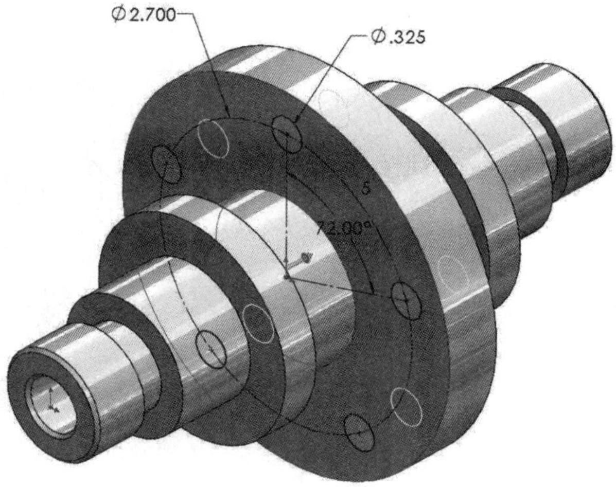

- Click **OK**.

- Rotate the model to different orientations to verify the cut feature.

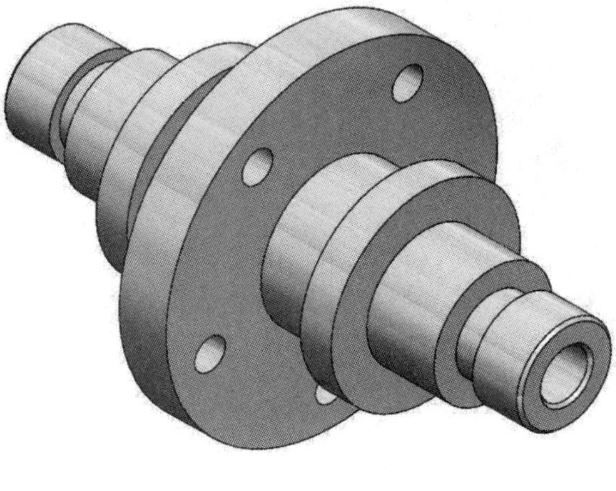

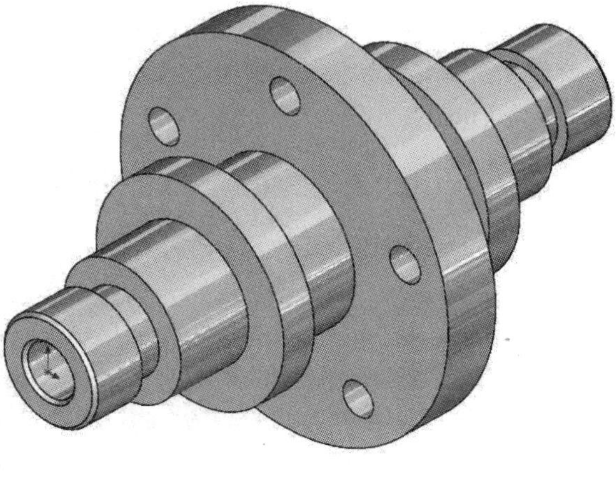

5. Adding threads:

- The Thread feature was added in SOLIDWORKS 2016. Its icon can be added to the Features tool tab by selecting: Tools, Customize, Commands, Features, and drag drop the icon on to the toolbar.

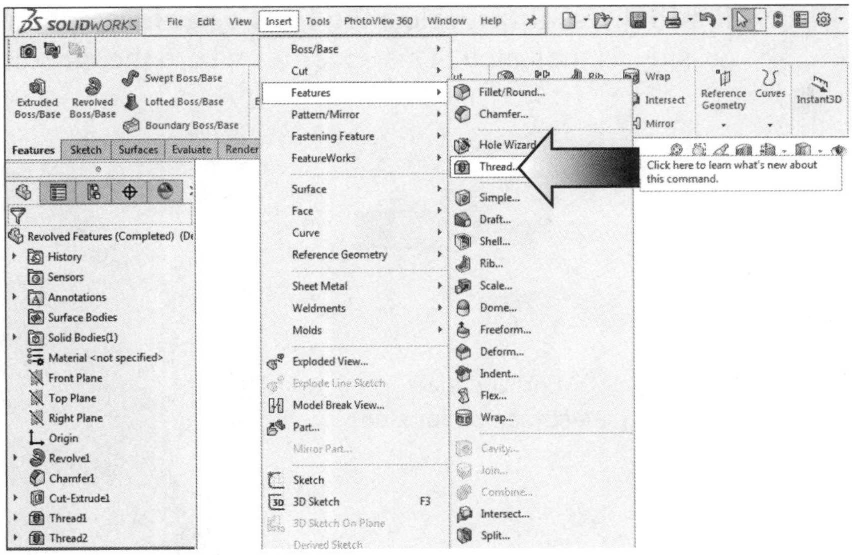

- Threads can be created with the "traditional method" by moving the thread profile along a helical path or by using the new Thread feature. The next couple of steps will discuss the use of the Thread feature.

- Select: **Insert / Features / Thread** (arrow).

- For Thread Location, click the **Edge** as noted.

- For Start Location, click the **Face** shown.

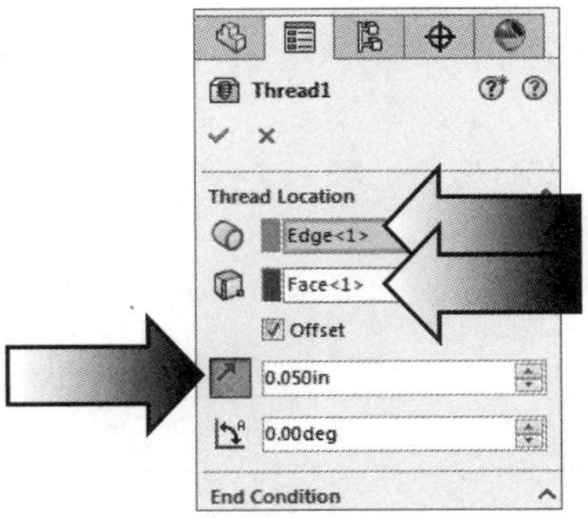

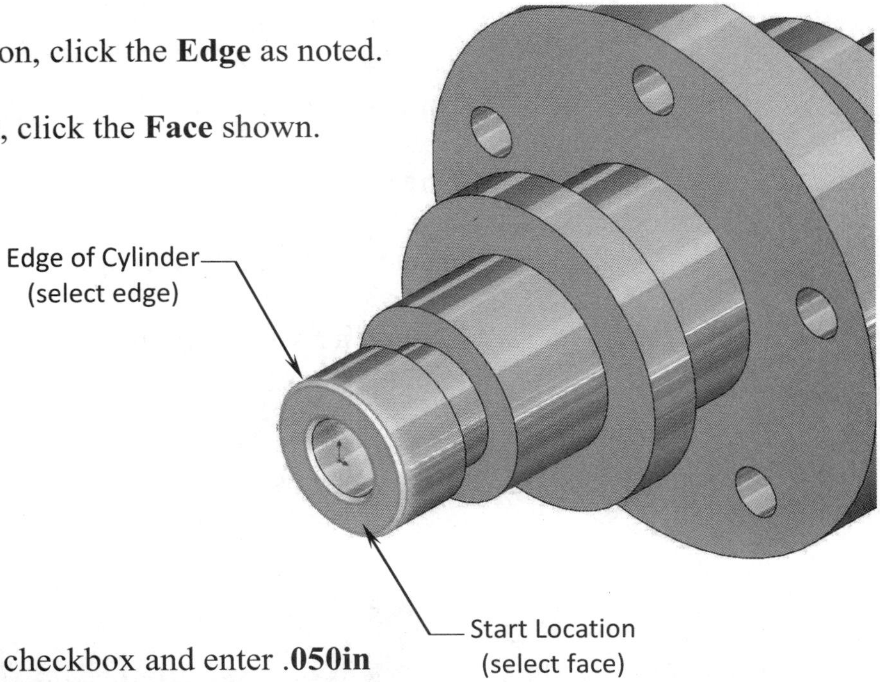

- Enable the **Offset** checkbox and enter **.050in** for clearance, click **Reverse** direction. This dimension moves the starting location outward to clear the front face.

More...

- For End Condition, select the **Up To Surface** option and click the **face** on the far side as indicated. This specifies where the threads will end.

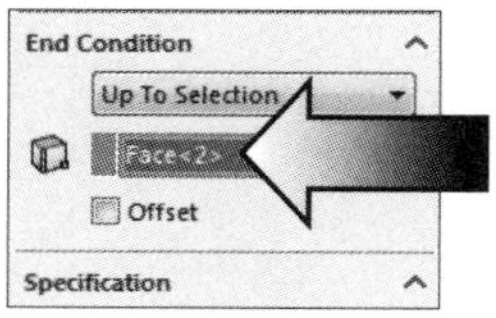

End Location
(select face on far side)

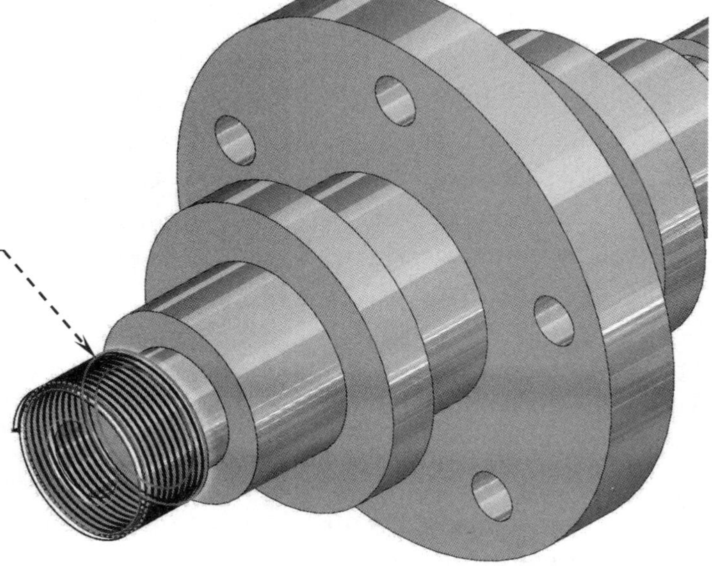

- Select the following under the Specification section:

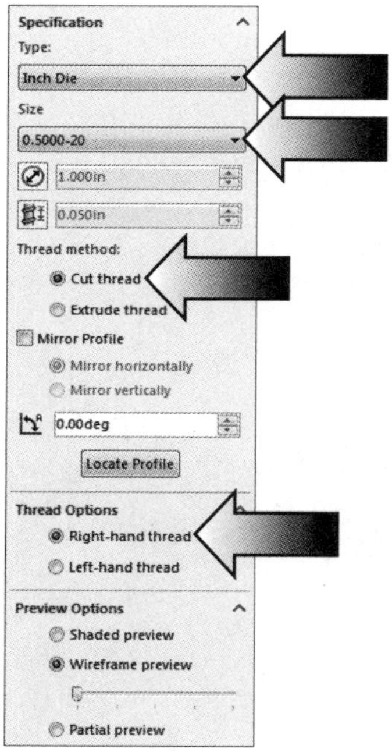

* Type: **Inch Die**.

* Size: **0.5000-20**.

* Thread Method: **Cut Thread**.

* Thread Options: **Right-Hand Thread**.

* Preview Options: **Wireframe**.

* Keep other settings at their default values.

- Click **OK**.

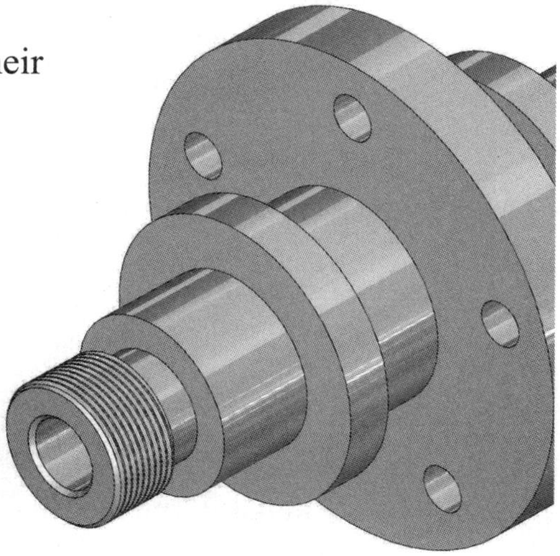

- Change to the **Right** orientation (Ctrl+4) to verify the details of the threads.

6. Adding threads to the opposite end:

- Change back to the isometric view (Ctrl+7) and press the hotkey Shift+Up Arrow twice. This shortcut will rotate your orientation precisely 180°.

- Select: **Insert / Features / Threads** once again.

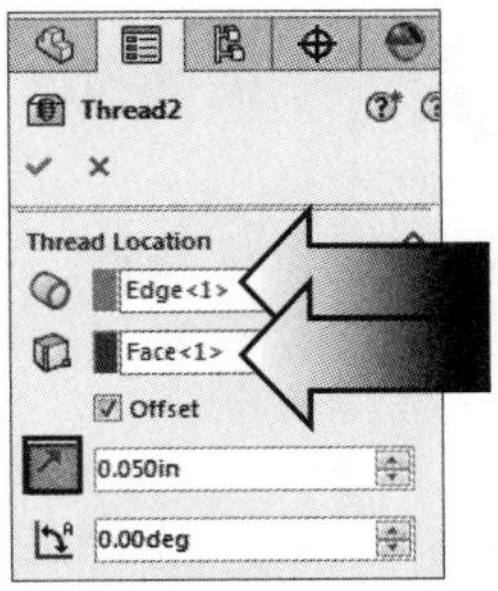

- For Thread Location, click the **Edge** as noted.

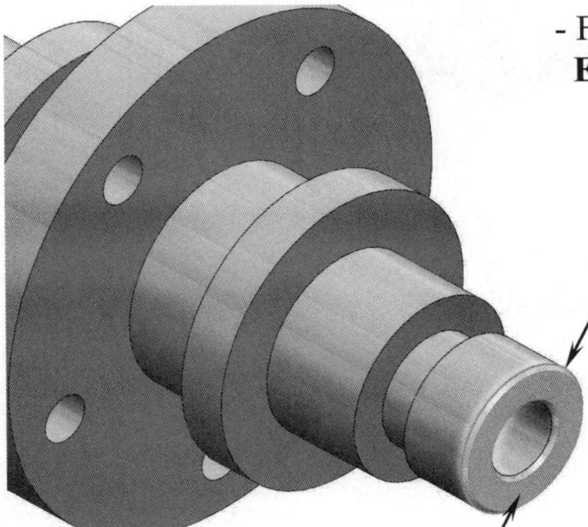

- For Start Location, click the **Face** shown.

- Enable the **Offset** checkbox and enter **.050in** for clearance, click **Reverse** direction. This dimension moves the starting location outward to clear the front face.

- For End Condition, select the **Up To Surface** option and click the face on the far side as indicated. This specifies where the threads will end.

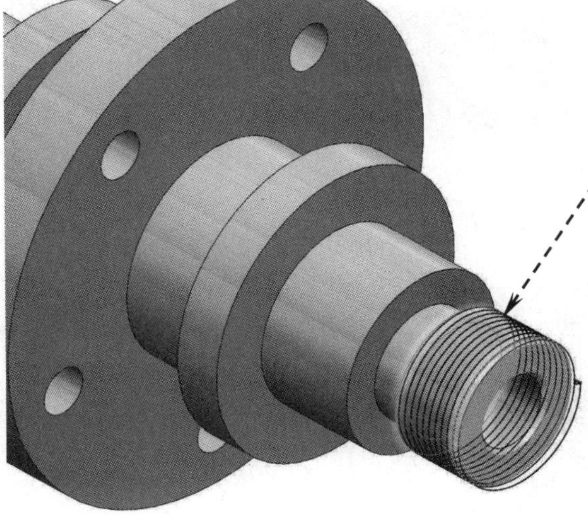

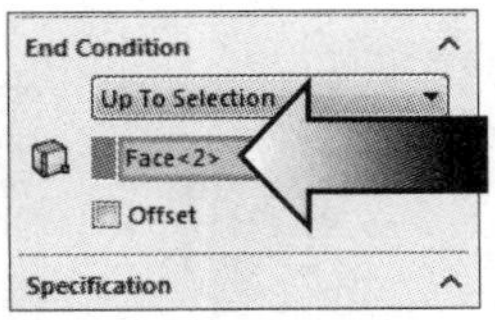

More...

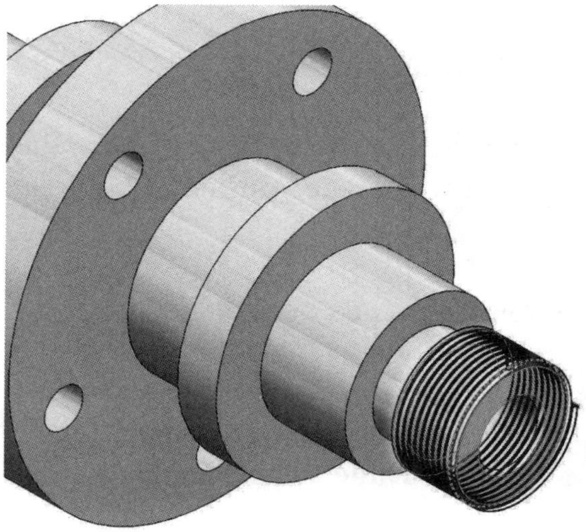

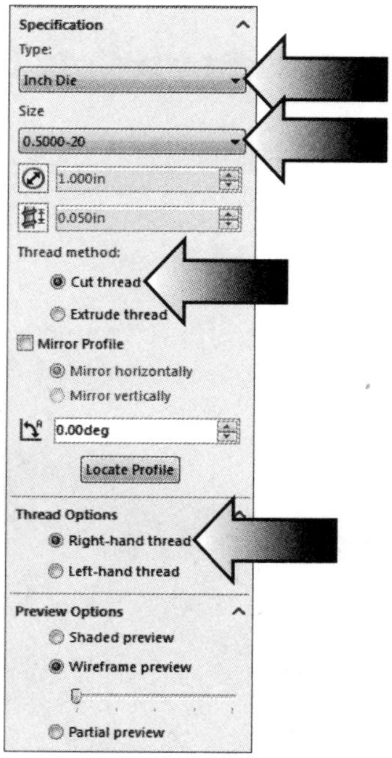

- Select the following under the Specification section:

  * Type: **Inch Die**.

  * Size: **0.5000-20**.

  * Thread Method: **Cut Thread**.

  * Thread Options: **Right-Hand Thread**.

  * Preview Options: **Wireframe**.

  * Keep other settings at their default values.

- Click **OK**.

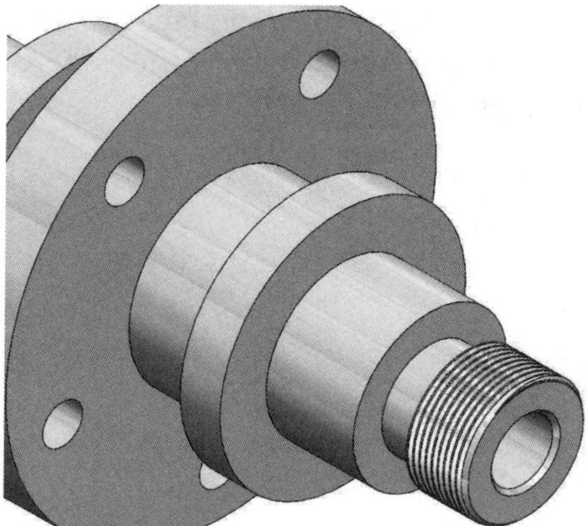

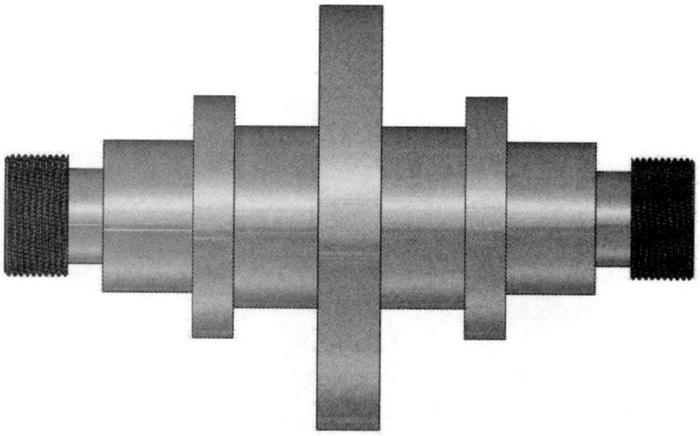

- Change to the **Right** orientation (Ctrl+4) to verify the details of the threads.

7. Creating a Zonal Section View:

- You can create section views in a model by cutting away multiple areas of the model. These multiple areas are defined by "intersection zones."

- Click the Section View command from the **View (Heads-Up)** toolbar (arrow).

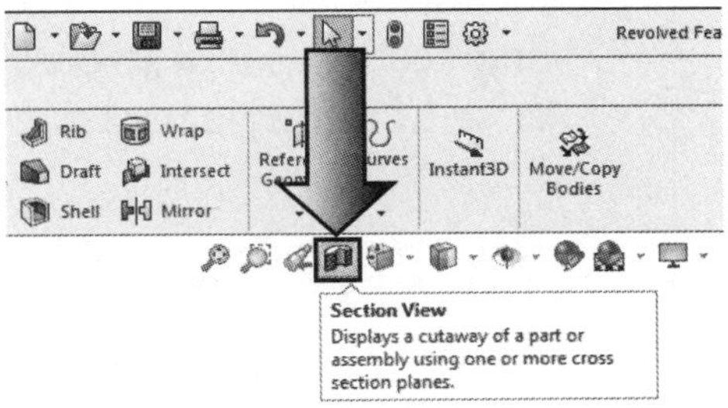

- For Section Method, select the **Zonal** option.

- For Section 1, select the **Top** plane.

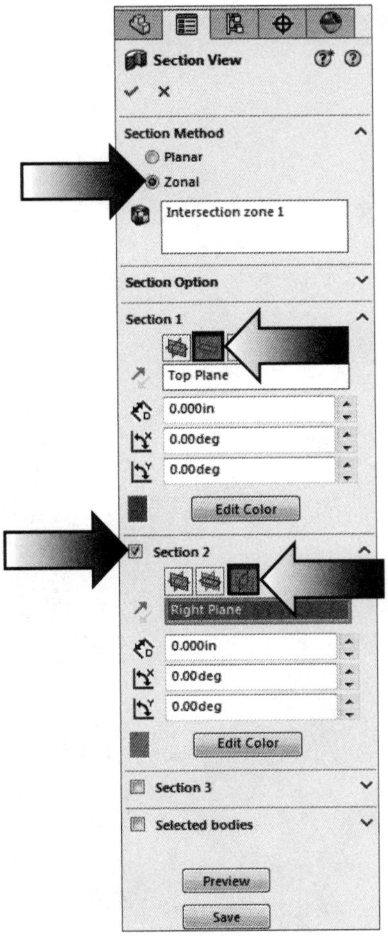

- Enable the Section 2 checkbox and select the **Right** plane.

- Click **OK**.

- When you select section planes or faces, the bounding box of your selections is the intersection zone. You can use the intersection zones to create a section view of multiple areas of a model.

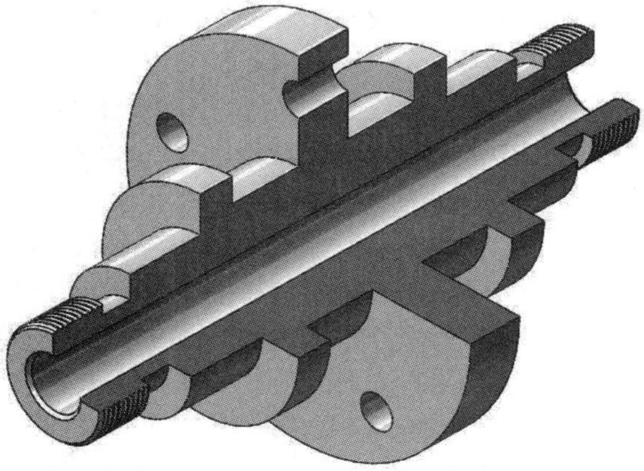

8. Saving your work:

- Click **File / Save As**.

- Use the same file name and press **Save**.

- Overwrite the existing one when prompted.

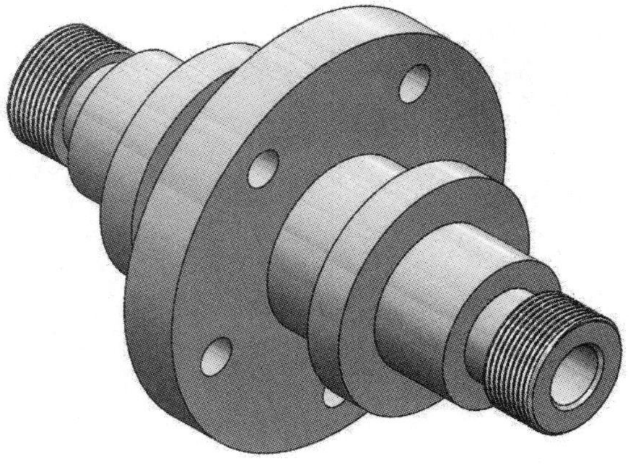

CHAPTER 6

Flex Bending

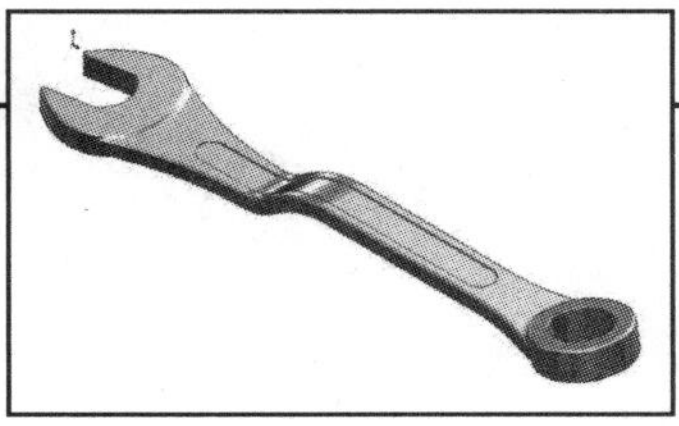

Flex Bending - Overview

Flex features are useful for modifying complex models with predictable, intuitive tools for many applications including concepts, mechanical design, industrial design, stamping dies, molds, and so on.

There are 4 flex types available:

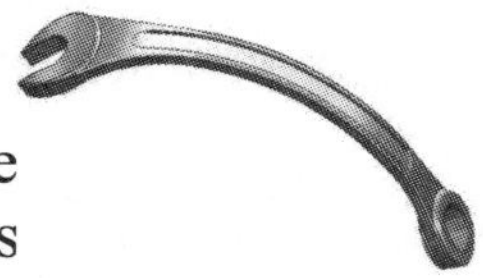

* **Flex Bending**  Bends one or more solid or surface bodies about the bend axis (Red X-Axis). The neutral plane of the bend passes through the triad Origin and corresponds to the triad's X-Z plane. The arc length between the trim planes along the neutral plane stays constant throughout the bending operation.

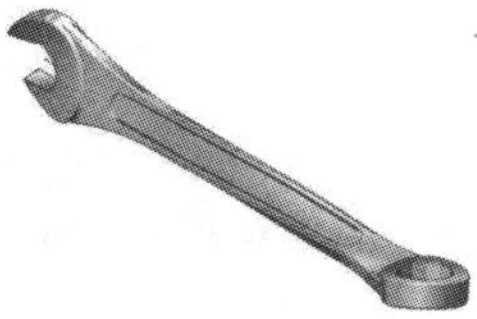

* **Flex Twisting**  Twists solid and surface bodies around the blue Z-axis of the triad. Position the triad and trim planes to control the degree, location, and extent of twisting.

* **Flex Tapering**  Tapers solid and surface bodies along the blue Z-axis of the triad. Position the triad and trim planes to control the degree, location, and extent of tapering.

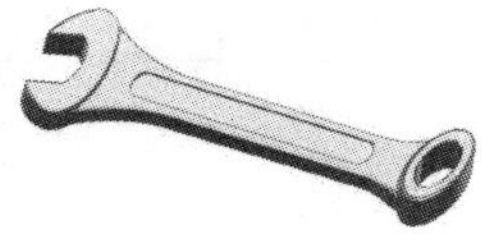

* **Flex Stretching**  Stretches solid and surface bodies along the blue Z-axis of the triad. Specify a distance or drag the edge of a trim plane with the left mouse button.

- The Flex feature calculates the extent of the part using a bounding box. The trim planes are then initially located at the extents of the bodies, perpendicular to the Z-axis of the triad. The Flex feature affects the region between the trim planes only.

Spanner
Flex Bending

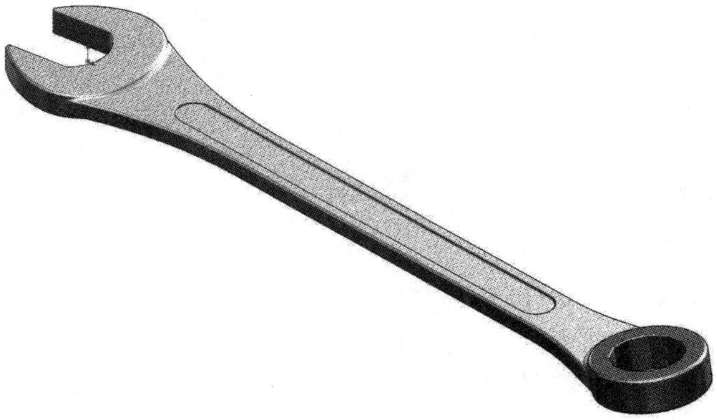

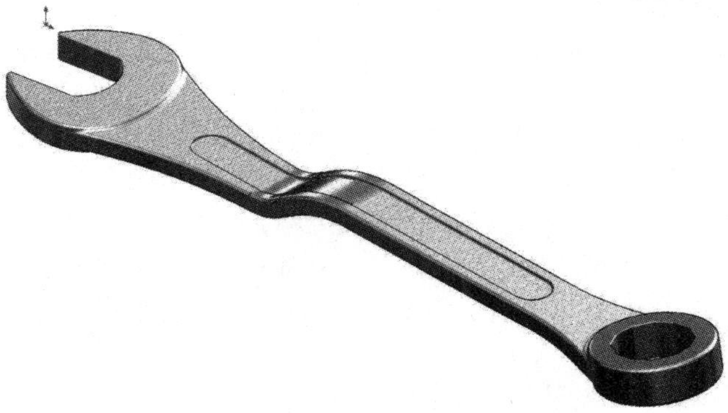

View Orientation Hot Keys:

Ctrl + 1 = Front View
Ctrl + 2 = Back View
Ctrl + 3 = Left View
Ctrl + 4 = Right View
Ctrl + 5 = Top View
Ctrl + 6 = Bottom View
Ctrl + 7 = Isometric View
Ctrl + 8 = Normal To Selection

Dimensioning Standards: **ANSI**

Units: **INCHES** – 3 Decimals

Tools Needed:

Flex

Bending

Flex Bending – Part 1

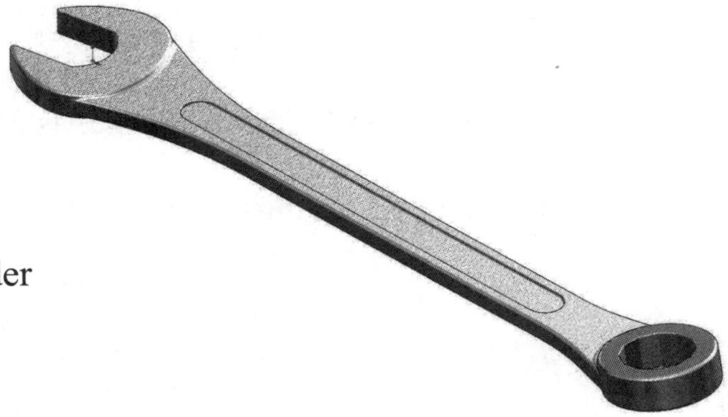

1. Opening a part document:

- Select **File / Open**.

- Browse to the **Training Files** folder and open a part document named: **Flex Bending 1.sldprt**

2. Creating the 1st Flex-Bending feature:

- The Flex features deform complex models in an intuitive manner. The tool is useful for modifying complex models with predictable, intuitive tools for many applications including concepts, mechanical design, industrial design, stamping dies, molds, and so on. Flex features can change single body or multibody parts.

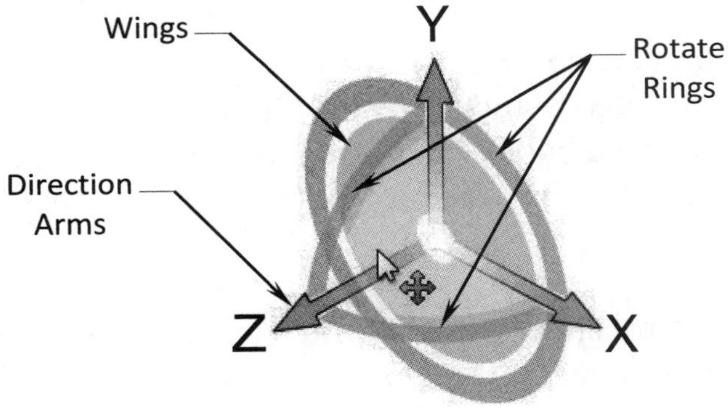

The Triad

- The Flex command also uses the Triad to facilitate manipulating various objects such as 3D sketch entities, bodies, parts, certain features, and components in assemblies.

- The rings and wings are displayed when rotation and dragging along the wings' planes are possible.

- Select **Insert / Features / Flex** (arrows).

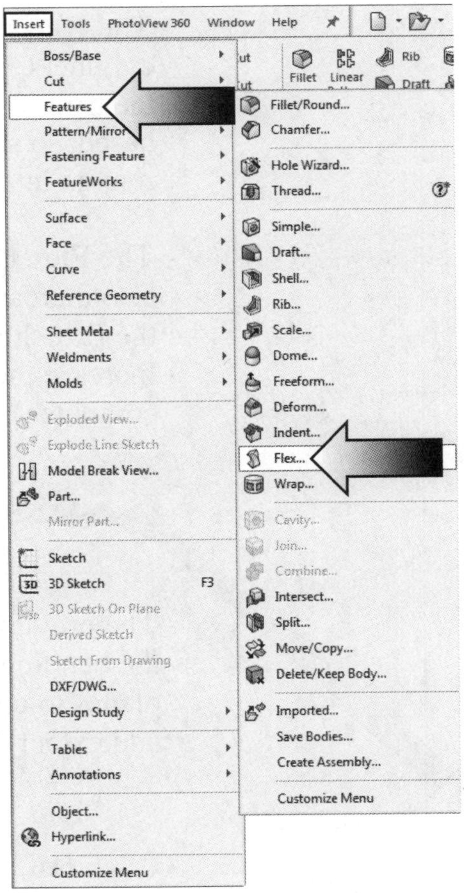

- Select the model in the graphics area for Flex Input.

- Click the **Bending** option (arrow).

- Enter **45deg** for Angle, the Radius is adjusted automatically.

- Leave all other settings at their default values.

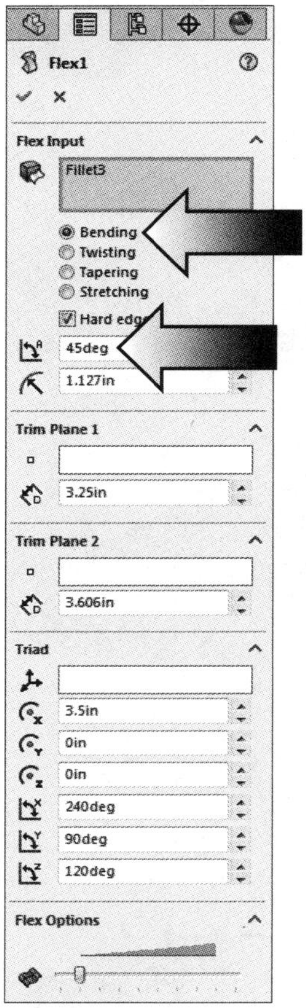

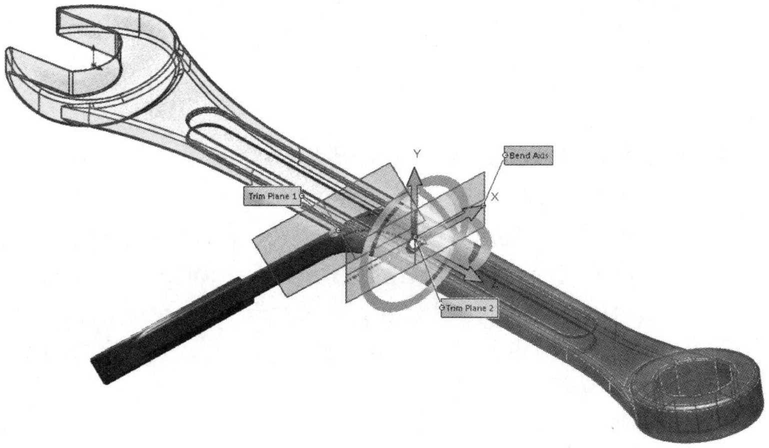

- The **Hard Edge** option creates analytical surfaces (cones, cylinders, planes, and so on), which often result in split faces where the trim planes intersect the bodies. If cleared, results are spline-based, so surfaces and faces may appear smoother and original faces remain intact.

- The **Flex Options** control surface quality. Increasing the quality also increases the success rate of the flex feature. For example, if the flex shows an error message, move the slider towards the right. Increase the quality only as needed because this may decrease the computer performance.

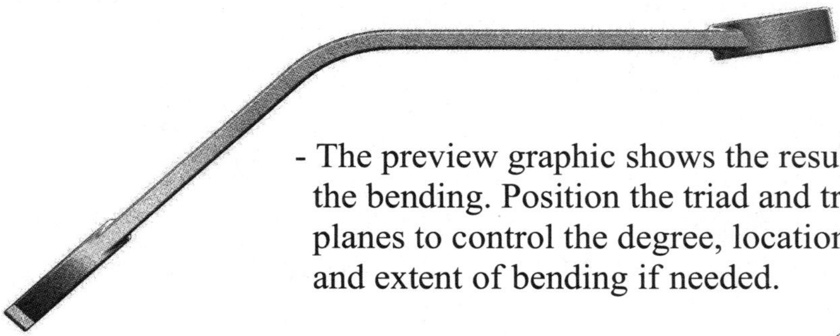

- The preview graphic shows the result of the bending. Position the triad and trim planes to control the degree, location, and extent of bending if needed.

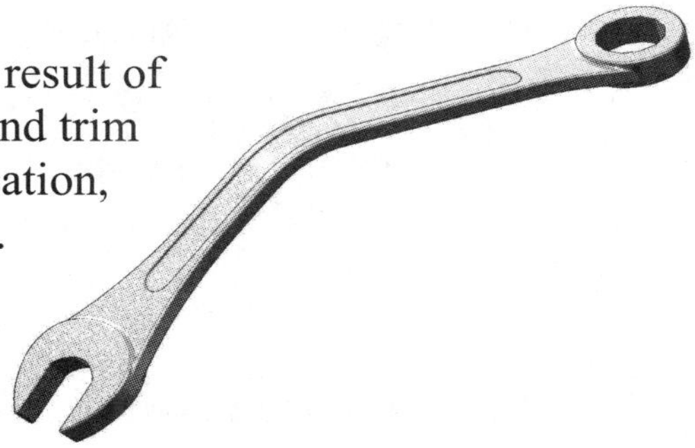

- Click **OK**.

3. Creating the 2nd Flex-Bending feature:

- Select **Insert / Features / Flex** once again.

- Select the model from the graphics area.

- Click the **Bending** option (arrow).

- Enter **45deg** for Angle, the Radius is adjusted automatically.

- Leave all other settings at their default values.

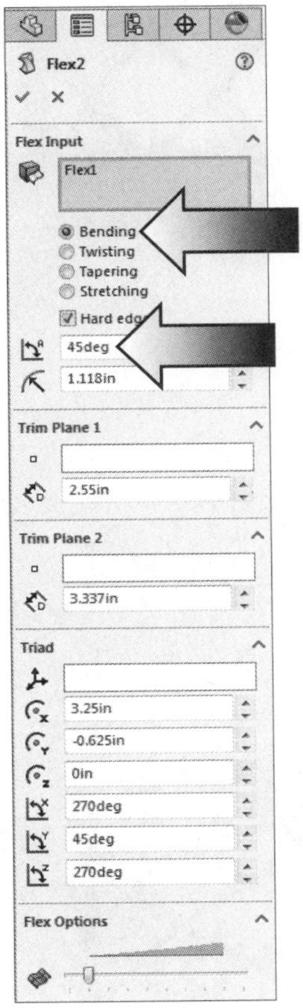

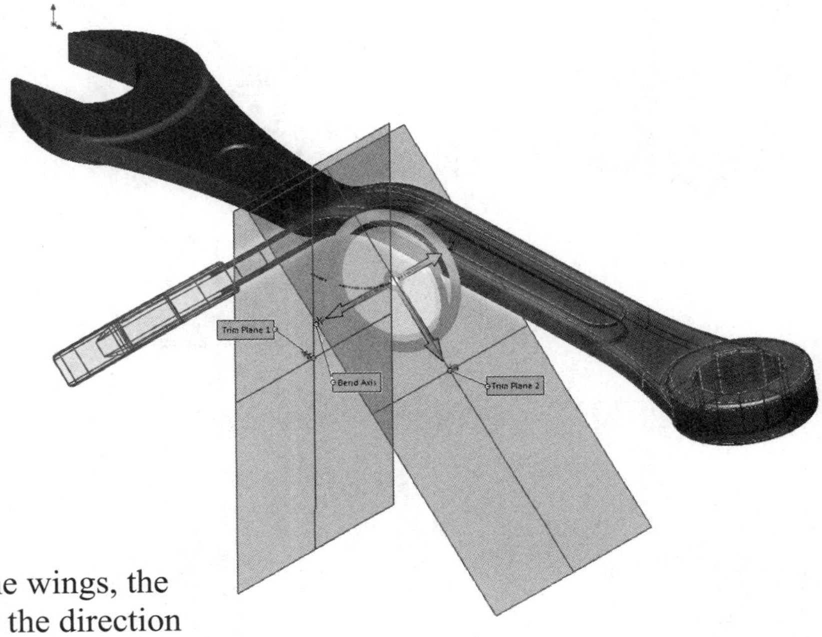

- Move the wings, the rings, or the direction arms to see the dynamic changes to the model.

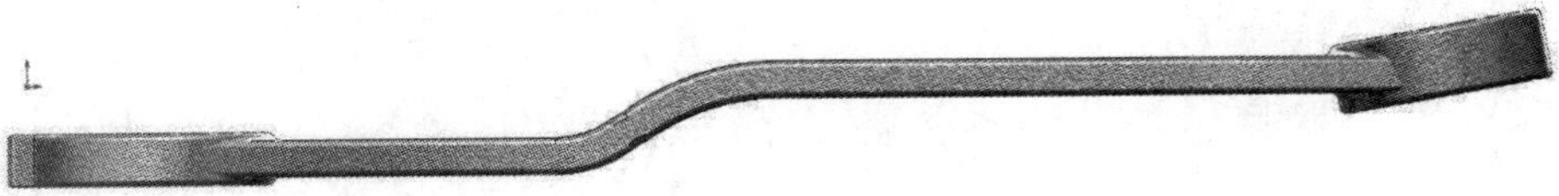

- Click **OK**.

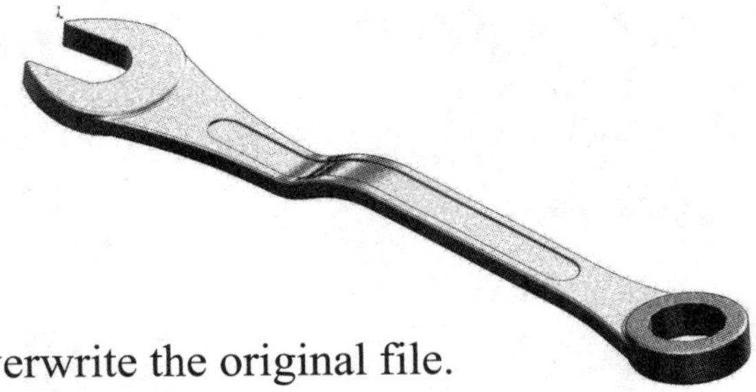

4. Saving your work:

- Save your work as **Flex Bending 1** and overwrite the original file.

Flex examples

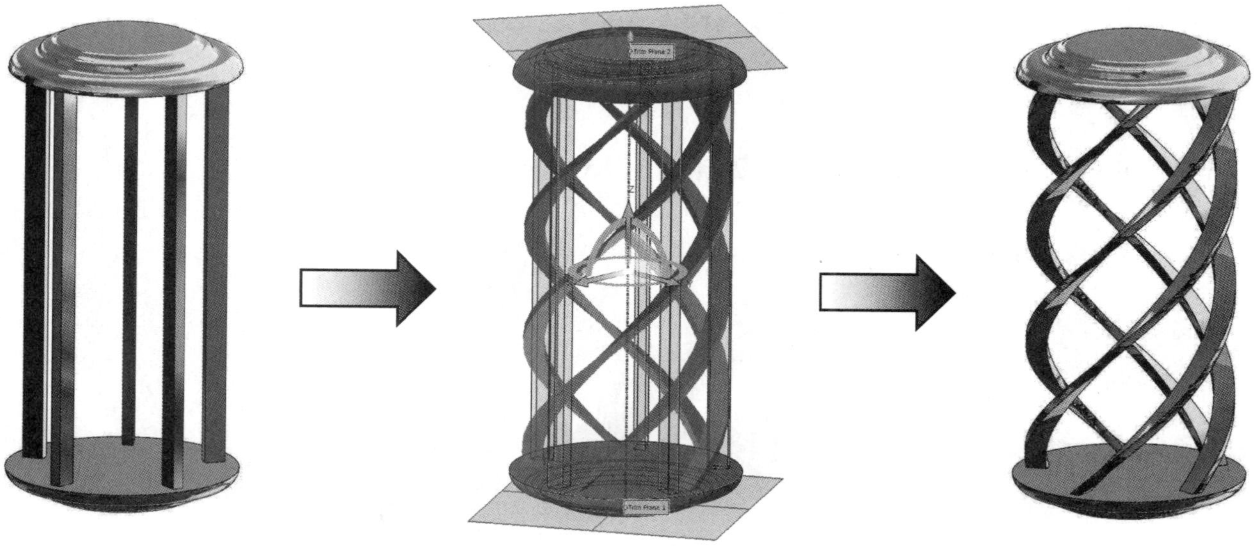

Flex Twisting

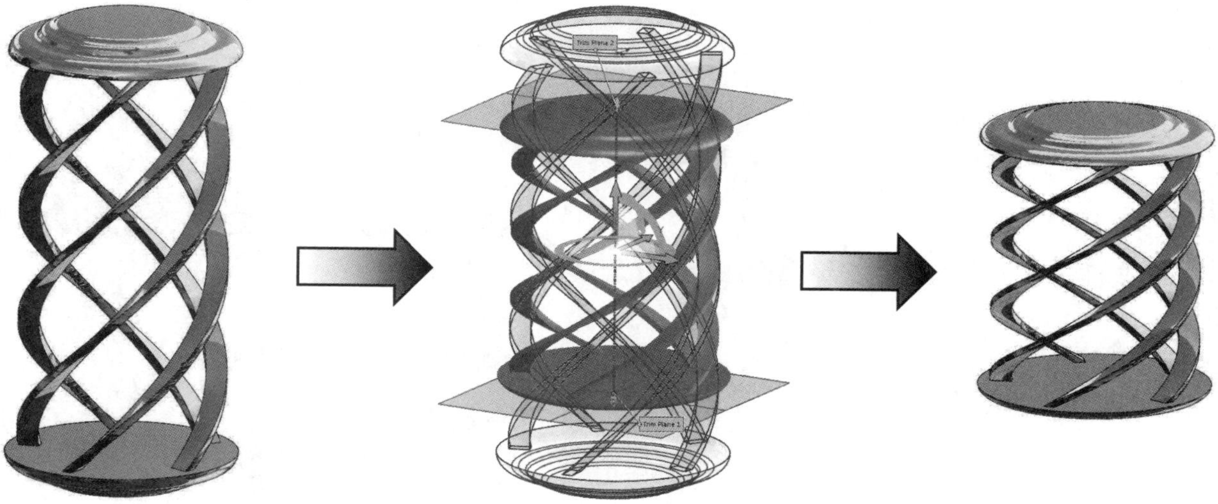

Flex Stretching

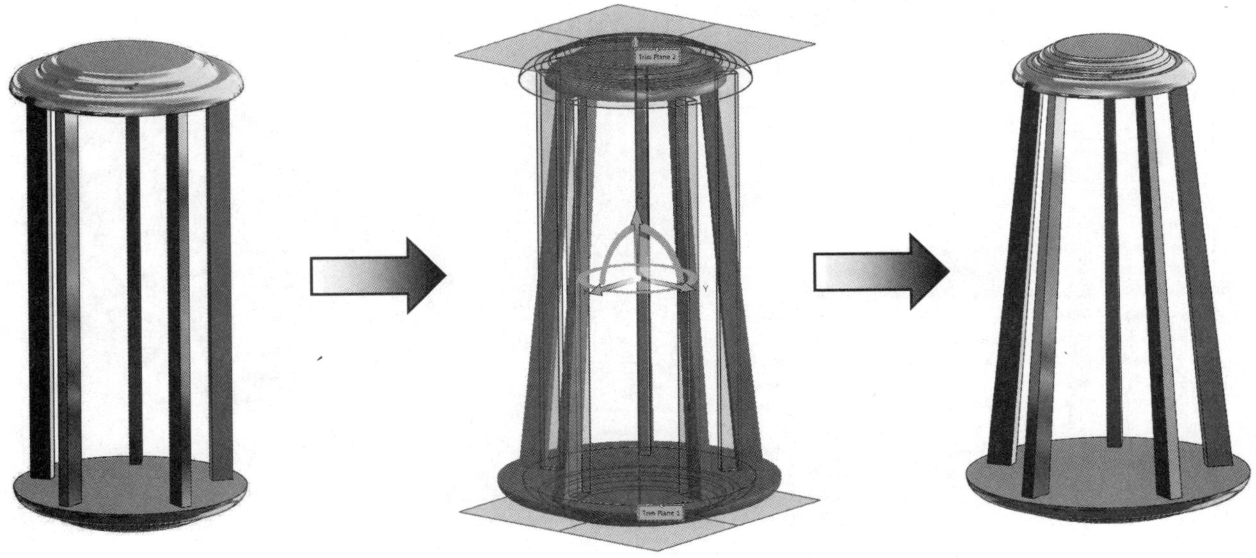

Flex Tapering

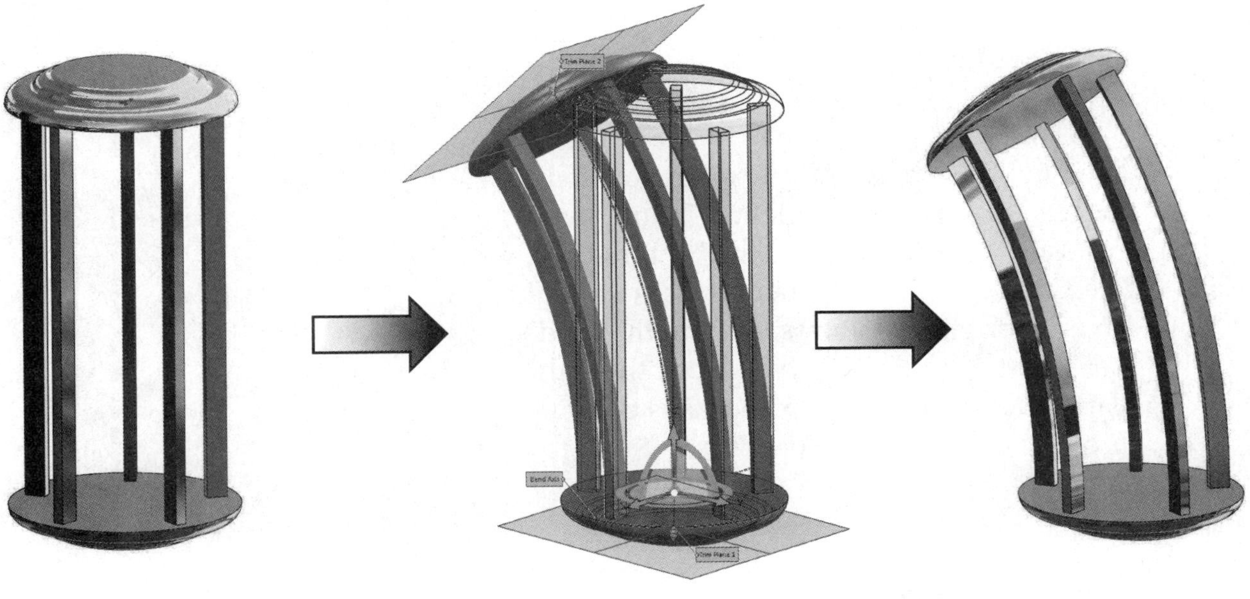

Flex Bending

Flex Bending – Part 2

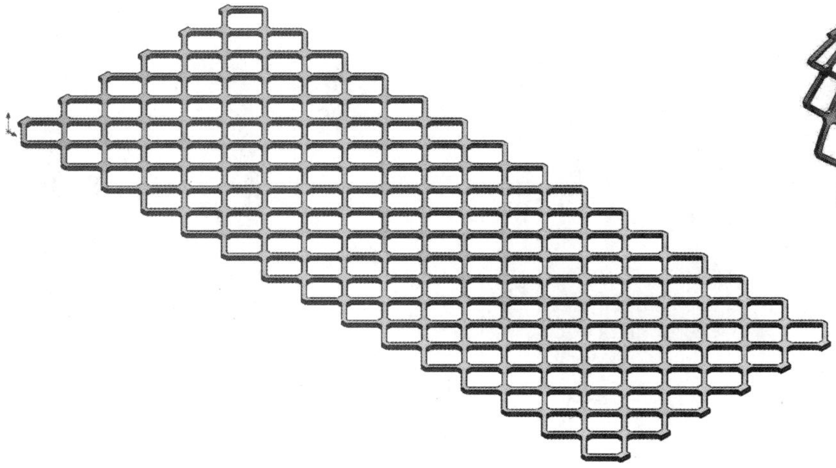

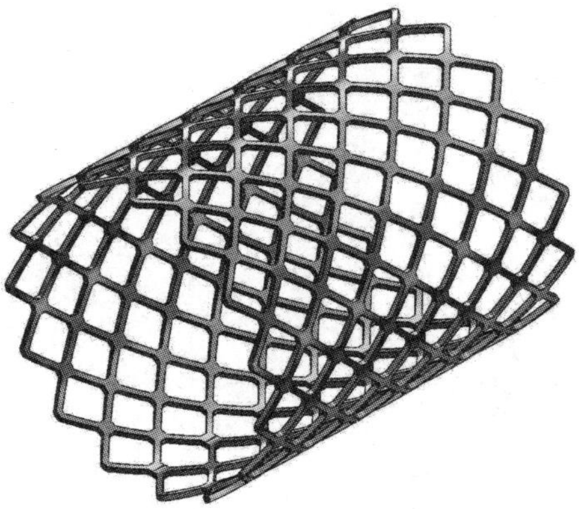

1. Opening a part document:

- Select **File / Open**.

- Browse to the **Training Files** folder and open a part document named: **Flex Bending 2.sldprt**

- The Flex feature uses the Triad to position the center of the bend and the 2 Trim Planes to define the bend angle or the bend radius. The neutral plane of the bend passes through the triad origin and corresponds to the triad's X-Z plane. The arc length between the trim planes along the neutral plane stays constant throughout the bending operation.

2. Creating a Flex-Bending:

- Select **Insert / Features / Flex** (arrows).

- Select **Insert / Features / Flex** once again.

- Select the model from the graphics area.

- Click the **Bending** option (arrow).

- Enter **359.9deg** for Angle, the Radius is adjusted automatically.

- Leave all other settings at their default values.

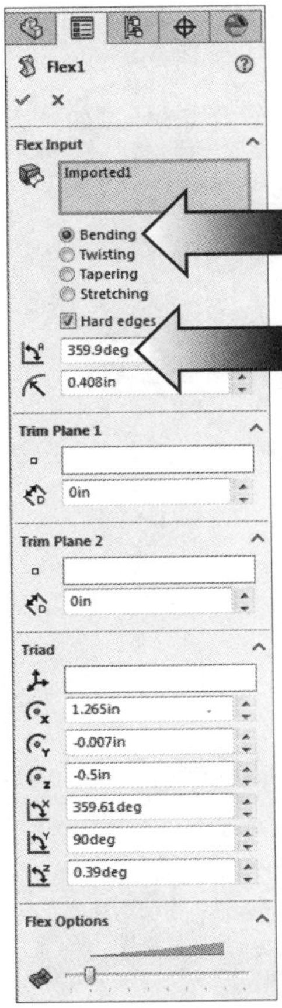

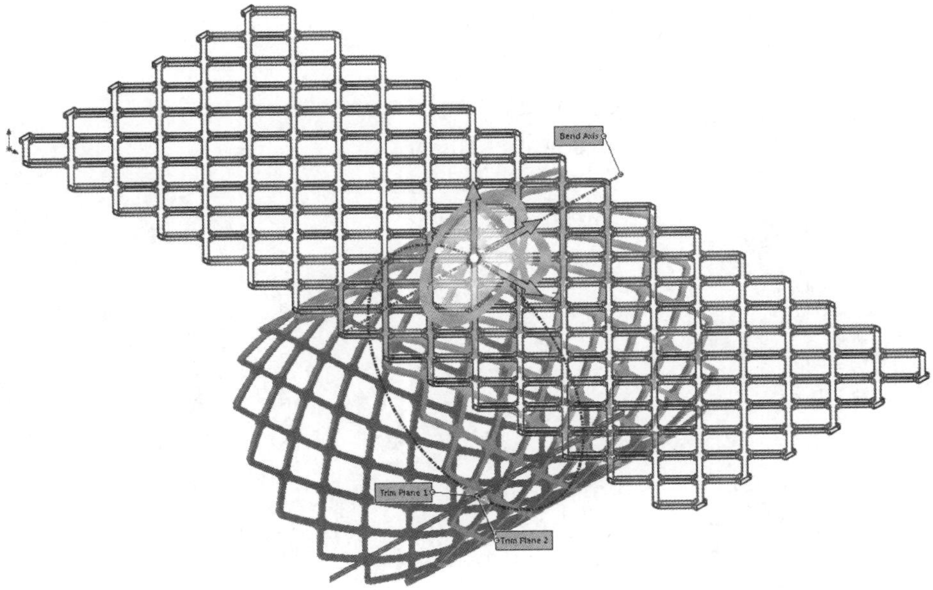

- Click **OK**.

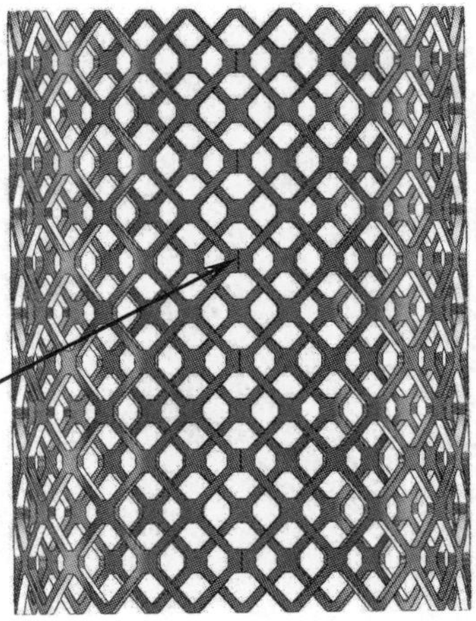

Press Ctrl+6 to see the slit from the back side

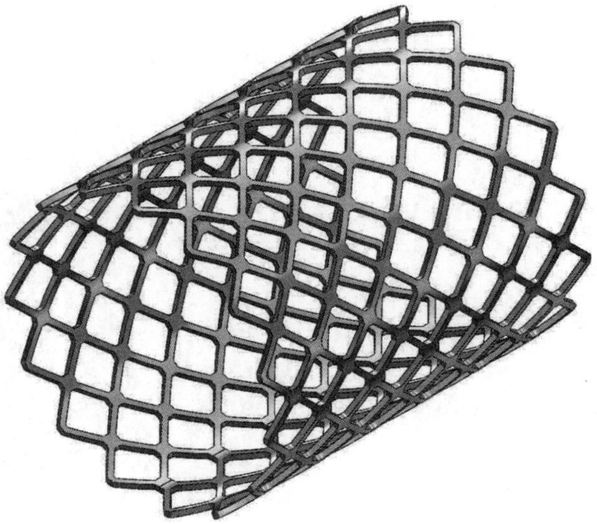

3. Creating a Linear Pattern:

- Switch to the **Features** tool tab.

- Select **View / Hide/Show / Temporary Axis**. We will use the temporary axis in the center of the model as the pattern direction.

- Click the **Linear Pattern** command and enter the following parameters:

  * Pattern Direction: Select the **Temporary Axis** in the center of the model.

  * Enter **1.0225in** for Spacing.

  * Click the **Bodies** checkbox and <u>select the model</u> from the graphics for Bodies to pattern.

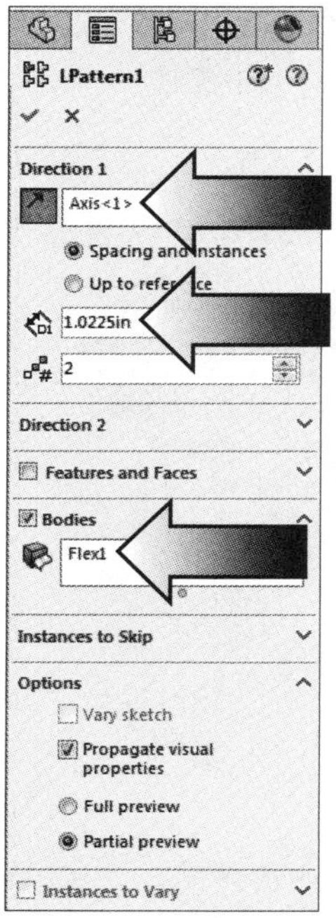

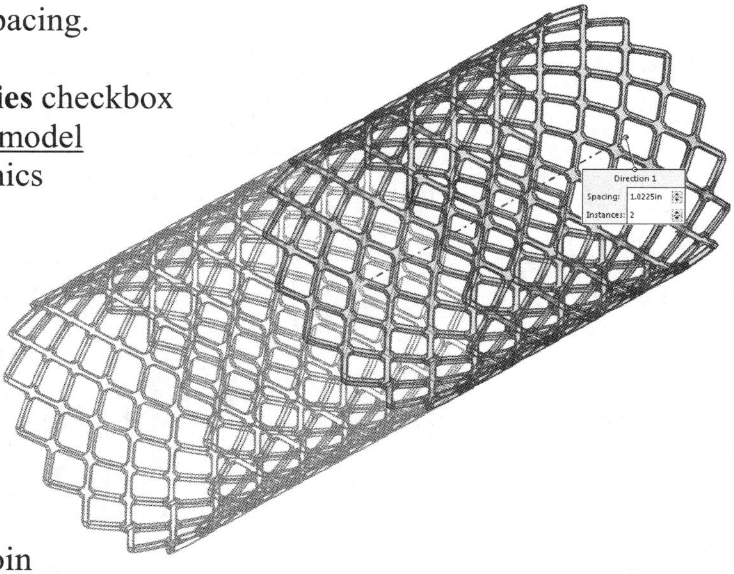

- The pattern created a second solid body. Use the Combine-Add Command to join them into one body if needed.

- Click **OK**.

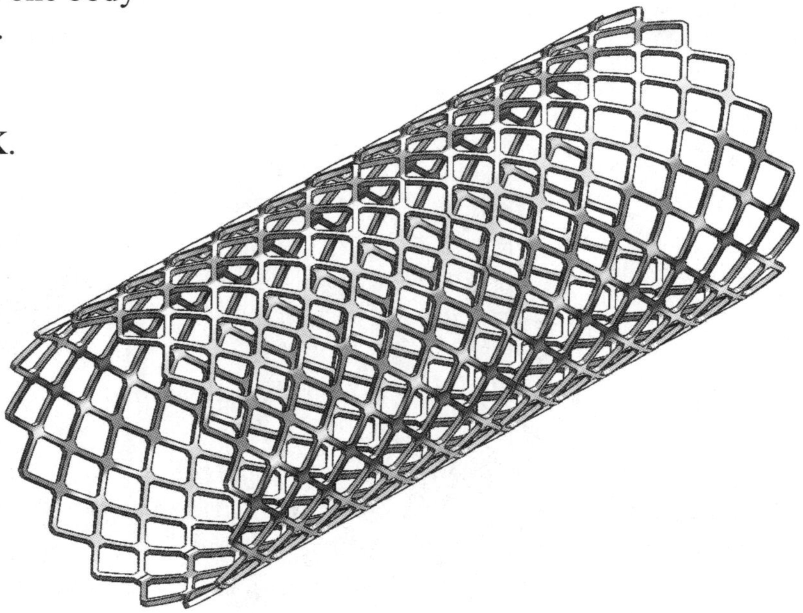

4. Saving your work:

- Save your work as **Flex Bending 2** and overwrite the original file when prompted.

- Close all documents.

CHAPTER 7

Sweep with Guide Curves

Sweep with Guide Curves - Overview

Plastic Bottle

A sweep creates a base, boss, cut, or surface by moving a profile along a path, or by specifying a path and a diameter.

For a circular profile, you do not need to sketch the profile. You only need to select an existing path and specify a diameter for the profile.

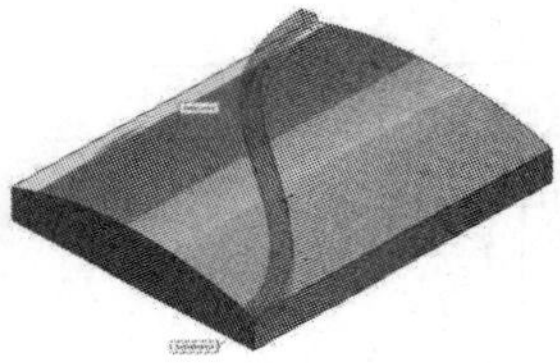

If the path is a 3D curve, one or more guide curves are used to help control the twisting in the sweep. The profile must be constrained to the guide curves with either a coincident or a pierce relation.

There are three types of sweeps: Sweep Boss/Base, Cut Sweep, and Surface Sweep. The Swept Boss/Base tool is used when creating the external threads; and the Swept Cut is used to make the internal threads.

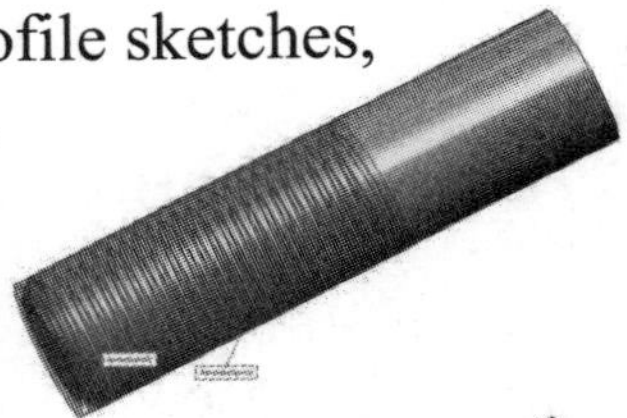

You can create helical threads on cylindrical faces using profile sketches, and you can store custom thread profiles as library features.

Using the new Thread tool in 2016, you can define the start thread location, specify an offset, set end conditions, specify the type, size, diameter, pitch and rotation angle, and choose options such as right-hand or left-hand thread.

You can create sweeps for a mid-path profile in either direction or the entire path using Direction 1, Direction 2, or Bidirectional. The bidirectional option is available for swept boss/base, swept surface, and swept cut in parts and assemblies.

Sweep with Guide Curves
Plastic Bottle

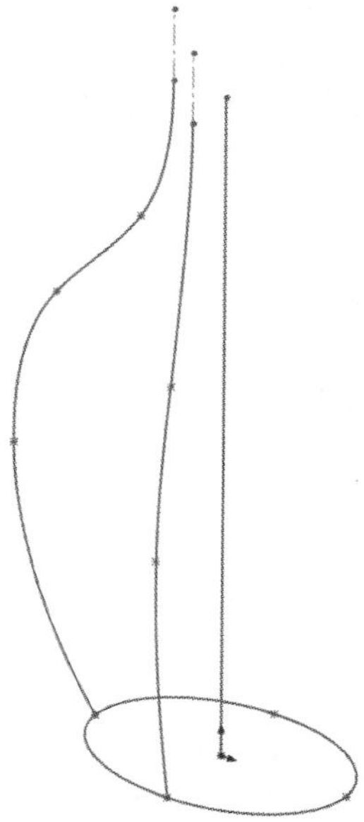

View Orientation Hot Keys:

Ctrl + 1 = Front View
Ctrl + 2 = Back View
Ctrl + 3 = Left View
Ctrl + 4 = Right View
Ctrl + 5 = Top View
Ctrl + 6 = Bottom View
Ctrl + 7 = Isometric View
Ctrl + 8 = Normal To Selection

Dimensioning Standards: **ANSI**

Units: **INCHES** – 3 Decimals

Tools Needed:

- Swept Boss/Base
- Ellipse
- Cut with Surface
- Plane
- Split Line
- Offset Surface
- Revolved Boss/Base
- Helix/Spiral
- Fillet
- Knit Surface
- Shell

1. Opening a part document:

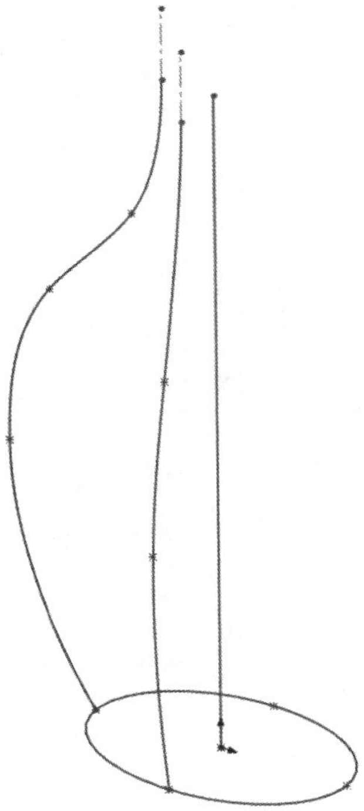

- Select **File / Open**.

- Browse to the Training Files location and open the part document named: **Sweep with Guide Curves.sldprt**

- Some of the sketches have been created to help focus on the key feature: Sweep.

2. Creating the main body:

- Switch to the **Features** tool tab.

- Select the **Swept Boss/Base** command .

- For Sweep Profile, select the **Ellipse** (or Sketch4).

- For Sweep Path, select the **Vertical Line** (or Sketch3).

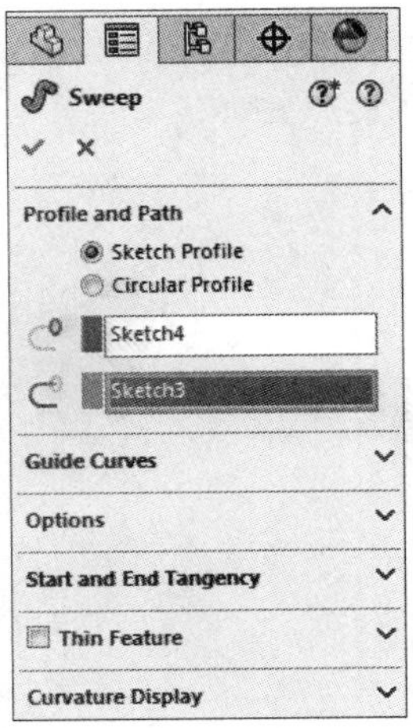

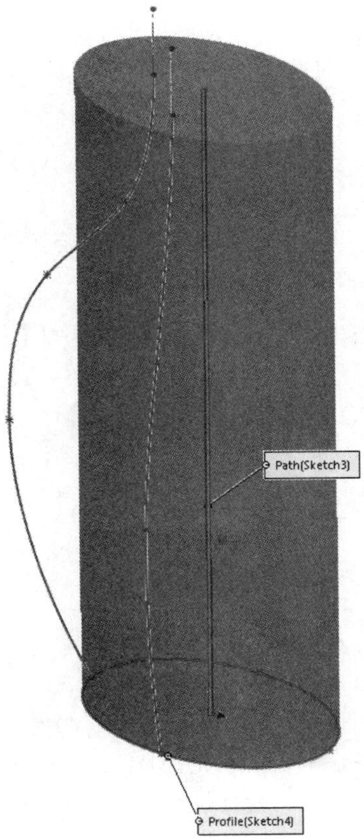

(More settings on the next page…)

- Expand the Guide Curves section and select **Sketch1** and **Sketch2** either from the graphics area or from the Feature tree.

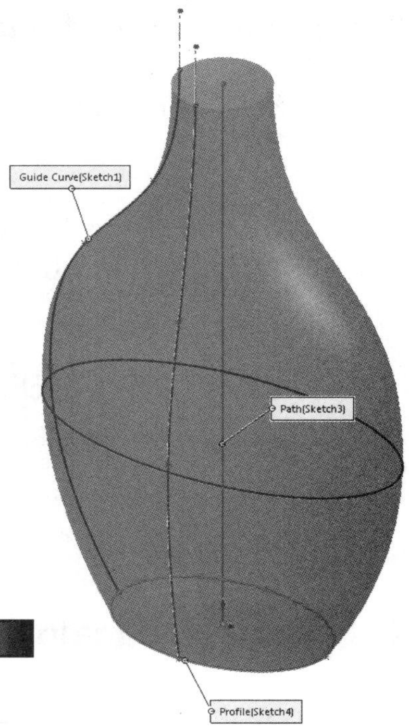

- Click the **Preview Sections** button (arrow) and press the Up / Down arrow to see the preview graphics on how the profile is moved along the path.

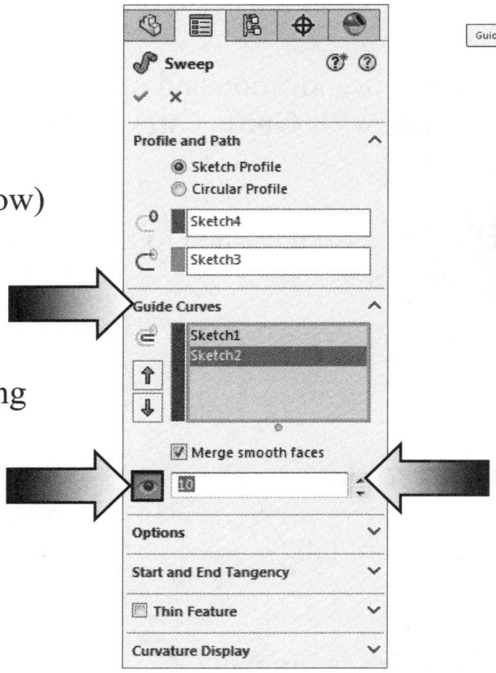

- Click **OK**.

<u>Note:</u> The Swept feature is shown with RealView Graphics enabled.

(RealView Graphics is hardware [graphics card] support of advanced shading in real time, including self-shadowing and scene reflections).

3. Creating the 1st split line:

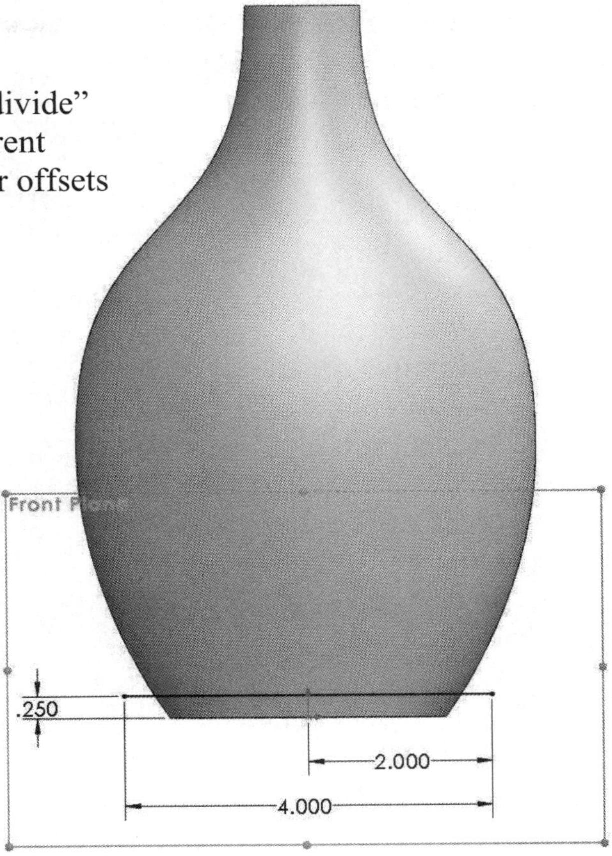

- The Split Line command is used to "divide" a single face into 2 faces so that different operations such as fillets, chamfers, or offsets can be applied to the individual faces.

- Select the **Front** plane and open a new sketch.

- Sketch a horizontal **Line** across the bottom of the model.

- Add the **Dimensions** shown to fully define the sketch.

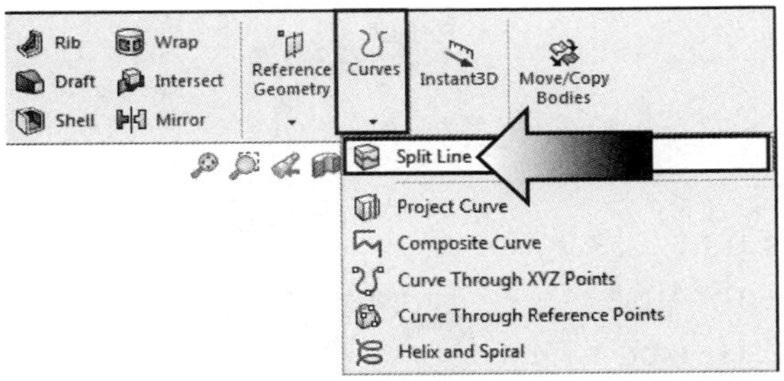

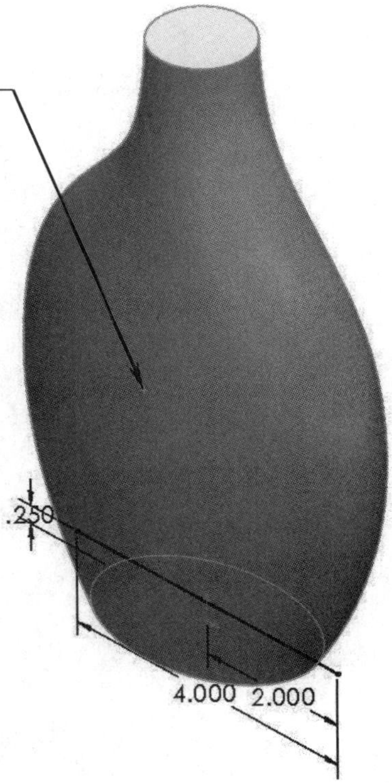

- Switch to the **Features** tool tab.

- Select the **Split Line** command under the **Curves** drop down.

- For Type of Split, click **Projection** type.

- For Selections, use the **Current Sketch**.

- For faces to Split, click **the body** of the model as noted.

- Click **OK**.

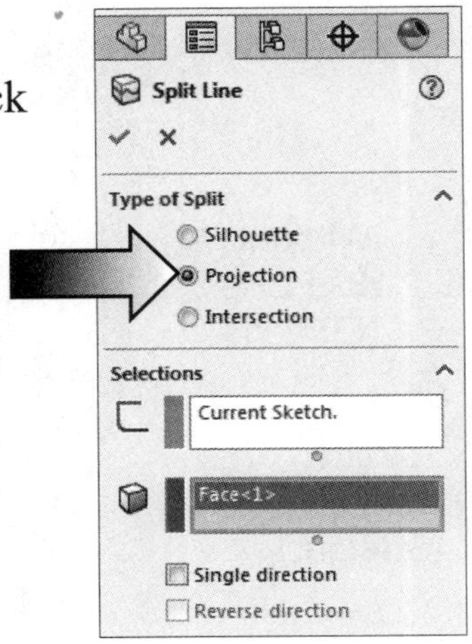

4. Creating a Face Fillet:

- Select the **Fillet**  command.

- Click the Face Fillet option (arrow).

- For Face Set 1, select the **upper portion** of the split face as noted.

- For Face Set 2, select the **bottom face** of the model

- For Fillet Parameters, select **Hold Line**.

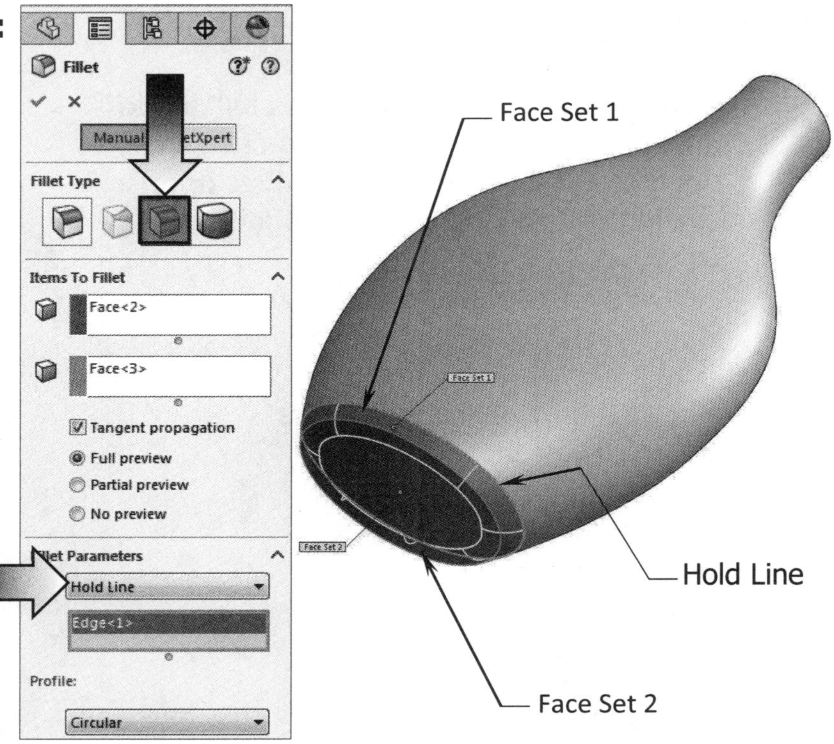

- Select the **edge** that was created by the split line. (The Hold Line is used to determine the shape and size of the fillet.)

- Click **OK**.

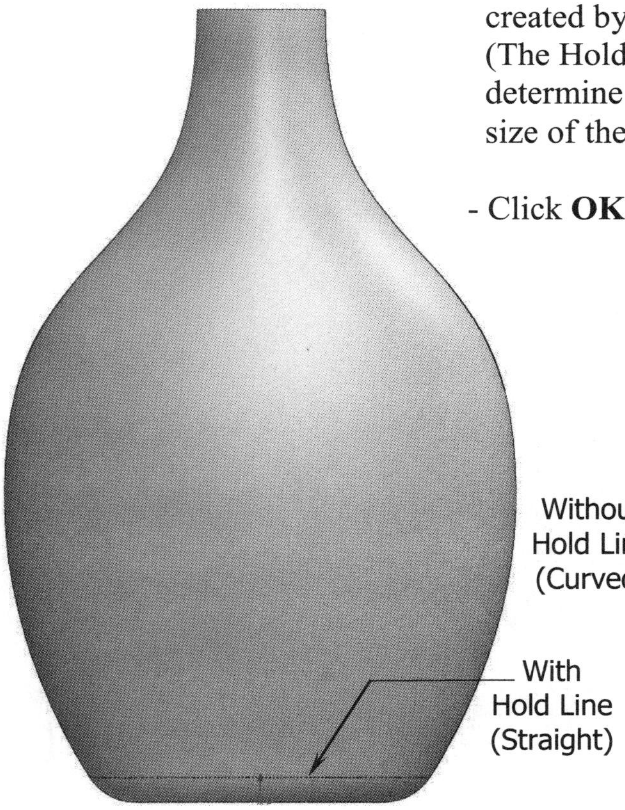

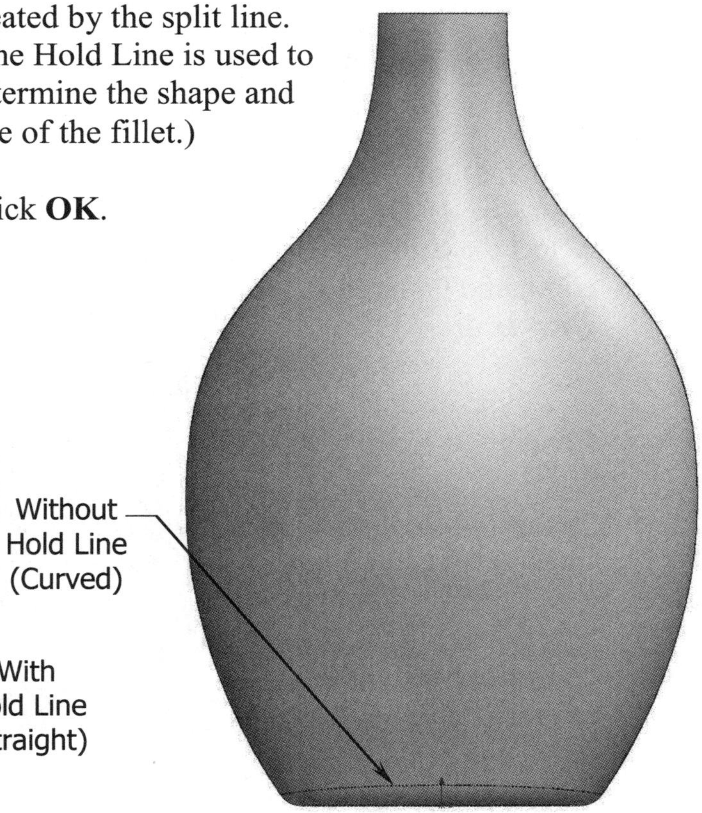

5. Creating the 2nd split line:

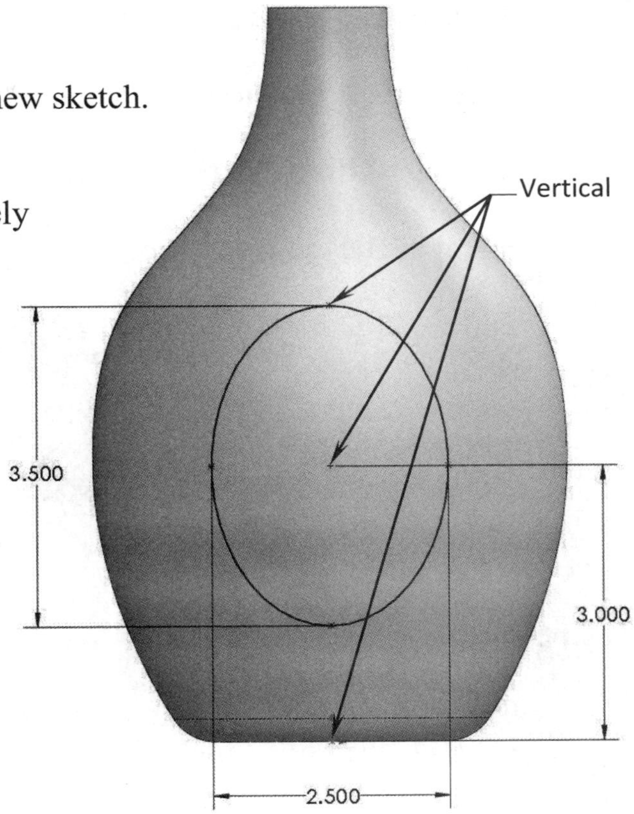

- Select the **Front** plane and open a new sketch.

- Sketch an **Ellipse**  approximately as shown.

- Add a **vertical relation** as noted to keep the ellipse from rotating.

- Add the **dimensions** shown to fully define the sketch.

- Switch to the **Features** tool tab.

- Select the **Split Line** command below the Curves tool.

- Use the default **Projection** type and the **Current Sketch**.

- Select the **face** as indicated to split.

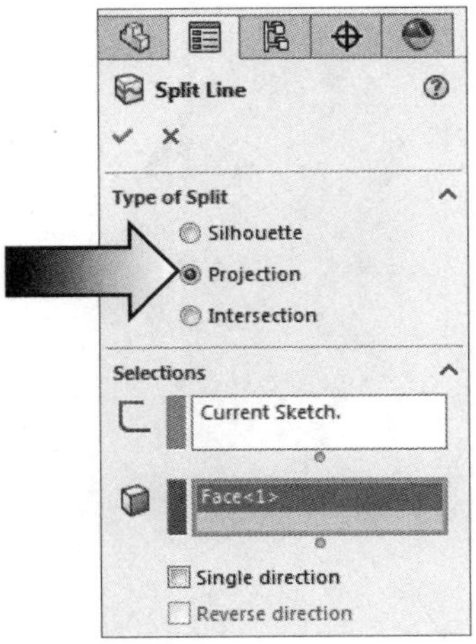

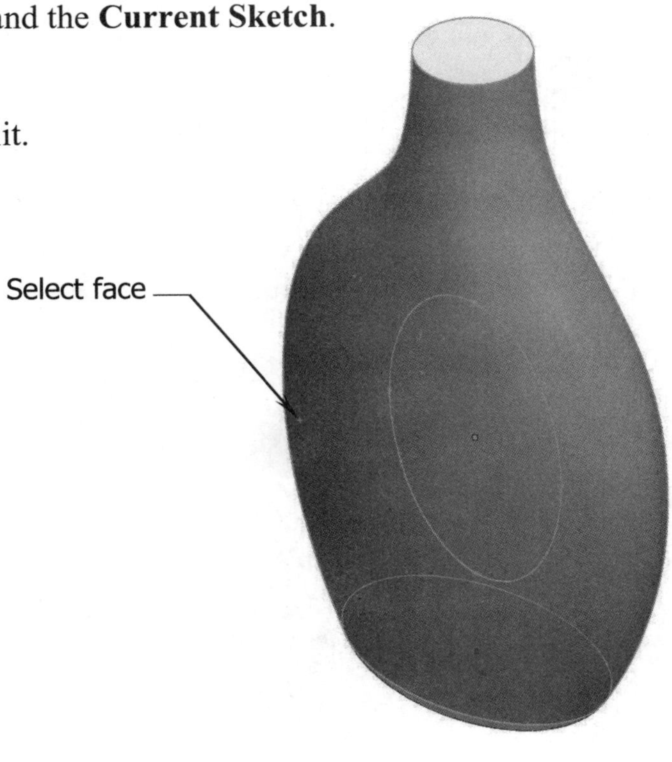

- Click **OK**.

6. Creating the 1st offset surface:

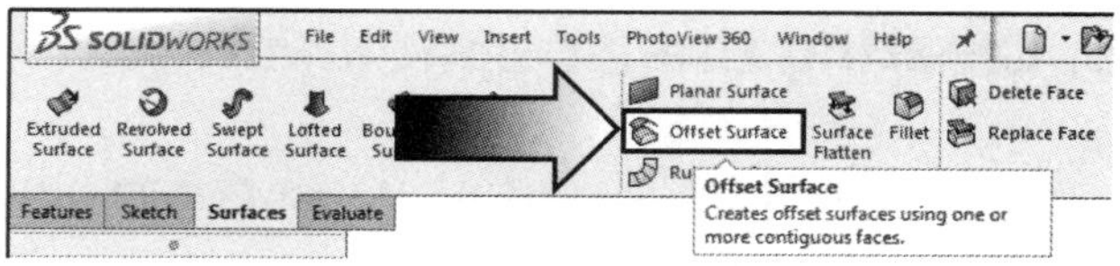

- Switch to the **Surfaces** tool tab.

- Select the **Offset Surface** command.

- Select the **inside face** as noted.

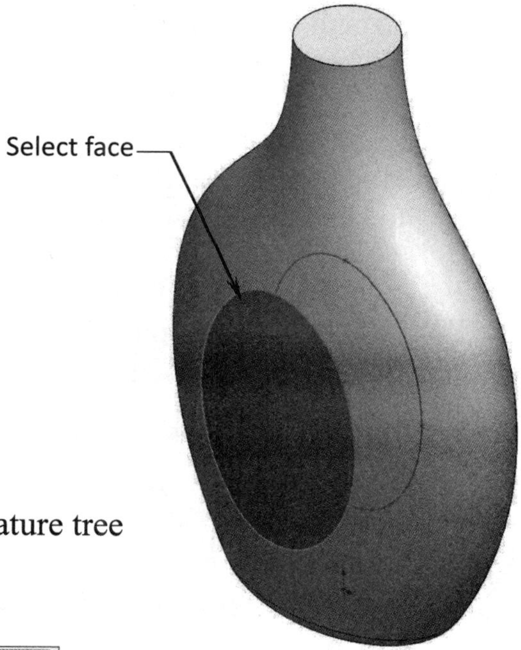

- Enter **.040in**. for Offset Distance.

- Click the **Reverse** button (arrow).

- Click **OK**.

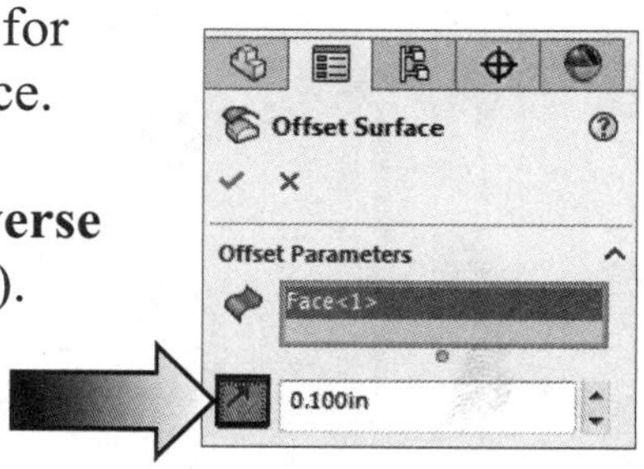

7. Creating a ruled surface:

- Expand the Solid Bodies folder from the Feature tree and **Hide** the **Split Line2** (the main body).

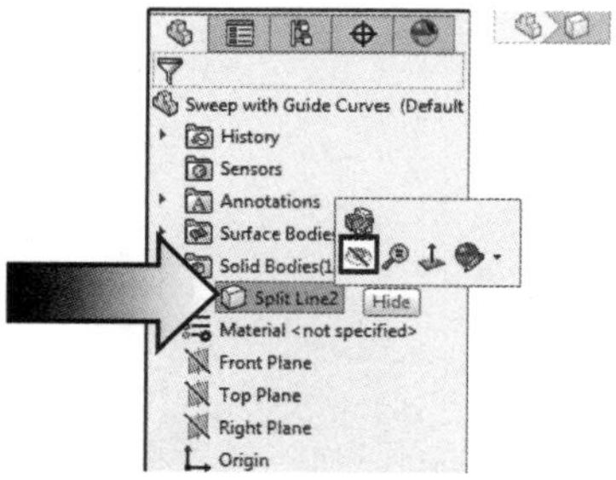

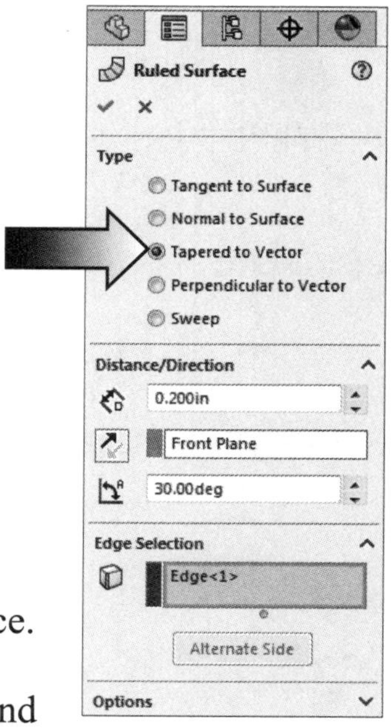

- Select **Ruled Surface**.

- Click **Taper to Vector**.

- Enter **.200in**. for Distance.

- Select the **Front** plane and enter **30.00deg** for Angle.

- Select the **edge** as indicated.

- Click **OK**.

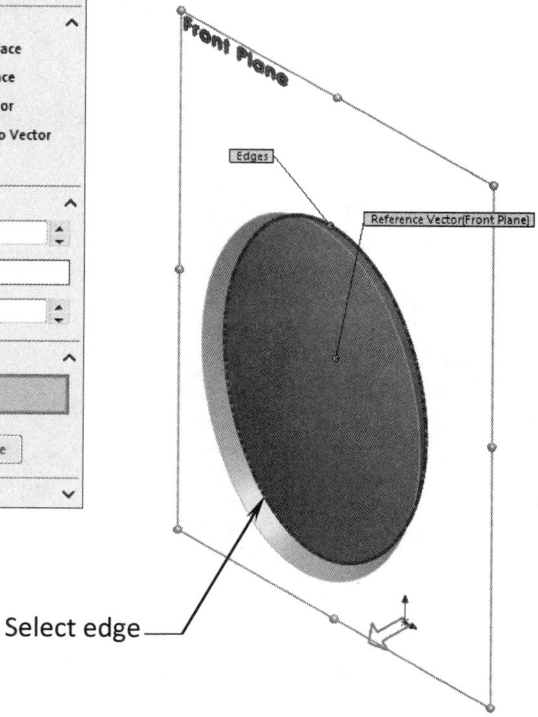

8. Creating the 1st knit surface:

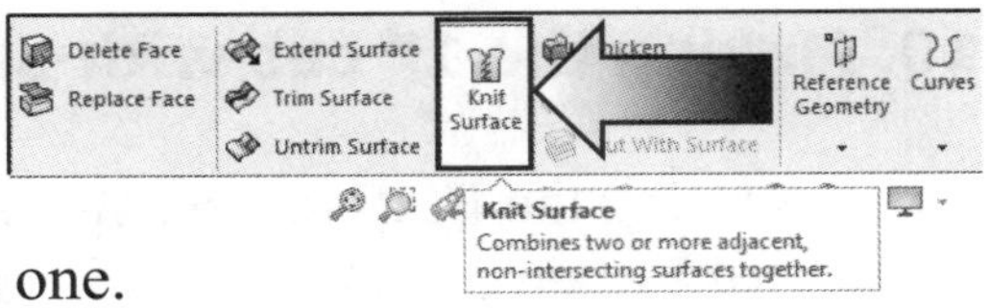

- The Knit Surface command is used to combine two or more faces and surfaces into one.

- Click the **Knit Surface** command.

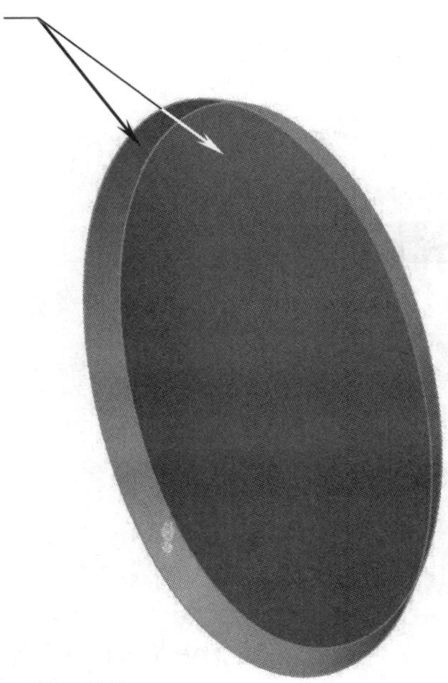

- Select the **2 surfaces** as noted.

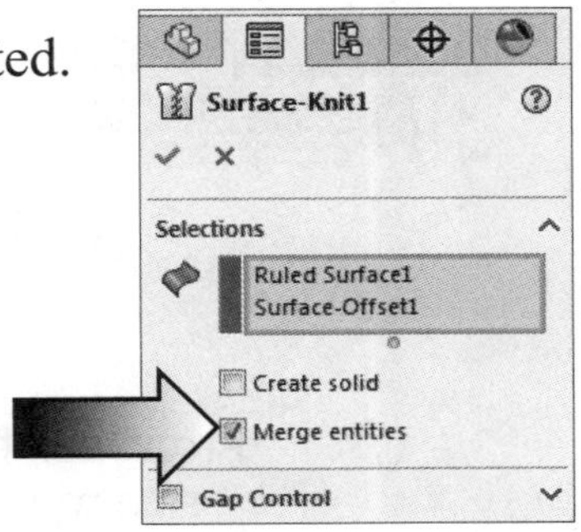

- Enable the **Merge Entities** checkbox (arrow).

- Click **OK**.

9. Adding the 1st .175" fillet:

- Click the **Fillet** command and select the **Constant Radius Size** button (arrow).

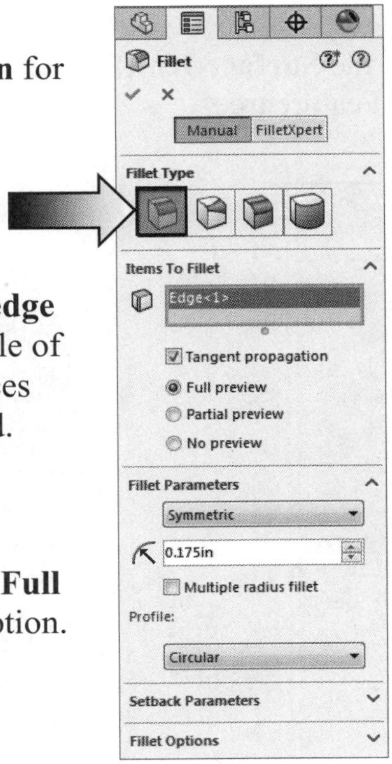

- Enter **.175in** for radius.

- Select the **edge** in the middle of the 2 surfaces as indicated.

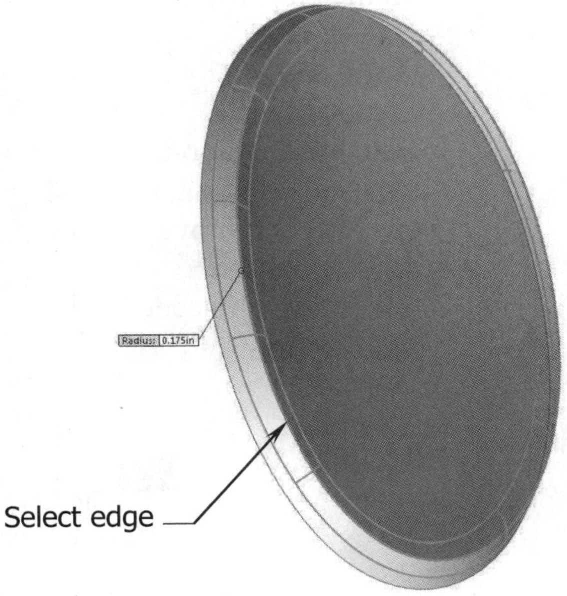

- Enable the **Full Preview** option.

- Click **OK**.

10. Making the 1st cut-with-surface:

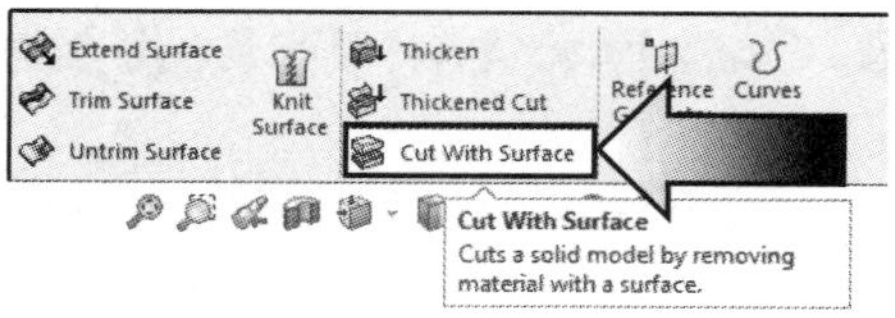

- Using the Feature tree, **show** the **Split Line2** (the main body).

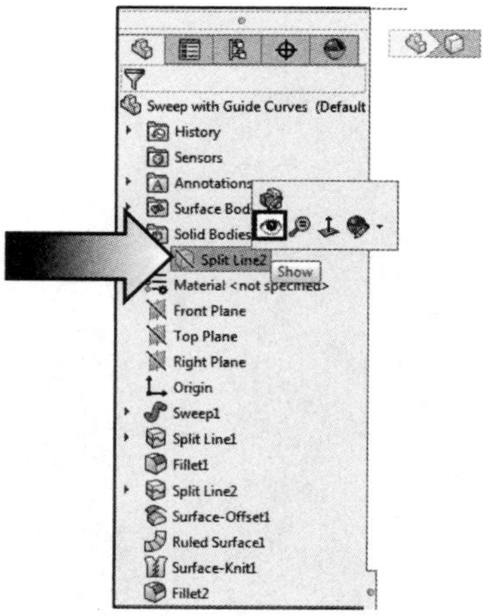

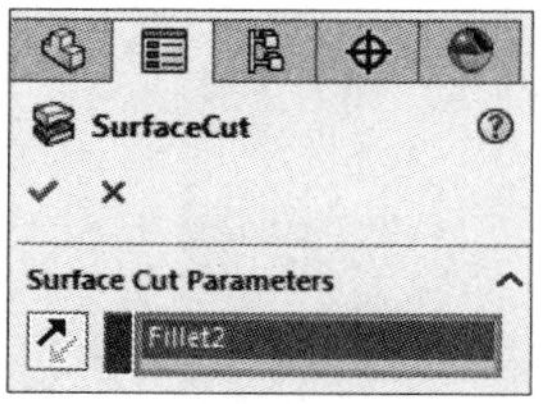

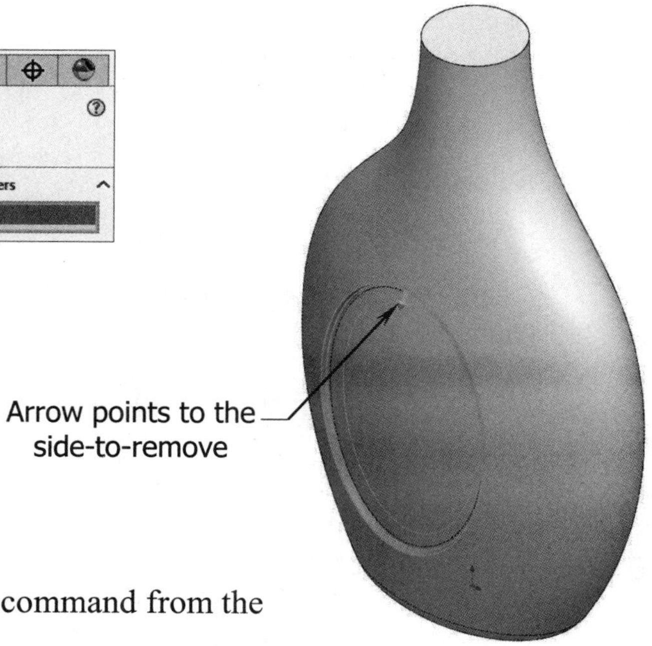

- Click the **Cut With Surface**  command from the **Surfaces** tool tab.

- For Surface Cut Parameters, select the **Surface-Knit1** either from the graphics area or from the Feature tree.

- Locate the Direction Arrow and point it downward to remove the inside portion. Click Reverse if needed.

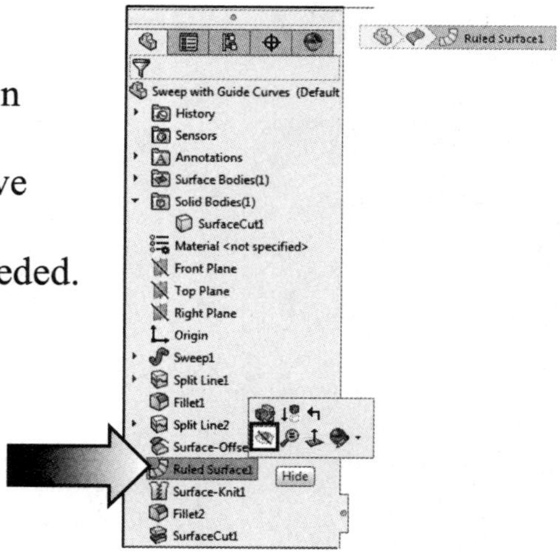

- Click **OK**.

- **Hide** the Ruled Surface (arrow).

11. Creating the 2nd offset surface:

- Repeat step number 6 and create a 2nd offset surface on the opposite side.

- Use the same offset distance of **.100in**.

- Click **Reverse** to place the new surface <u>**inside**</u> of the model.

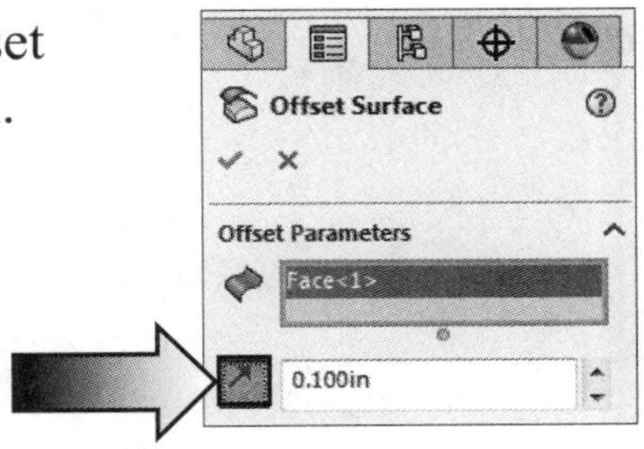

- Click **OK**.

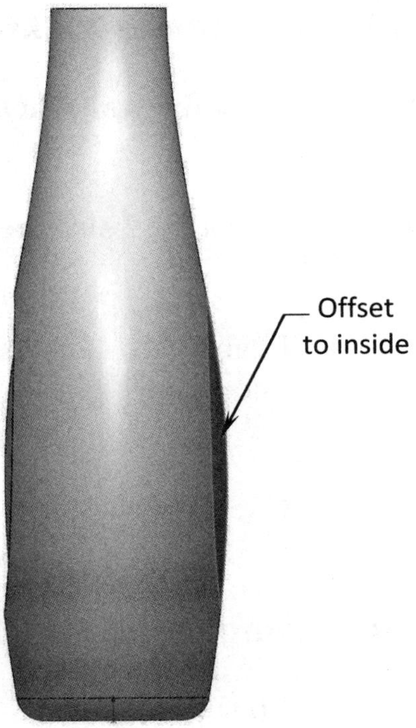

12. Creating the 2nd offset surface:

- **Hide** the SurfaceCut1 (arrow).

- Click **Ruled Surface**.

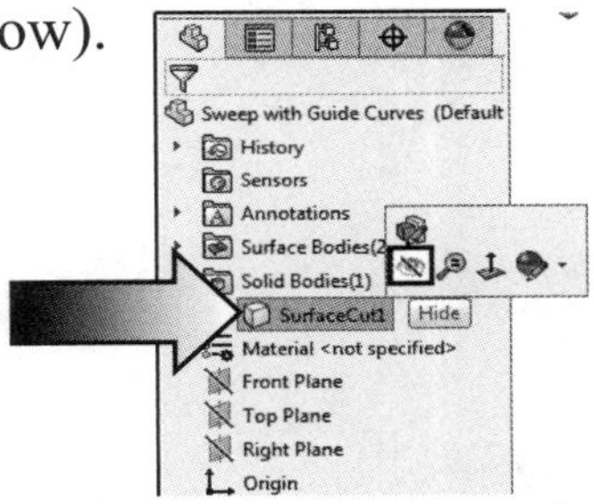

- Use the default **Taper to Vector** option.

- Enter **.200in** for distance

- Select the **Front** plane for Direction.

- Enter **30deg** for Taper Angle.

- Select the <u>**edge**</u> as noted

- Click **OK**.

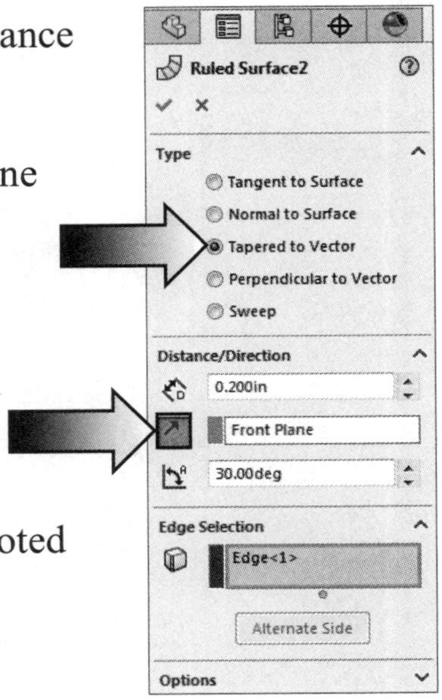

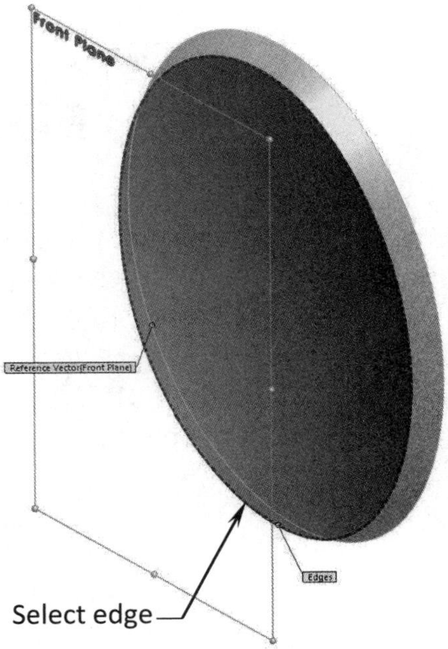

13. Creating the 2nd knit surface:

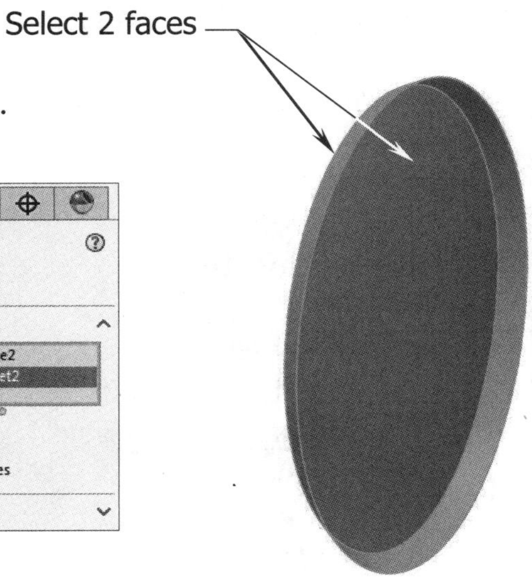

- Click the **Knit Surface** command once again.

- Select the **2 surfaces** as noted.

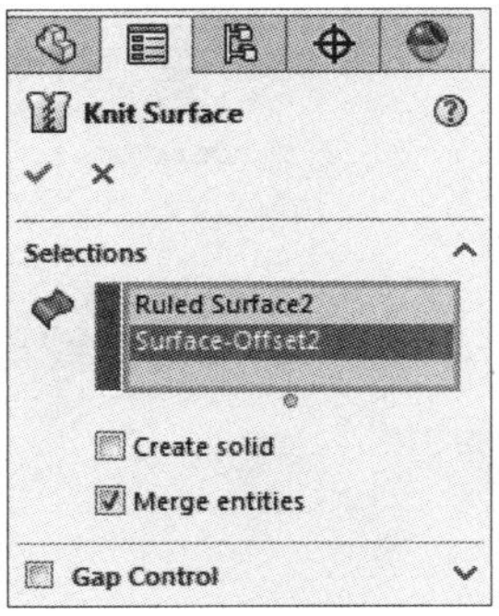

- Enable the **Merge Entities** Checkbox.

- Click **OK**.

14. Adding the 2nd .175" fillet:

- Click the **Fillet** command and select the **Constant Radius Size** button (arrow).

- Enter **.175in** for radius.

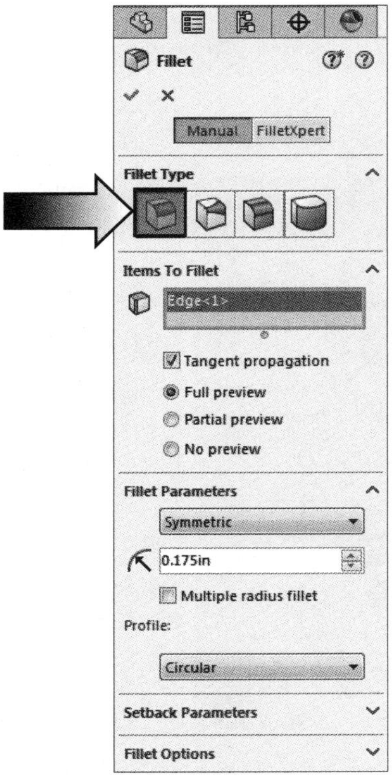

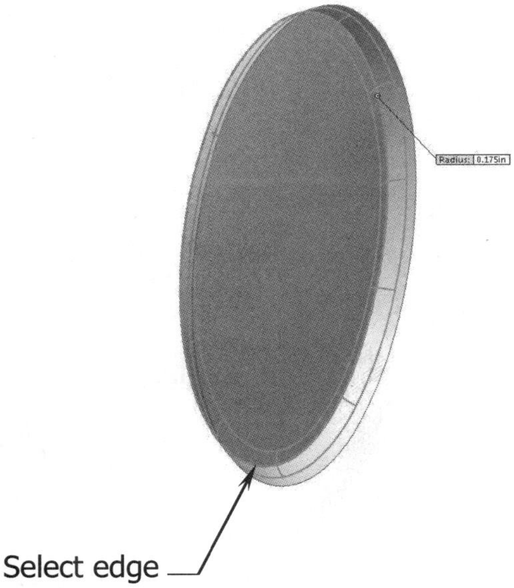

- Select the **edge** in the middle of the 2 surfaces as indicated.

- Enable the **Full Preview** option.

- Click **OK**.

15. Making the 2nd cut-with-surface:

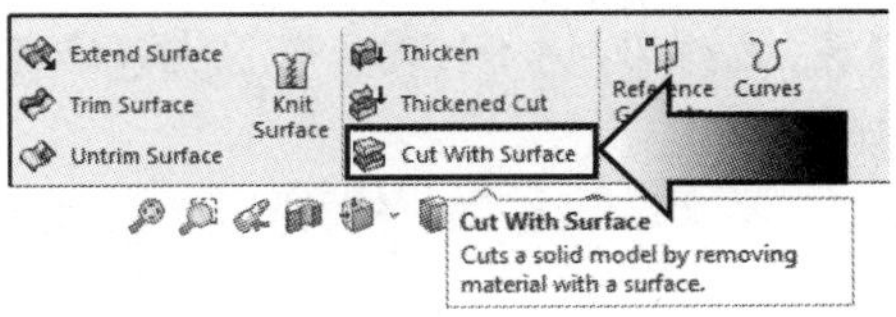

- Using the Feature tree, **show** the main solid body.

- Click the **Cut With Surface** command  .

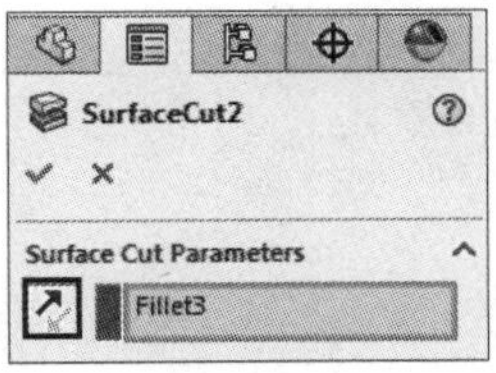

- For Surface Cut Parameter, select the **Surface-Knit2** either from the graphics area or from the Feature tree.

- Locate the Direction Arrow and point it upward to remove the inside portion. Click the arrow to reverse direction.

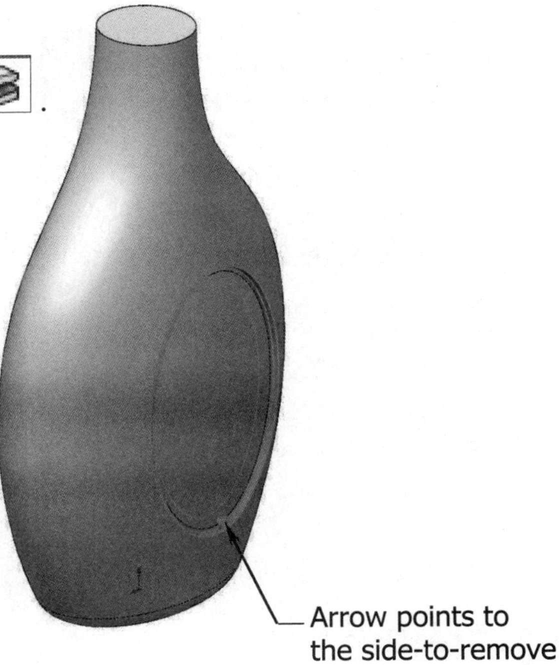

- Click **OK**.

- **Hide** the Ruled Surface (arrow).

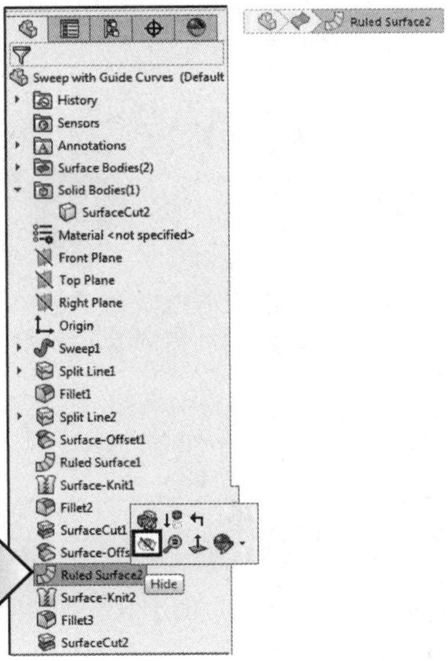

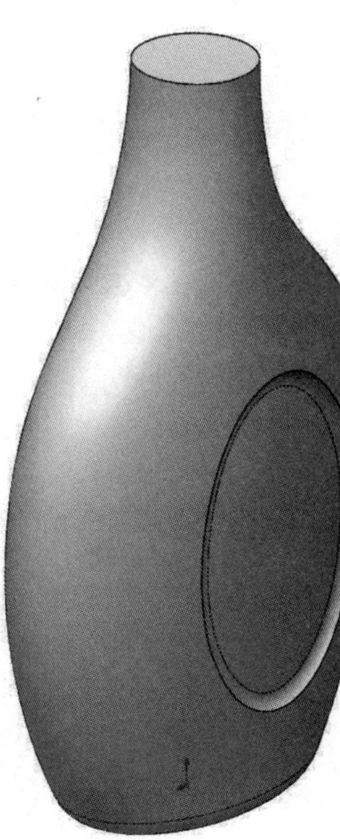

Note: The recessed feature can be easily mirrored, but for the purpose of practicing, we went ahead and created both of them individually.

16. Adding the 3rd .175" fillet:

- Click the **Fillet** command.

- Use the default **Constant Size Radius** type (arrow).

- Select the **2 edges** as noted.

- Enter **.175in**. for radius.

- Click **OK**.

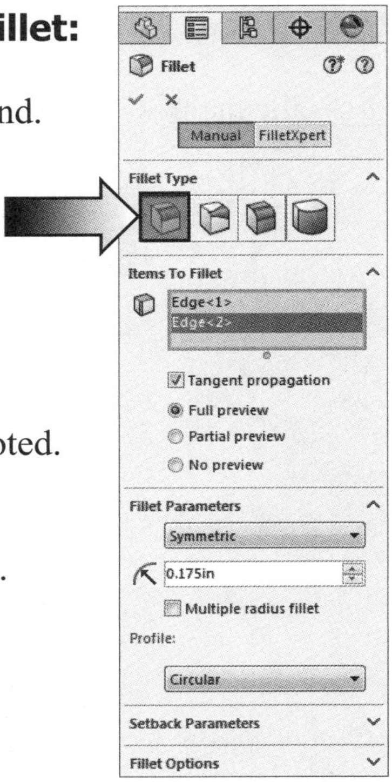

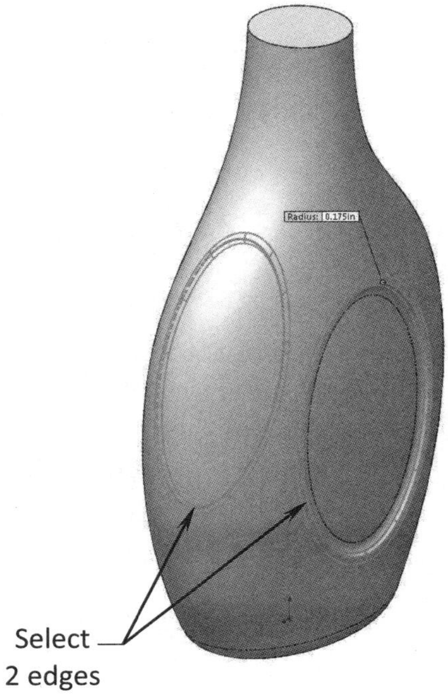

17. Creating a shell:

- The shell command hollows out a part, leaves open the faces you select, and creates thin-walled features on the remaining faces.

- Switch to the **Features** tool tab.

- Click the **Shell** command

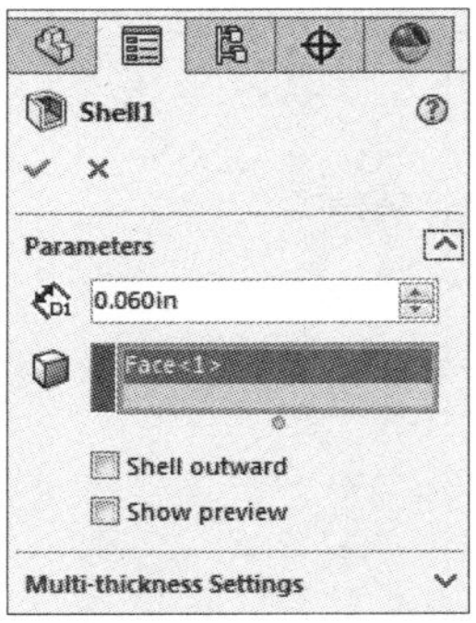

- Enter **.060in**. for wall thickness and select the upper surface to remove.

- Click **OK**.

18. Adding the neck feature:

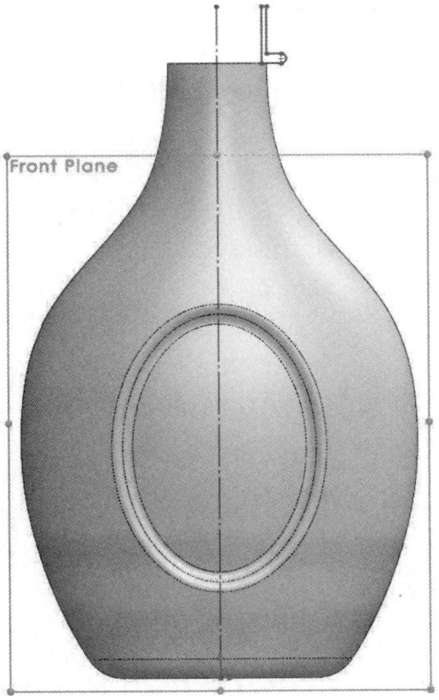

- The neck feature is added next so that the threads can be added after.

- Select the **Front** plane and open a new sketch.

- Sketch a **vertical centerline** that starts at the origin. This centerline will be used to add the dimensions and also to revolve the sketch.

- Sketch the profile below using the **Line** tool.

- Add the dimensions shown. Hold the **Shift** key when adding the dimension .875. The shift key attaches the dimension to the tangent of the arc (called Maximum Condition).

- Add the **Tangent** relation as noted to fully define the sketch.

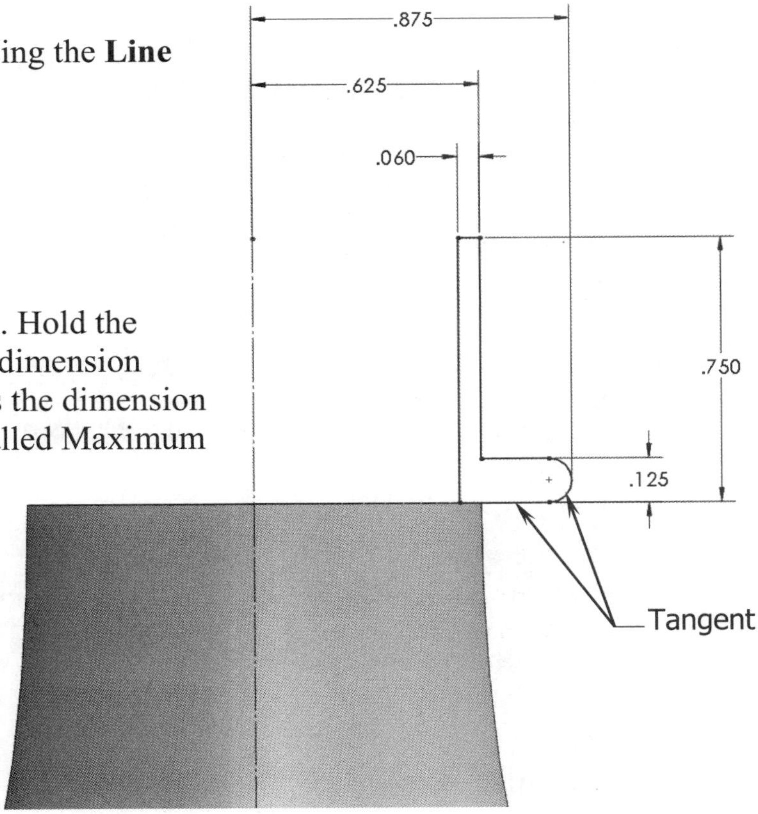

19. Revolving the sketch:

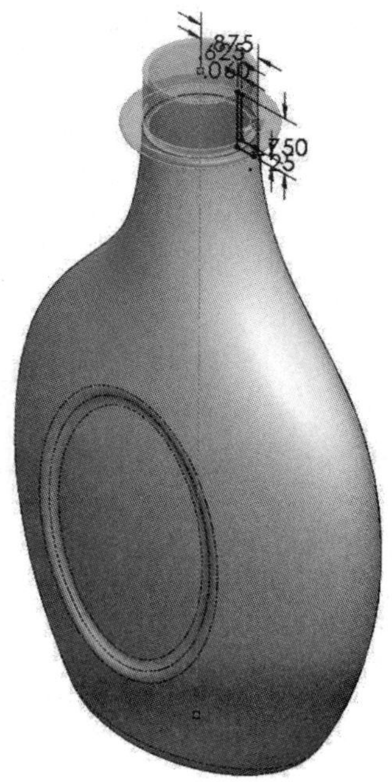

- Change to the **Features** tool tab.

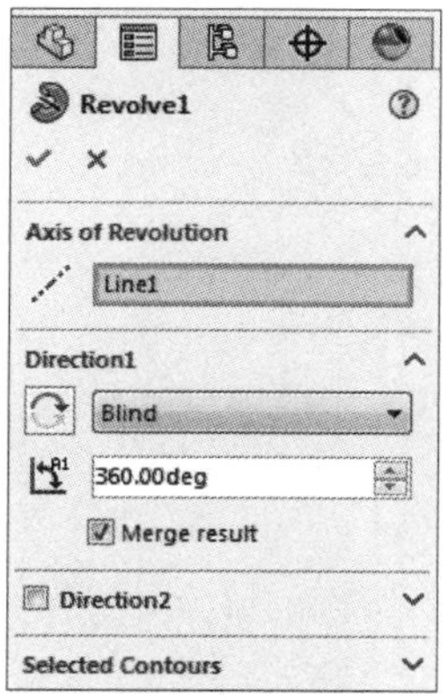

- Click the **Revolved Boss/Base** command.

- Keep the default **Blind** type and the Angle at **360º**.

- Click **OK**.

20. Creating a new plane:

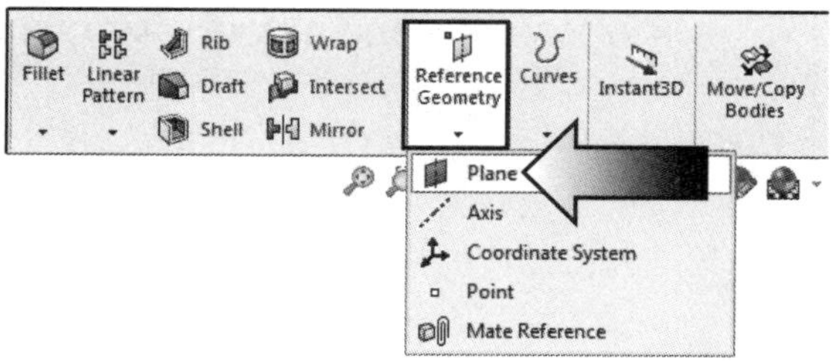

- Using the "traditional method" a plane is used to define the offset distance of the threads.

- Select **Reference Geometry / Plane** (arrow).

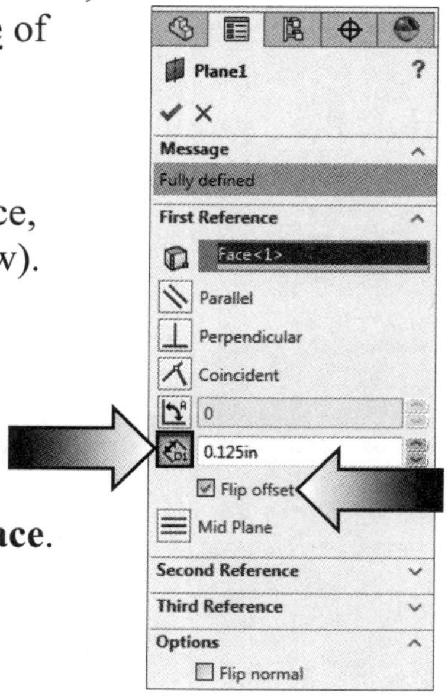

- For the First Reference, select the **<u>top face</u>** of the neck feature.

- For Offset Distance, enter **.125in** (arrow).

- Click the **Flip-Offset** checkbox to place the new plane **above the face**.

- Click **OK**.

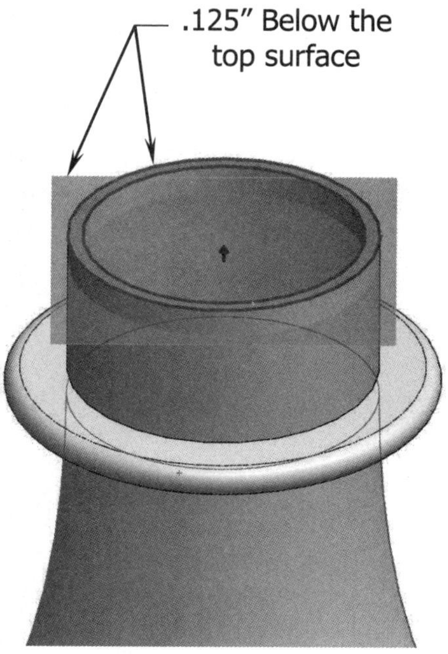

21. Creating a helix:

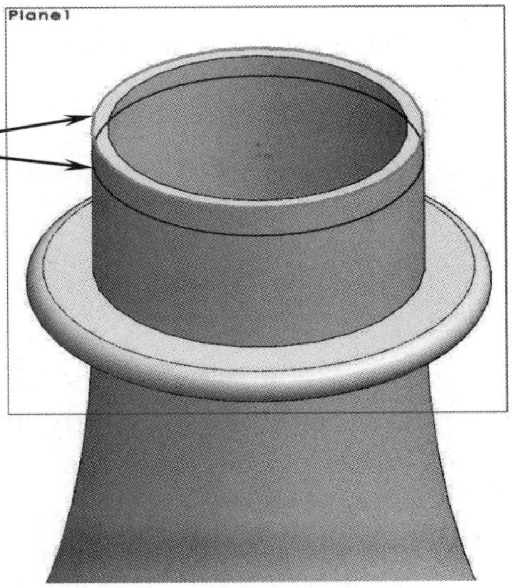

- Select the **new plane** (Plane1) and open a new sketch.

- Select the <u>upper circular</u> edge and press the **Convert Entities** command .

- The edge is converted to a circle. The circle is used to create the helix.

- Switch to the **Features** tool tab.

- Select the **Helix/Spiral** command under the **Curves** drop down list.

- For Defined by, select **Pitch and Revolution** (default).

- For Parameters, set the following:

  * **Constant Pitch**

  * Pitch: **.100in**.

  * Reverse Direction: **Enabled**.

  * Revolution: **3.5**

- Click **OK**.

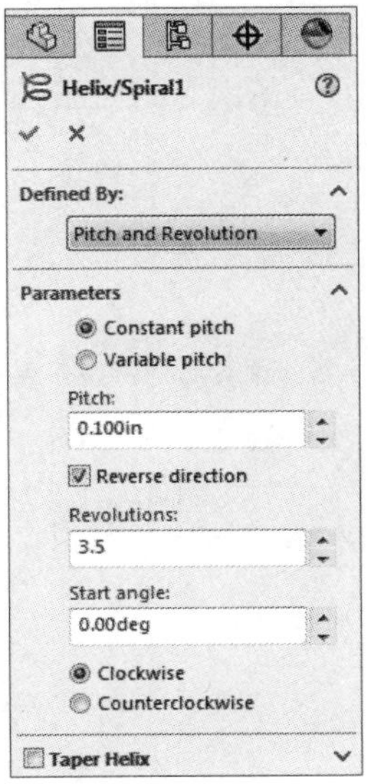

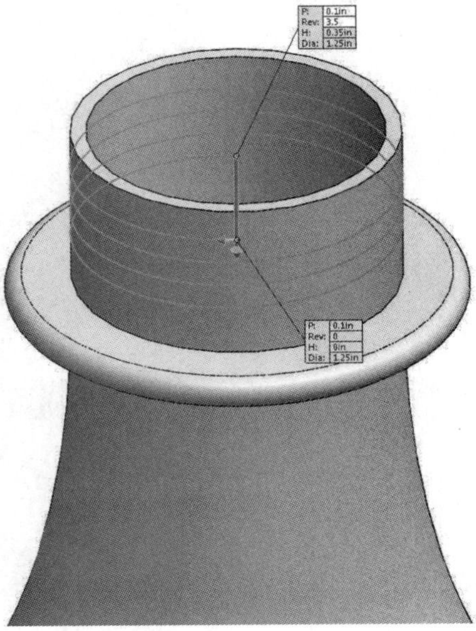

22. Sketching the thread profile:

- Select the **Right** plane and open a new sketch.

- Sketch the profile shown. Use the Mirror command to keep the entities Symmetric with each other.

- The 2 centerlines at the left corner are there for clarity only. Do not create them.

- Add the **dimensions** and the **Pierce** relation to fully define the sketch.

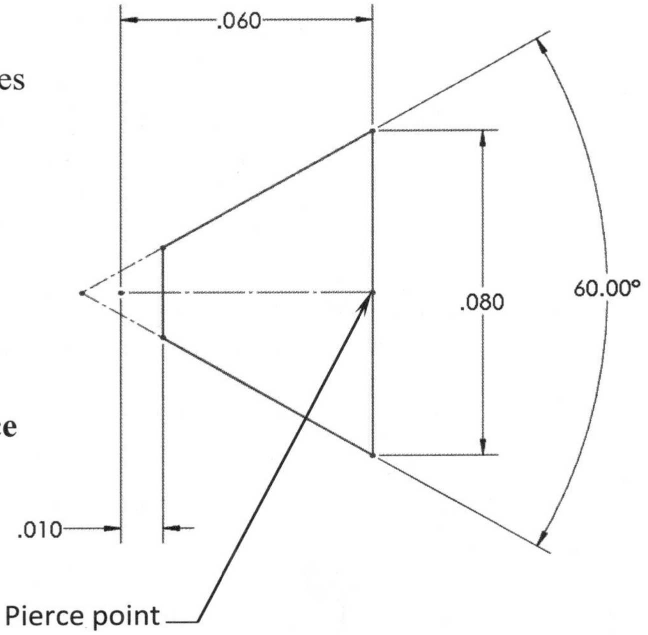

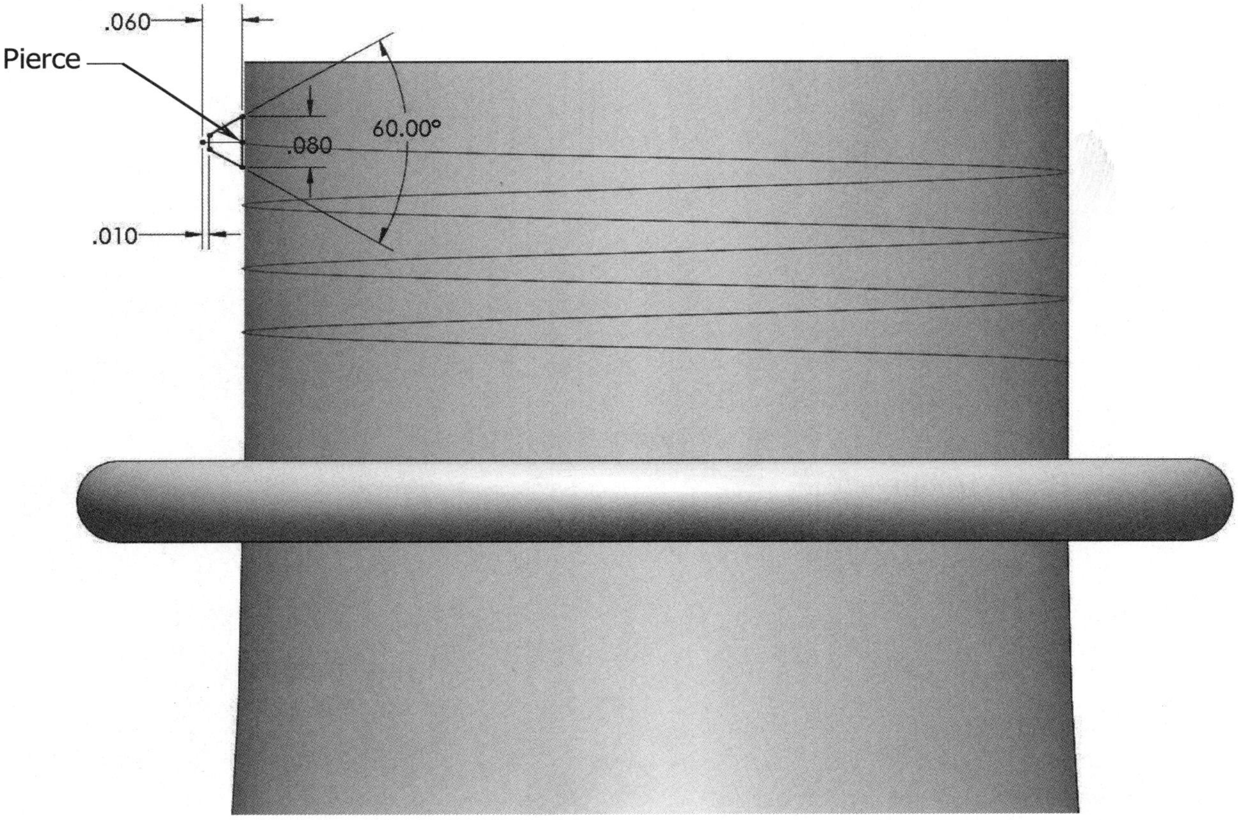

23. Making the Threads:

- Switch to the **Features** tool tab.

- Select the **Swept Boss/Base** Command.

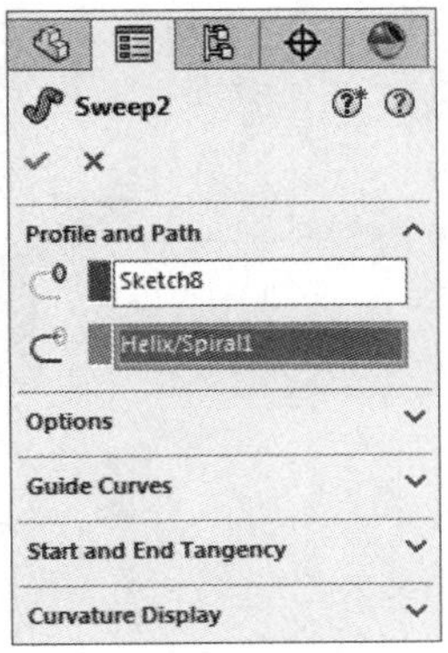

- For Sweep Profile, select the sketch of the **Triangle**.

- For Sweep Path, select the **Helix**.

- Click **OK**.

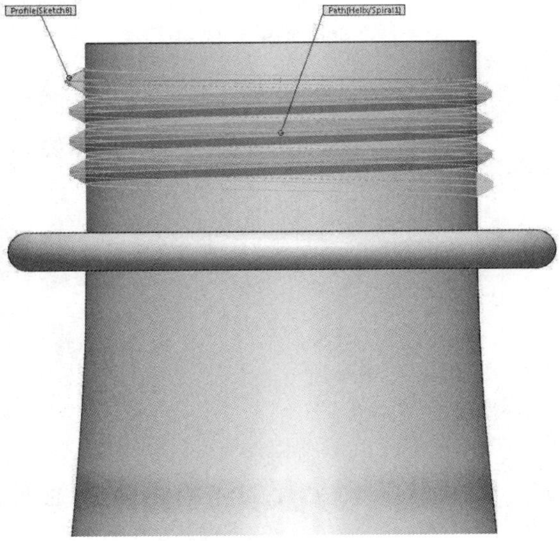

24. Rounding off the ends of the threads:

- The ends of the threads need to be rounded off so that the cap can screw on more easily.

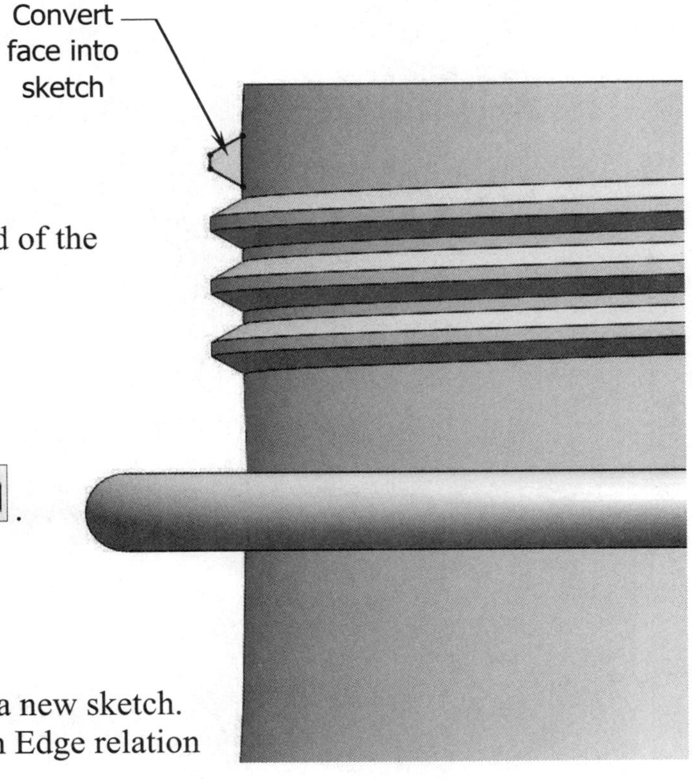

- Select the **planar face** at the end of the thread and open a new sketch.

- Highlight the planar face and press **Convert Entities** .

- The planar face is converted to a new sketch. Each converted entity has an On Edge relation added to them automatically.

25. Revolving the sketch:

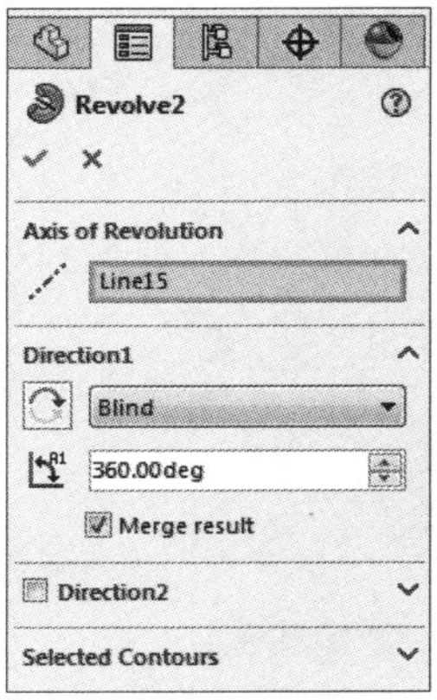

- Switch to the **Features** tool tab.

- Press **Revolved Boss/Base**.

- Keep the default **Blind** type and the angle of **360°**.

- Click **OK**.

26. Rounding off the opposite Side:

- Repeat steps 24 and 25 and close off the opposite side with the same revolved feature.

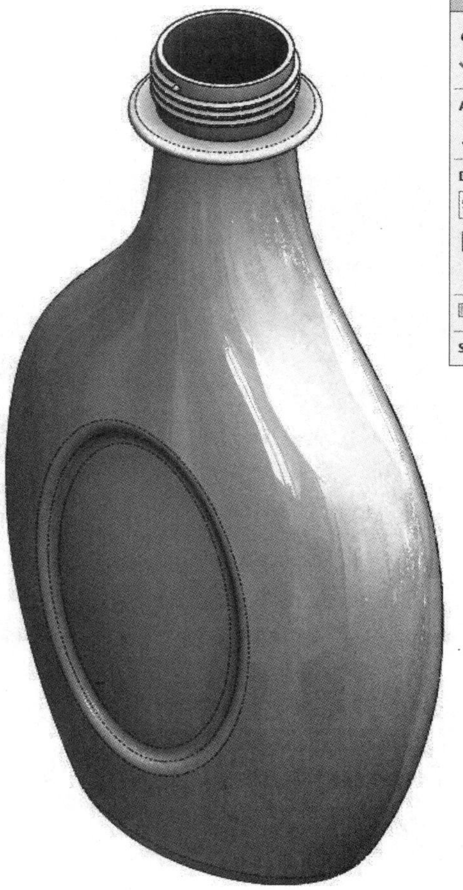

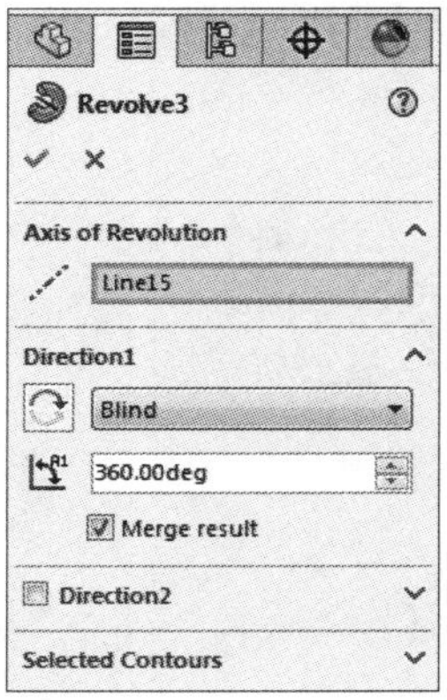

27. Saving your work:

- Select **File / Save As**.

- Use the same file name and overwrite the original document when prompted.

- Click **Save**.

CHAPTER 8

Lofts and Boundaries

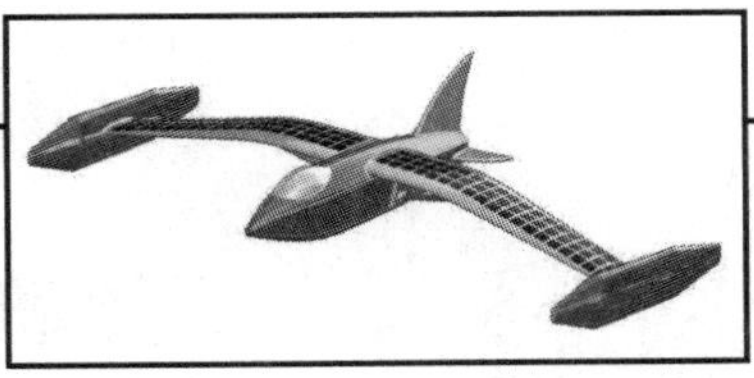

Lofts and Boundaries Overview

Solar Boat

- A loft feature is created by making transitions between two or more profiles. Only the first and last profiles can be points. The others must be closed sketches to create a solid feature, or opened sketches to create a surface feature.

- For a solid loft, the first and last profiles must be model faces or faces created by split lines, planar profiles, or surfaces. A loft can be a base, boss, cut, or surface.

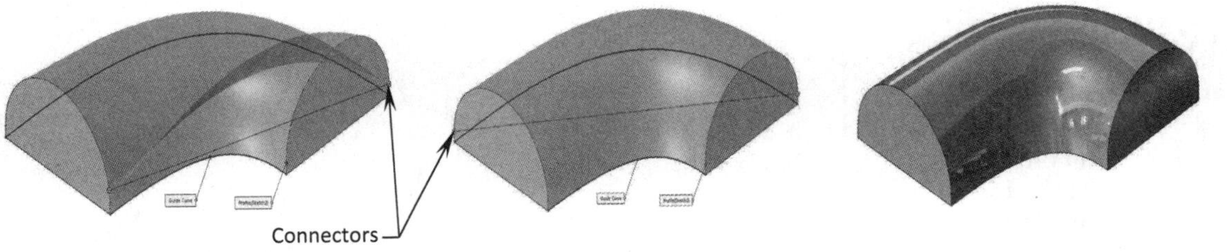

- The boundary command is similar to the loft but it produces higher quality and accurate features useful for creating complex shapes. It uses two or more profiles and curves in two directions to define the boundary.

- The Loft and Boundary commands use connectors to manipulate the twisting between the profiles. Right click a connector to get to the connectors options to reset them.

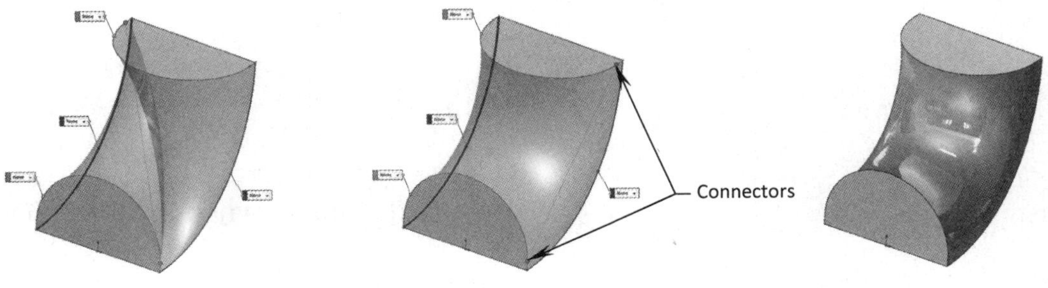

Solar Boat
Lofts and Boundaries

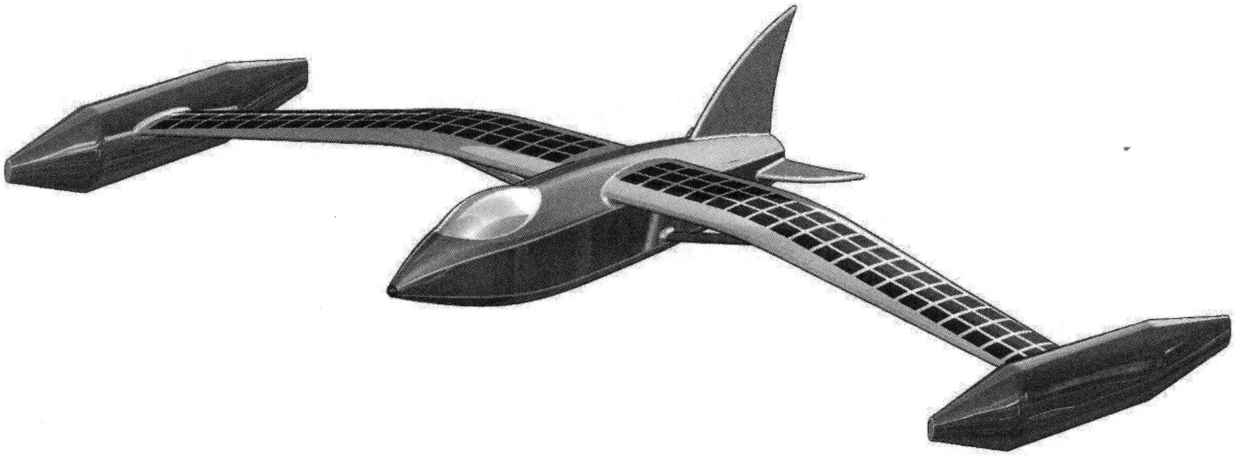

View Orientation Hot Keys:

Ctrl + 1 = Front View
Ctrl + 2 = Back View
Ctrl + 3 = Left View
Ctrl + 4 = Right View
Ctrl + 5 = Top View
Ctrl + 6 = Bottom View
Ctrl + 7 = Isometric View
Ctrl + 8 = Normal To Selection

Dimensioning Standards: **ANSI**

Units: **INCHES** – 3 Decimals

Tools Needed:

Insert Sketch	Split Lines	Extruded Boss/Base
Dimension	Add Relations	Plane
Mirror	Lofted Boss/Base	Boundary Boss/Base

1. Opening a part document:

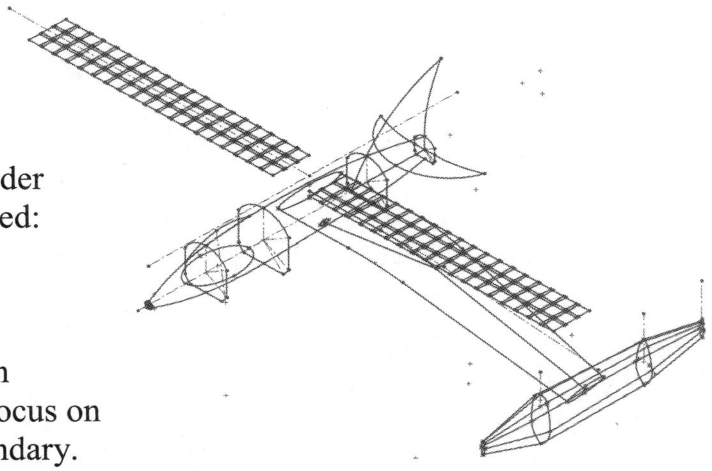

- Select **File / Open**.

- Browse to the training files folder and open a part document named: **Loft and Boundary.sldprt**.

- Most of the sketches have been created ahead of time to help focus on the main feature Loft and Boundary.

2. Creating a lofted feature:

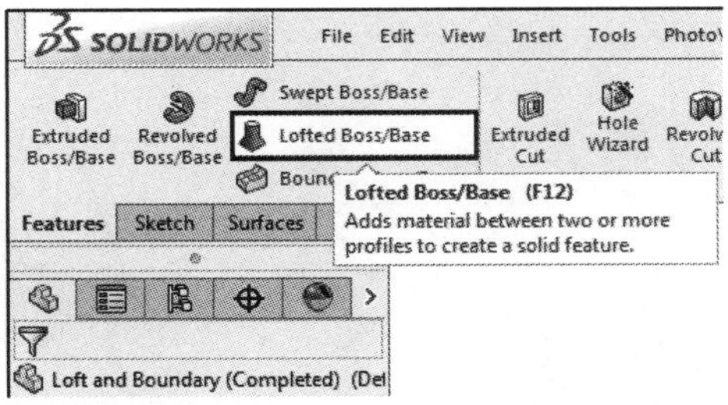

- A loft feature is created by making transitions between two or more profiles. Only the first, last, or first and last profiles can be points. The others must be closed sketches to create a solid feature, or opened sketches to create a surface feature.

- We will try to create the main body with the loft command. Switch to the Features tool tab and select the **Lofted Boss/Base** command.

- Select the profiles by clicking their common points to prevent the transition from twisting as noted below.

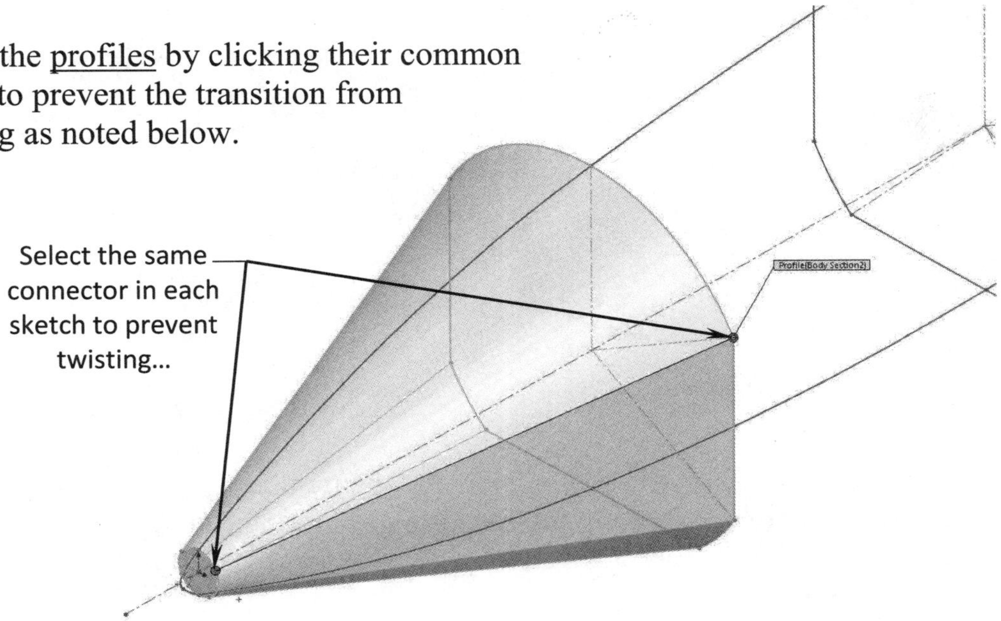

- When creating a loft, a sweep, or a boundary feature, the SelectionManager can be used to select entities across multiple sketches as well as in combination with model edges.

- Select the 5 loft-profiles as indicated.

- Expand the Guide Curves section and select the 2 guide curves as noted, click OK in the SelectionManager after selecting each guide curve.

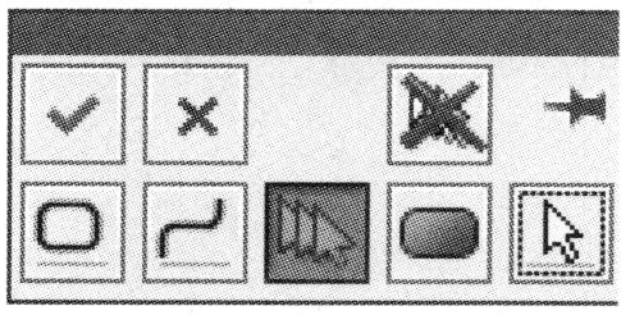

The SelectionManager

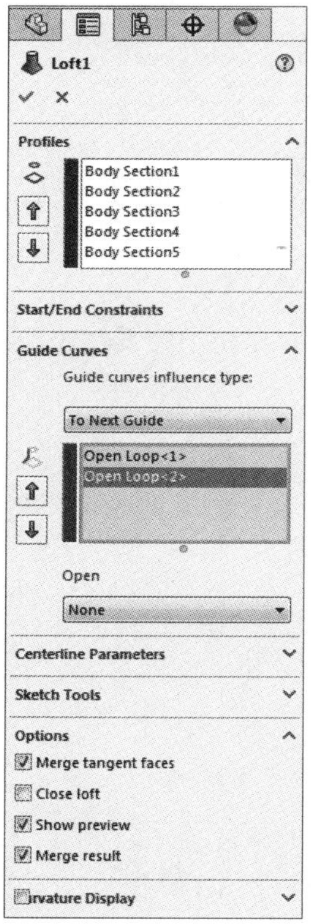

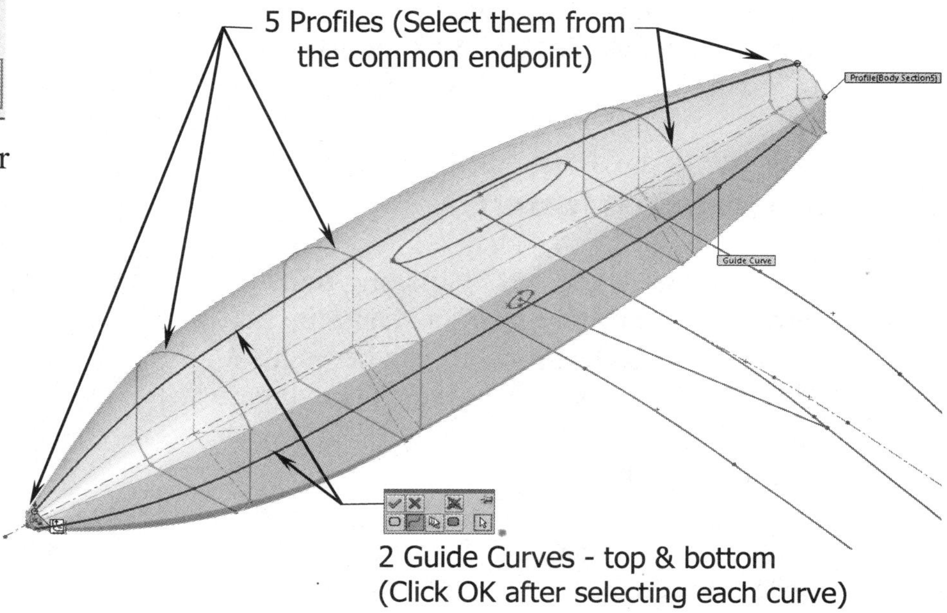

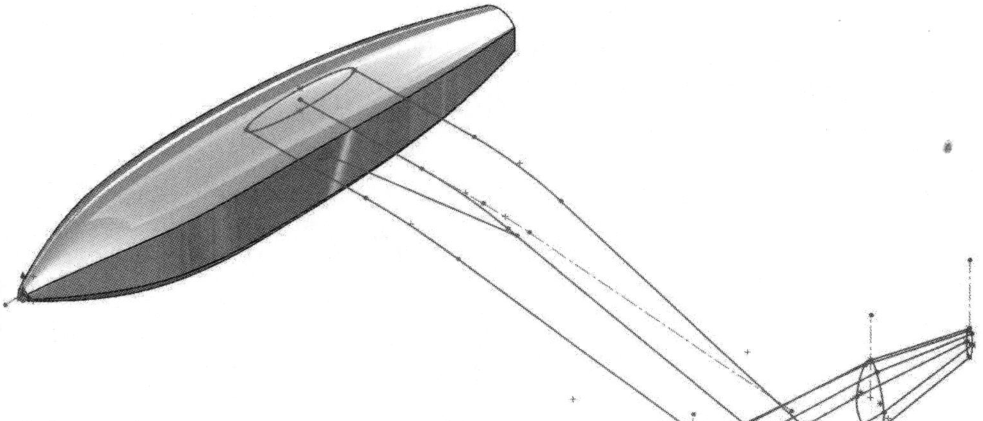

- A preview of the main body appears. Ensure that there is no twisting along the transition of the loft.

- Click **OK**.

3. Creating the boundary feature:

- The boundary command produces very high quality, accurate features useful for creating complex shapes. It uses two or more profiles and curves in two directions to define the boundary.

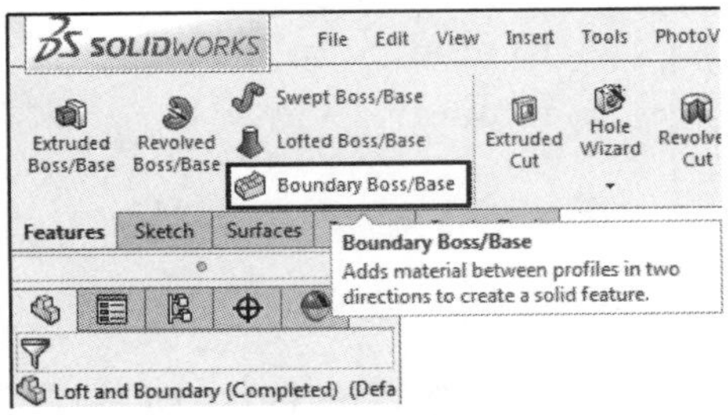

- We will try to create the float body with the boundary command. Click the **Boundary Boss /Base** command from the Features tool tab.

- For **Direction 1**, select the 4 profiles at their common points as noted.

- For **Direction 2**, select the 6 guides as indicated, click OK in the SelectionManager after selecting each guide.

- Check the preview graphics to ensure that there is no twisting in the boundary.

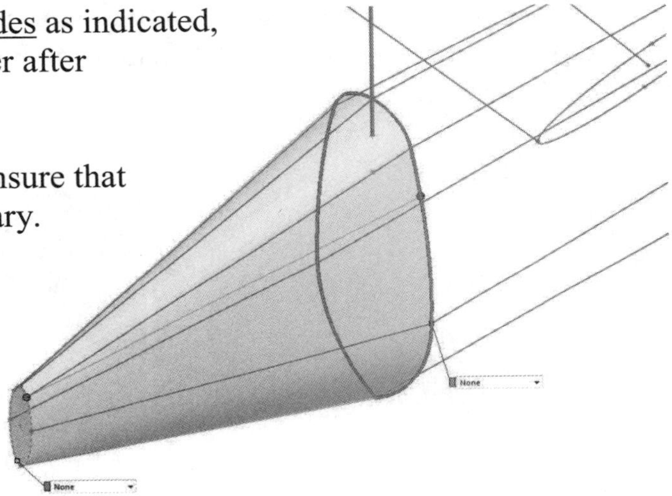

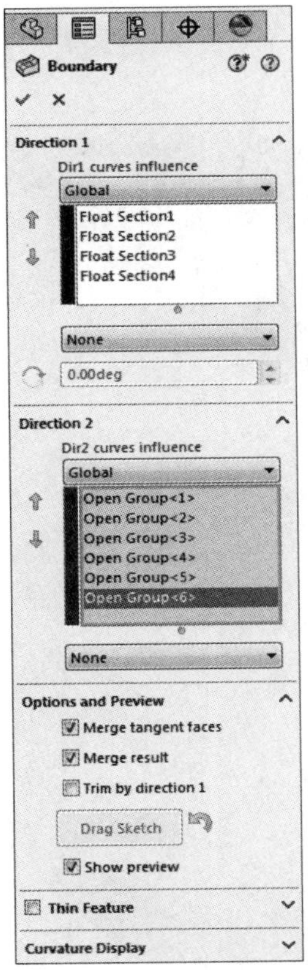

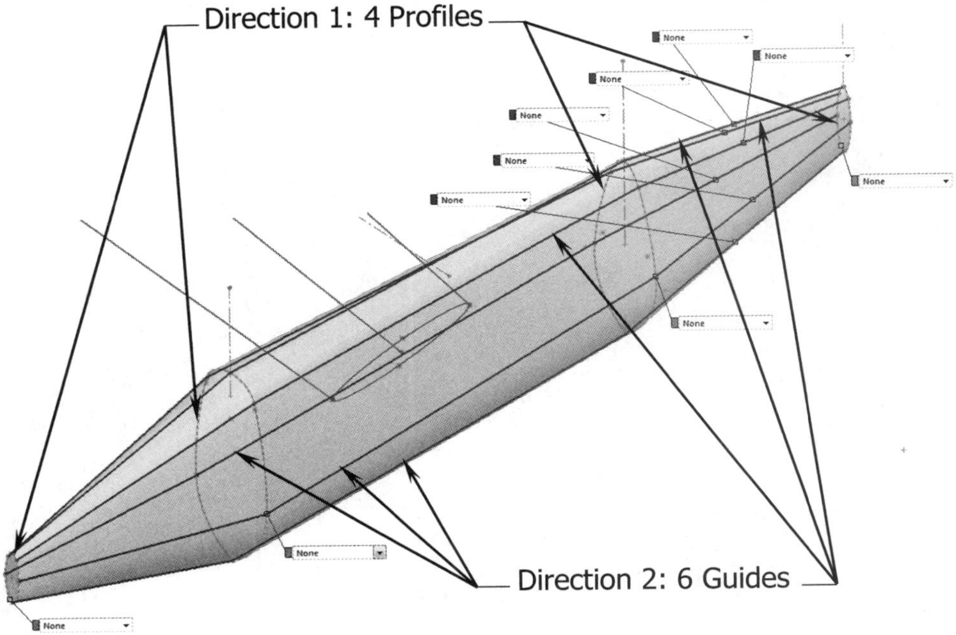

- Click **OK**.

The resulted Boundary feature

- Press Ctrl+7
 to change to the
 Isometric view.

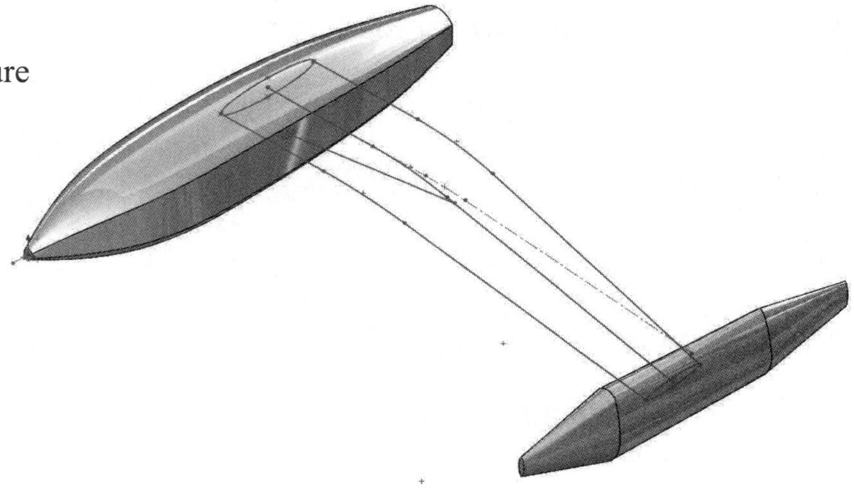

4. Creating the wing:

- The wing will be created using the loft command.
 While creating the loft, the Centerline Parameter is used to guide the loft shape.

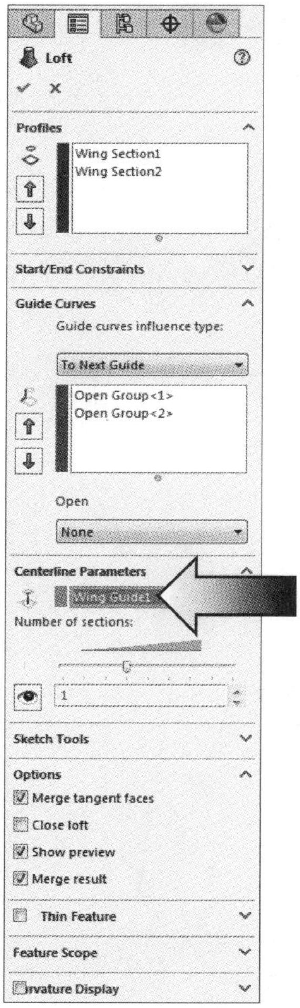

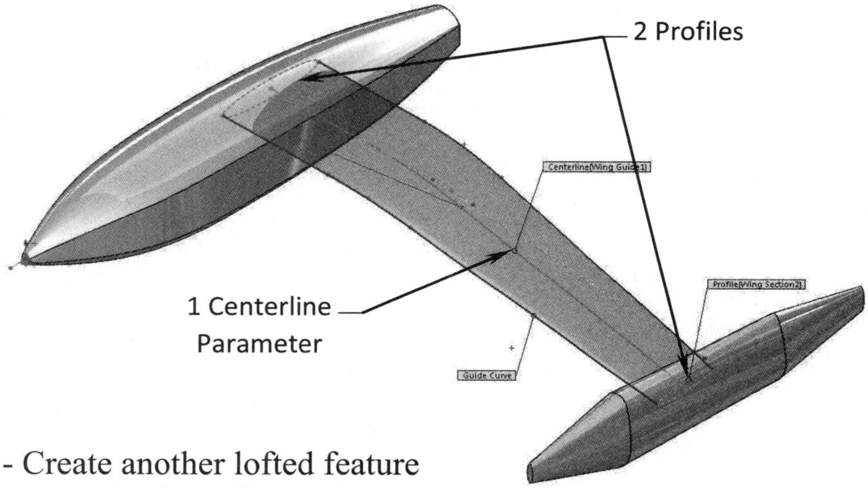

- Create another lofted feature
 using the 2 profiles and 1
 Centerline Parameter
 as indicated.

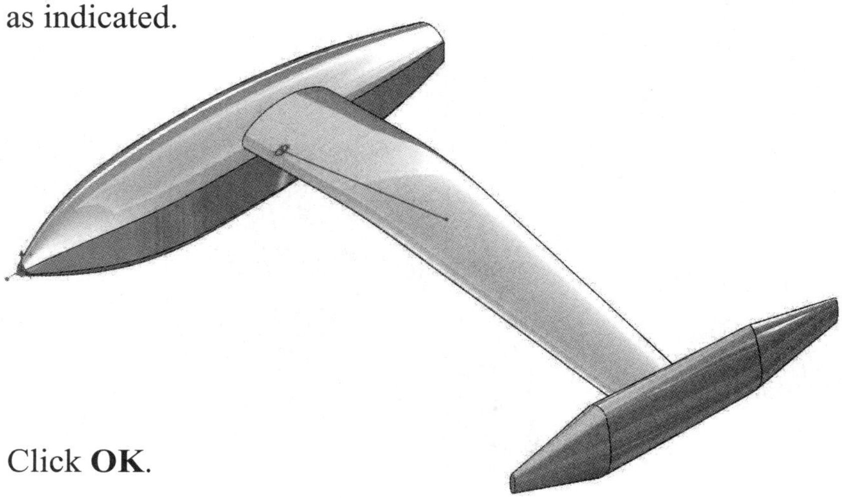

- Click **OK**.

5. Creating the wing-support:

- The wing support is much simpler than the wing itself. It can be created using a simple sweep operation.

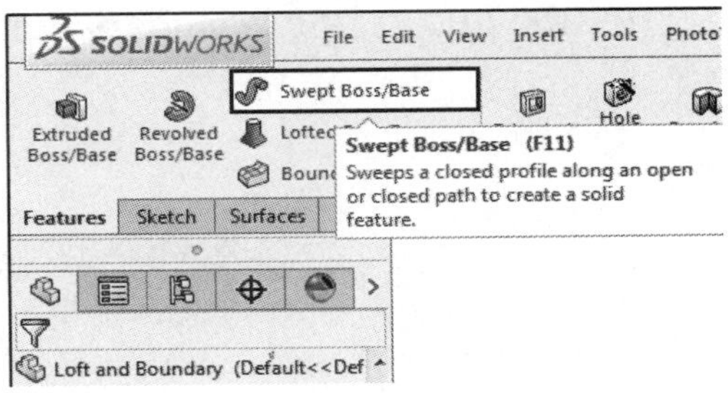

- The sweep command creates a feature by moving a profile along a path.

- Click **Swept Boss/Base**.

- Select the **Ellipse** for profile.

- Select the **Line** for sweep path.

- Leave all other settings at their default values.

- Click **OK**.

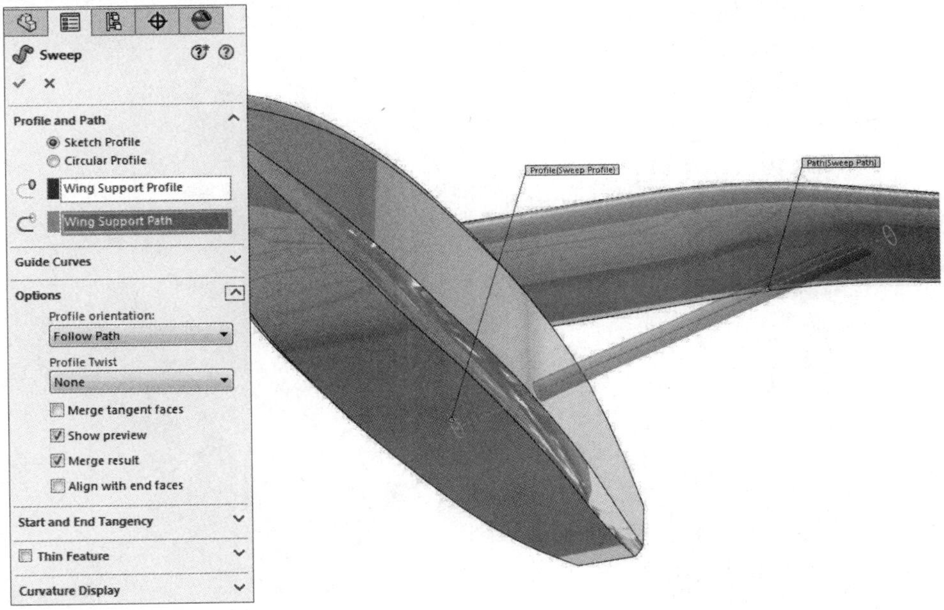

- Press Ctrl+1 to change to the front orientation.

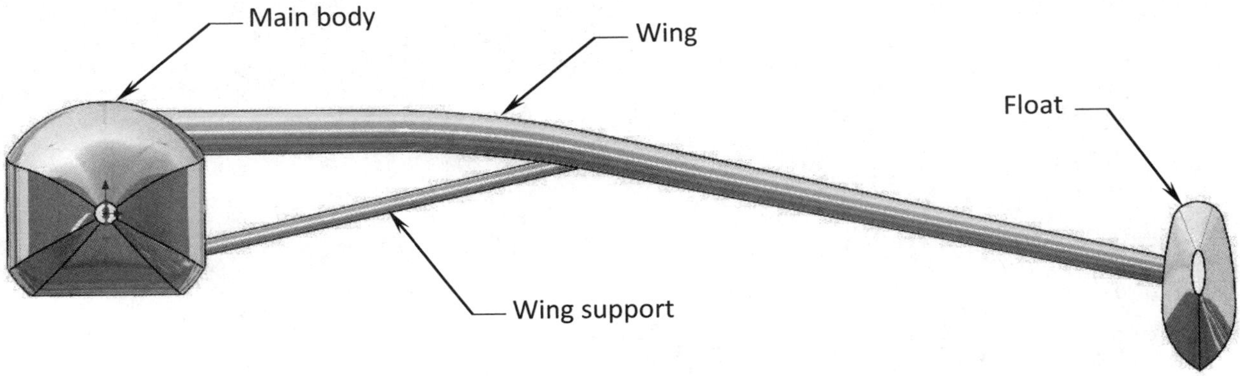

6. Constructing the nose feature:

- The following examples will demonstrate the slightly different results created by the loft vs. the boundary commands.

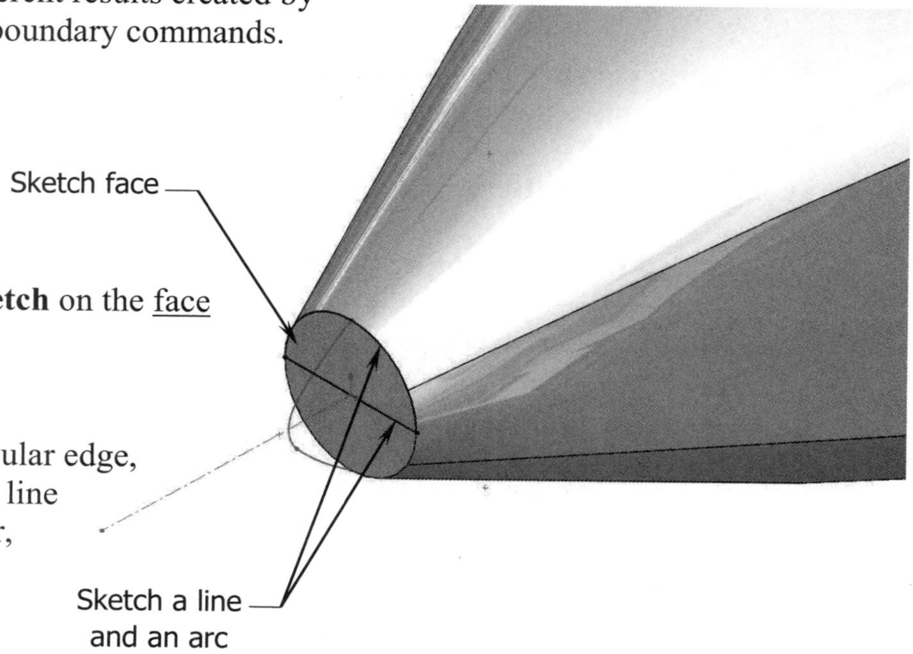

- Open a **new sketch** on the face as noted.

- Convert the circular edge, add a horizontal line across the center, and trim the circle to create a closed sketch.

- **Exit** the sketch.

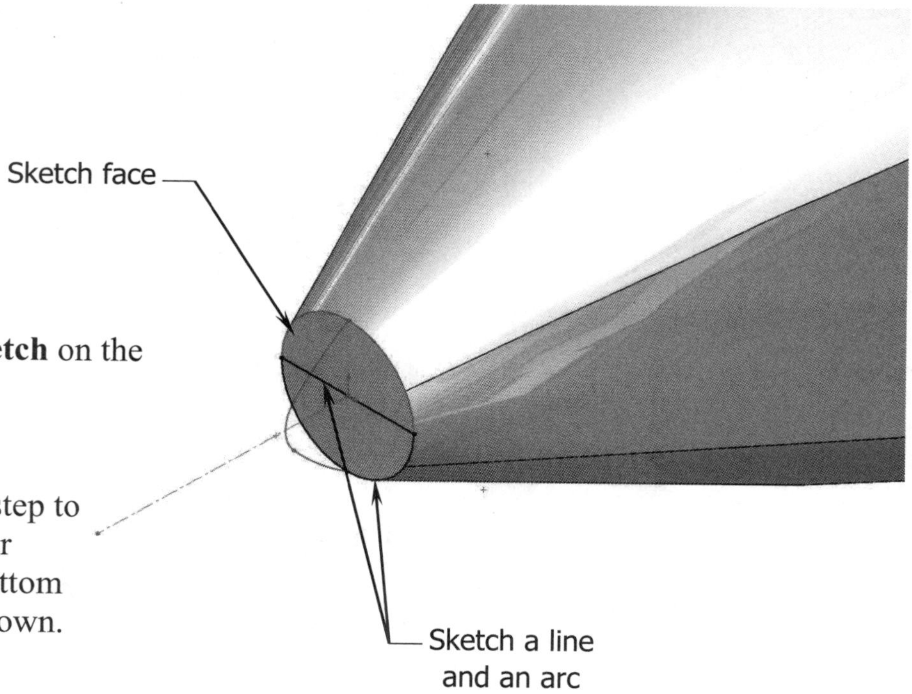

- Open a **new sketch** on the face once again.

- Repeat the last step to create the similar sketch on the bottom of the face as shown.

- **Exit** the sketch.

- Click the **Boundary Boss/Base** command.

- For **Direction 1**: select the 2 nose profiles that were created in the last step.

- For **Direction 2**: select the Nose Guide sketch from the Feature tree.

- The preview graphic shows the result of the nose tip that may need further adjustments.

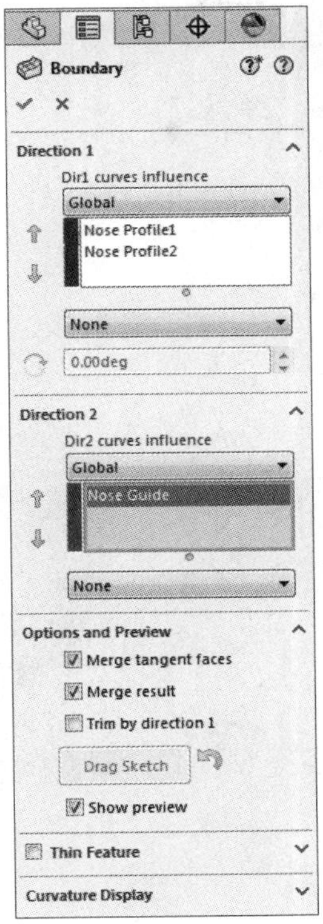

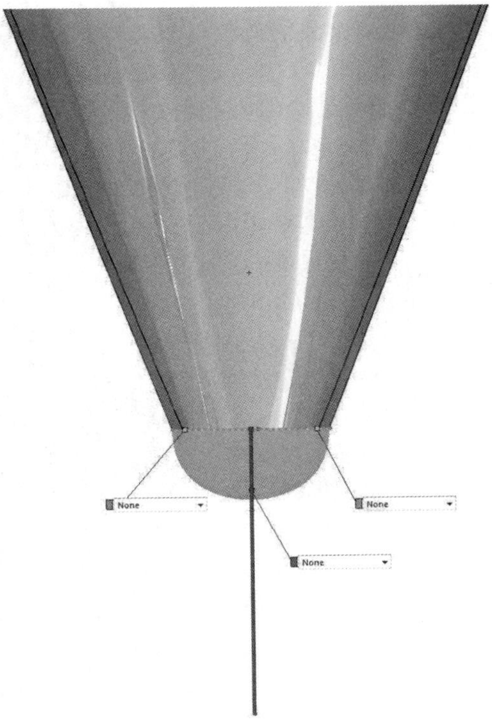

- Click **Cancel**. We will try creating the nose tip as a lofted feature instead.

- Click **Lofted Boss/Base**.

- For **Loft Profile**, select the 2 Nose Profiles that were created in the last step.

- For **Guide Curve**, select the Nose Guide sketch from the Feature tree.

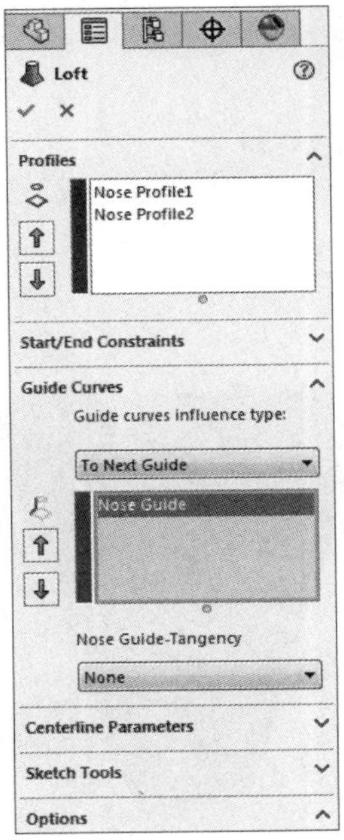

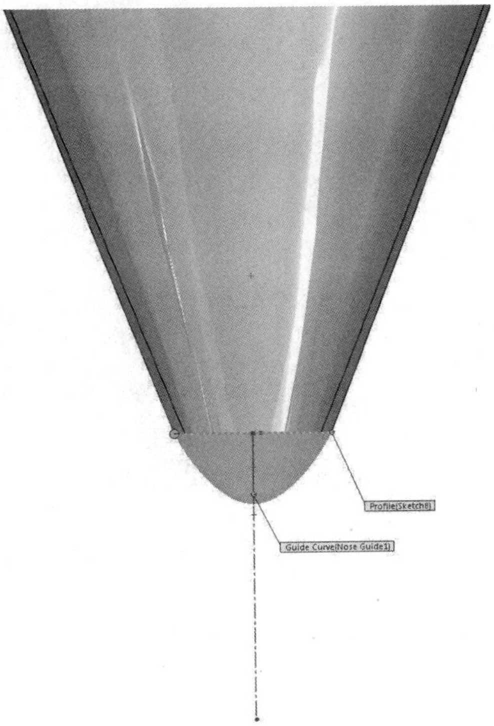

- The preview graphics shows a much better result of the nose tip than the one created with the boundary command.

- Click **OK**.

- The Boundary command can create higher quality and more accurate features than the loft can, but for this particular feature the loft is quicker and it produces an acceptable result.

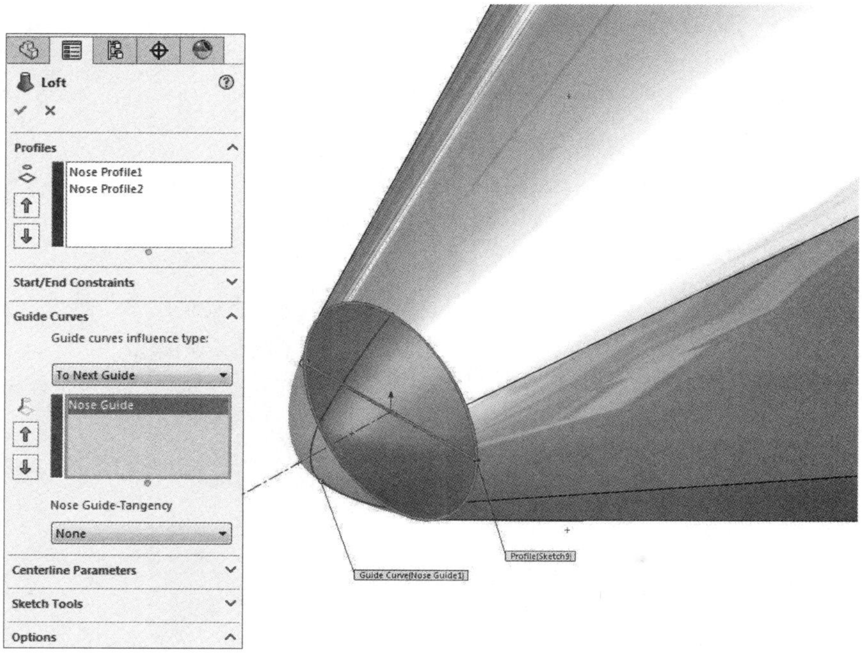

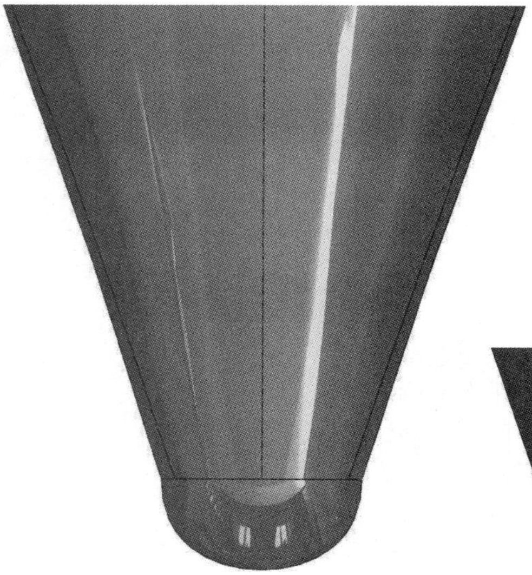

Boundary

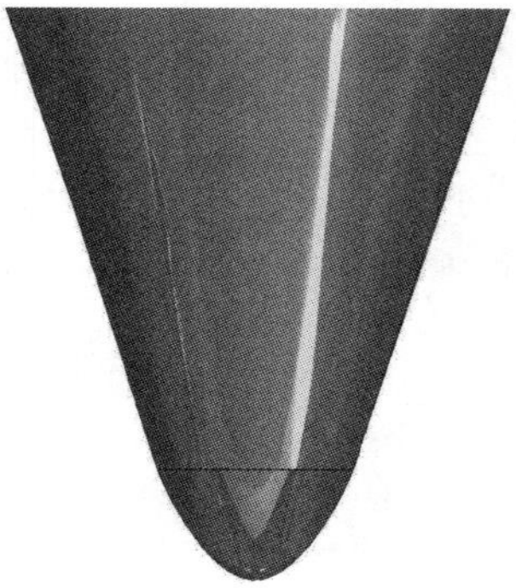

With additional guides

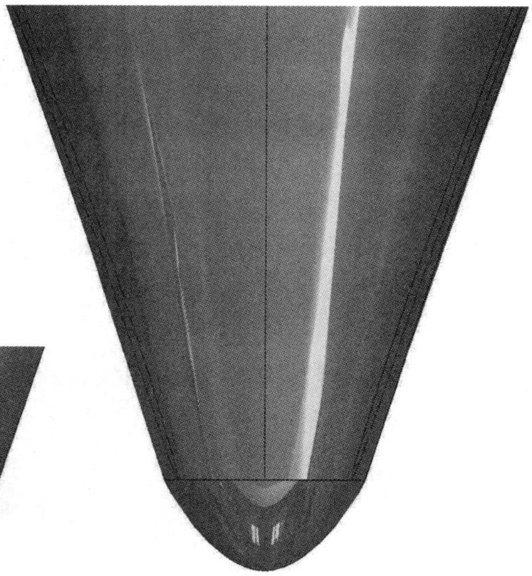

Loft

- Both the Loft and Boundary require additional guide curves to better control the transition between the nose tip to the body.

7. Creating the horizontal tail fins:

- Open a new sketch on the **Top** plane. Press Ctrl+5 to change to the top orientation.

- Sketch the profile shown.

- Use the mirror option to keep the sketch entities symmetrical with each other.

- Add the dimensions and relations shown to fully define the sketch.

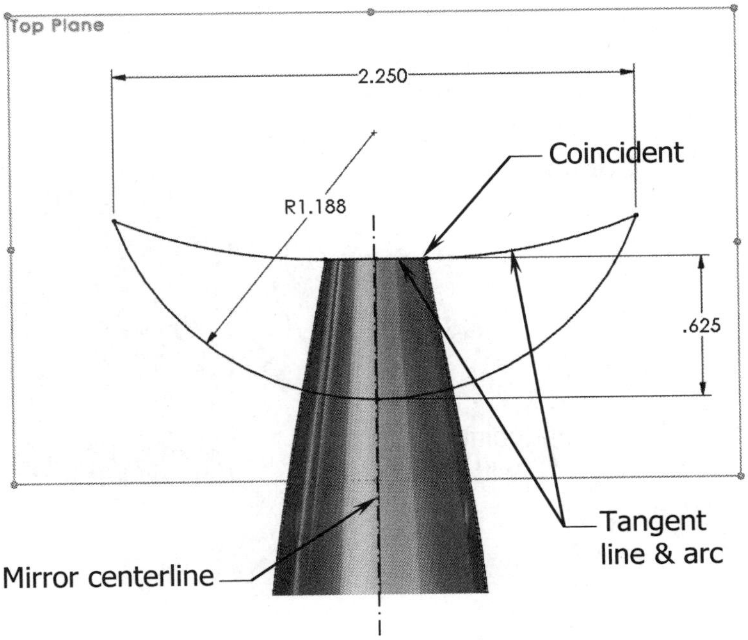

- Switch to the **Features** tool tab.

- Select **Extruded Boss/Base**.

- Select the **Mid Plane** condition.

- Enter **.060in** for extrude depth.

- Enable the **Merge Result** checkbox.

- Click **OK**.

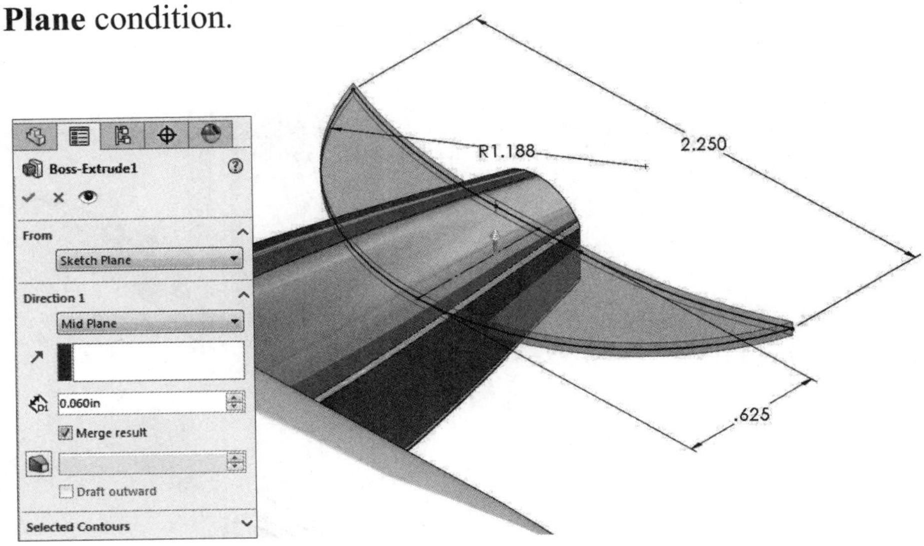

8. Creating the vertical tail fin:

- Open a new sketch on the **Right** plane. Press Ctrl+4 to change to the right orientation.

- Sketch the profile using the 3-Point Arc and the Line Commands.

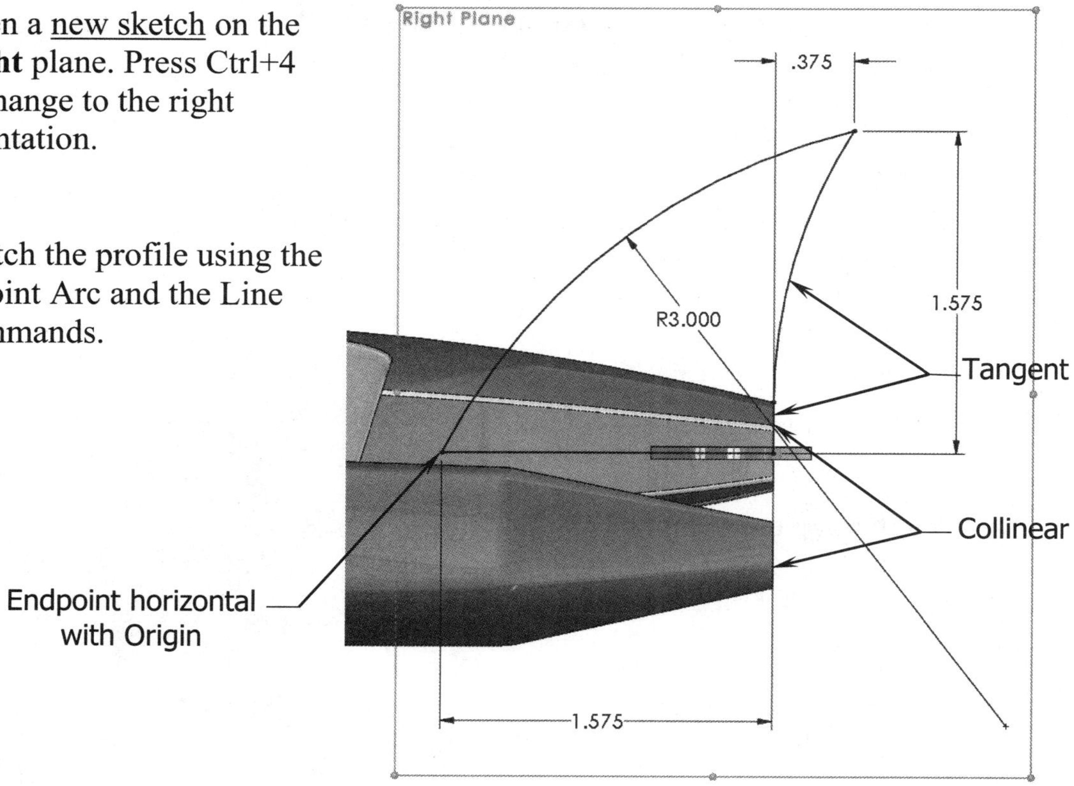

- Add the dimensions and relations indicated to fully define the sketch.

- Extrude the sketch with the **Mid Plane** condition.

- Enter **.060in** for extrude depth.

- Enable the **Merge Result** checkbox.

- Click **OK**.

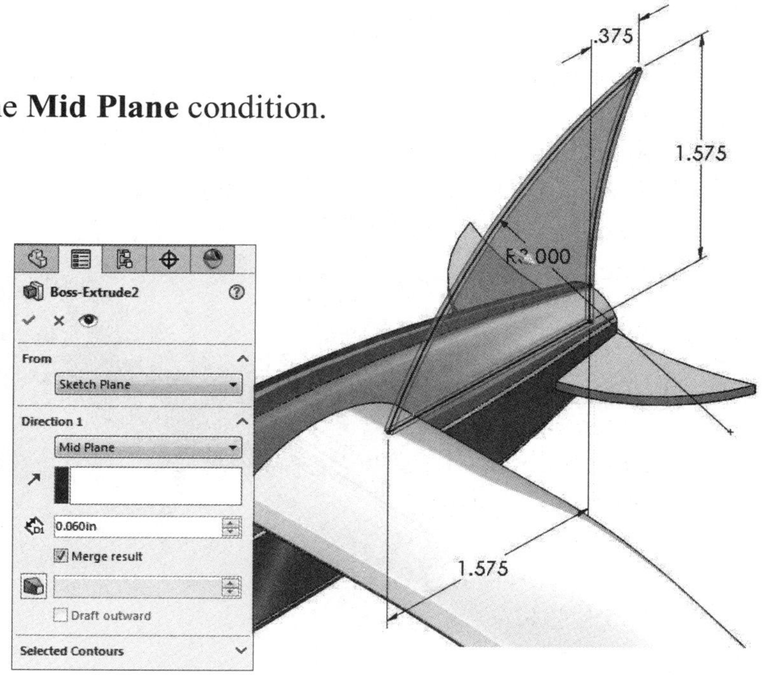

9. Creating a split line:

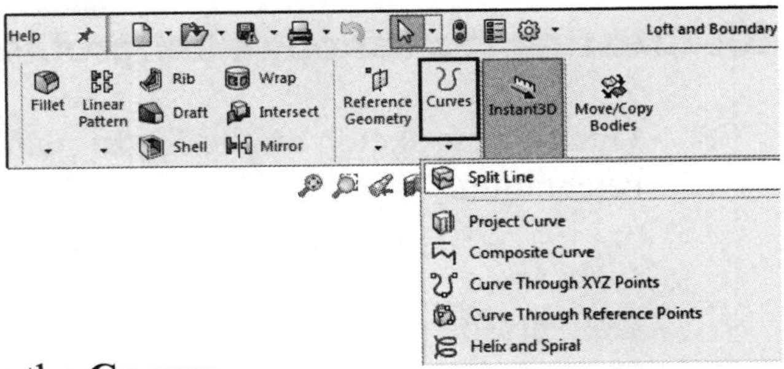

- The split line is used to define the the shape, size, and location of the canopy feature.

- Select the Split Line command from the **Curves** pull down menu.

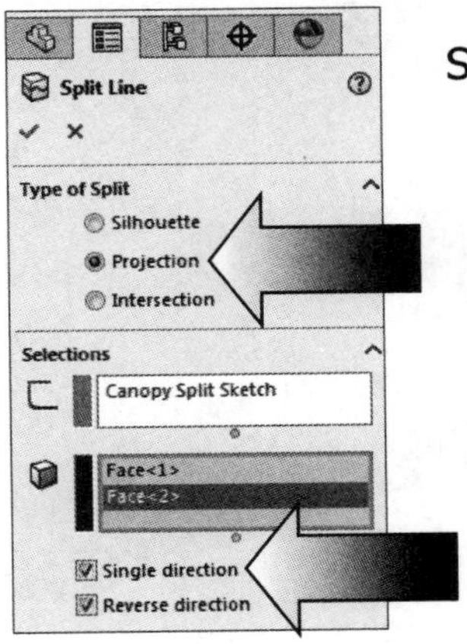

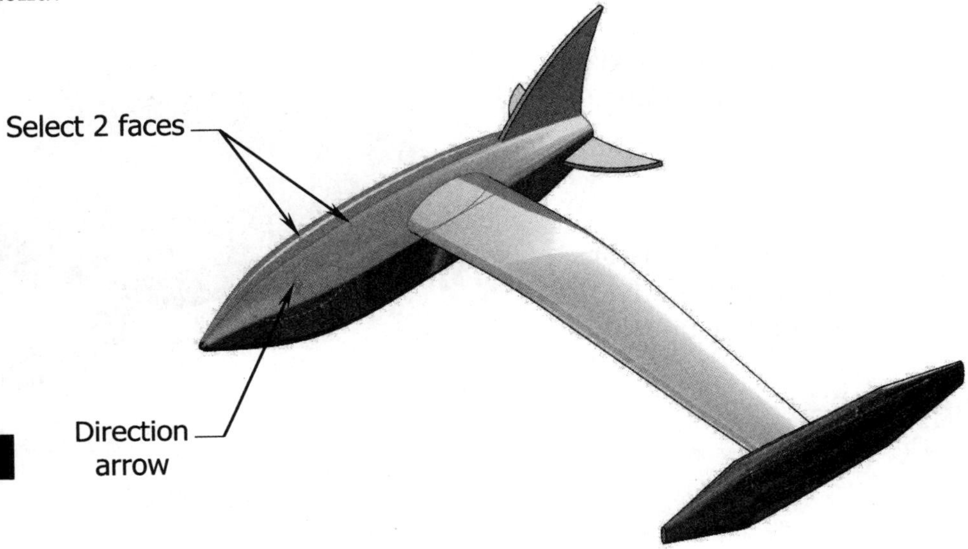

- For Type of Split, select the **Projection** type.

- For Sketch Selection, select the **Canopy Split Sketch** from the Feature tree.

- For Faces To Split, select the **2 upper Faces** of the main body as noted.

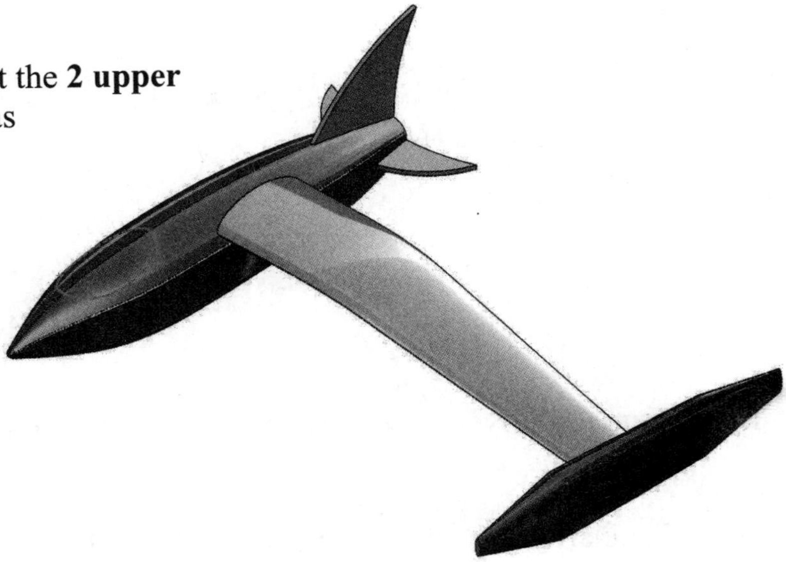

- Enable the **Single Direction** checkbox and click the direction arrow to reverse it.

- Click **OK**.

10. Creating the canopy's 1st profile:

- Open a new sketch on the **Right** plane. Press Crtl+4 to change to the right orientation.

- Convert the upper edge of the body to a curve.

- Add a **3-Point-Arc** and a **Centerline** shown.

- Add the dimensions indicated to fully define the sketch.

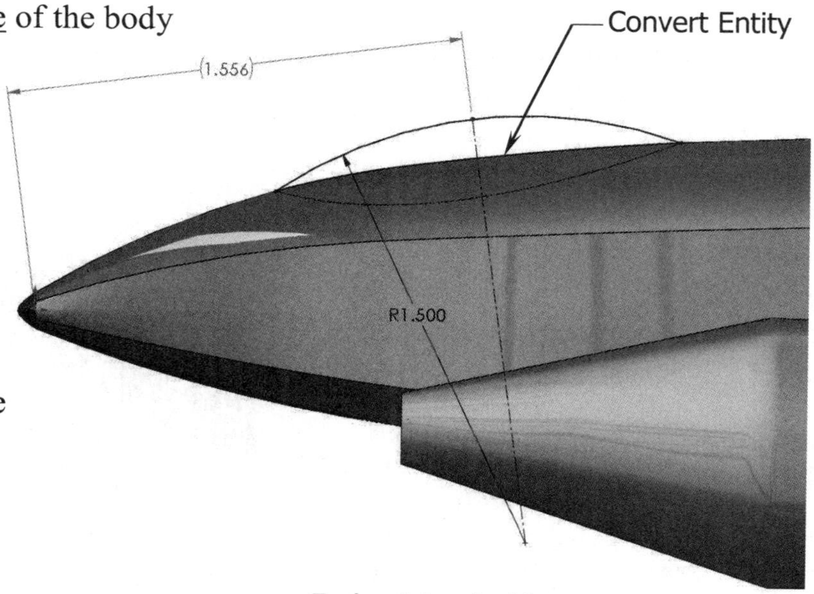

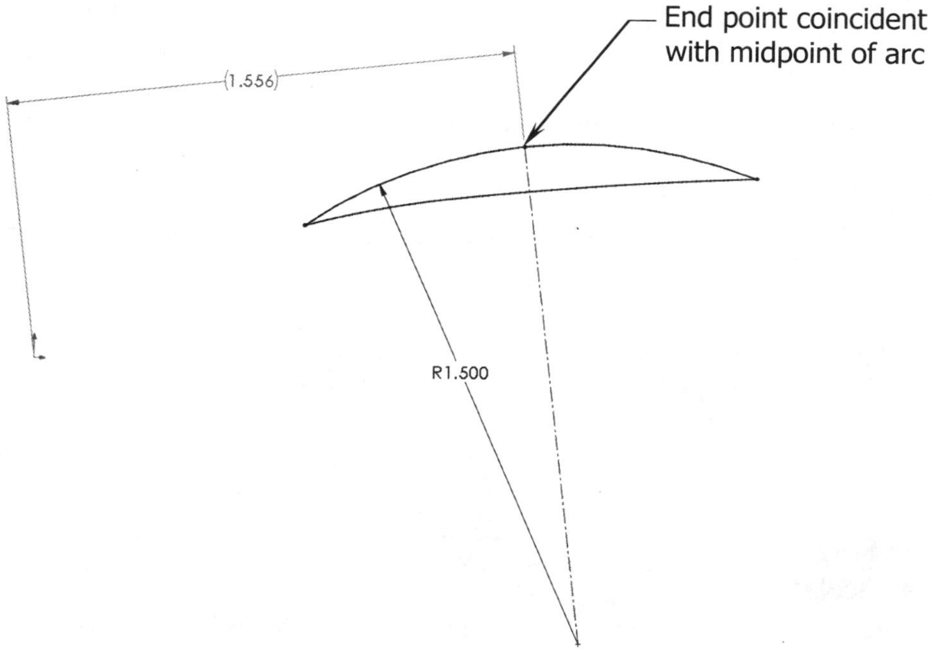

- Trim the curve to meet the ends of the arc and form a closed sketch profile.

- For clarity, the model is hidden to show only the sketch.

11. Creating a new plane:

- A new plane is needed to sketch the guide curve.

- Select the **Plane** command from The Reference Geometry drop down menu, or select: **Insert / Reference Geometry / Plane**.

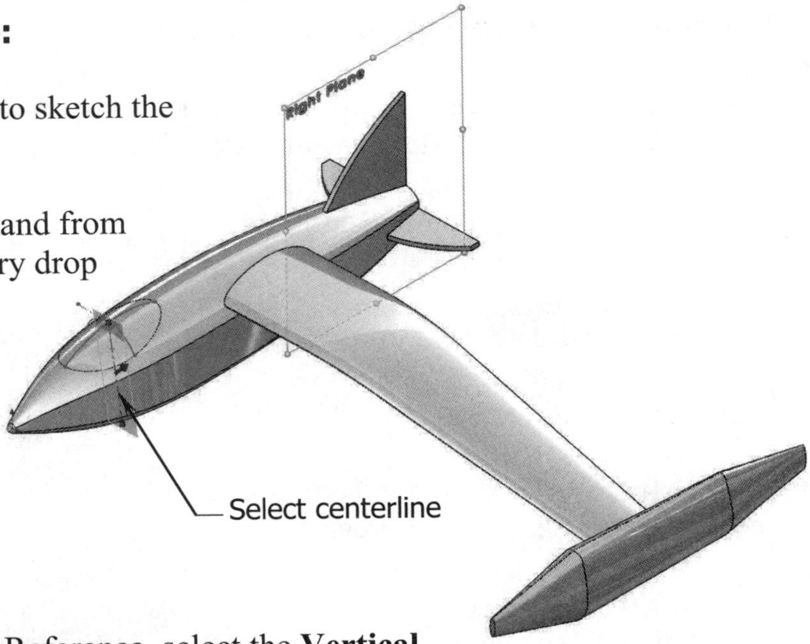

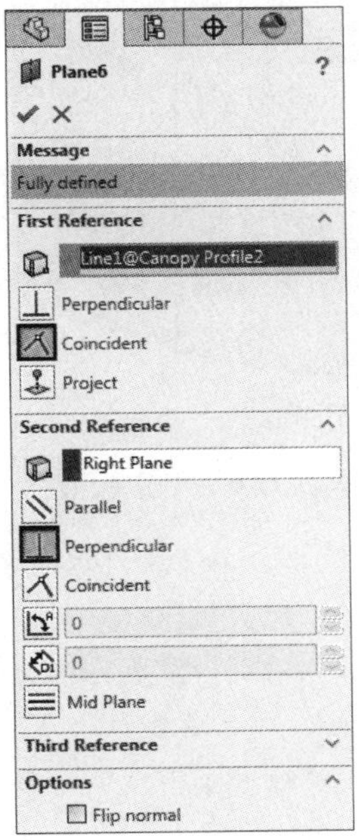

- For First Reference, select the **Vertical Centerline** from the previous sketch.

- For Second Reference, select the **Right** plane from the Feature tree.

- SOLIDWORKS automatically places the new plane on the vertical centerline and rotates it to the perpendicular position with the right reference plane.

12. Sketching the guide curve:

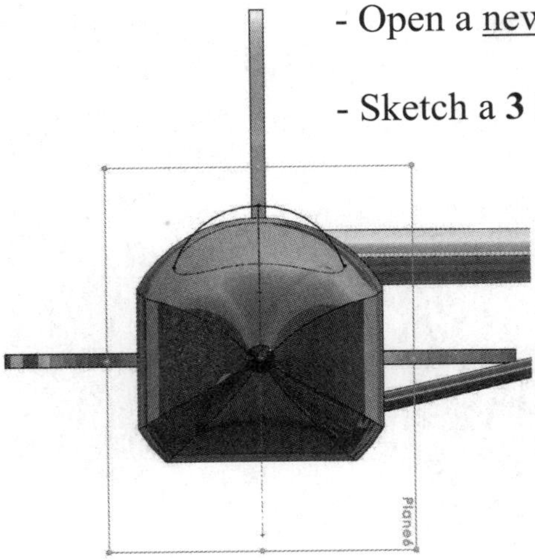

- Open a <u>new sketch</u> on the new plane.

- Sketch a **3 Point-Arc** and a vertical **Centerline** as shown in the images.

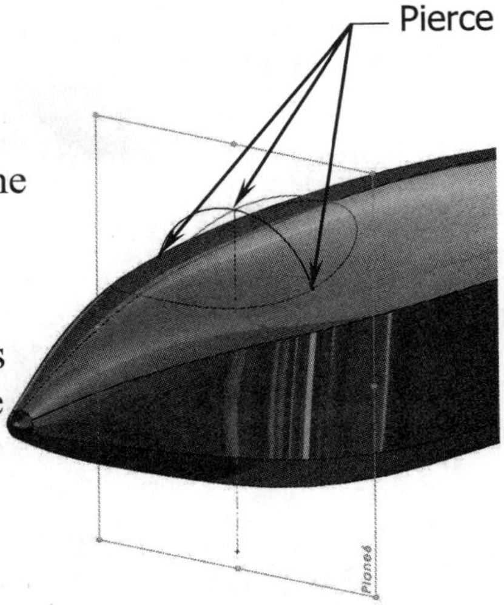

- Add the **Pierce** relations (3 places) to fully define the sketch.

- **<u>Exit</u>** the sketch.

13. Creating the canopy's 2nd loft profile:

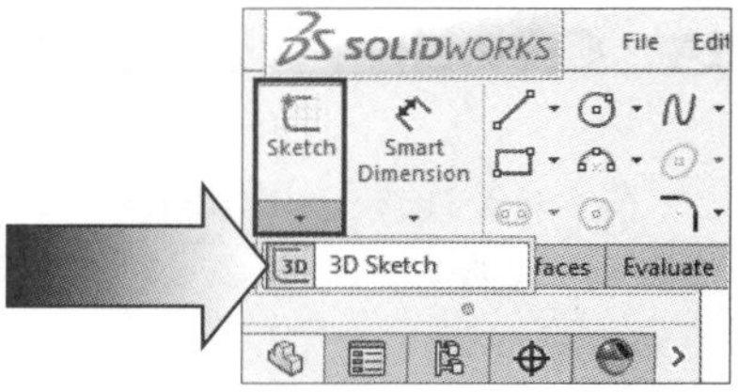

- When working on non-planar surfaces, sometimes it is quicker to create the geometry in 3D sketch rather than creating them on a plane and then later projecting onto the surfaces.

- We will create the 2 loft profiles as 3D sketch profiles.

- Select the **3D sketch** command from the Sketch drop down.

- Select the 2 edges shown and click **Convert Entities**.

- The 2 selected edges are converted to 2 splines.

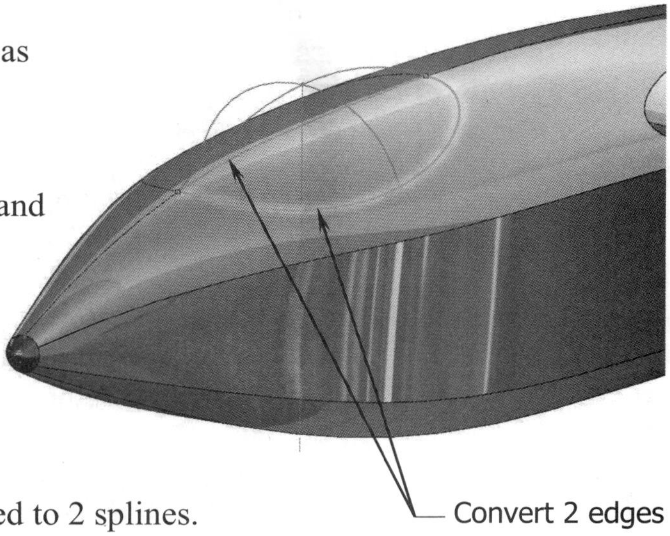

- **Exit** the 3D-Sketch or press Ctrl+Q.

14. Creating the canopy's 3rd loft profile:

- Repeat the last step and create the 2nd loft profile the same way.

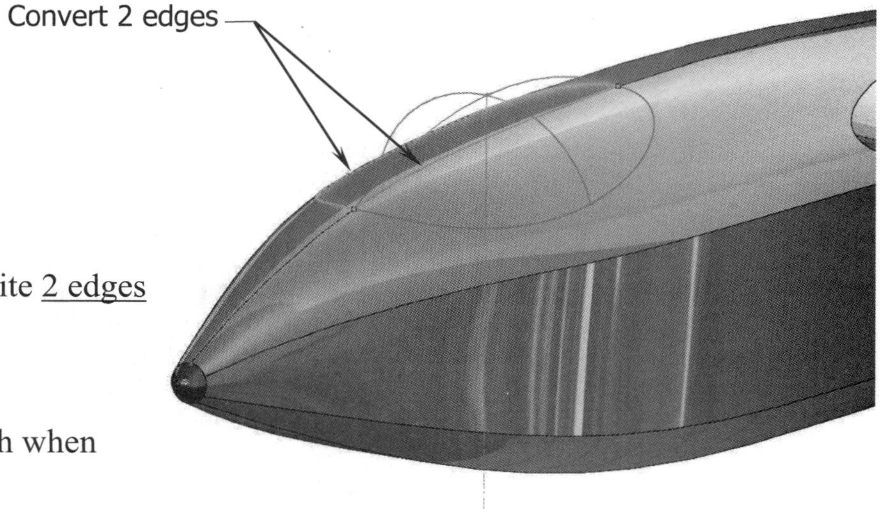

- Convert the opposite 2 edges to 2 splines.

- **Exit** the 3D-Sketch when finished.

15. Creating the canopy:

- Select the **Lofted Boss/Base** command from the Features tool tab.

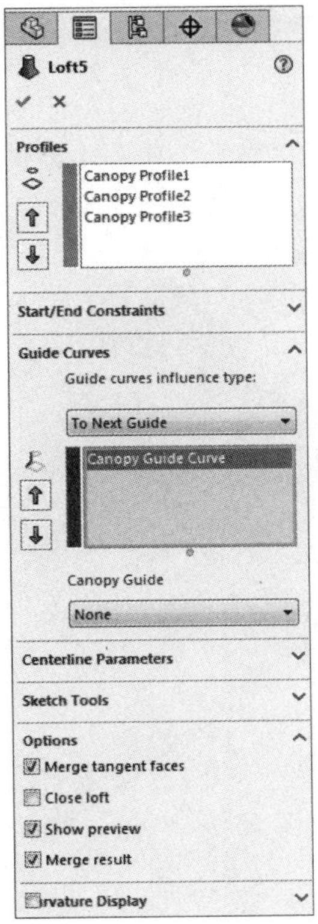

- For Profiles, select the sketches of the **3 loft profile**.

- For Guide Curves, select the **arc** as noted.

- Click **OK**.

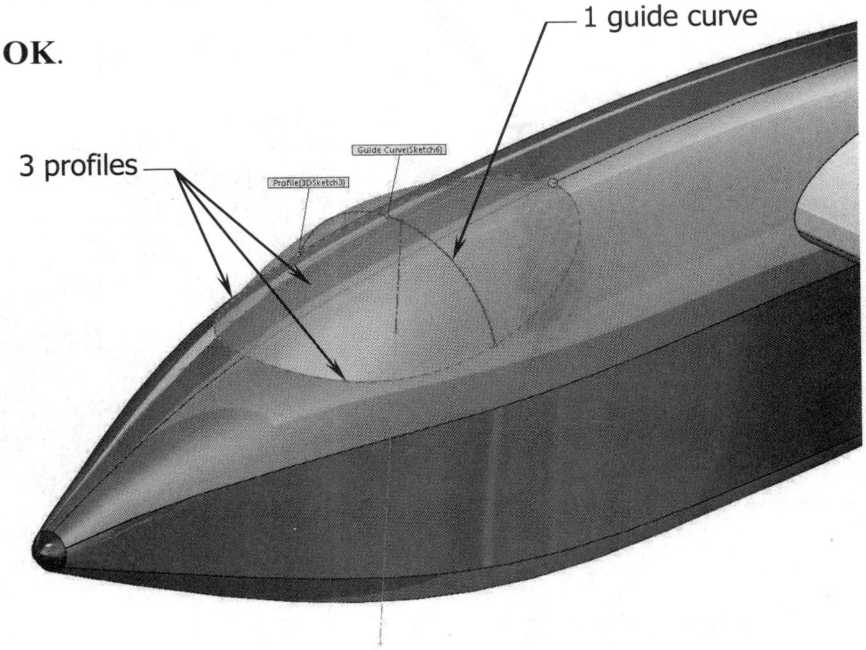

16. Creating a mirror feature:

- Select the **Mirror** command from the Features tool tab.

- For Mirror Face/Plane, select the **Right** plane from the Features tree.

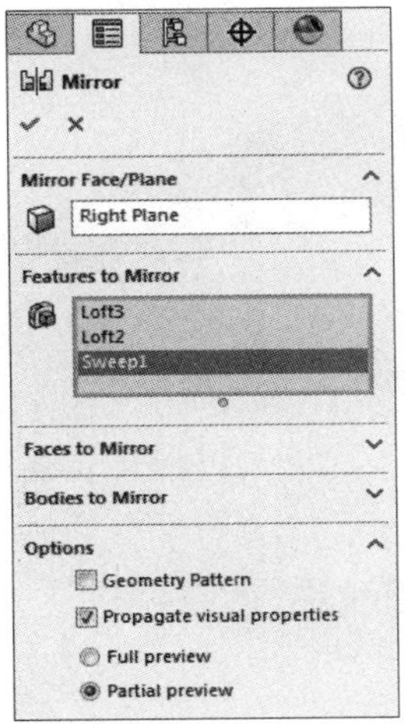

- For Features to Mirror, select from the graphics area: the **Wing**, the **Float**, and the **Wing Support** features.

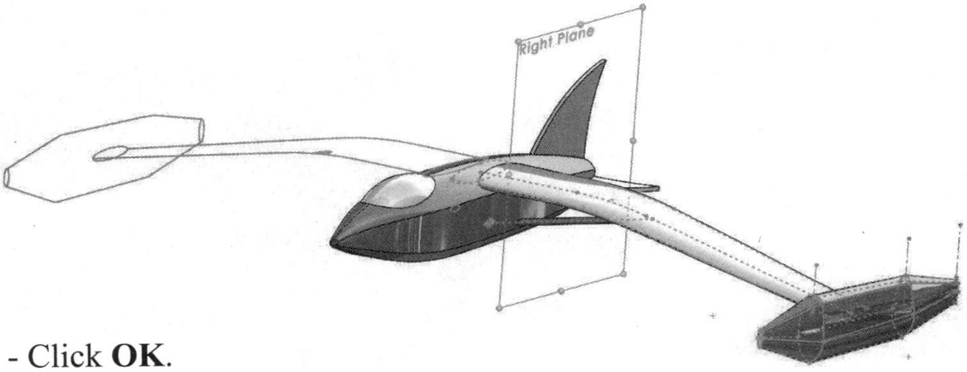

- Click **OK**.

17. Adding fillets to the main body:

- Select the Fillet command from the Features tool tab.

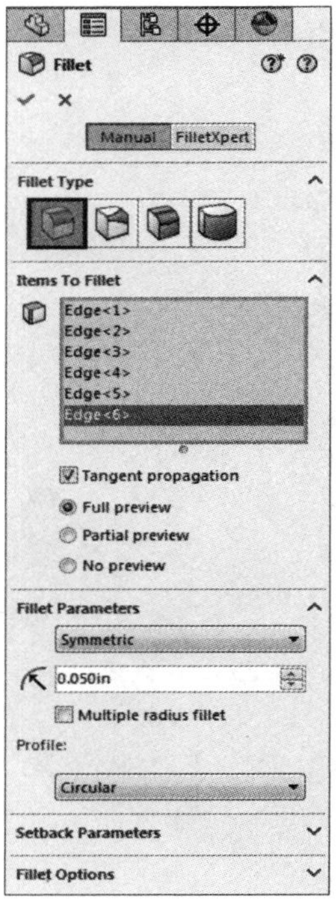

- The **Constant Size Fillet** should be the default type.

- Enter **.050in** for radius.

- Select the **6 edges** along the length of the main body.

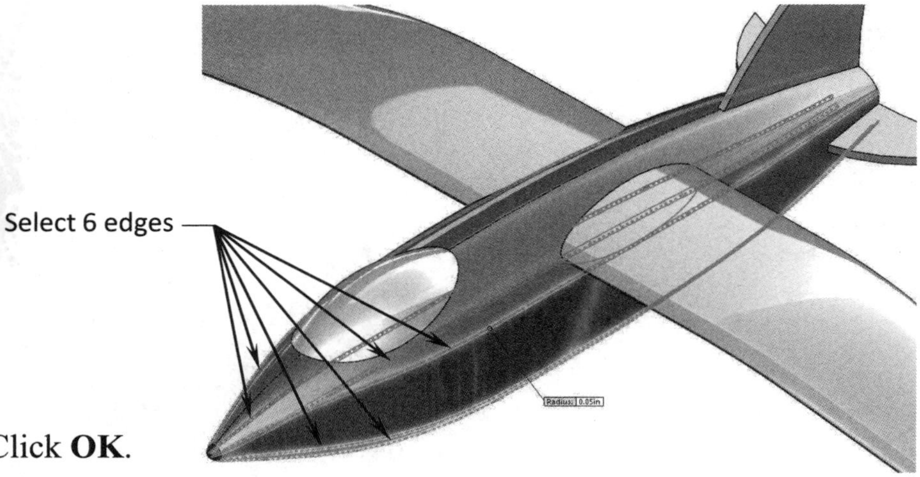

- Click **OK**.

18. Adding fillets to the float and wing:

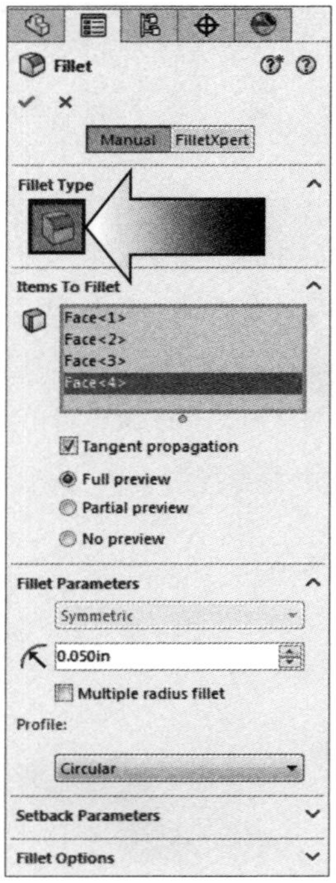

- Click the **Fillet** command and Enter **.050in** for radius.

- Select the **surfaces** of the **wing**, the **float**, and the **wing** support to add the fillets to their edges.

<u>NOTE:</u> It is quicker to select a face of a feature and add the fillets to all of its edges then selecting one edge each time.

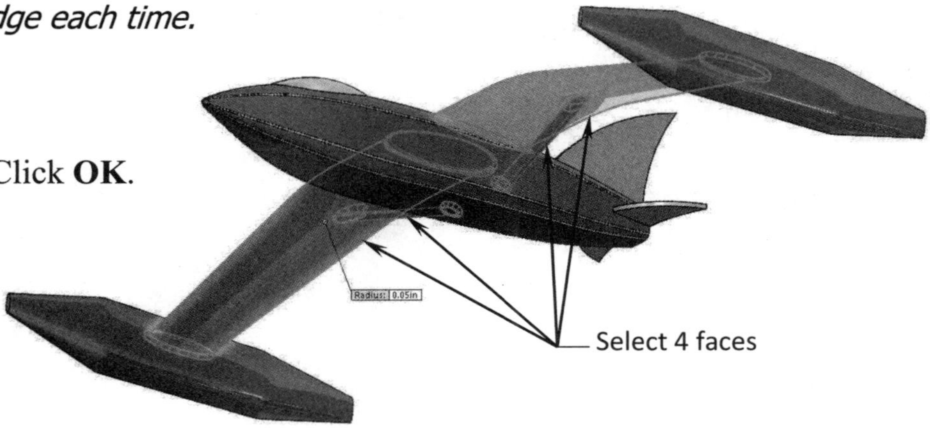

- Click **OK**.

19. Adding fillets to the ends of the floats:

- Add a fillet of **.008in** to the left and right ends of both floats.

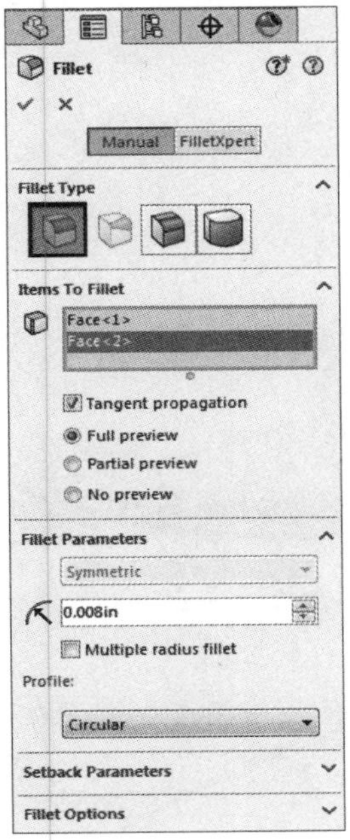

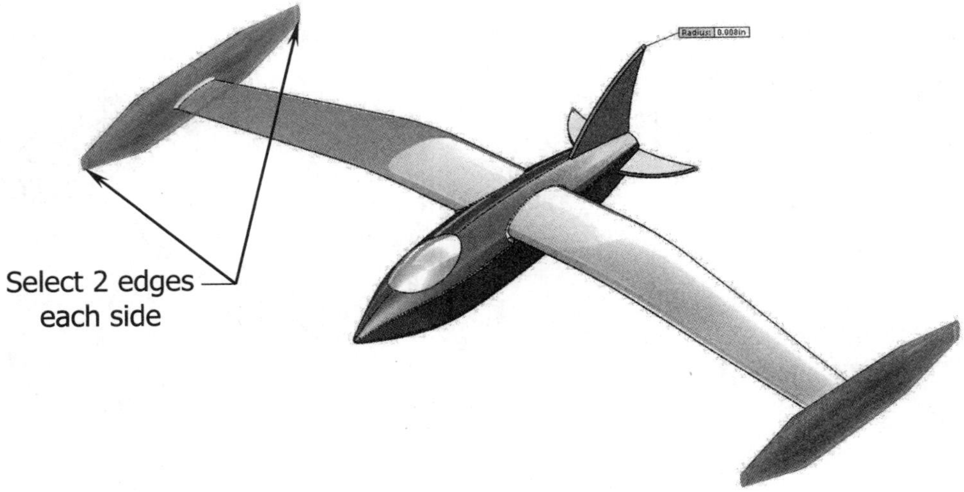

- Click **OK**.

20. Adding fillets to the tail fins:

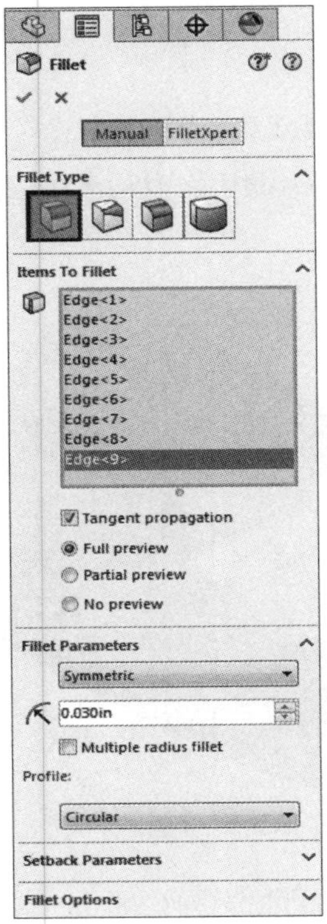

- Add a fillet of **.030in** to <u>all edges</u> of the 3 fins.

- There should be a total of 9 edges.

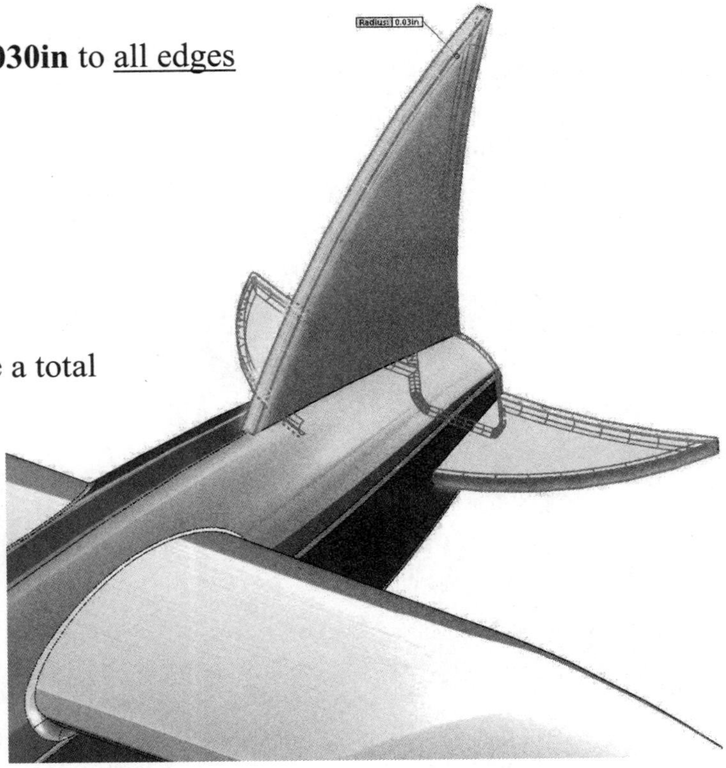

- Click **OK**.

21. Adding fillets to the ends of the fins:

- Add another fillet of **.030in** to the ends of the 3 fins.

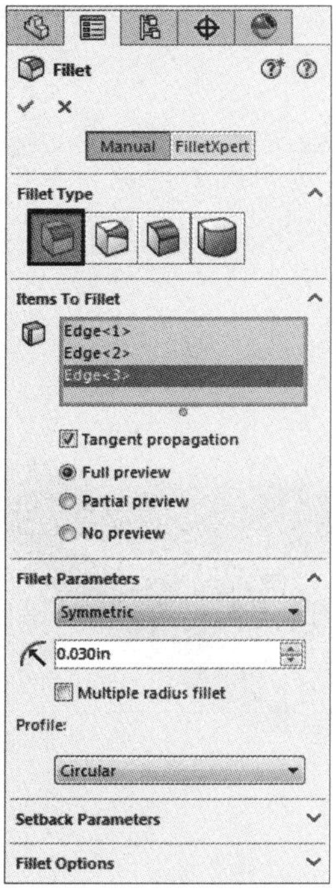

- There should be a total of 3 edges.

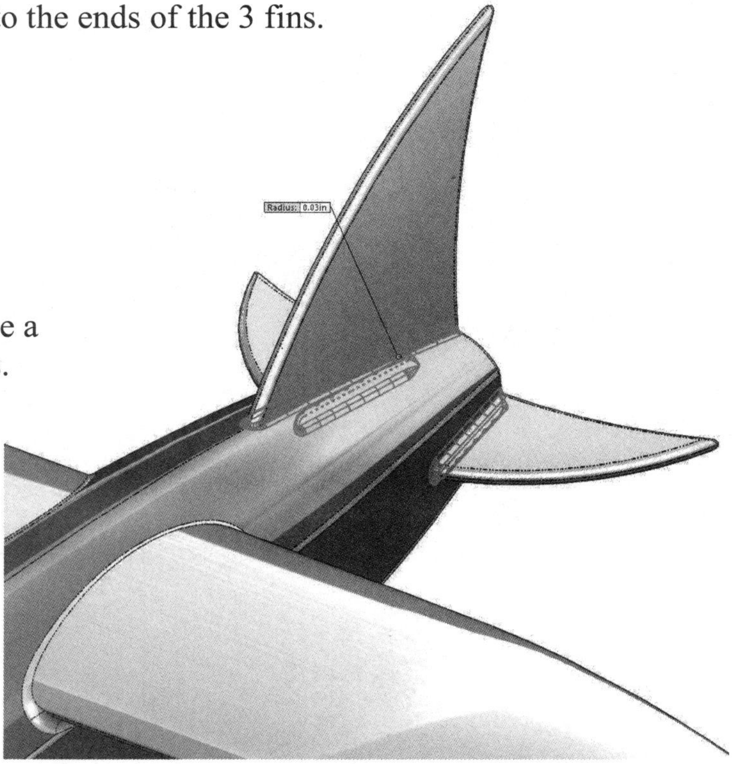

- Click **OK**.

22. Creating a face fillet:

- The examples below show 2 different types of fillet used to create the blend between the canopy and the main body. One of them was created using the Constant Size Fillet, and the other was Face Fillet.

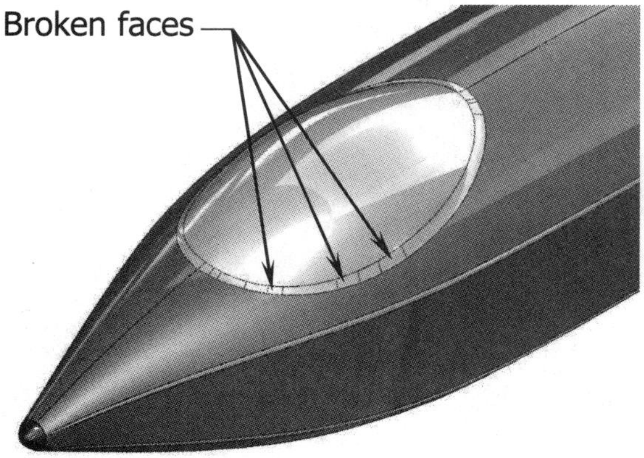

Constant Size Fillet

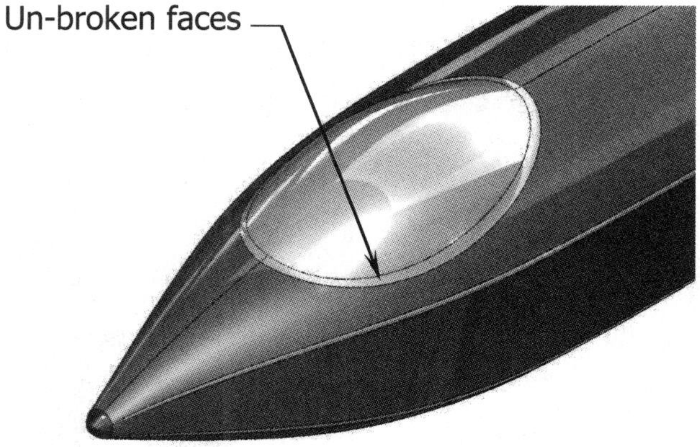

Face Fillet

- We will use the Face Fillet option to create a smoother blend between the canopy and the main body.

- Select the **Fillet** command once again.

- Click the **Face Fillet** option (arrow).

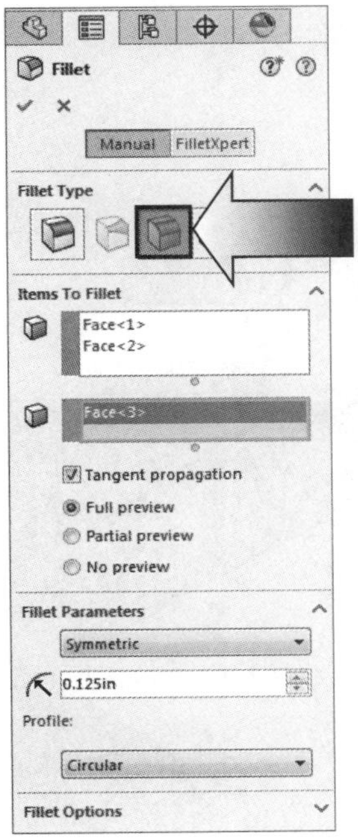

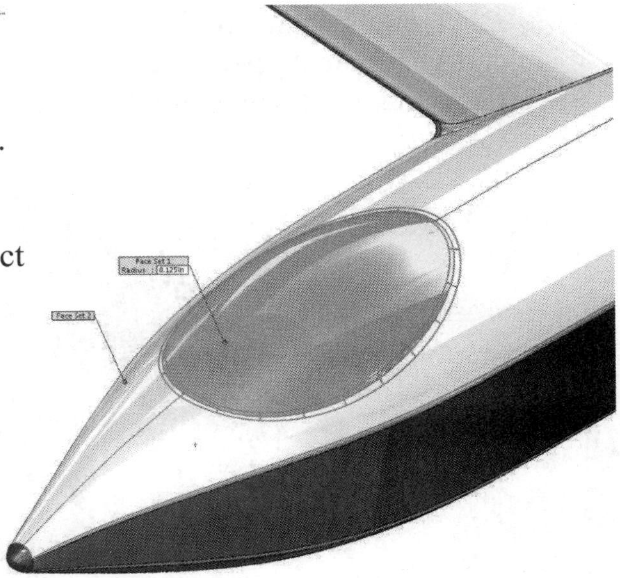

- Enter **.125in** for radius.

- For Face Group 1, select the **upper 2 faces** of the main body.

- For Face Group 2, select the face of the canopy.

- Click **OK**.

23. Creating a split line for the solar panels:

- From the Features tool tab, select the **Split Line** command from the Curves pull down menu

- Use the default **Projection** type.

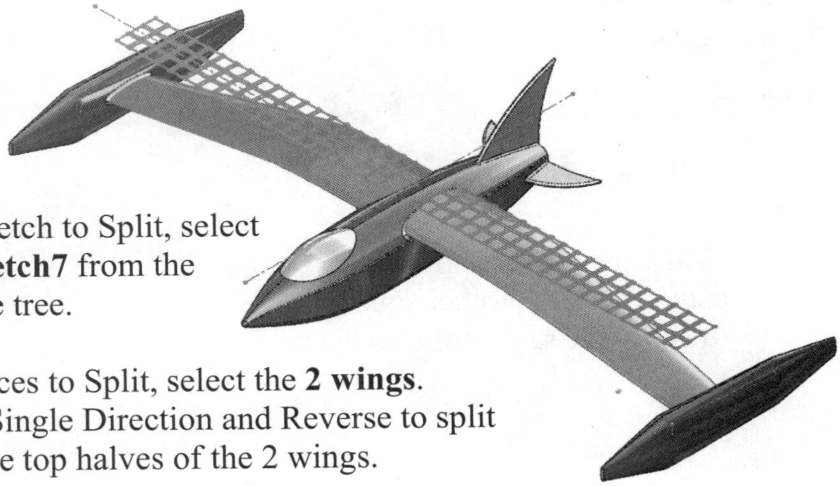

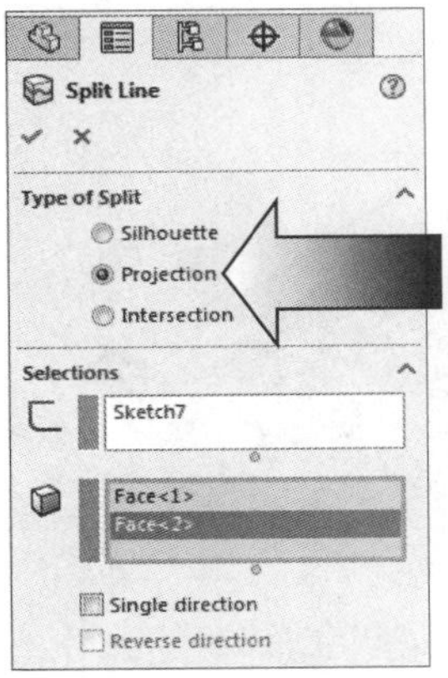

- For Sketch to Split, select the **Sketch7** from the Feature tree.

- For Faces to Split, select the **2 wings**. Click Single Direction and Reverse to split only the top halves of the 2 wings.

- Click **OK**.

24. Changing the color of the solar squares:

- The color of any faces, features, or bodies can be changed at any time. To further enhance the look of the solar squares, we will change them to the black color.

- Click on the inside of one of the squares and select the **Appearance** button, and then click the **Face** option (arrows).

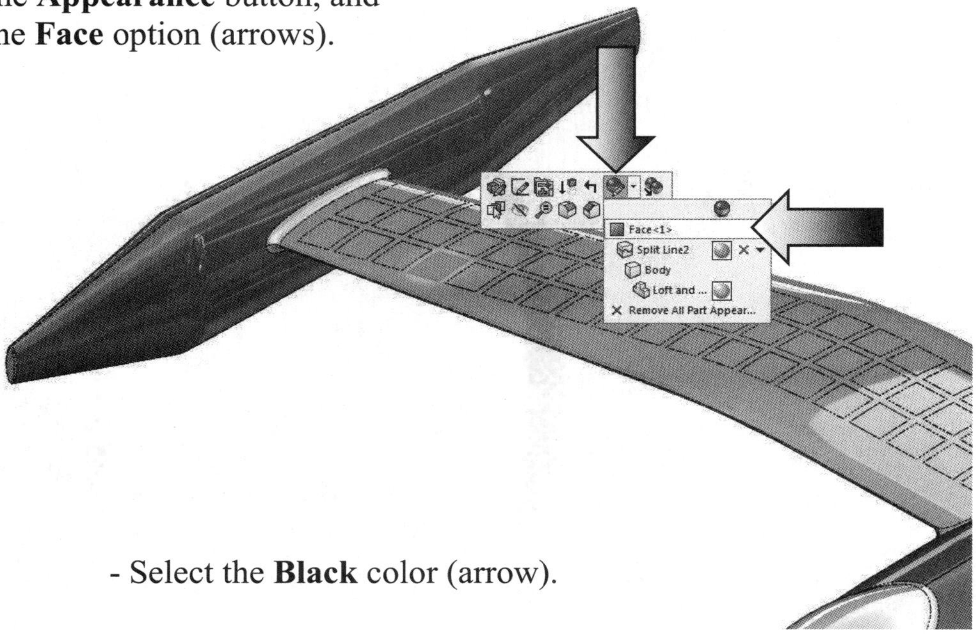

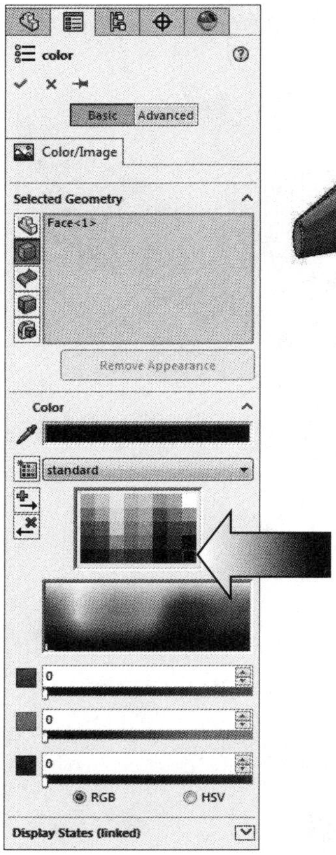

- Select the **Black** color (arrow).

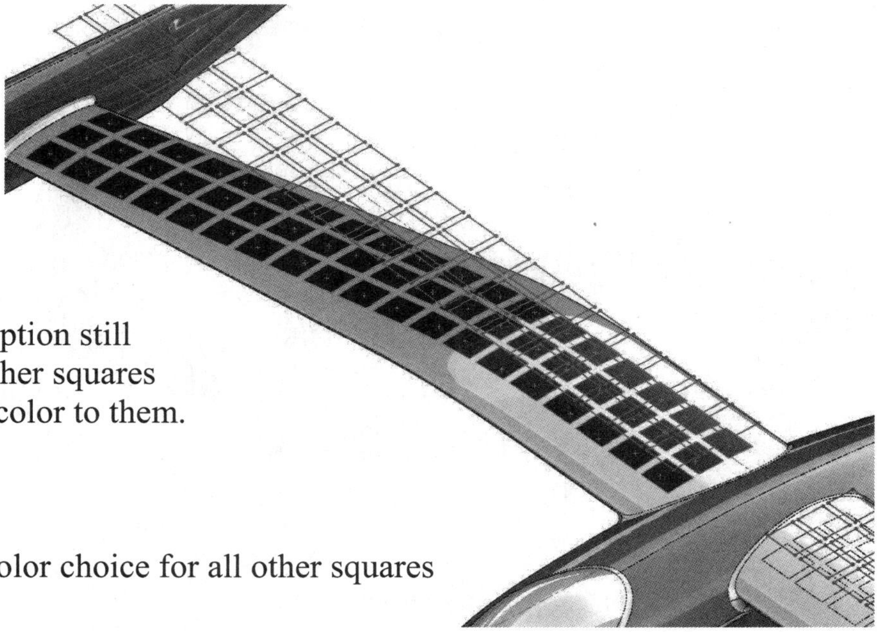

- While the colors option still active, select all other squares to apply the same color to them.

- Repeat the same color choice for all other squares on the other wing.

25. Changing the edge display:

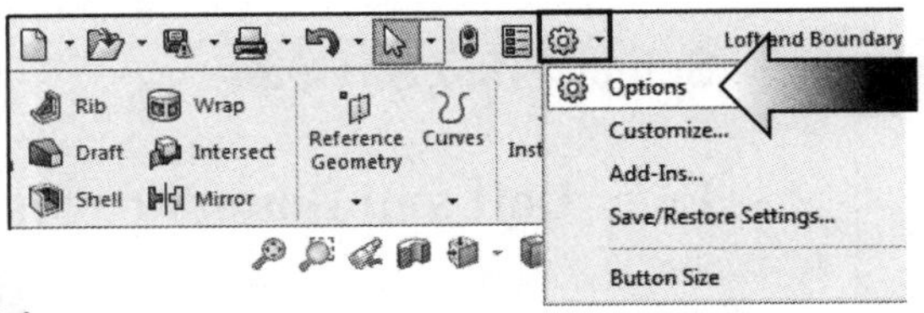

- While creating the model we often use the option Shaded with Edges for convenience, but when the model is completed we should change the display to Tangent Edges Remove. Not only will this shading option make the model look a little more realistic but it also helps improve the computer performance.

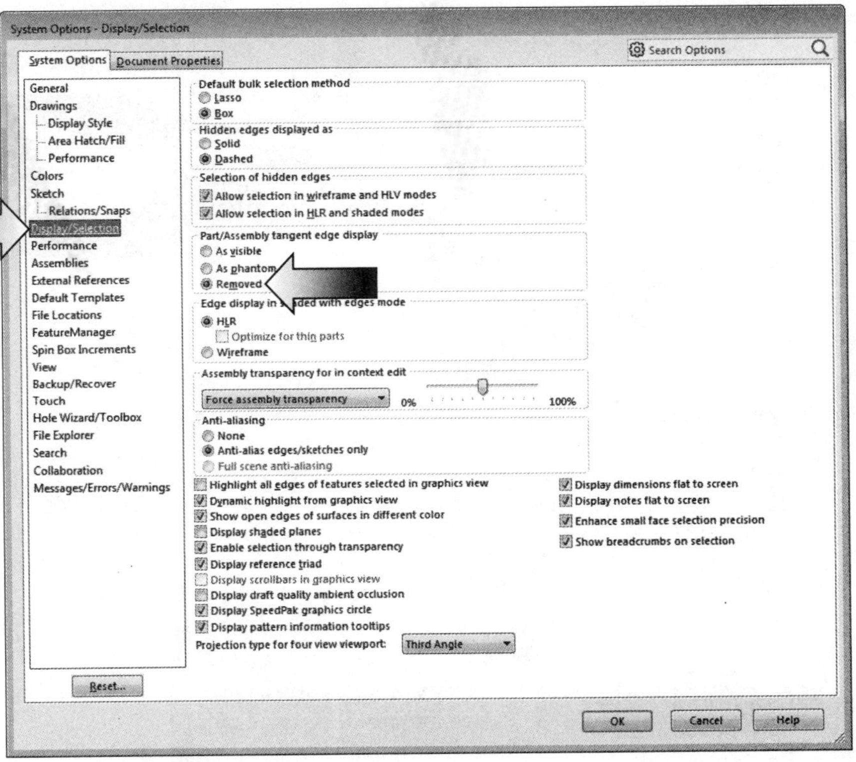

- Click **Options** (arrow).

- Select the option **Display Selection**.

- Click the **Remove** option under the Part/Assembly Tangent Edge Display.

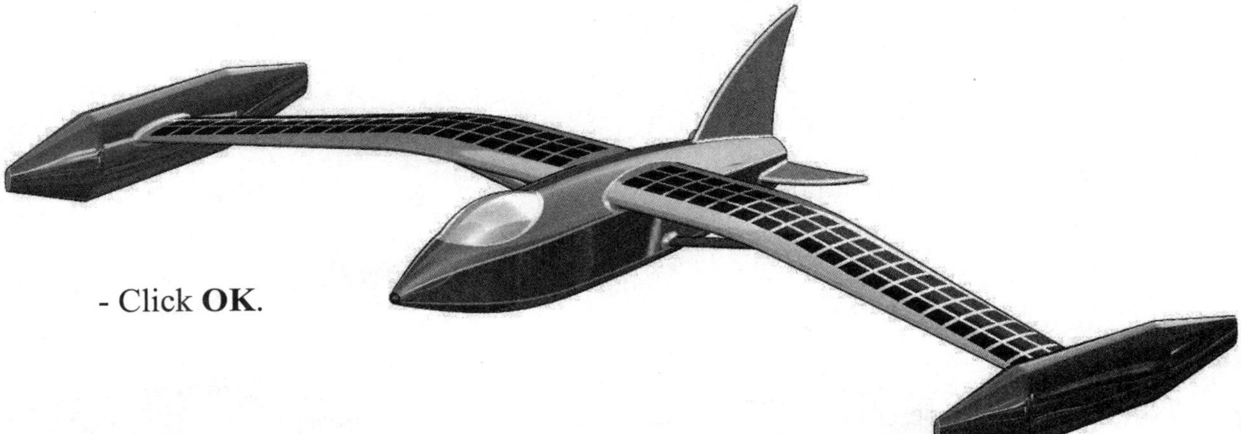

- Click **OK**.

- The Tangent edges are removed from the model.

26. Saving your work:

- Select **File / Save As**.

- Enter **Loft and Boundary** for the name of the file.

- Press **Save** and click **Yes** to overwrite the old file if prompted.

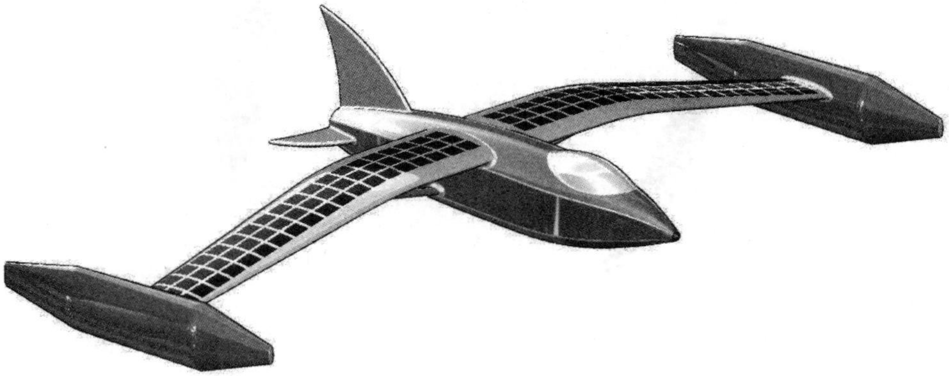

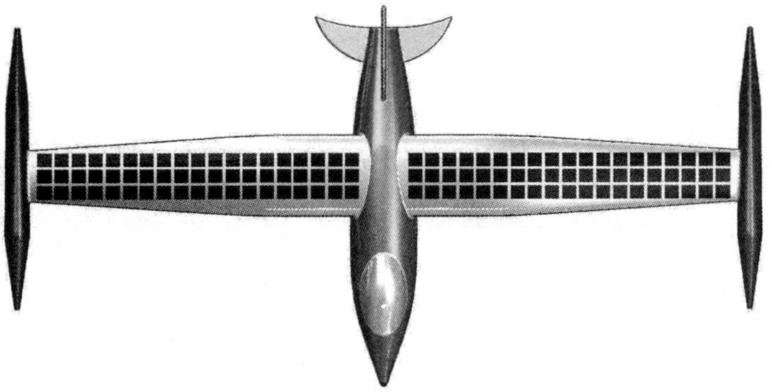

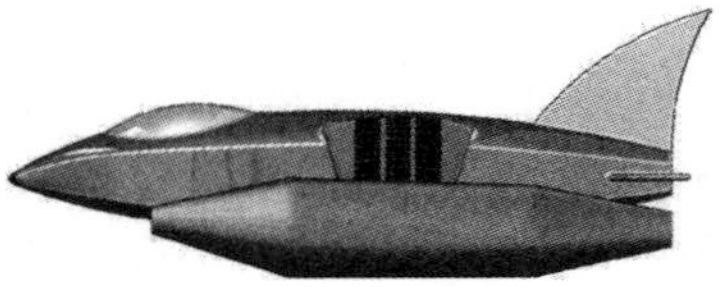

CHAPTER 9

Surfaces & Patches

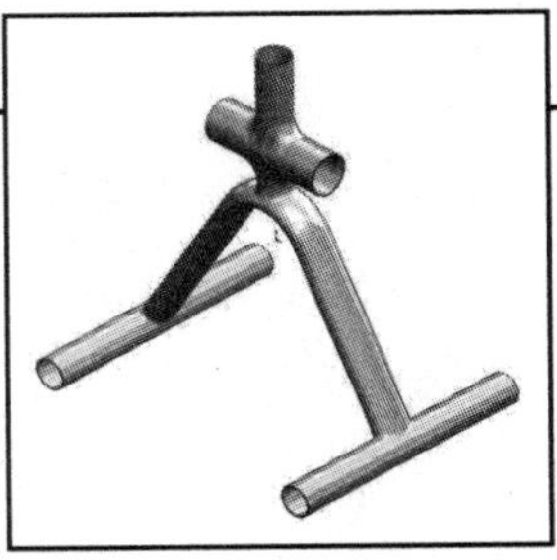

Surfaces & Patches - Overview
Welding Fixture

When creating models in SOLIDWORKS, it is best to combine both Solid and Surfaces tools to develop the geometry.

Solid and Surface bodies are made up of two types of entities: Geometry and Topology.

* Geometry describes shape, flat or curved.

* Topology describes relationships such as: Which edges form the boundary of which face, or which edges meet at which vertices / endpoints.

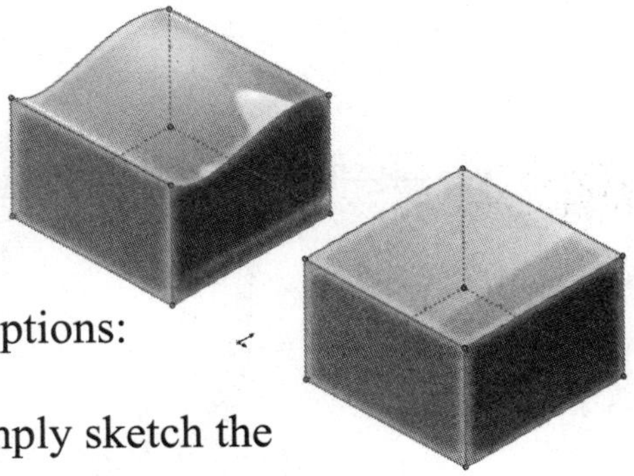

Look at the 2 images on the right, geometrically they have different shapes, but topologically they are identical. Both are composed of 6 faces, 12 edges, and 8 vertices.

Creating the surface bodies are very similar to creating the solid bodies but there are some exceptions:

* If you wish to add a cut in a solid body, simply sketch the geometry and extrude-cut it.

* If you wish to cut a surface body, you will need to sketch the geometry and either use the sketch to trim the surface body – or – extrude the sketch as a new surface, and then use it to trim the surface body.

This lesson discusses the use of the surface tools to create the surface bodies, trim, knit and thicken them into a solid body.

Surfaces & Patches
Welding Fixture

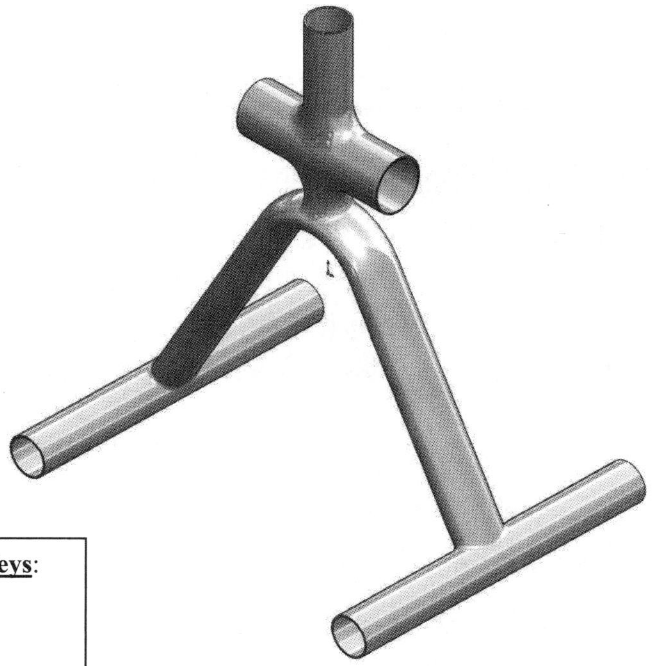

View Orientation Hot Keys:

Ctrl + 1 = Front View
Ctrl + 2 = Back View
Ctrl + 3 = Left View
Ctrl + 4 = Right View
Ctrl + 5 = Top View
Ctrl + 6 = Bottom View
Ctrl + 7 = Isometric View
Ctrl + 8 = Normal To Selection

Dimensioning Standards: **ANSI**

Units: **INCHES** – 3 Decimals

Tools Needed:

Extruded Surface	Swept Surface	Lofted Surface
Boundary Surface	Trim Surface	Filled Surface
Fillet	Thicken Surface	Section View

1. Opening a part document:

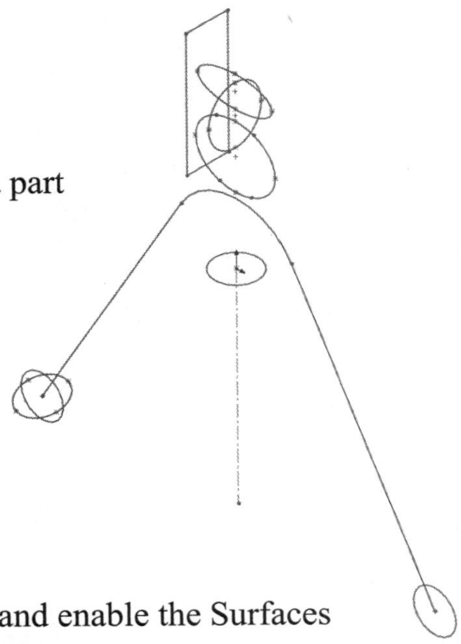

- Select **File / Open**.

- Browse to the Training Files location and open a part document named: **Surfaces & Patches.sldprt**.

- The sketches have been previously created to help focus on the main topics: Surfaces and Patches.

2. Creating a swept surface:

- Right click either the Sketch or the Features tab and enable the Surfaces tool tab.

- Select the **Swept Boss/Base** from the Surfaces tool tab (arrow).

- For Sweep Profile, select the **Sketch2** from the Feature tree (arrow).

- For Sweep Path, select the **Sketch1** also from the Feature tree (arrow).

- Click **OK**.

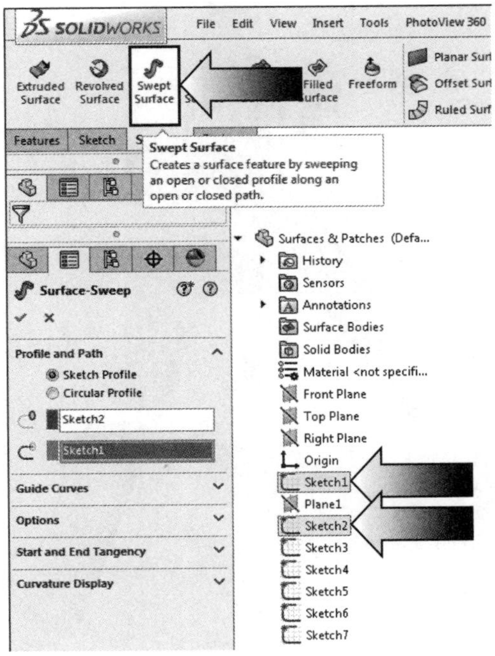

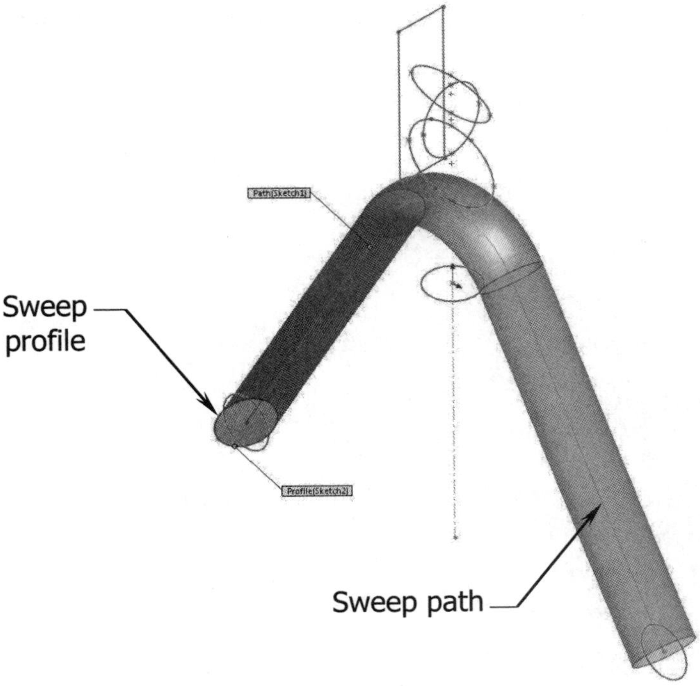

3. Creating the 1st extruded surface:

- Select the **Sketch3** from the FeatureManager tree, click **Extruded Surface** .

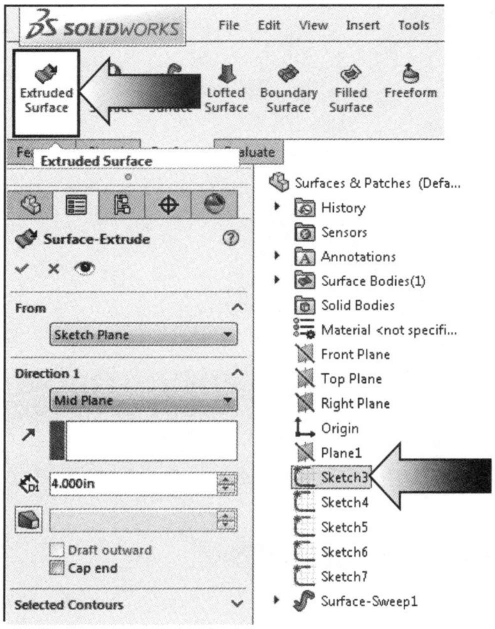

- Select the **Mid Plane** extrude type.

- Enter **4.00in.** for extrude depth.

- Click **OK**.

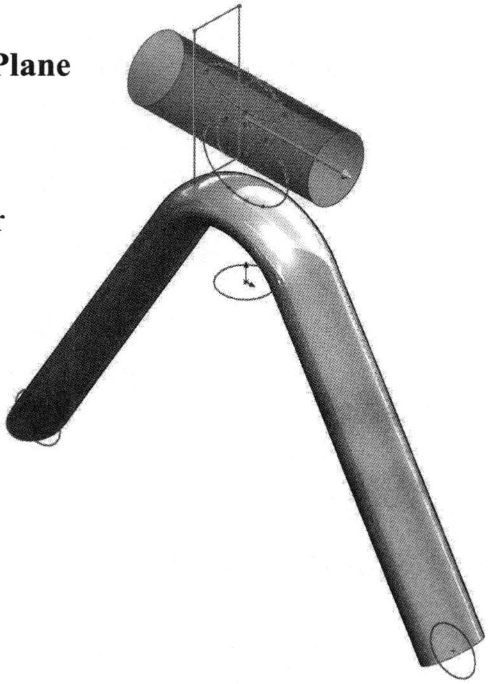

4. Creating the 2nd extruded surface:

- Select the **Sketch4** and click the **Extruded Surface** command  once again.

- Select the **Blind** type and enter the depth of **6.500in**.

- Click **OK**.

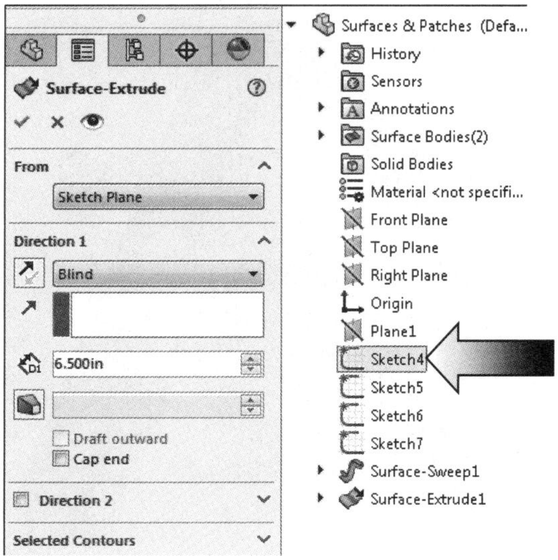

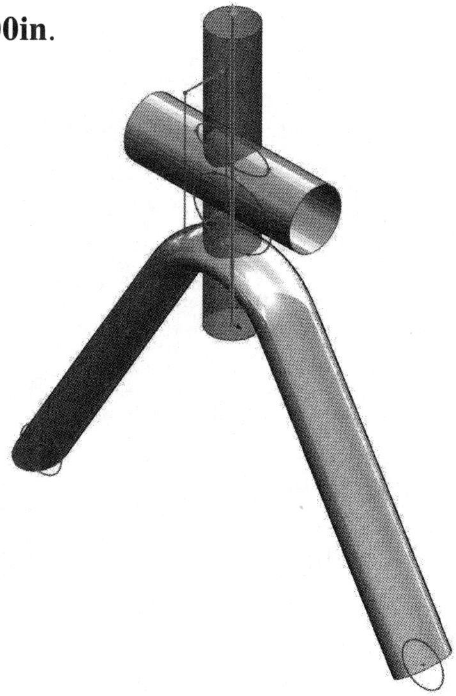

5. Creating the 3rd extruded surface:

- Select the **Sketch5** from the Feature tree and click **Extruded Surface**  .

- Select the **Mid Plane** type and a depth of **8.00in**.

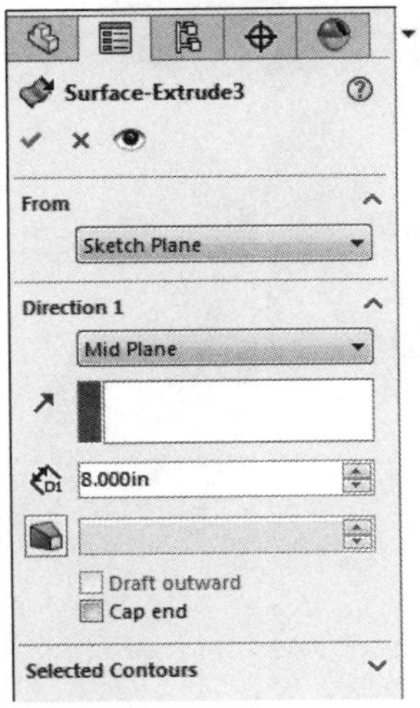

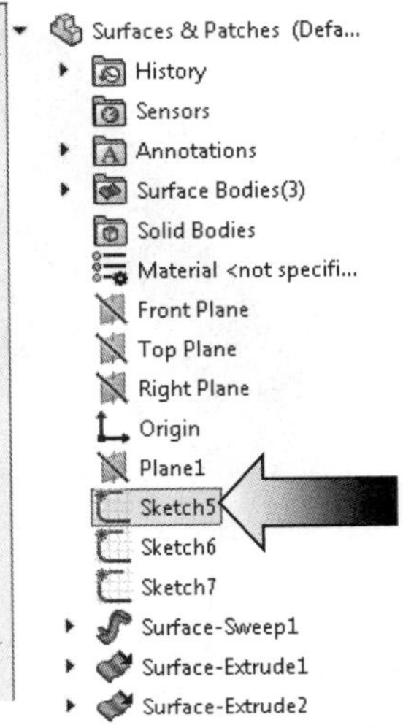

- Click **OK**.

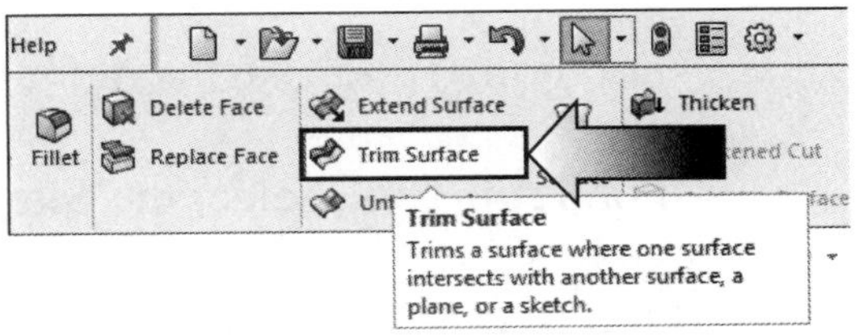

6. Creating the 1st trimmed surface:

- Select the **Trim-Surface** command from the Surfaces tool tab (arrow).

- For Trim Type, select **Standard Trim**.

- For Trim Tool, select the **Sketch6** from the Feature tree.

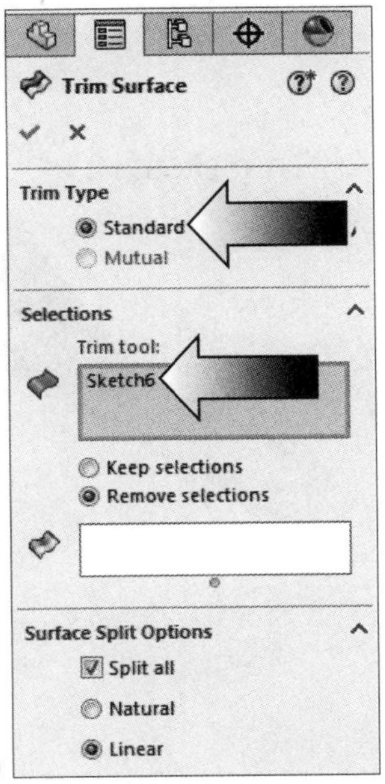

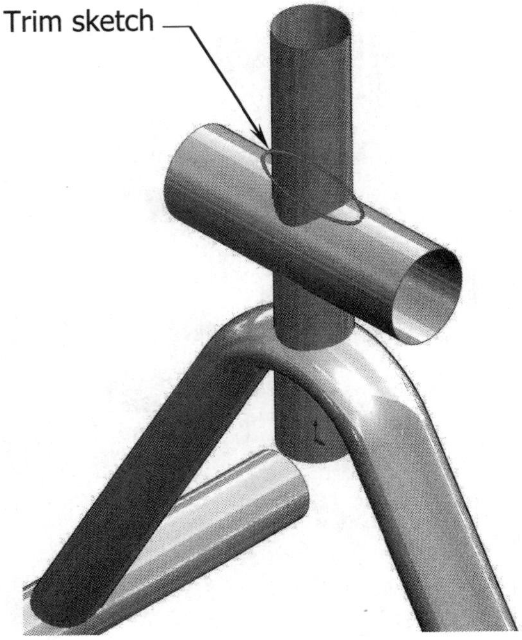

(more settings on next page…)

- Click the **Keep Selections** option (arrow).

- Select the **2 Extruded Surfaces** to keep (arrow).

- Click the **Natural** option (arrow).

- Click **OK**.

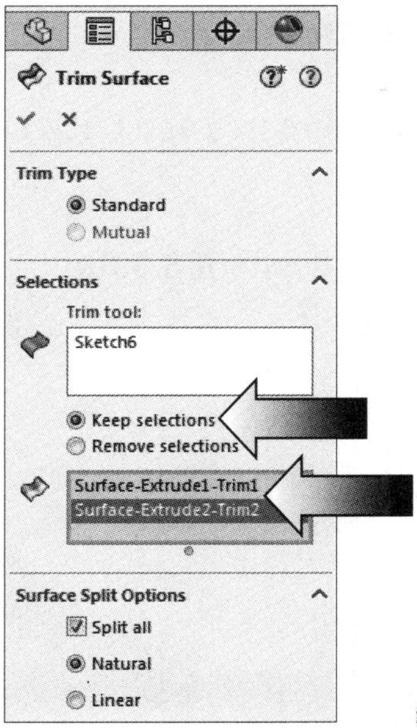

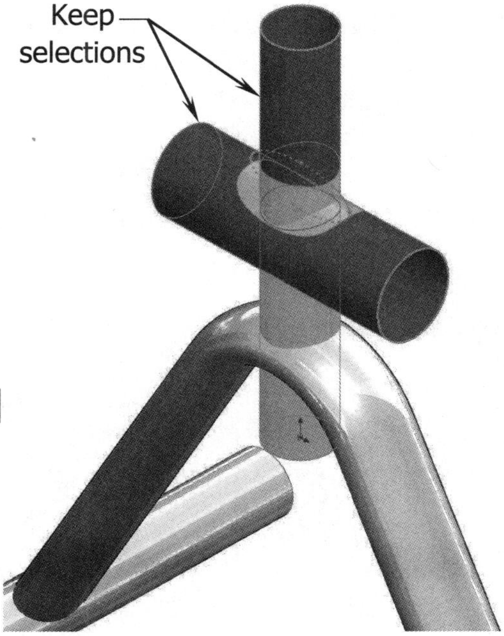

7. Creating the 2nd trimmed surface:

- Click the **Trim Surface** command  once again.

- For Trim Type, use the default **Standard Trim** option.

- For Trim Tool, select the **Sketch7** from the Feature tree.

(more settings on next page…)

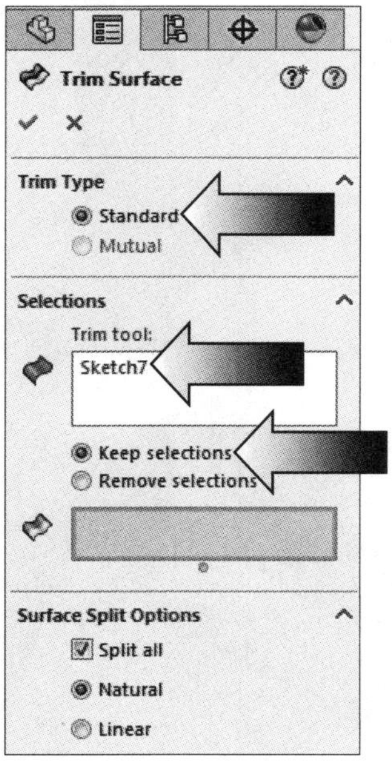

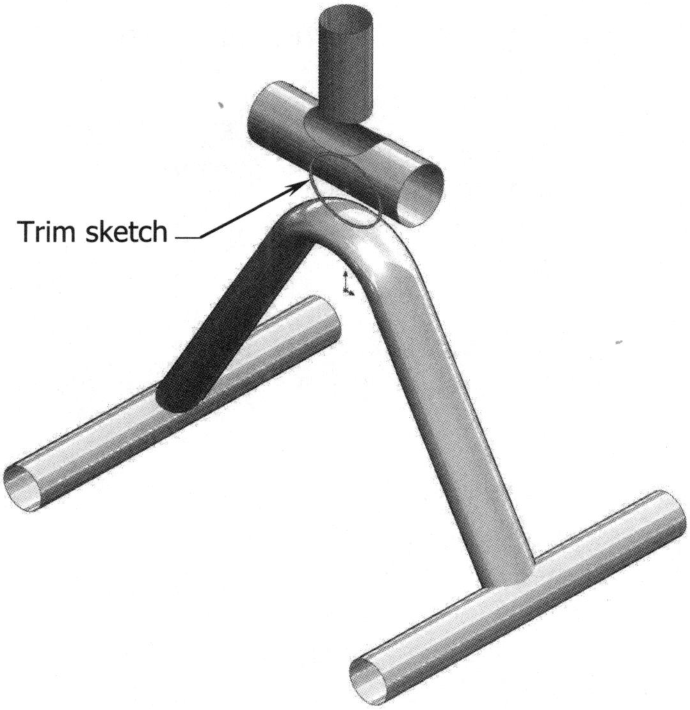

- Click the **Keep Selections** option (arrow).

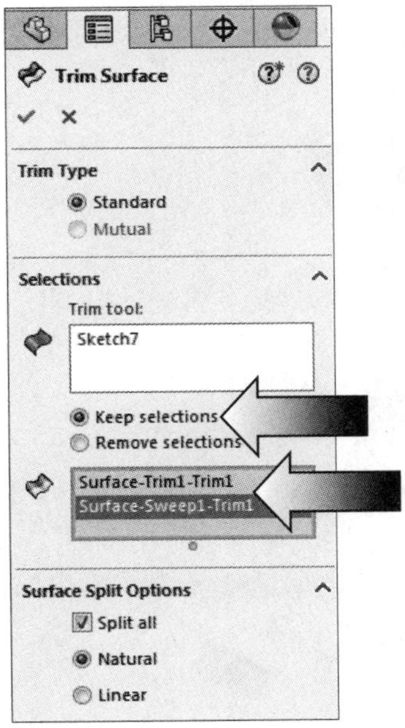

- Select the **2 surfaces** as indicated.

- Keep the Surface Split Options at **Natural**.

- Click **OK**.

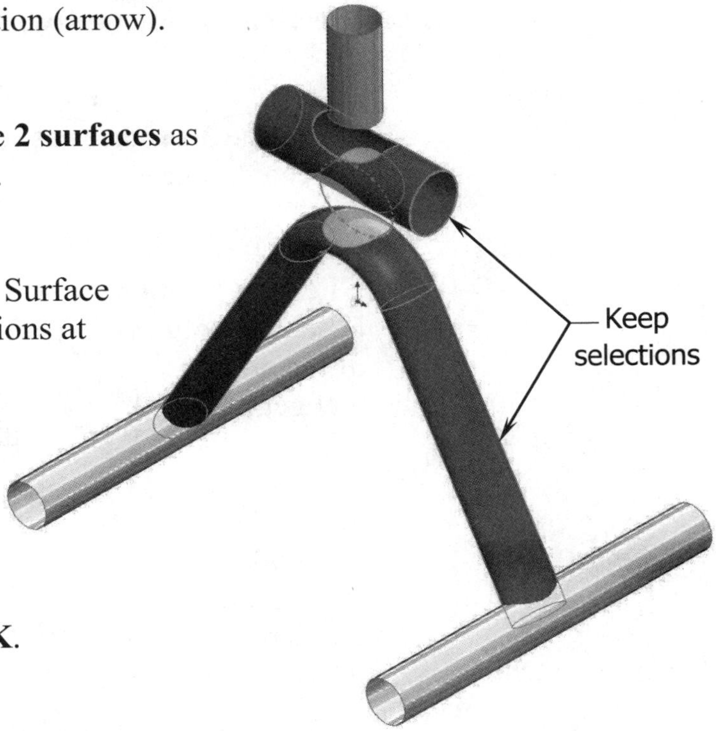

8. Creating the 3rd trimmed surface:

- Click the **Trim Surface** command again.

- For Trim Type, select the **Mutual** option (arrow).

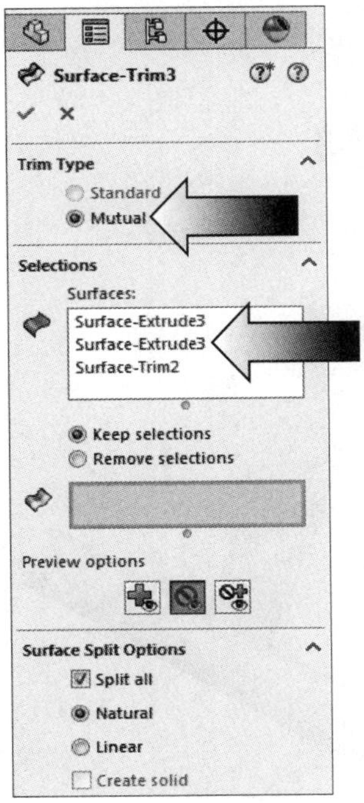

- For Surfaces Selections, select the **3 surfaces** as noted.

(More settings on next page…)

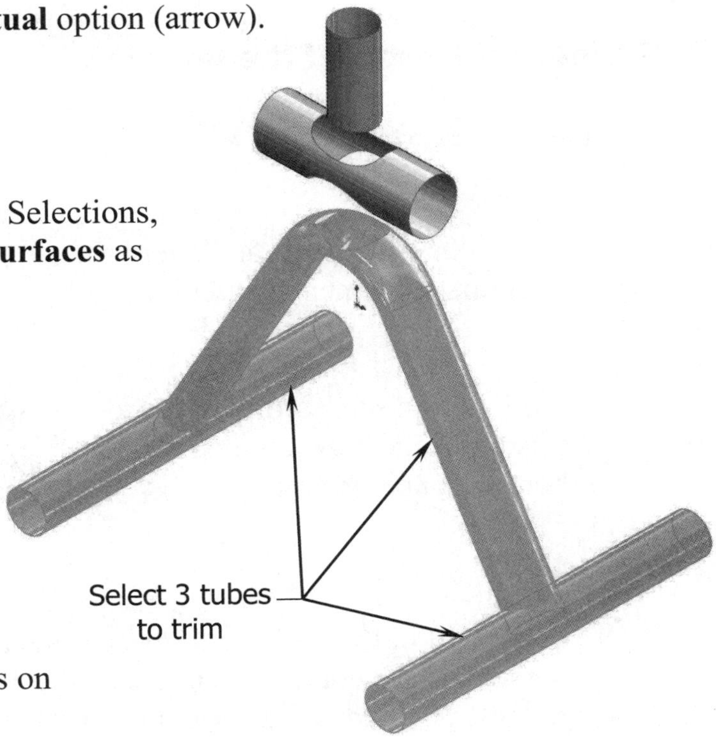

- Click the **Keep Selections** option (arrow).

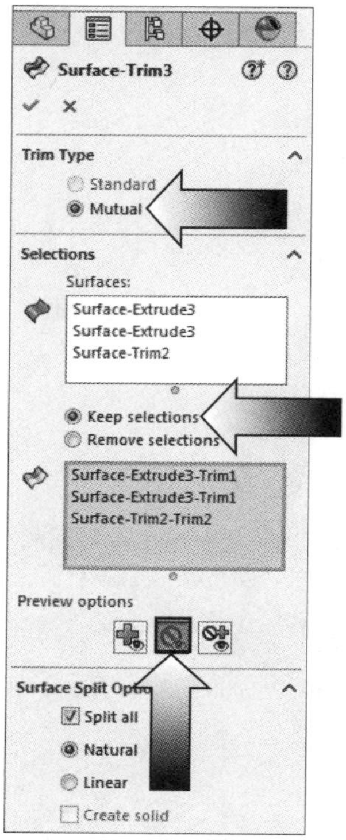

- Select the **3 surfaces** as indicated to keep.

- Click the * button to see the preview of the portions that get removed.

- Keep the **Natural** split option enabled.

- Click **OK**.

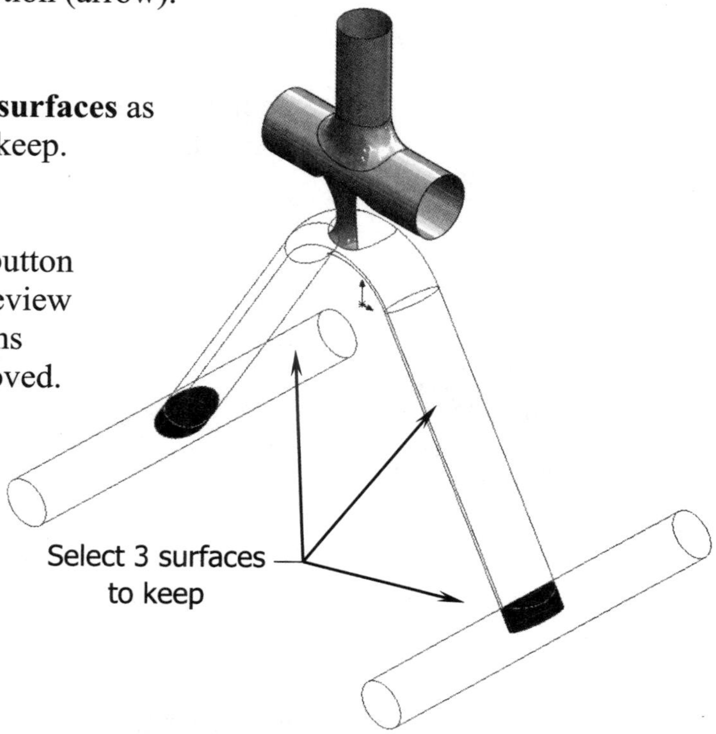

9. Saving the 1st half of the lesson:

- Click **File / Save As**.

- Use the same file name and overwrite the original document when prompted.

* The 1st half of the lesson discussed the use of some basic methods for creating and trimming the surfaces.

* The 2nd half of the lesson will discuss the use of different surface commands to create the 4-sided patches to fill some of the openings in the model.

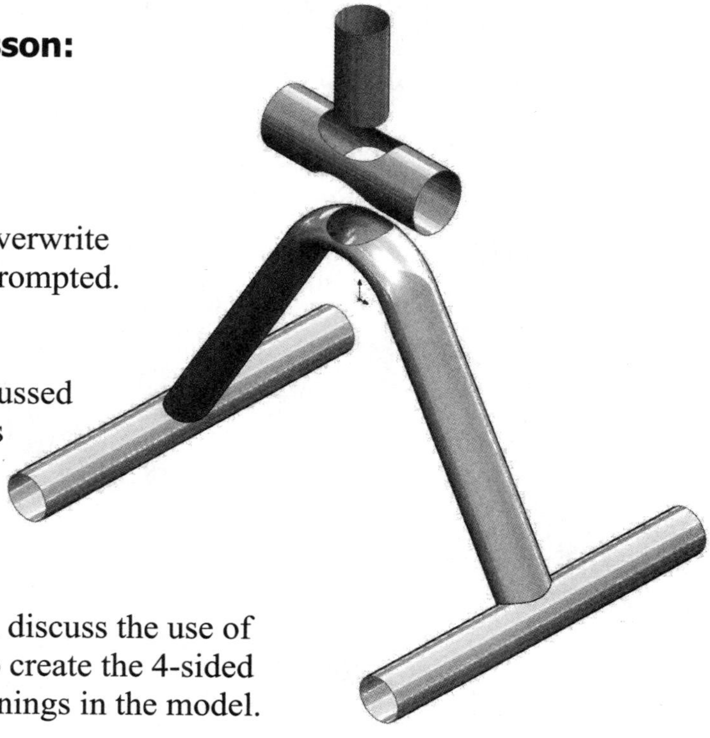

10. Creating a lofted surface:

- Click the **Lofted Surface** command  from the surfaces tool tab.

- For Loft Profiles, select the **2 edges** near the centers of the 2 surfaces as noted.

> **Lofted Surface**
>
> A Lofted Surface is created by making transitions between two or more profiles, and guided by guide curves.

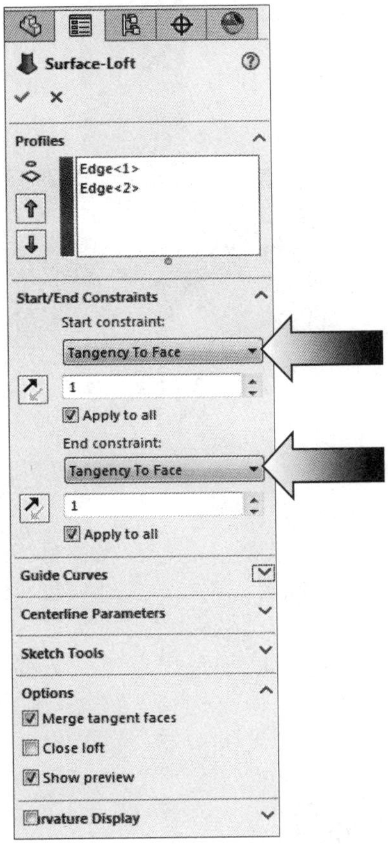

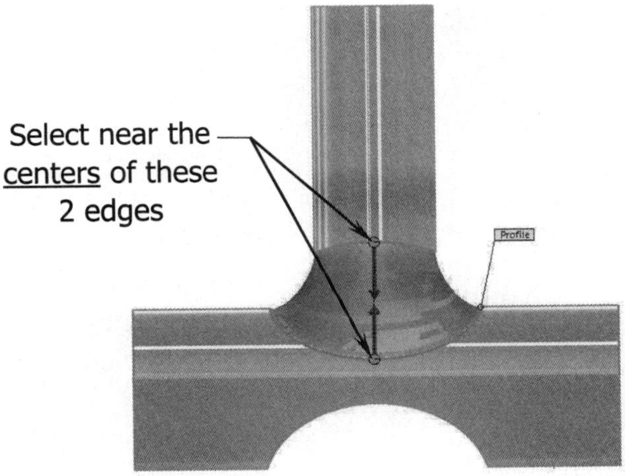

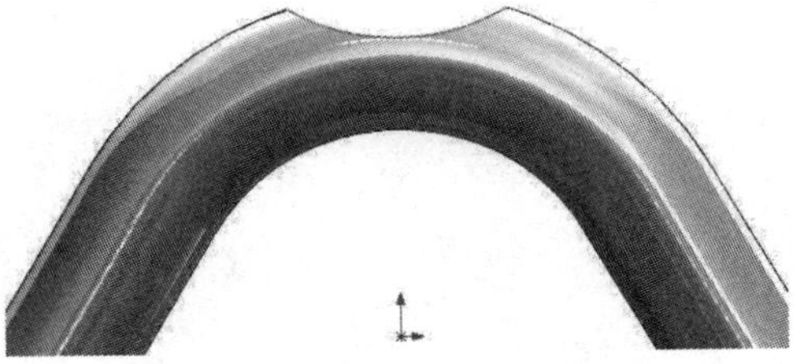

- Expand the Start/End Constraints section and select **Tangent To Face** for both directions (arrow).

- Keep the **Tangent Weight** at their default value of 1. Enable the **Apply To All** check boxes for both directions.

- Click **OK**.

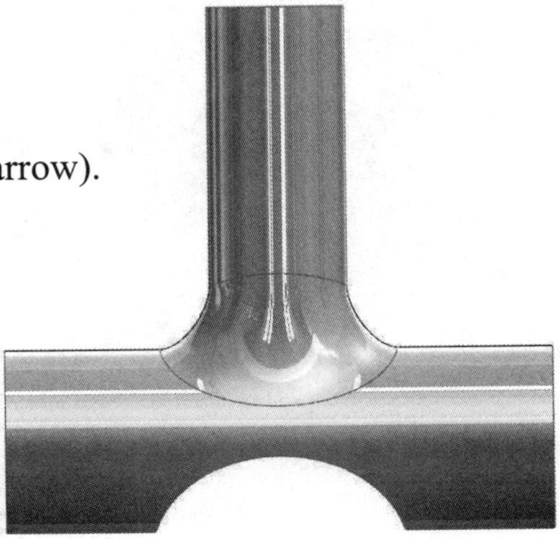

11. Creating the 1st boundary surface:

- Click the Boundary **Surface command**  from the Surfaces tool tab, and change to the Front orientation (Ctrl+1).

> **Boundary Surface**
>
> Boundary Surface uses 2 or more profiles and curves in two directions to define the boundary.

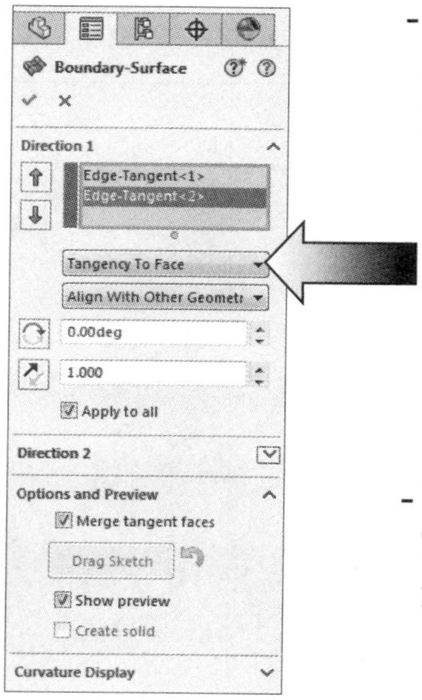

- For Direction 1, select the **2 edges** near the ends to prevent twisting.

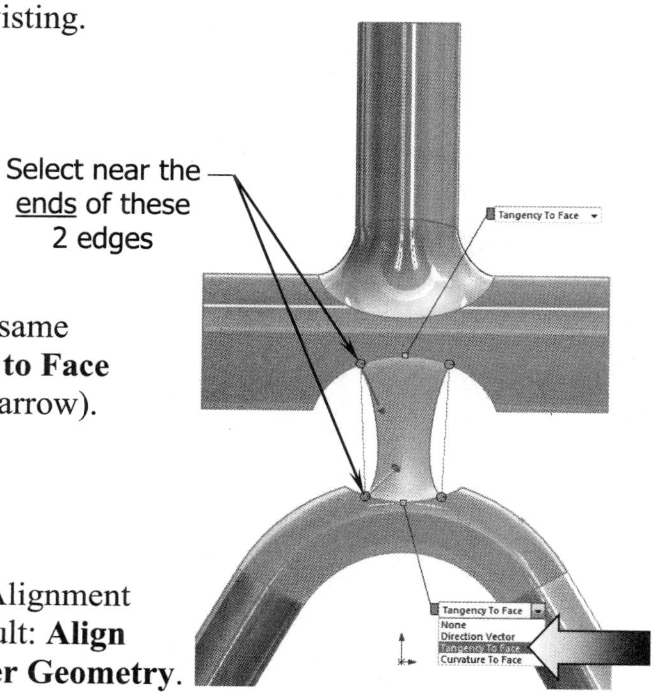

- Select the same **Tangency to Face** for edges (arrow).

- Keep the Alignment at the default: **Align With Other Geometry**.

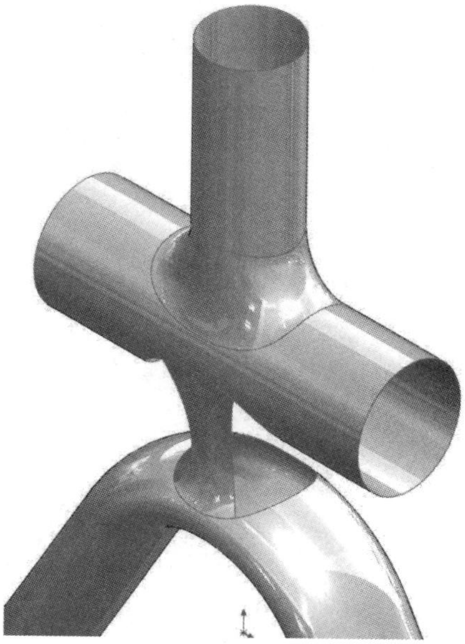

- Keep the Tangent Weight at the default value of **1** for both edges.

- Enable **Apply to All** for both edges.

- Click **OK**.

12. Creating the 2nd boundary surface:

- Click the **Boundary Surface** command from the Surfaces tool tab, and change to the Back orientation (Ctrl+2).

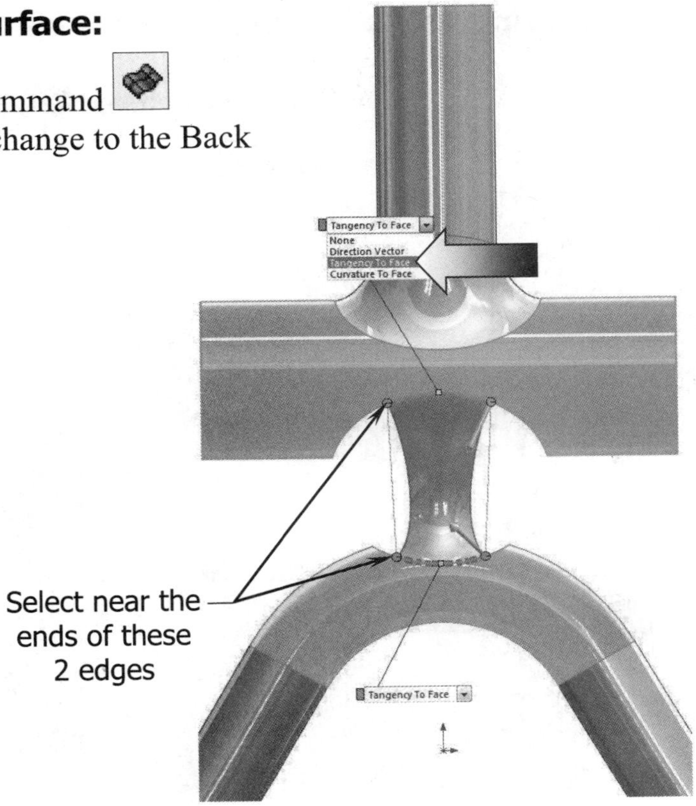

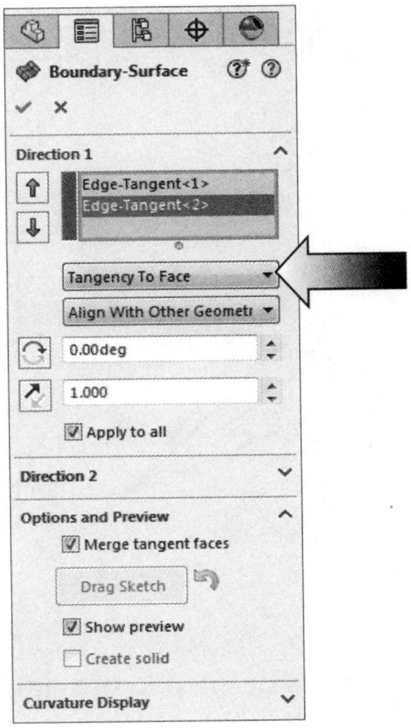

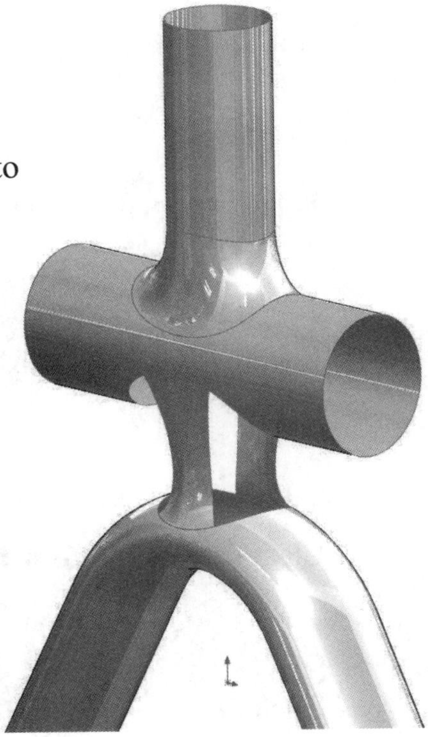

- For Direction 1, select the **2 edges**, near the ends to prevent twisting.

- Select the same **Tangency to Face** for both edges (arrow).

- Keep all other settings at their default values.

- Click **OK**.

13. Creating the 1st filled surface:

- Click the **Filled Surface** command  from the Surfaces tool tab.

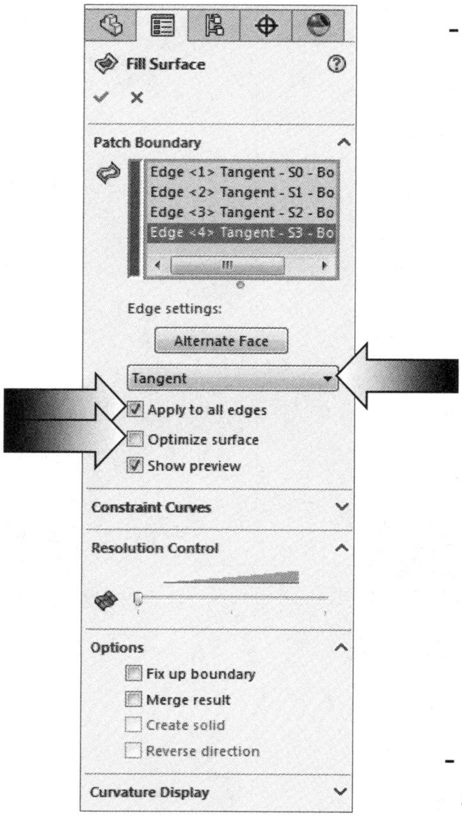

- Select the **4 edges** on the right side of the opening.

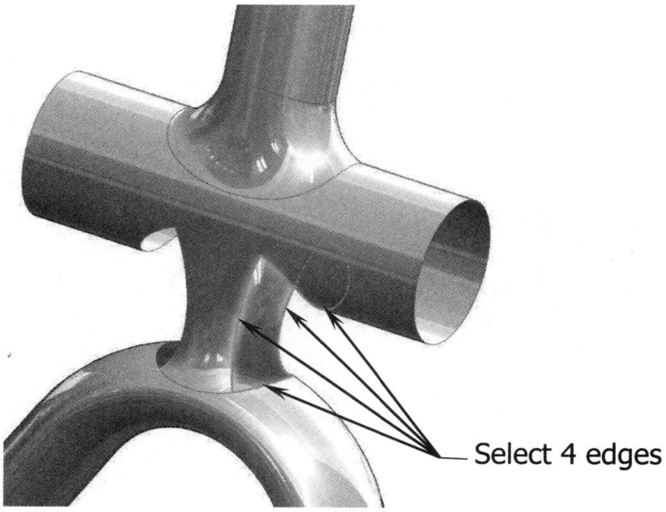

- When a closed boundary is defined, a preview mesh appears showing a patch surface is being generated.

- Select **Tangent** from the list (arrow).

- Enable the **Apply to All Edges** checkbox.

- Clear the **Optimize surface** checkbox.

- Click **OK**.

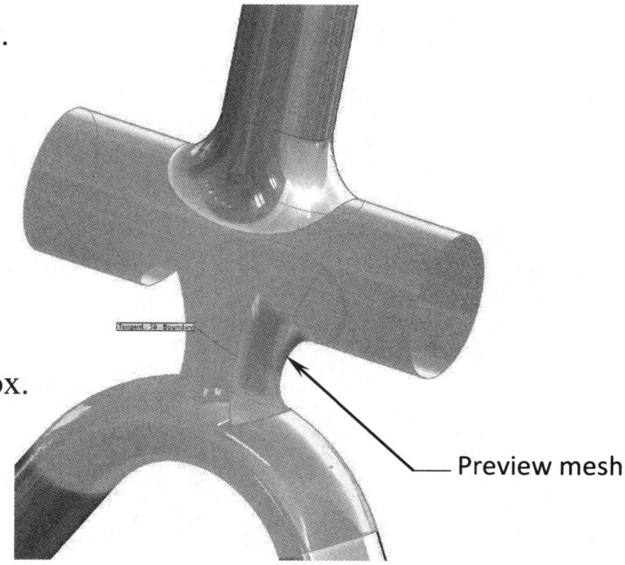

14. Creating the 2nd filled surface:

- Click the **Filled Surface** command  from the Surfaces tool tab.

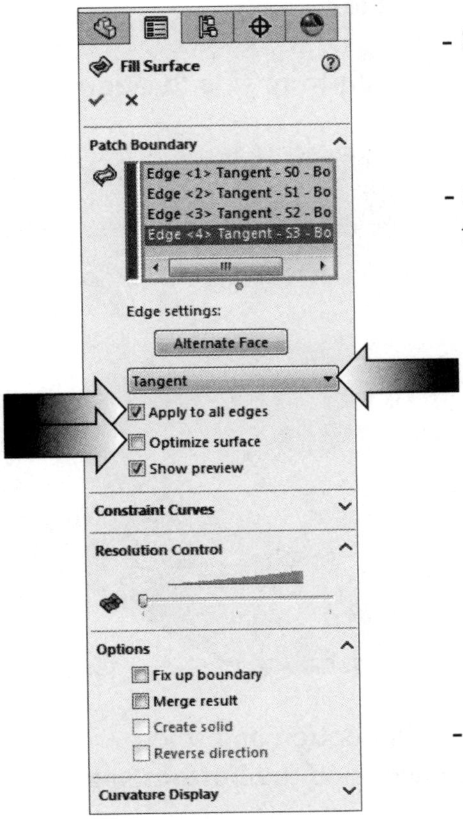

- Select the **4 edges** on the left side of the opening.

- Select **Tangent** from the list (arrow).

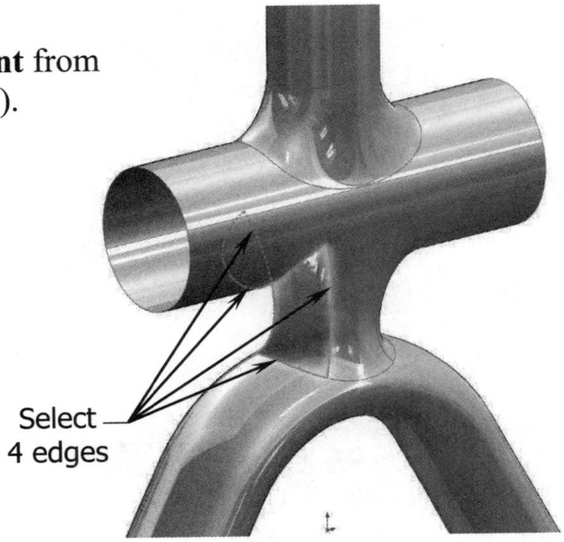

- Enable the **Apply to All Edges** checkbox.

- <u>Clear</u> the **Optimize surface** checkbox.

- Click **OK**.

- The opening is now filled with a 4-sided patch.

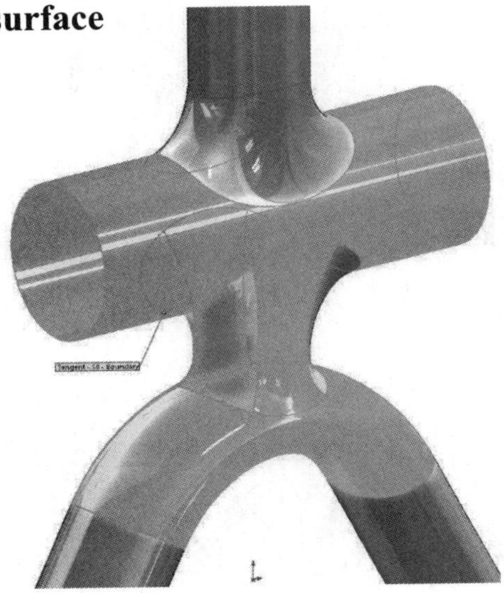

15. Creating a face fillet:

- Switch to the Features tool tab and click the **Fillet** command .

- Add a **Constant Radius Size** of **.125"** to the edge shown.

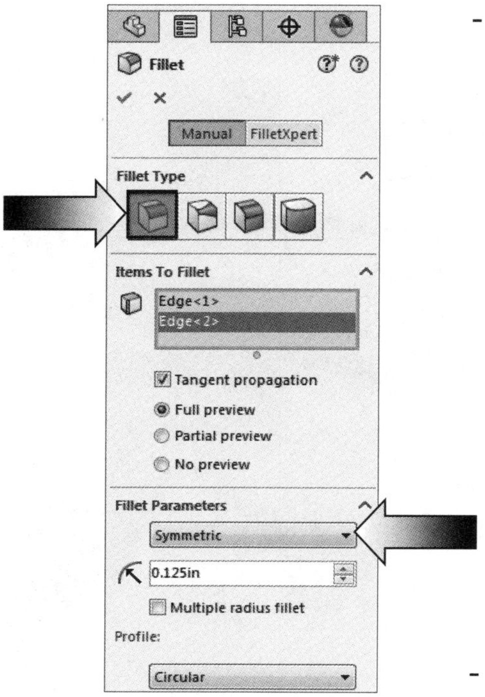

- Notice the "uneven" width from side to side?

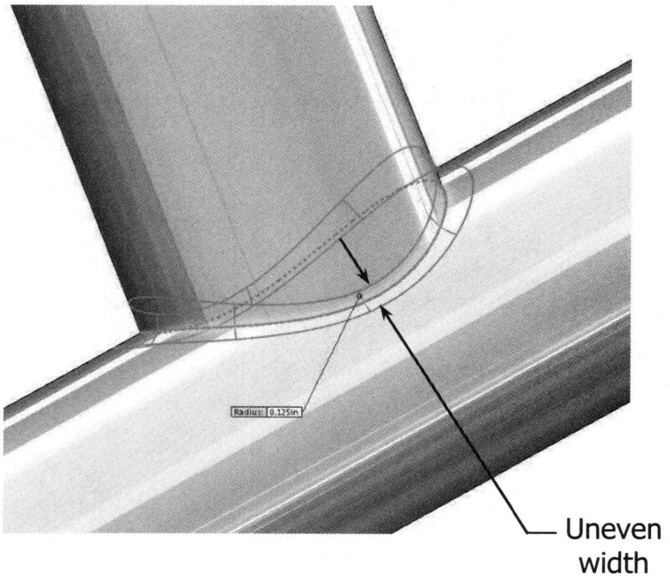

- Change to the Face Fillet option and select the **top surface** for Face1 and the **bottom surface** for Face2.

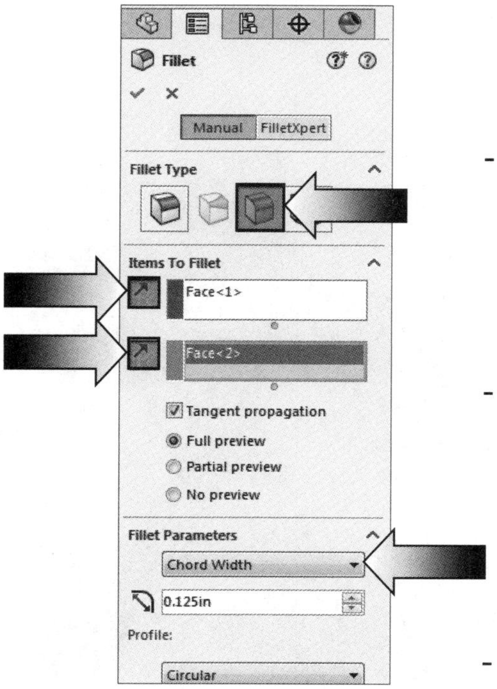

- Set all the parameters as shown.

- Notice an even width all around?

- Click **OK**.

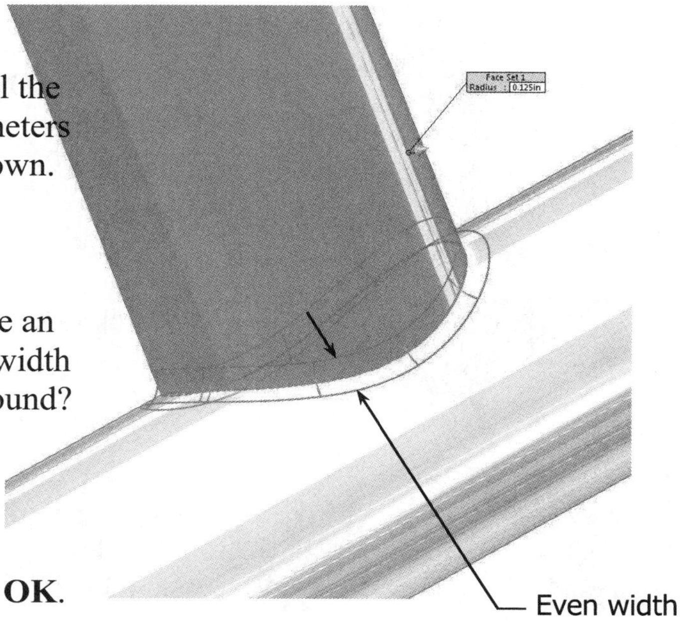

- The completed Surface-Model.

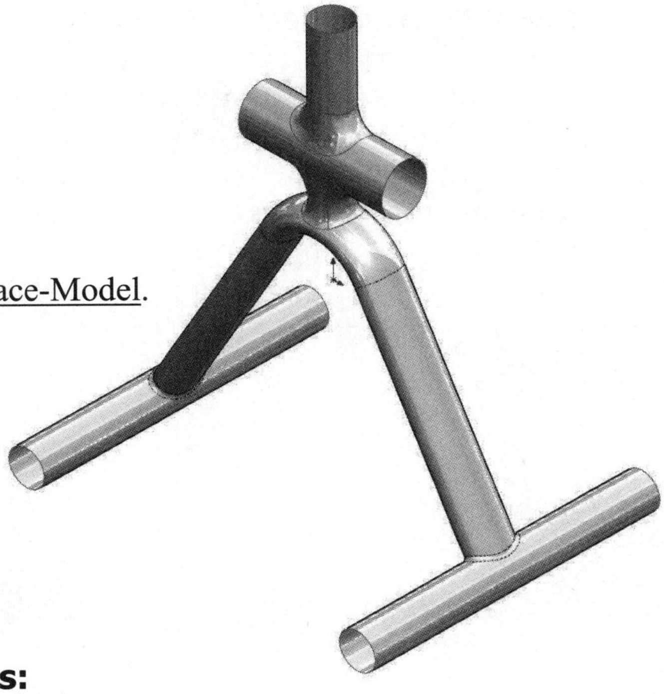

16. Knitting all surfaces:

- Select the **Knit Surface** command.

- Change to the **Surfaces** tool tab.

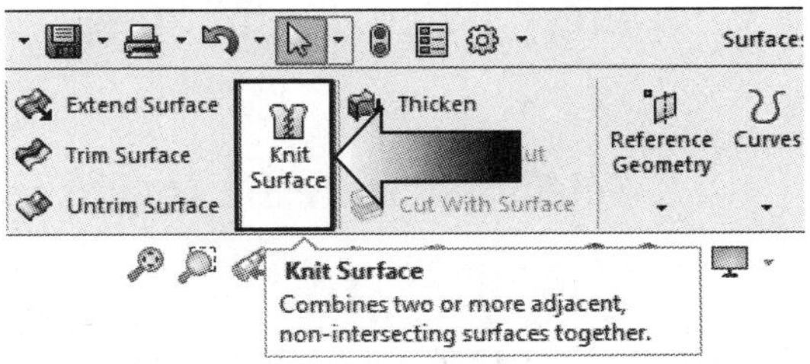

- Select **all surfaces** from the graphics area. (Make sure all surfaces are highlighted.)

- Enable the Merge Entities checkbox.

- Click **OK**.

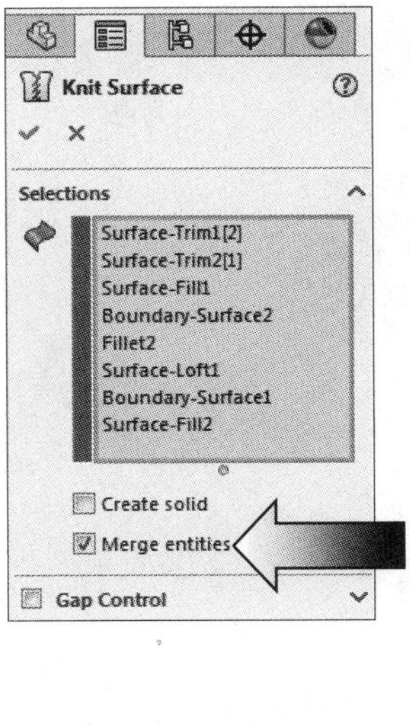

17. Thickening the surface model:

- Click the **Thicken** command .

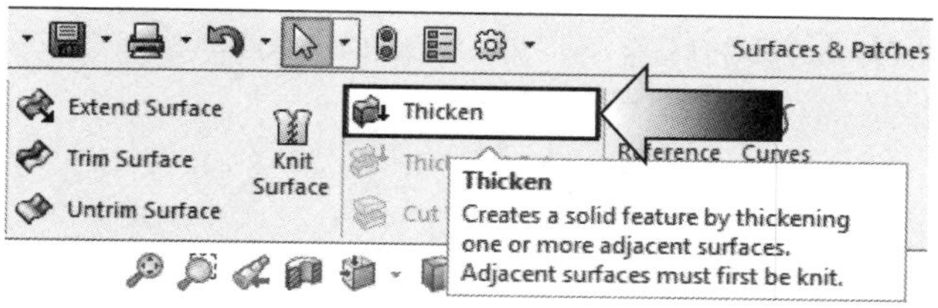

- Select the model from the graphics area.

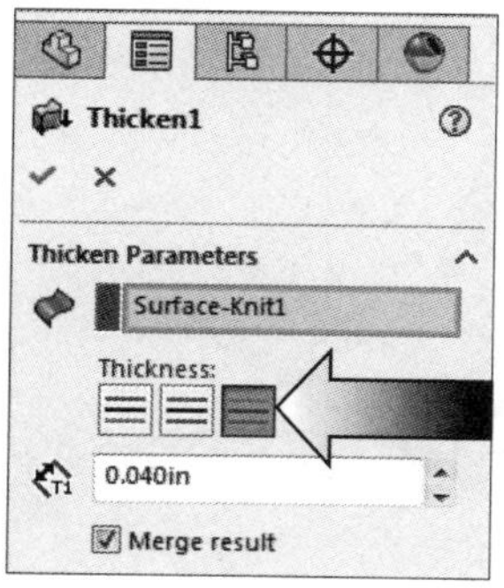

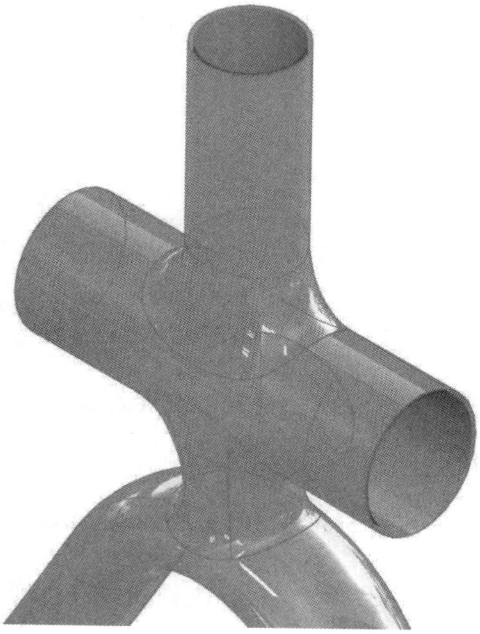

- Enter **.040in**. for thickness.

- Select the **Material Inside** option (arrow).

- Click **OK**.

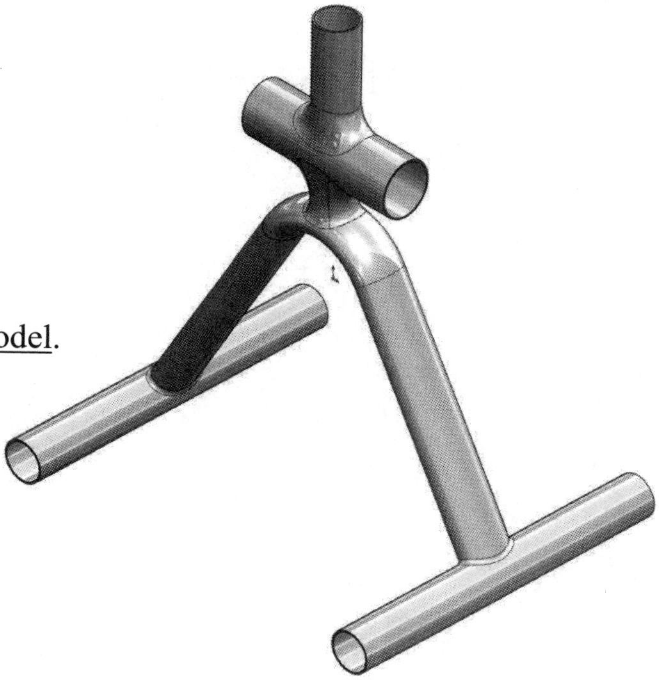

- The completed Solid-Model.

18. Creating a section view:

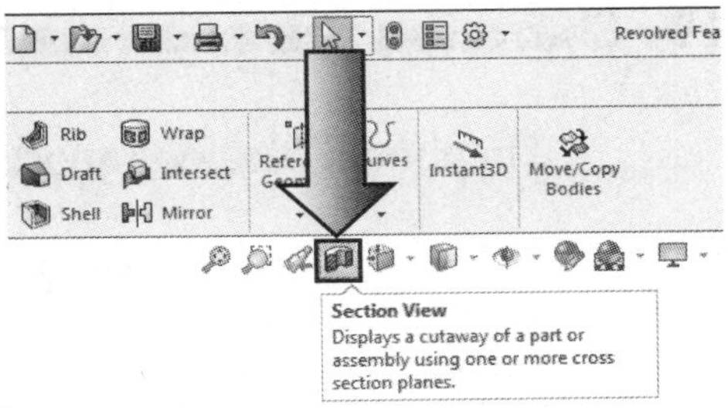

- Click the **Section View** command from the View (Heads-Up) toolbar (arrow).

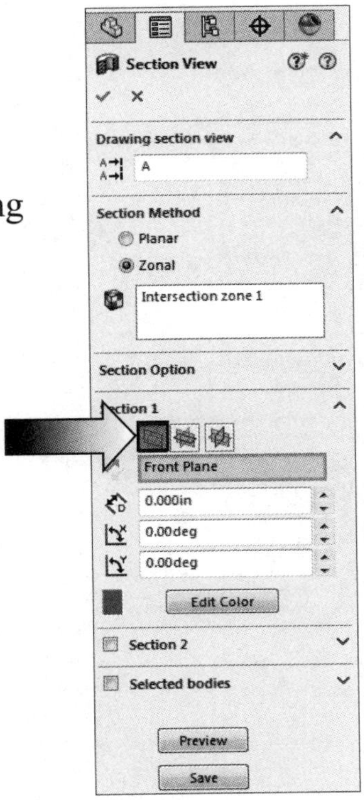

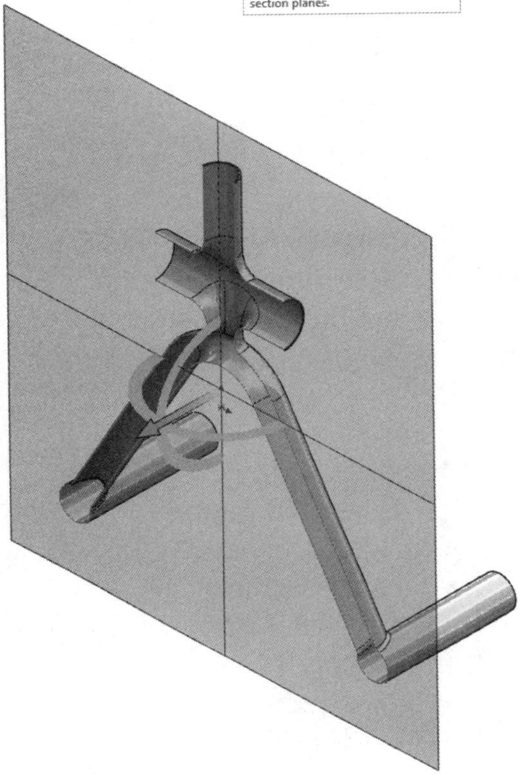

- Select the **Front** plane as the cutting plane.

- Keep the section location at Zero (default).

- The preview graphics show a half section of the model.

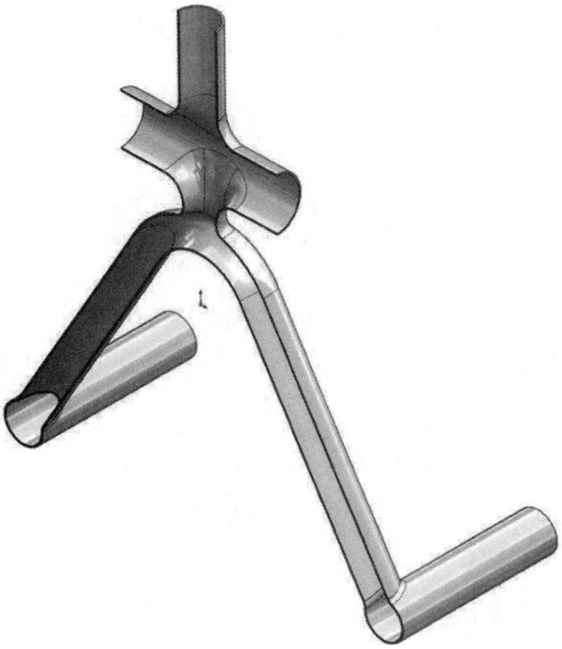

- The red color is the wall thickness of the solid model.

- Click off the section view command to return to the full view.

19. Changing the edge display:

- The model can look more realistic simply by changing the edge display.

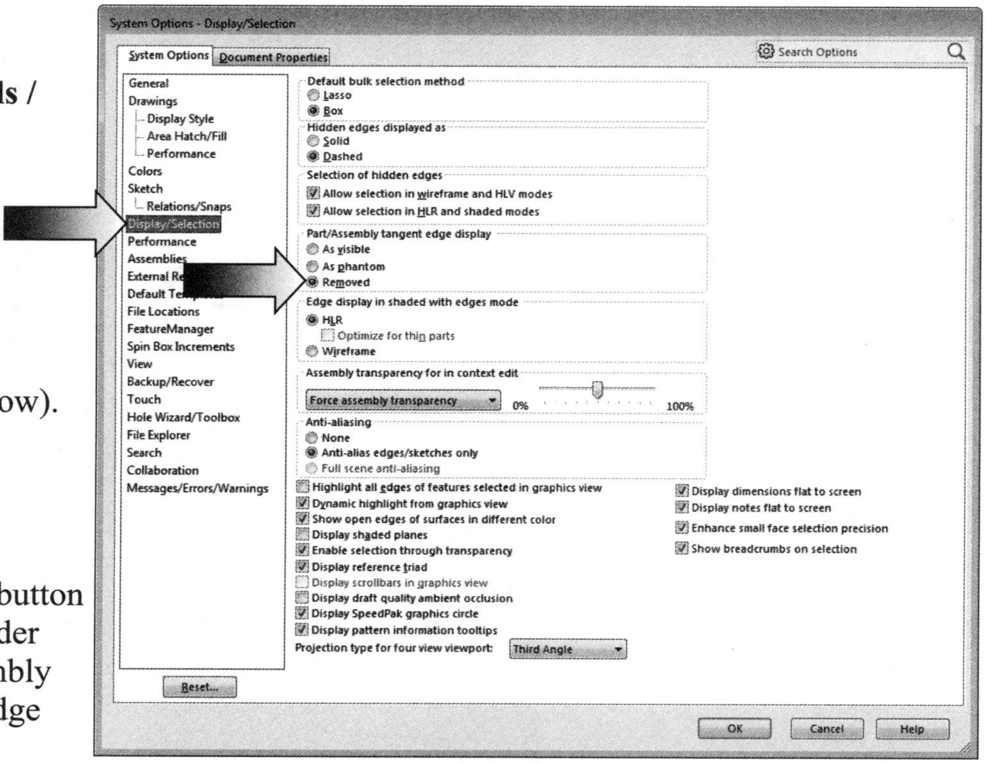

- Click **Tools / Options**.

- Select the **Display / Selection** option (arrow).

- Click the **Removed** button (arrow) under Part/Assembly Tangent Edge Display.

- Click **OK**.

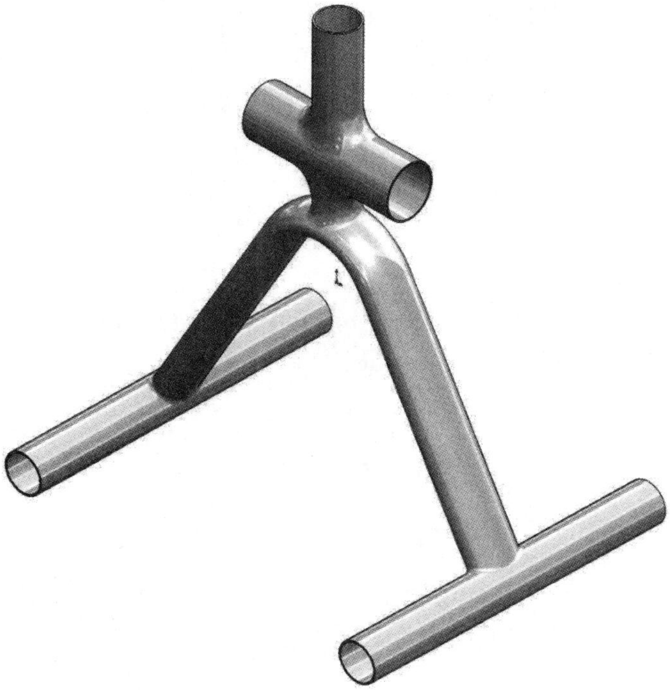

20. Saving your work:

- Select **File / Save As**.

- Keep the same file name and overwrite the previous document when prompted.

- Click **Save**.

CHAPTER 10

Configure Features

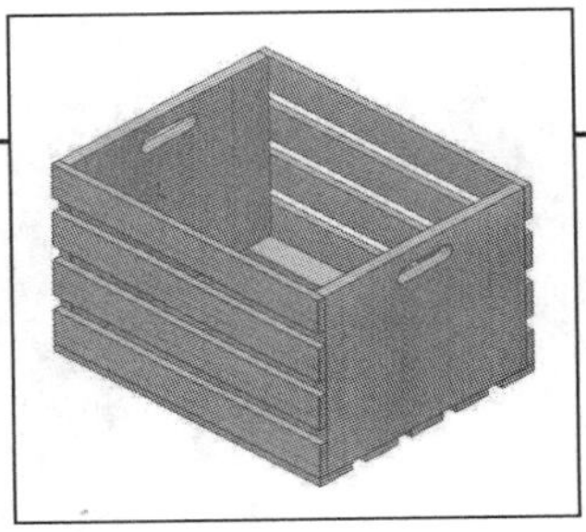

Configure Features - Overview
Wooden Crate

- The Configure Feature uses the Modify Configuration dialog box to create and modify configurations for commonly configured parameters in parts and assemblies.

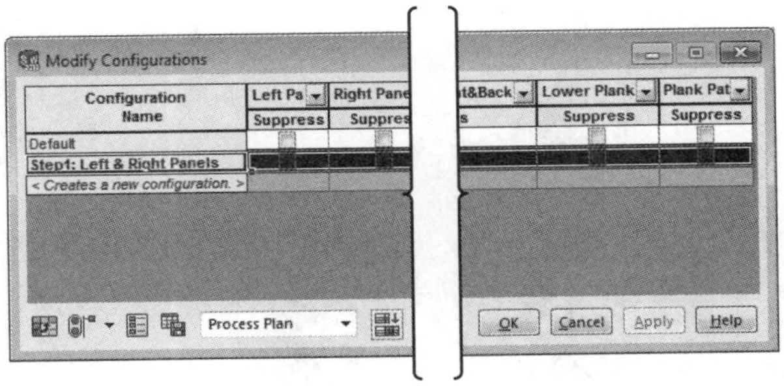

- To create or modify a configuration do one of the following: Right-click an item and select Configure Dimension, Configure Feature, Configure Component, or Configure Material.

- Not all items can be configured in the Modify Configuration dialog box. Valid items to right-click and start Modify Configuration, or to double-click and add to Modify Configuration include:

  * For parts: features, sketches, dimensions, and material.
  * For assemblies: components, assembly features, mates, and dimensions of assembly features and mates.

- The Modify Configuration dialog box lists the Configurations of the model in one column and configurable parameters in other columns.

- New columns can be added by double-clicking items in the graphics area or FeatureManager design tree. Click at the top of a column to select other parameters of a feature to configure.

- A column can be added for every configured parameter in the model at once by clicking All-Parameters at the bottom of the dialog box.

Wooden Crate
Configure Features

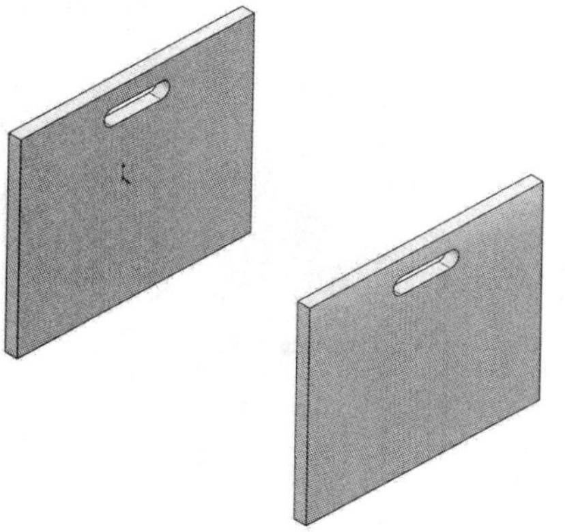

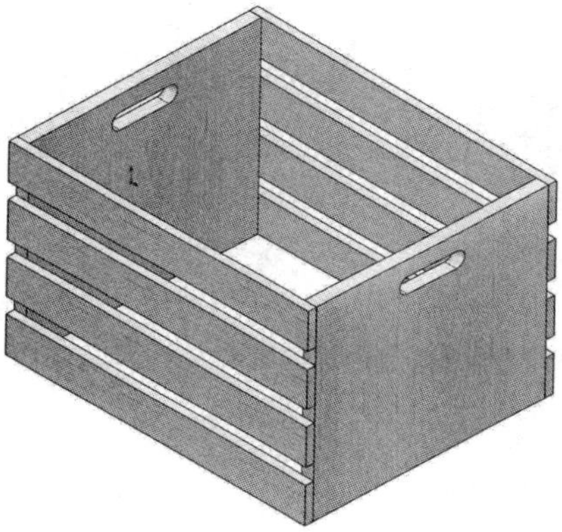

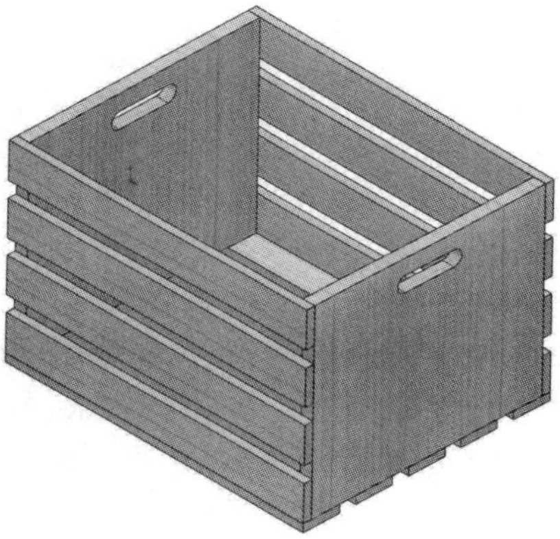

Dimensioning Standards: **ANSI**

Units: **INCHES** – 3 Decimals

Tools Needed:

Modify Configurations   Design Table

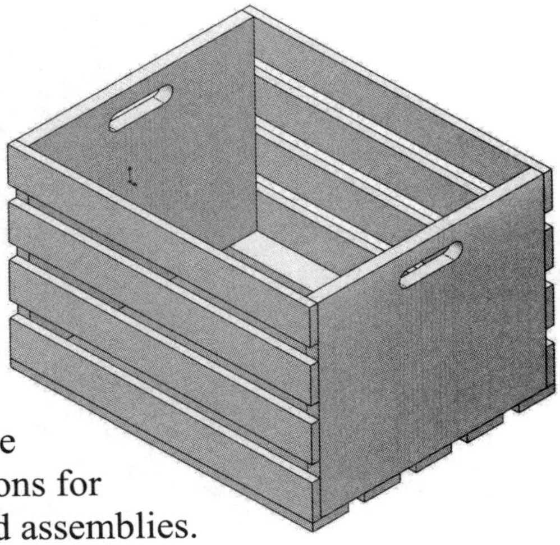

1. Opening a part document:

- Select **File / Open**.

- Locate the part document named: **Configure Features.sldprt** and open it.

2. Configuring features:

- The Configure Feature option provides a table where you can create and modify configurations for commonly configured parameters in parts and assemblies.

- In a part, you can configure dimensions of features and sketches, suppression states of features and sketches, material, and custom properties. Alternatively, you can create and modify configurations manually or with a design table.

- Right click the feature named: **Left Panel** and select **Configure Feature** (arrow).

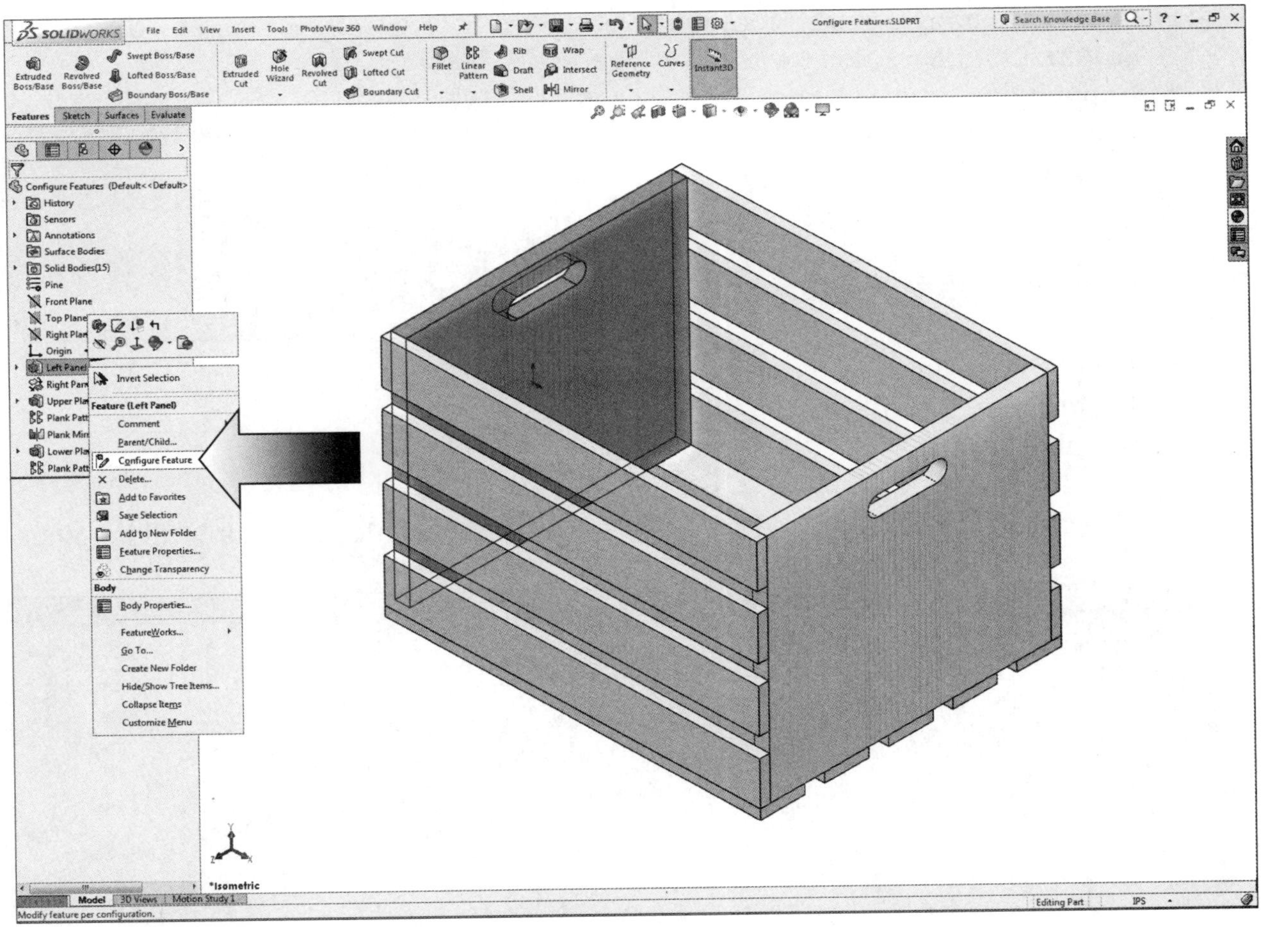

The Modify-Configurations Dialog Box

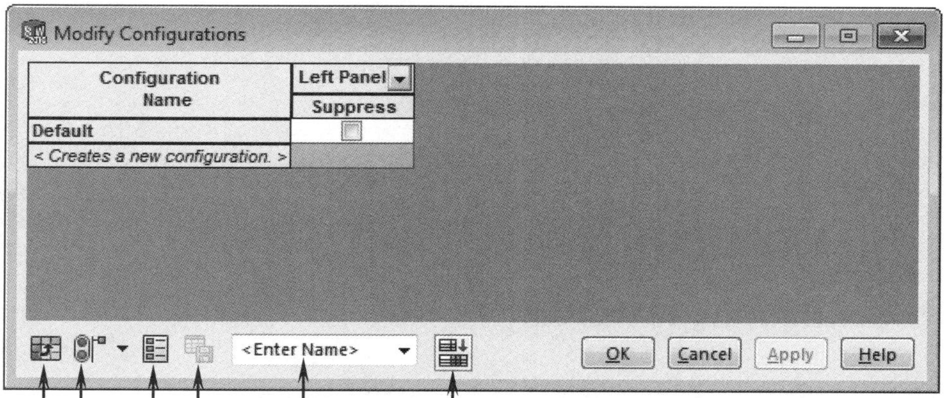

- A new column is created for the feature Left Panel along with a Suppression state checkbox.
  If the checkbox is left blank, the feature will be unsuppressed.

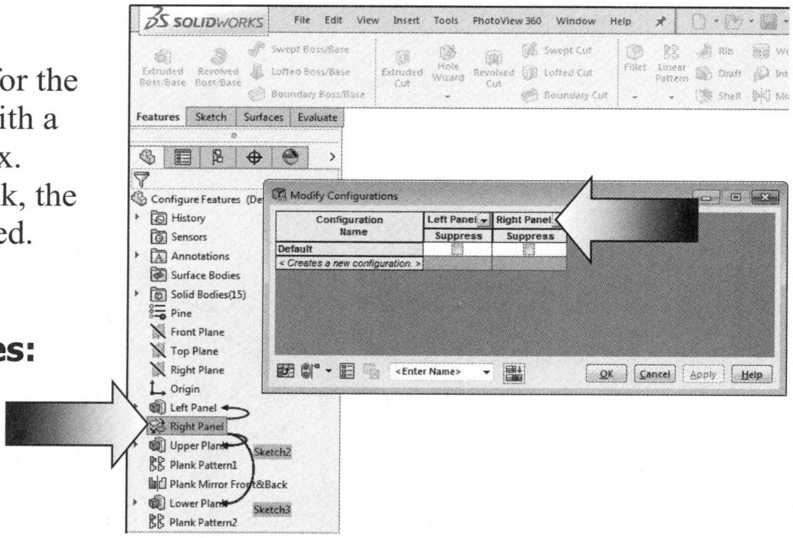

3. Configuring other features:

- Double click on the **Right Panel** to add it to the table (arrow).

- Repeat the same step to add all other features to the table. (7 features all together.)

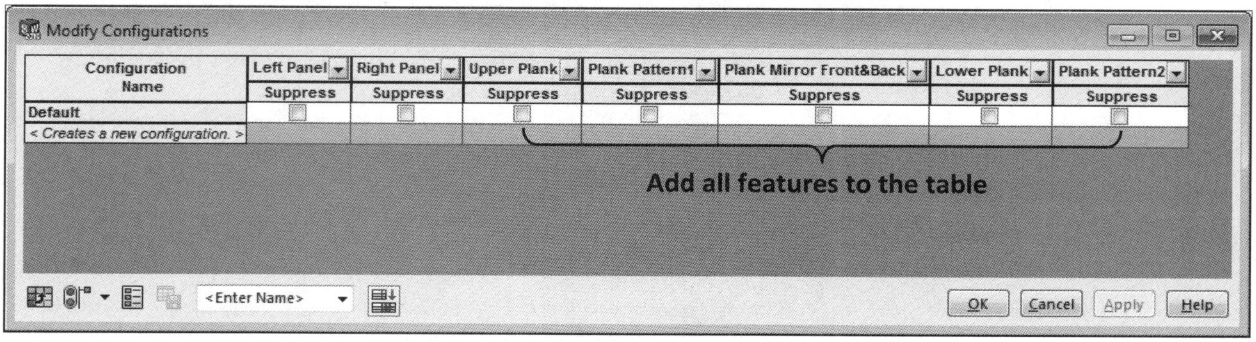

4. Saving the table:

- Enter **Process Plan** as the name of the table and press **Save Table View.**

- As good practice, always click the Save Table View after adding or changing the content of the table.

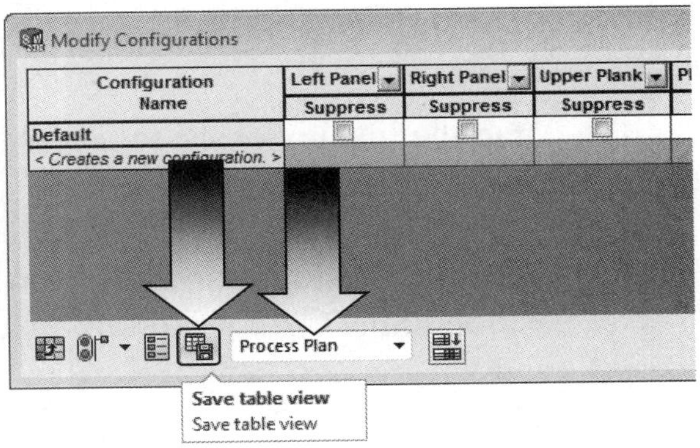

5. Adding new configurations:

- Click in the cell under the Default configuration and enter the name of the new configuration: **Step1: Left & Right Panels** (arrow).

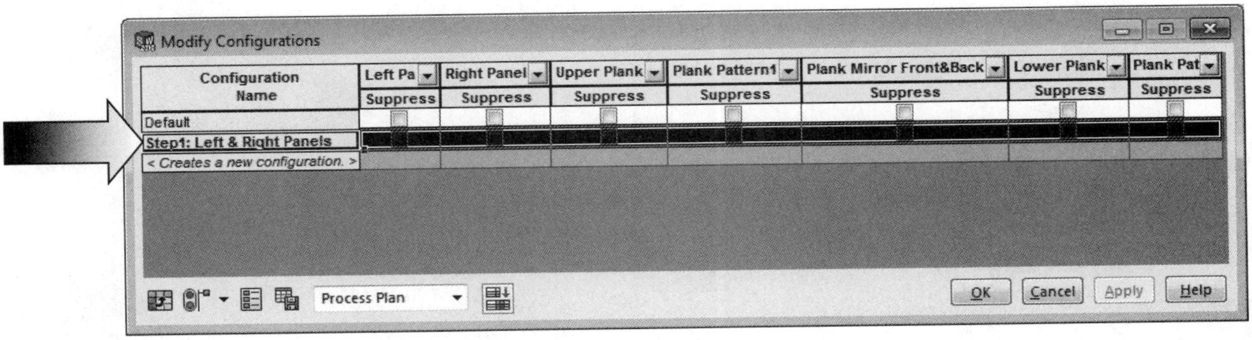

- Select the Suppress checkboxes for the last <u>5 features</u> as indicated (arrows).

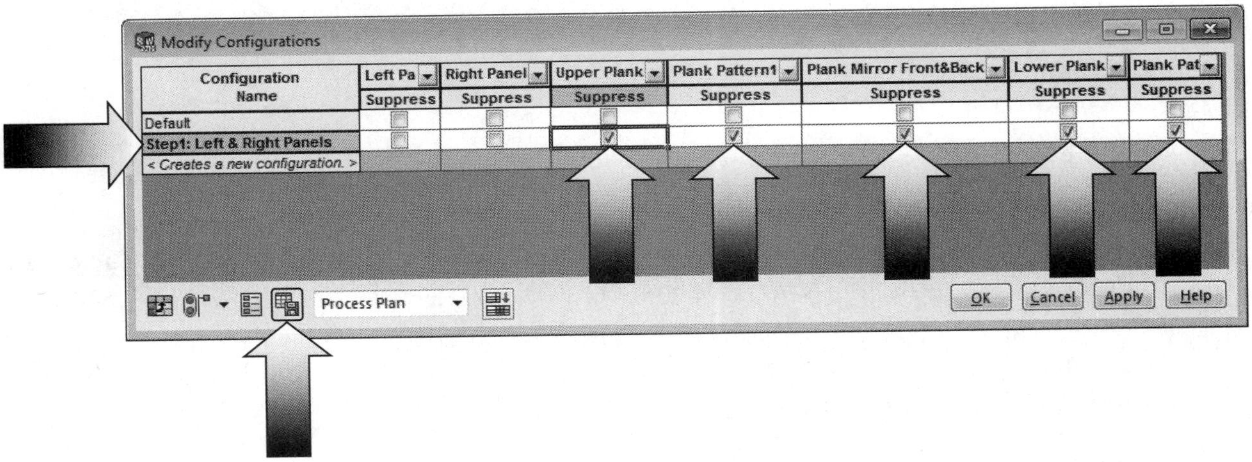

- Click the **Save Table View** again to re-save the table, and click **OK** to close it.

6. Viewing the new configuration:

- Drag the line under the tool tabs halfway down the tree to split the FeatureManager into 2 sections (see note below).

- Click the Configuration tab to change the lower section to the ConfigurationManager.

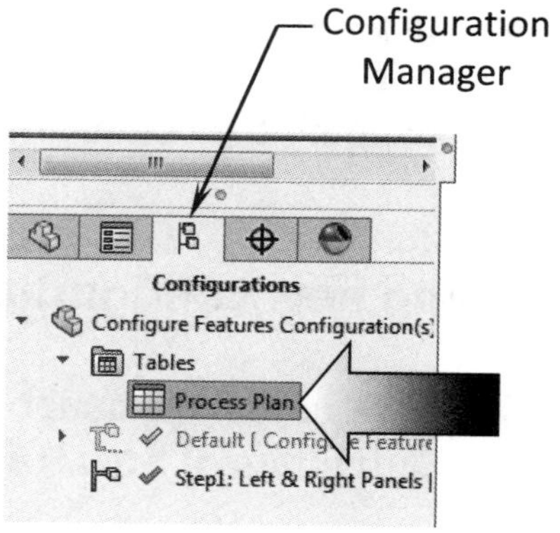

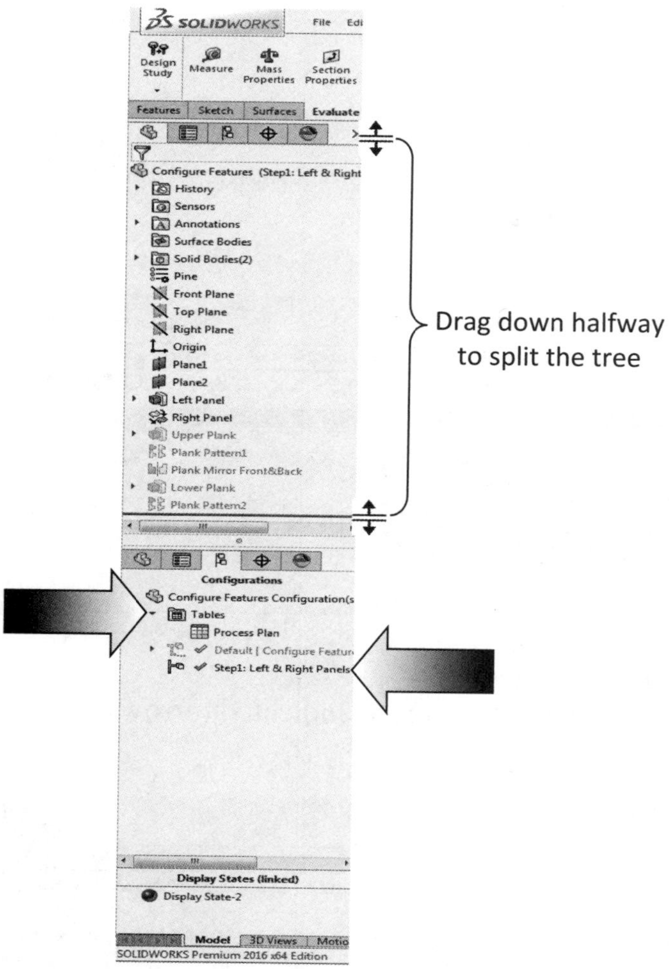

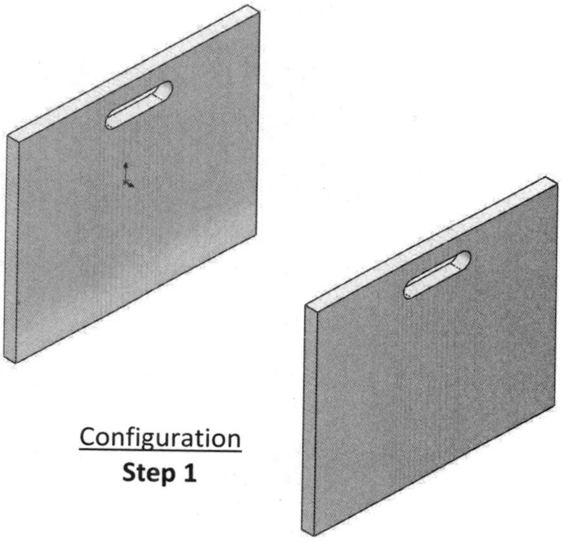

Configuration
Step 1

- A folder is created automatically to store the table(s). Expand the folder to see the Process Plan table that you have just created.

- The new configuration Step1 is displayed under the table. Double click it to activate this configuration.

- The new configuration displays only the features that did not have the check mark in their suppress boxes. The other features are suppressed in this configuration.

7. Adding more configurations:

- Double click the Process Plan table to re-activate it.

- Enter the name of the new configuration: **Step 2: Upper Planks Front**.

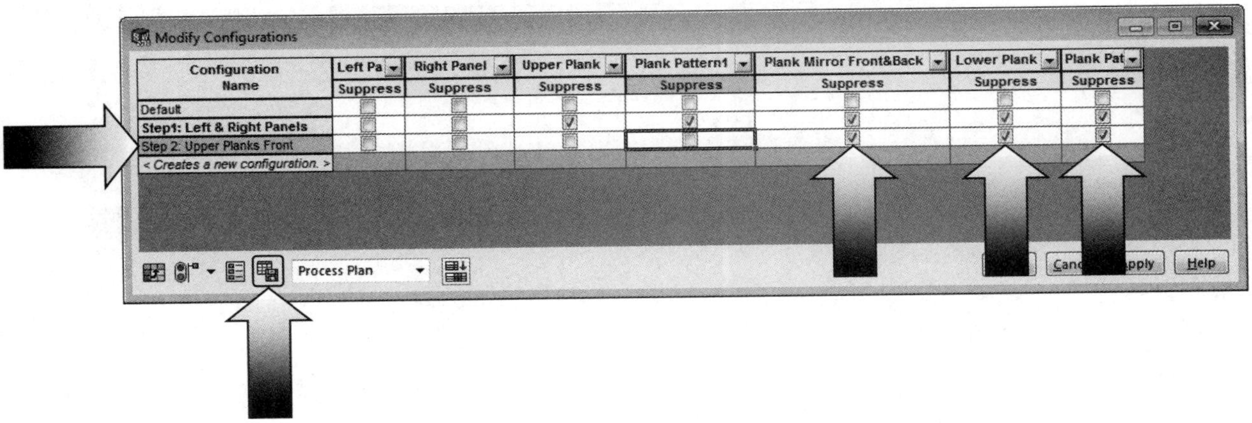

- Leave the first 4 checkboxes blank and suppress the last 3 features.

- Click **Save Table View** to update the table.

- Click **OK** to close the table.

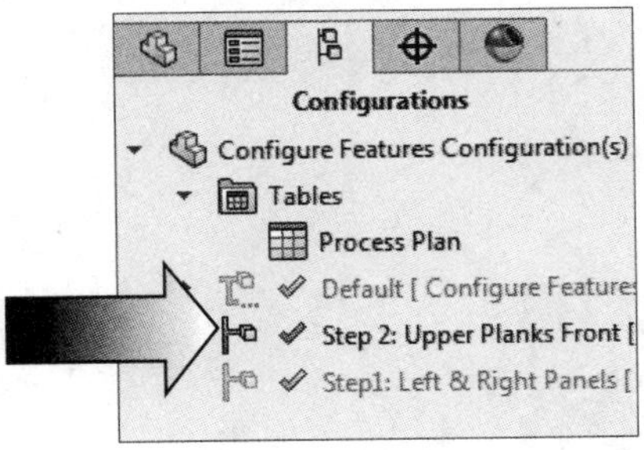

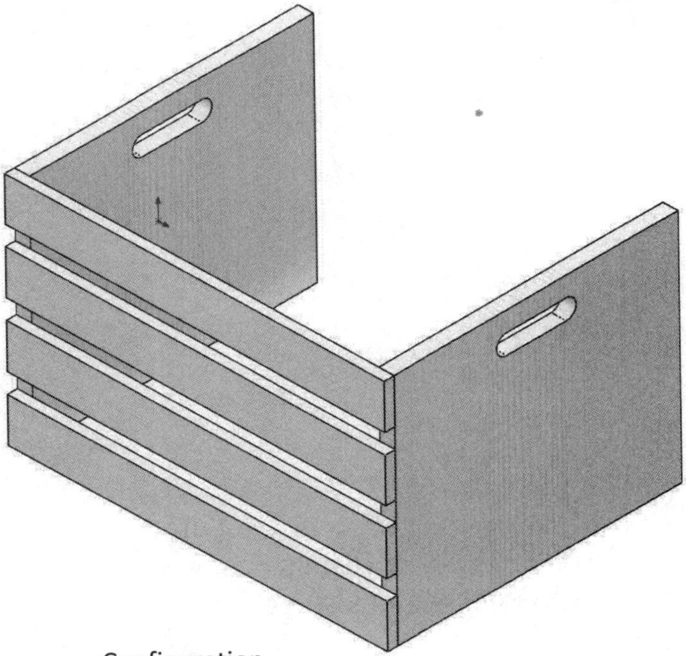

- Locate the new configuration Upper Planks Front and double click on its icon to activate it.

- The 4 planks in the front of the crate are displayed.

Configuration
Step 2: Upper Planks Front

- Double click the Process Plan table to re-activate it.

- Enter the name of the next configuration: **Step 3: Upper Planks Back**.

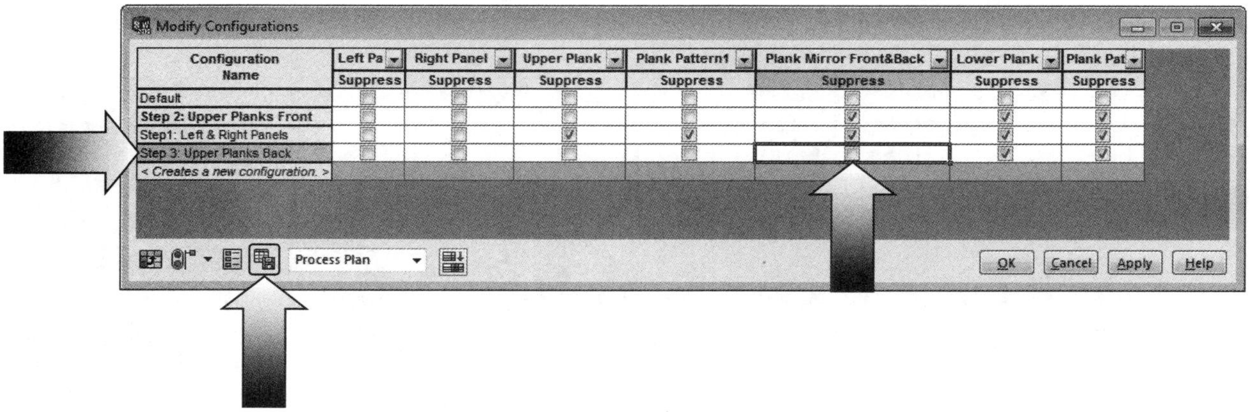

- Leave the first 5 checkboxes blank and suppress the last 2 features.

- Click **Save Table View** to update the table.

- Click **OK** to close the table.

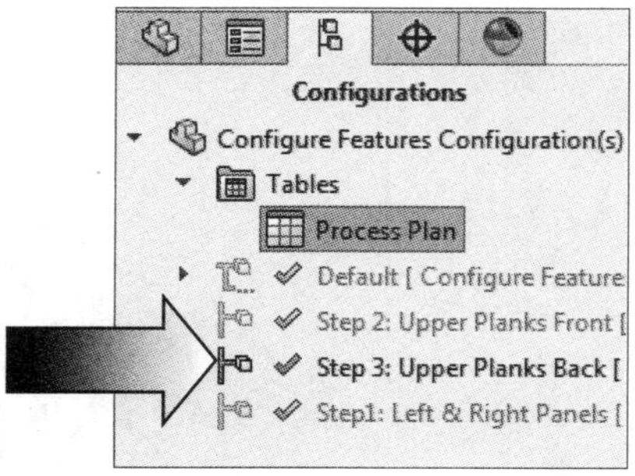

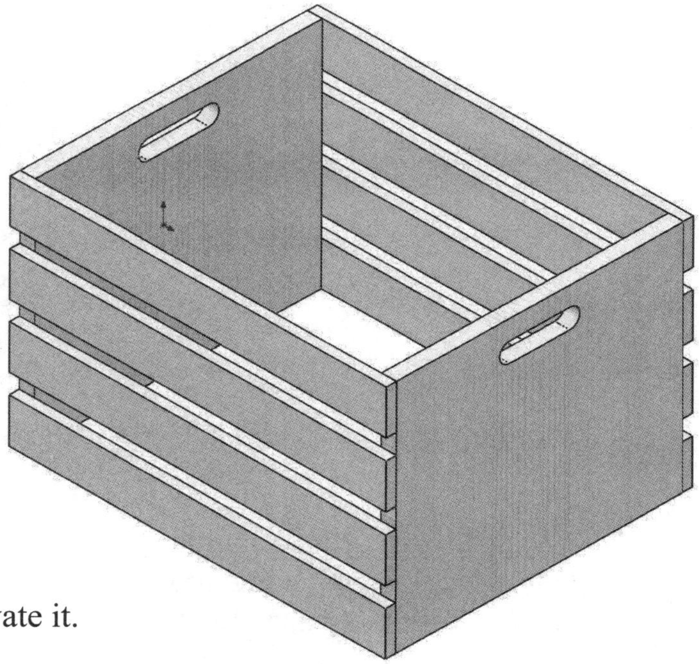

- Locate the new configuration Step 3: Upper Planks Back and Double click on its icon to activate it.

- The 4 planks in the back of the crate are displayed.

Configuration
Step 3: Upper Planks Back

8. Renaming a configuration:

- The Default configuration already has all the planks in it. It is quicker to rename it than to create another configuration.

- To rename, either click+pause+click on the name of the configuration, or use the hot key **F2** to rename it.

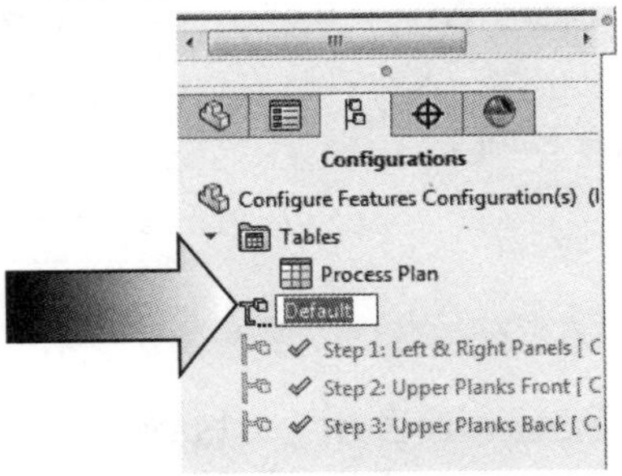

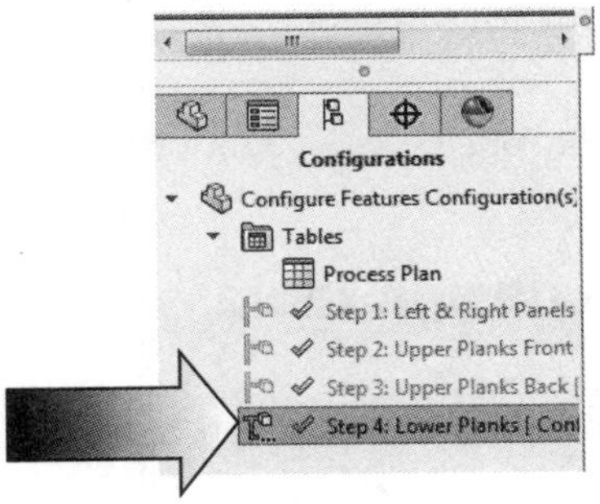

- Double click on the Default configuration to activate it.

- The active configuration will have a green check mark in front of its name, the inactive configuration will have the grey check mark instead.

- Rename the **Default** configuration to **Step 4: Lower Planks** (arrow).

- Rotate the model to see the planks at the bottom.

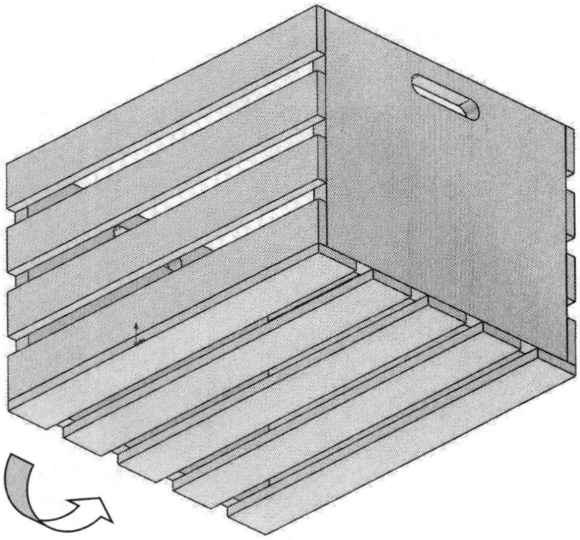

Configuration
Step 4: Lower Planks

NOTE:

The order of the configurations is displayed either numerically or alphabetically.
The configurations should be renamed in such a way that they appear in the correct order when sorted.

- Toggle between the configurations to see the changes in each one.

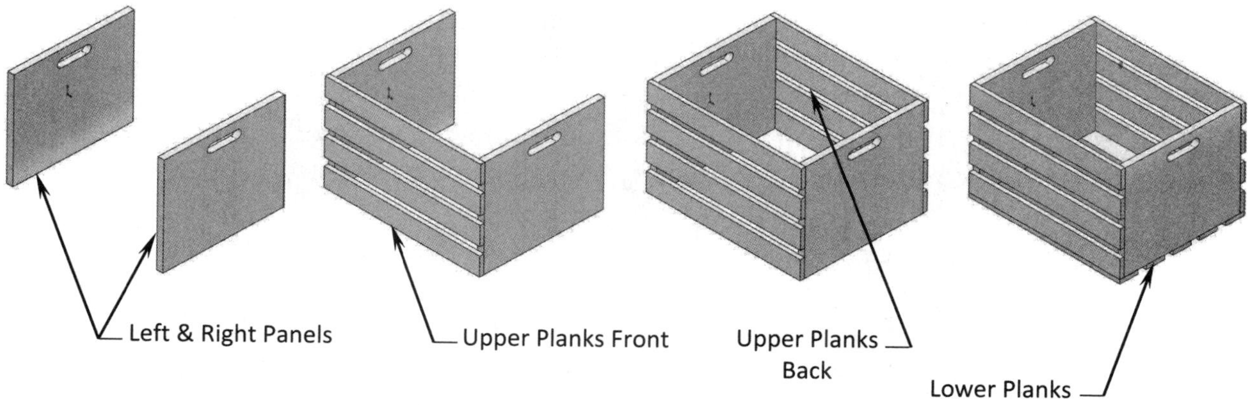

9. Inserting a design table:

- A design table allows you to build multiple configurations of parts or assemblies by specifying parameters in an embedded Microsoft Excel worksheet.

- Existing configurations in the model will be populated to the table automatically.

- Changes done to the model will update the table and vice versa, changes done to the table will be reflected in the model.

- To use design tables, you must have Microsoft Excel installed on your computer.

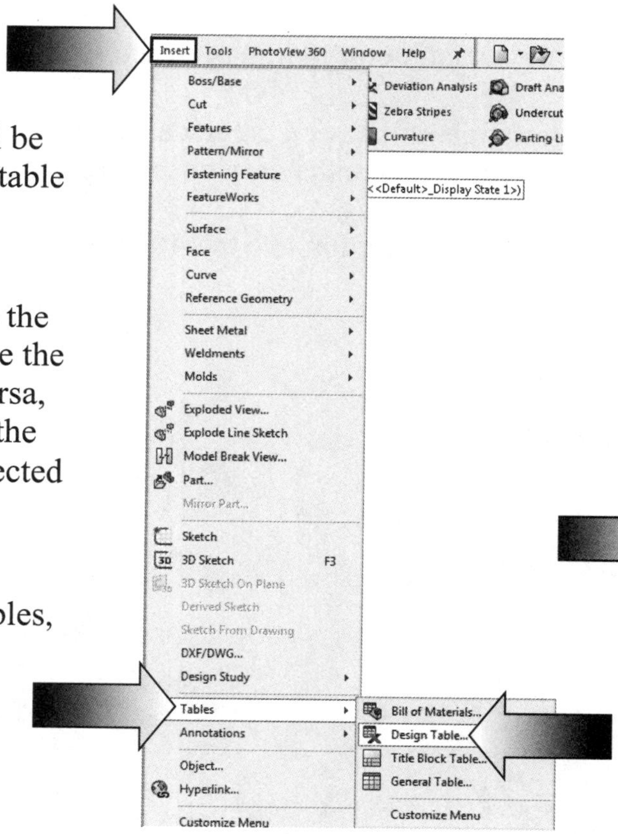

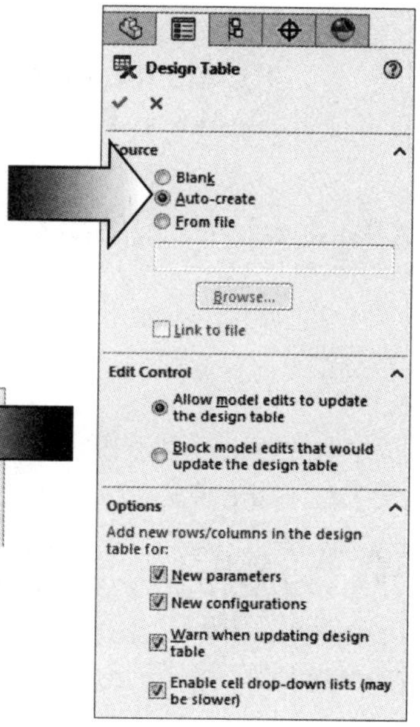

- Select **Insert / Tables / Design Table**.

- Click the **Auto Create** option under Source.

- Microsoft Excel is loaded; a new worksheet is created using the default template and all existing configurations are populated into the rows and columns, in the same order that they were created.

- A new design table is added to the ConfigurationManager (arrow).

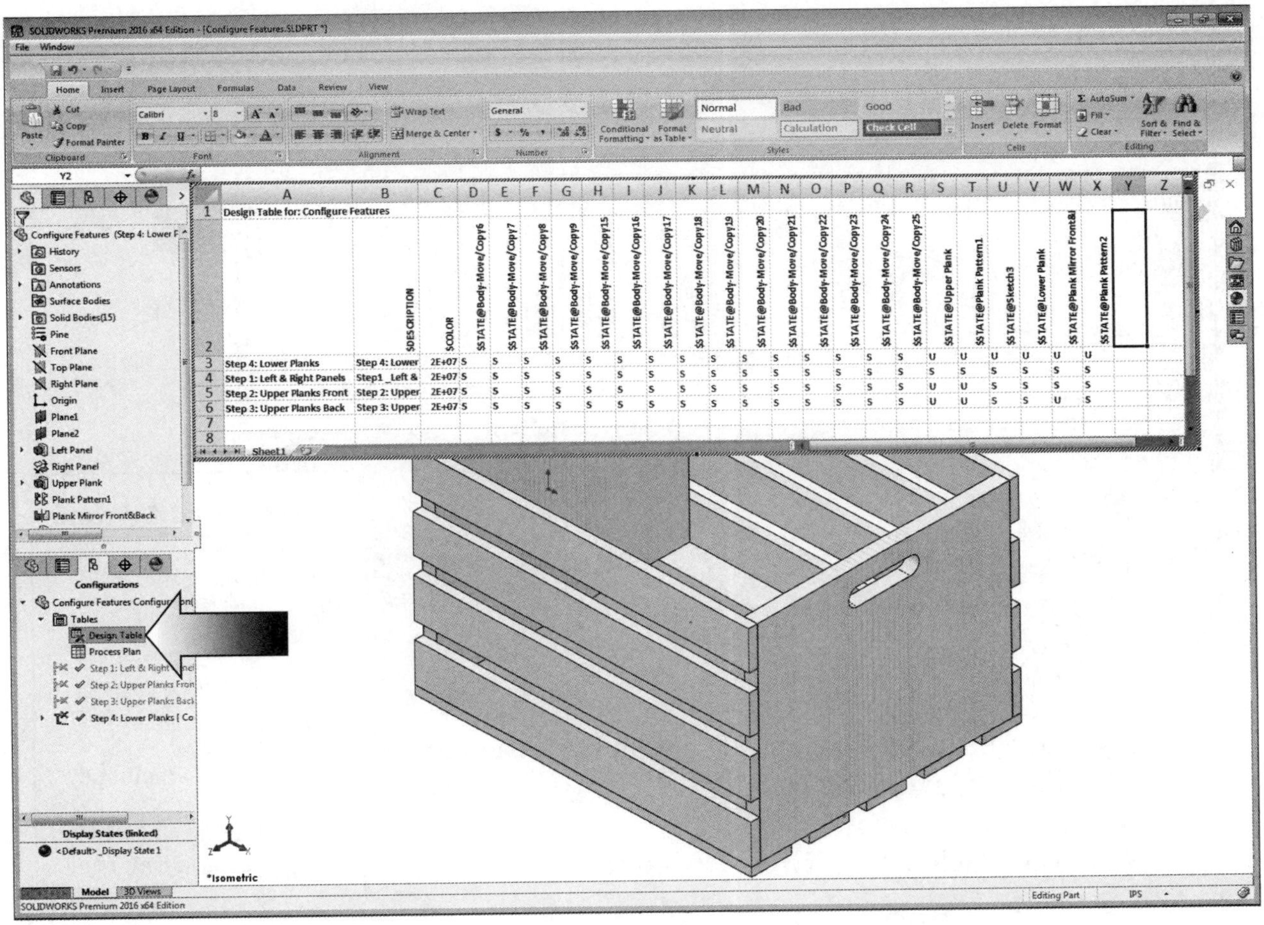

10. Adding a Material column:

- Using the design table, materials can be assigned to single and multi body parts per configuration.

- Click in a blank cell (arrow). We will create a new material for each configuration.

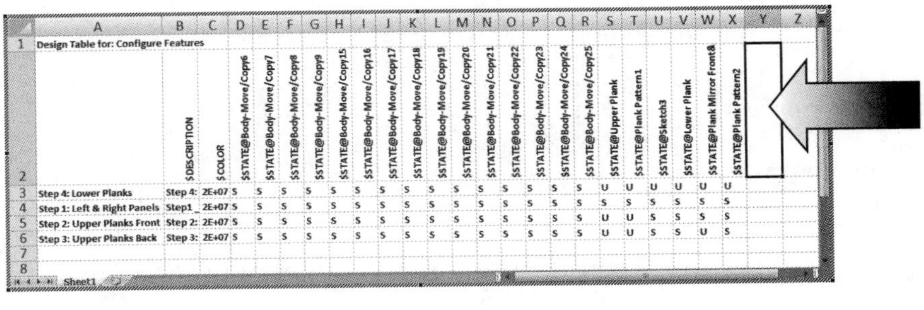

- In the Formula Bar (arrow), enter the following syntax:

$LIBRARY:MATERIAL@Configure Features.

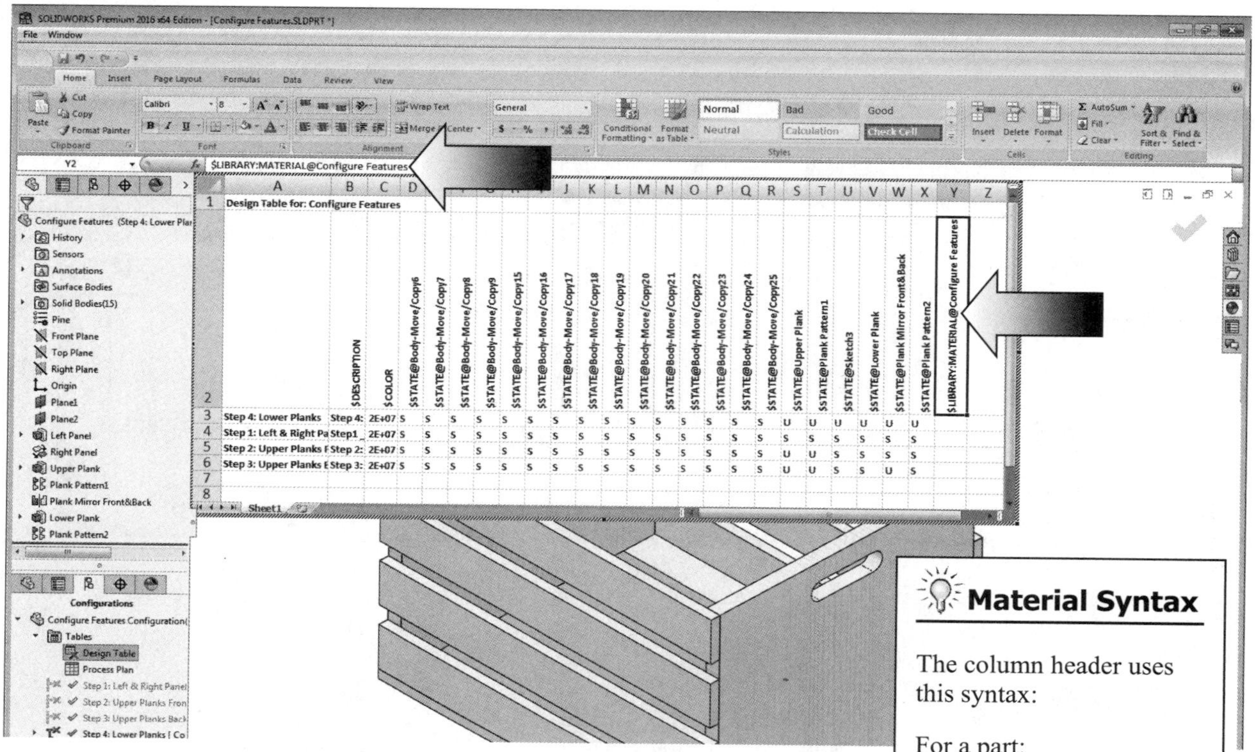

> **Material Syntax**
>
> The column header uses this syntax:
>
> For a part:
> $LIBRARY:MATERIAL @part_name
>
> For a body in a multibody part:
> $LIBRARY:MATERIAL @body_name@part_name

- Select the next cell under the Y column (Y3) and enter the following material:

SOLIDWORKS MATERIAL:Cedar.

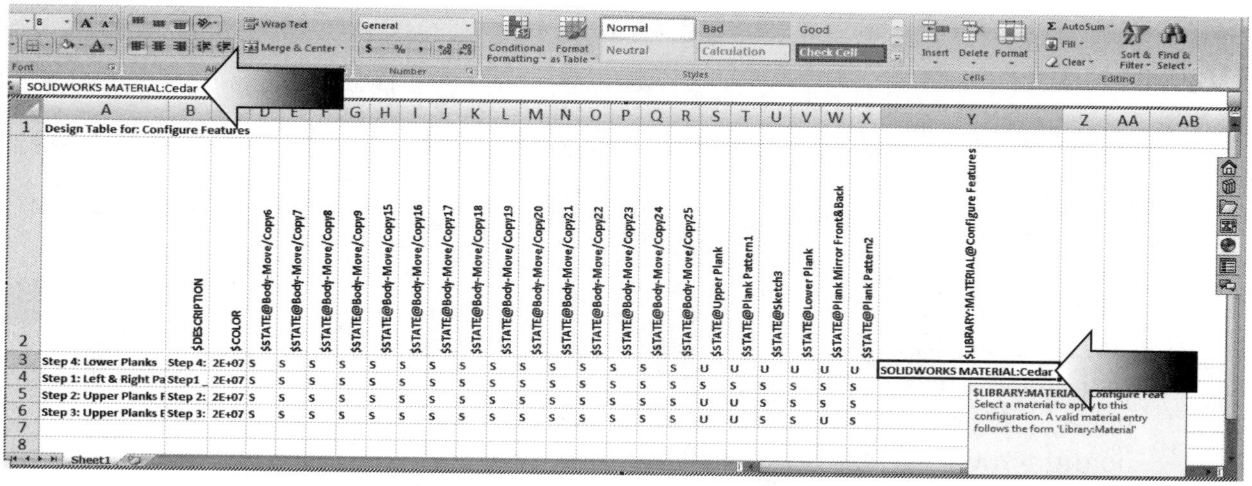

- Continue with adding the materials to the other configuration:

(Config 4 - Step 4: Lower Planks = **Cedar**)

Config 1 - Step 1: Left & Right Panels = **Pine**

Config 2 - Step 2: Left & Right Panels = **Oak**

Config 3 - Step 3: Left & Right Panels = **Maple**

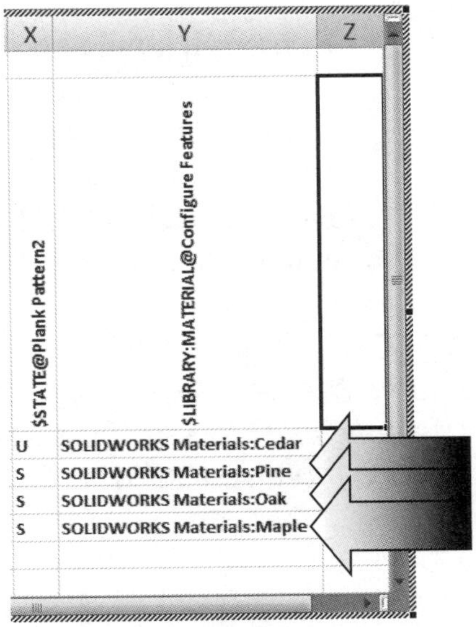

NOTE:
If you accidently exited the design table, simply right click the Design Table from the ConfigurationManager and select: ***Edit Table*** *(arrow).*

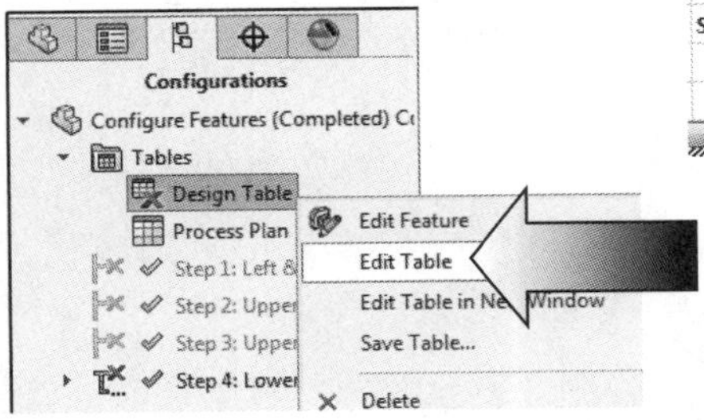

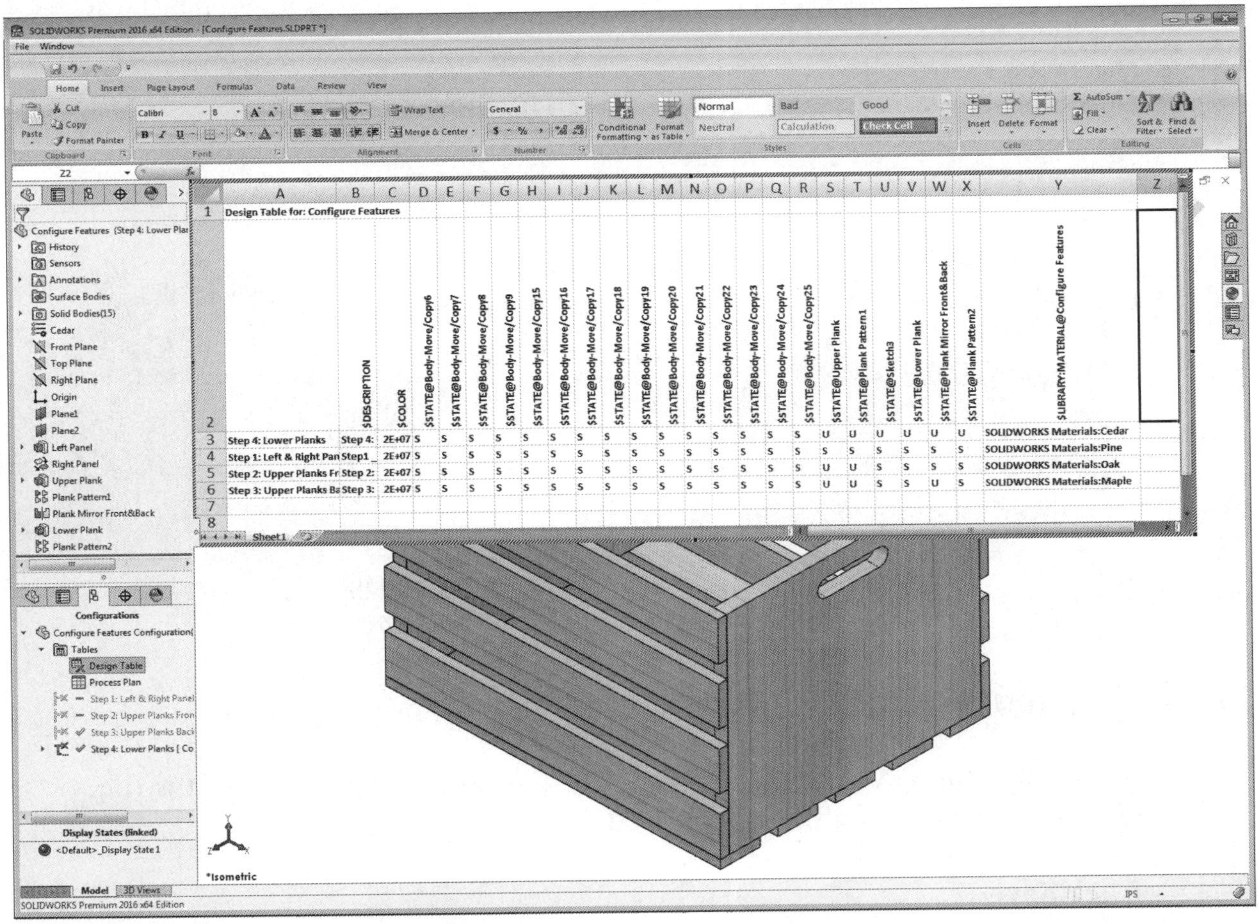

- Either click the check mark on the upper right corner of the screen to exit Excel (arrow) or simply click in the SOLIDWORKS background.

- Double click on each configuration to see the material changes.

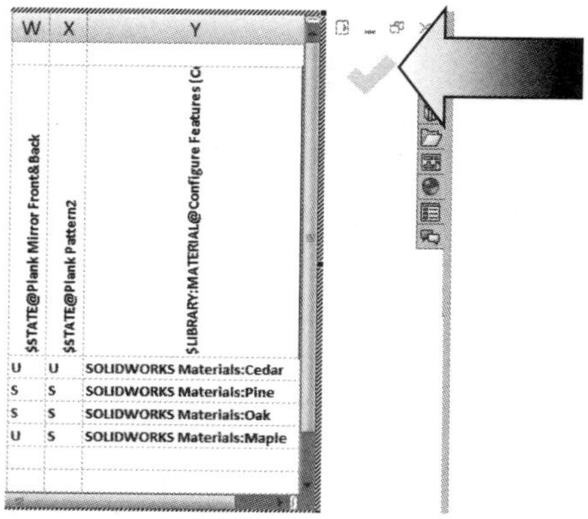

<u>NOTE:</u>
Enable the RealView Graphics option (if applicable) to see the material's texture more realistically.

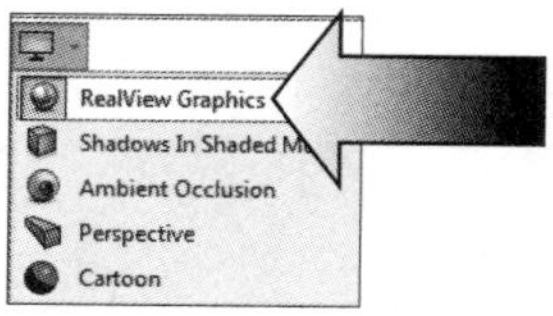

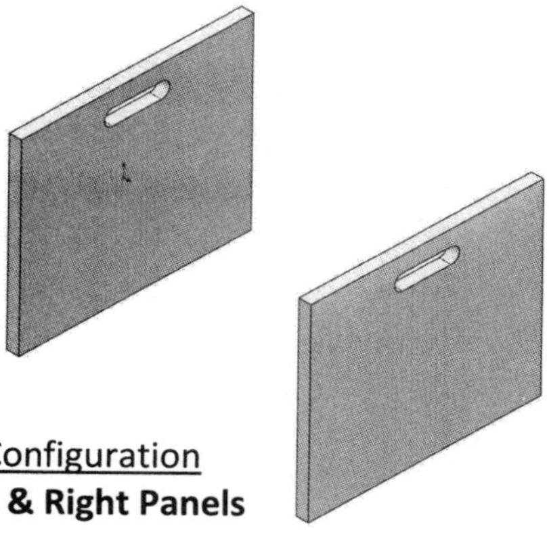

<u>Configuration</u>
Left & Right Panels

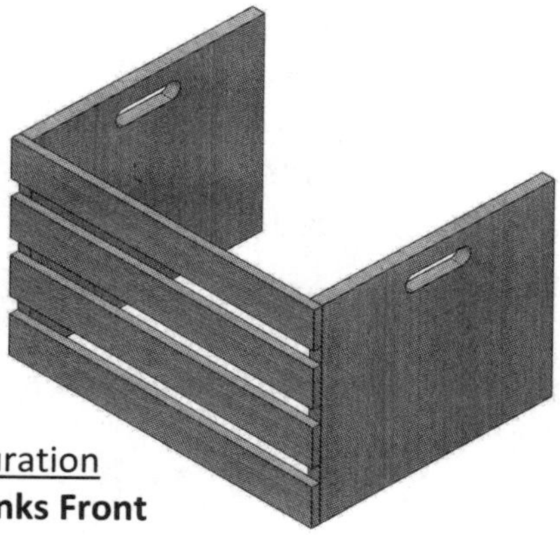

<u>Configuration</u>
Upper Planks Front

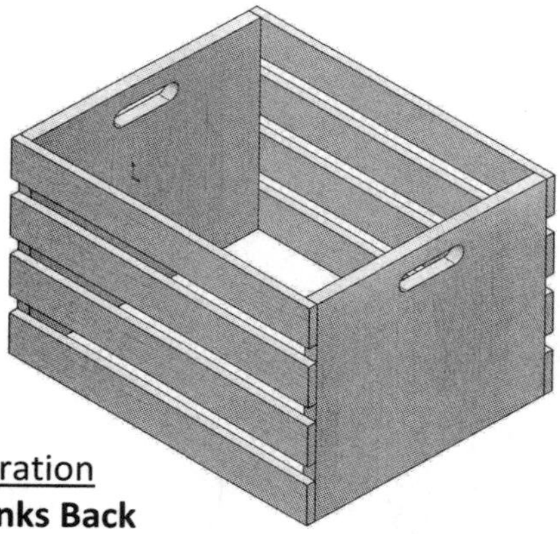

<u>Configuration</u>
Upper Planks Back

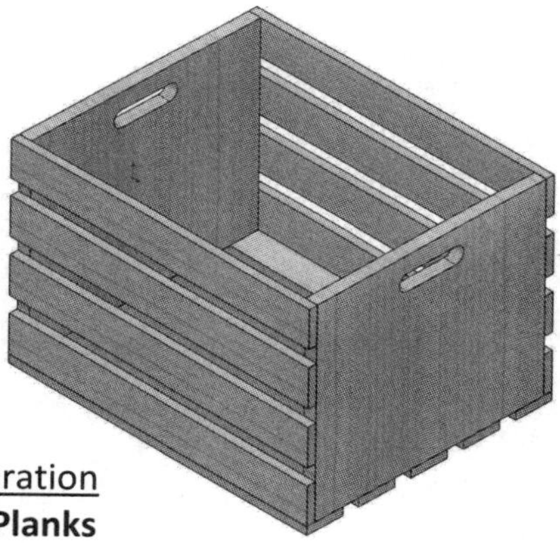

<u>Configuration</u>
Lower Planks

11. Saving your work:

- Click **File / Save As** and enter **Configure Features** for the name of the file. Overwrite the existing file if prompted.

- Click **Save**.

CHAPTER 11

Assembly Motions & Mates

Assembly Motions & Mates
HeliDrone

Add mates to the components in an assembly to assemble them. Mates create geometric relationships between assembly components. When adding mates, the user defines the allowable directions of linear or rotational motion of the components. They can then be moved within their degrees of freedom, visualizing the assembly's behavior.

There are 3 types of mates available in SOLIDWORKS:

* **Standard mates:** include angle, coincident, concentric, distance, lock, parallel, perpendicular, and tangent mates.

* **Advanced mates:** include limit, linear/linear coupler, path, symmetry, and width mates.

* **Mechanical mates:** include cam-follower, gear, hinge, rack and pinion, screw, and universal joint mates.

A Mates folder is automatically included in the FeatureManager design tree to store the mates. Mates can be edited, suppressed, or deleted.

When a component is over mated there will be a plus sign (+) added to its name on the Feature tree. If one or more degrees of freedom still exist in a component, a minus sign (-) appears next to its name, but a fully mated component does not have any sign next to its name.

This lesson discusses the use of some of the options in the 3 mate types: Standard, Advanced, and Mechanical Mates.

Assembly Motions & Mates
HeliDrone

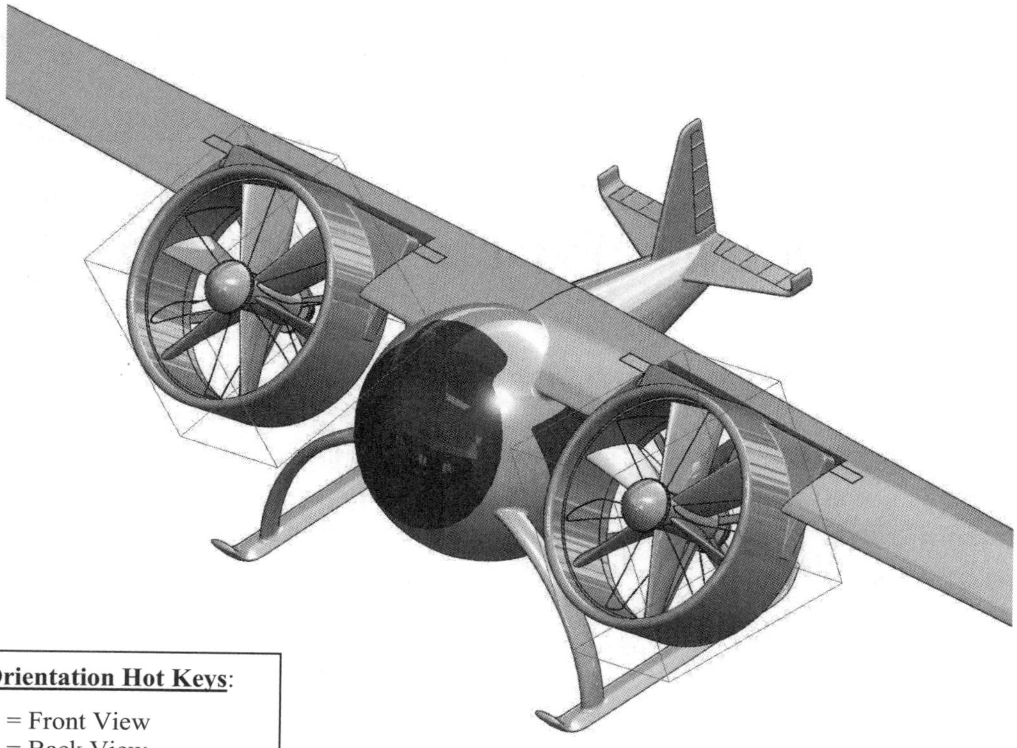

View Orientation Hot Keys:

Ctrl + 1 = Front View
Ctrl + 2 = Back View
Ctrl + 3 = Left View
Ctrl + 4 = Right View
Ctrl + 5 = Top View
Ctrl + 6 = Bottom View
Ctrl + 7 = Isometric View
Ctrl + 8 = Normal To Selection

Dimensioning Standards: **ANSI**

Units: **INCHES** – 3 Decimals

Tools Needed:

Mate	Width Mate	Concentric Mate
Coincident mate	Limit Angle Mate	Parallel Mate
Gear Mate	Pattern Driven Component pattern	Radial Explode

Assembly Motions & Mates

1. Opening an existing assembly document:

- Browse to the Training Files location and open the assembly document named: **HeliDrone Assembly.sldasm**

- This assembly contains one component and two sub-assemblies.

- The sub-assemblies are set to **Rigid** by default; they will need to be changed to **Flexible** so that the blades inside the fan housings can be rotated when needed.

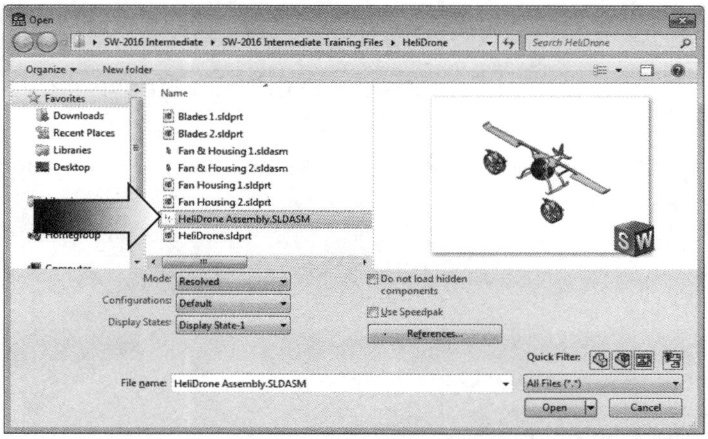

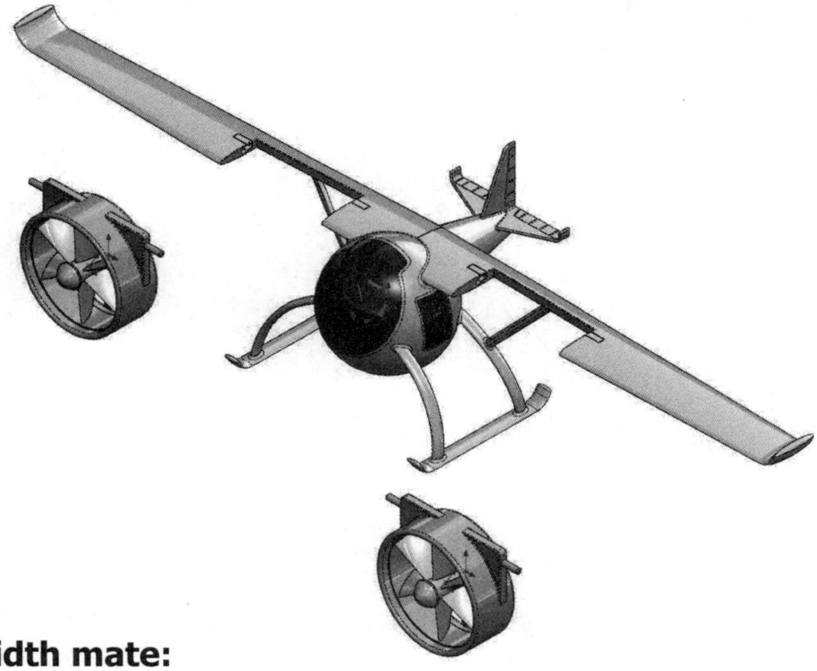

2. Using the Width mate:

- Use the following options to define the limits of the mate: (Note: A width mate must be created prior to selecting one of the options below.)

*** Centered:**	Centers a tab within the width of a groove.
*** Free:**	Lets the components move freely within the limits of the selected faces or planes with respect to the components.

*** Dimension:** Sets a distance or angle dimension from one selection set to the closest opposing selection set of faces or planes.

*** Percent:** Sets the distance or angle based on a percentage value dimension from one set of the selection set to the center of the other selection set.

- Select the **Mate** command and expand the **Advanced Mate** section.

- Click the **Width** button. For Width-Selection, select the <u>2 planar faces</u> on the left and right side of the Fan Housing as noted.

- For Tab-Selection, select the <u>2 planar faces</u> on the left and right side of the wing.

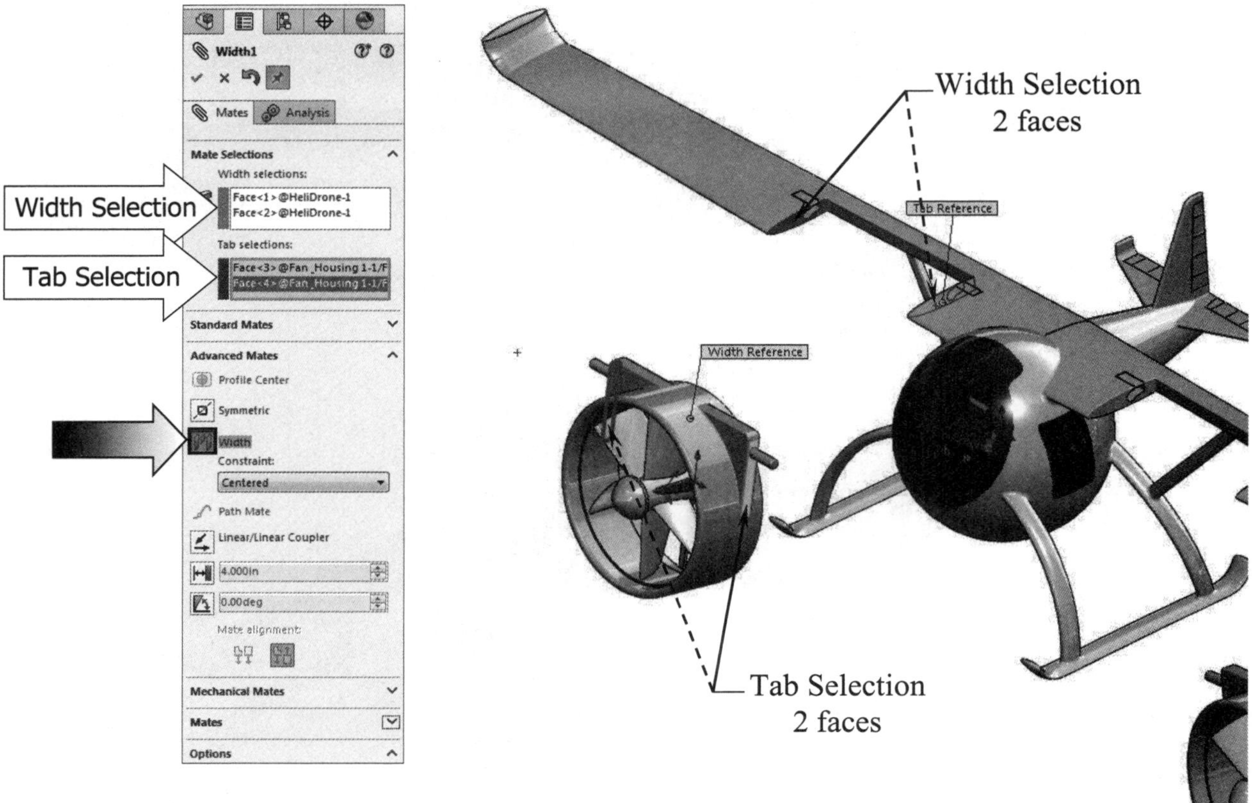

- The selected faces are centered between each other. Click **OK**.

3. Adding a Concentric mate:

- Concentric mates can be added between a circular edge, a cone or cylinder, a line, a point, or a sphere.

- Switch back to the **Standard Mates** section (arrow).

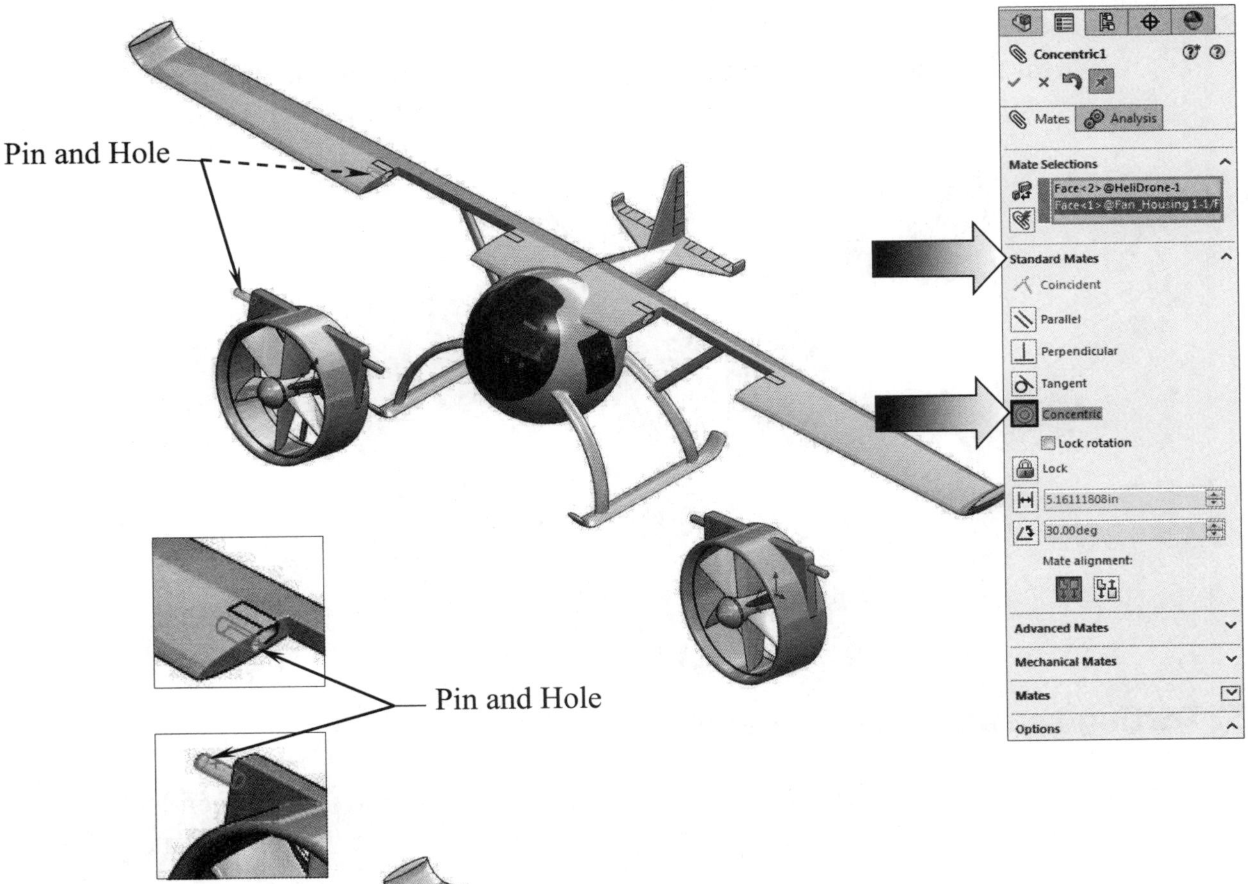

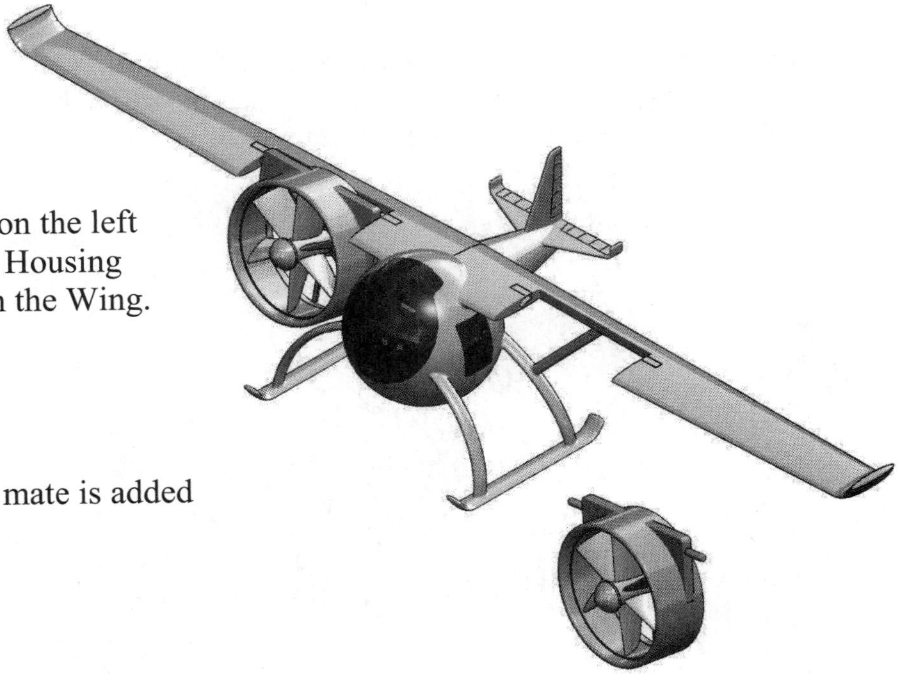

- Select the **Pin** on the left side of the Fan Housing and the **Hole** in the Wing.

- A **Concentric** mate is added automatically.

- Click **OK** to accept the mate and drag the Fan Housing up and down to test the mates.

4. Adding another Concentric mate:

- Repeat the last step and mate the second Fan Housing to the opposite wing.

5. Testing the assembly motions:

- Drag the two Fan Housings up and down. They are moved independently from each other. The Fan Blades are also rotated independently at this point.

- More mates need to be added so that they will move and rotate together instead. We will take a look at the other mate options such as: Limit mates, Parallel mates, and Gear mates in the next few steps.

6. Adding a Limit-Angle mate:

- Limit Angle mate allows components to move within a range of specified angles.

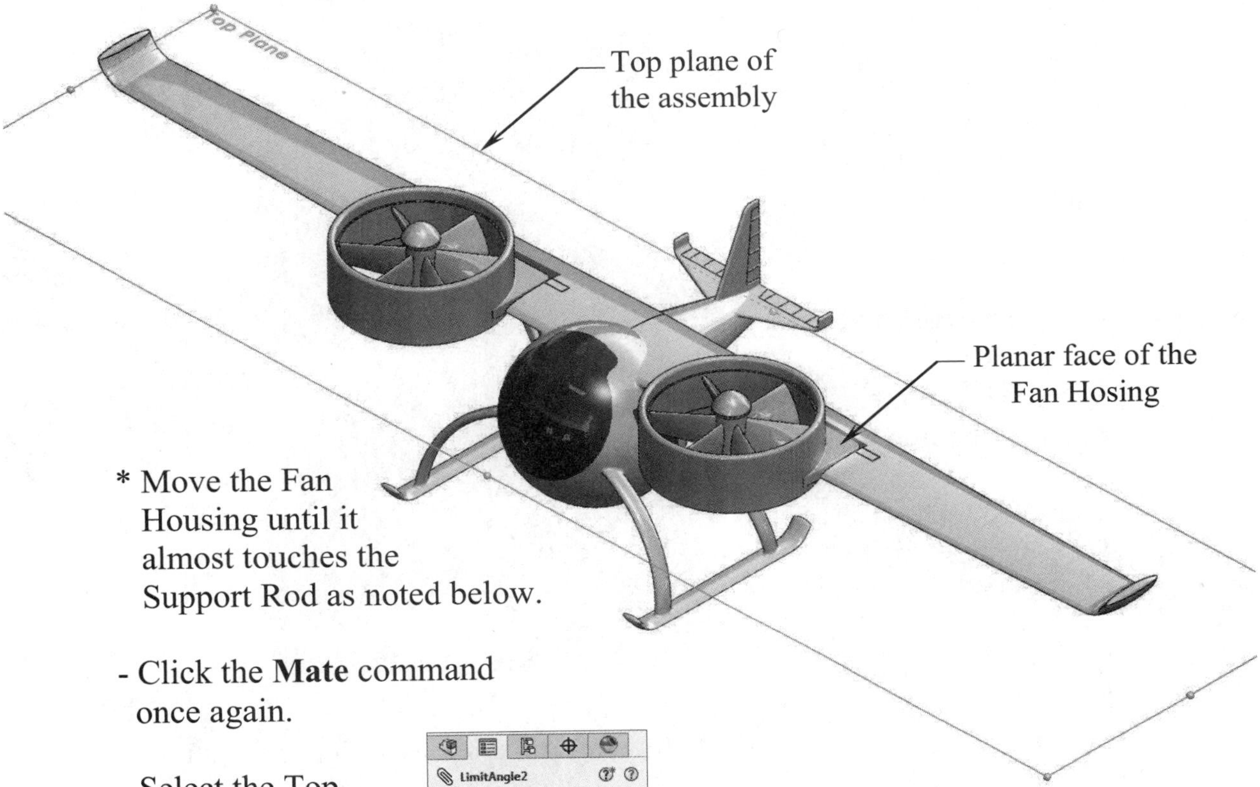

* Move the Fan Housing until it almost touches the Support Rod as noted below.

- Click the **Mate** command once again.

- Select the Top plane of the assembly and the planar Face of the Fan Housing as noted.

- Expand the **Advanced Mates** section and click the **Angle** button.

- Enter:

Angle: 83.00deg
Max: 83.00deg
Min: 0.00deg.

- Click **OK**.

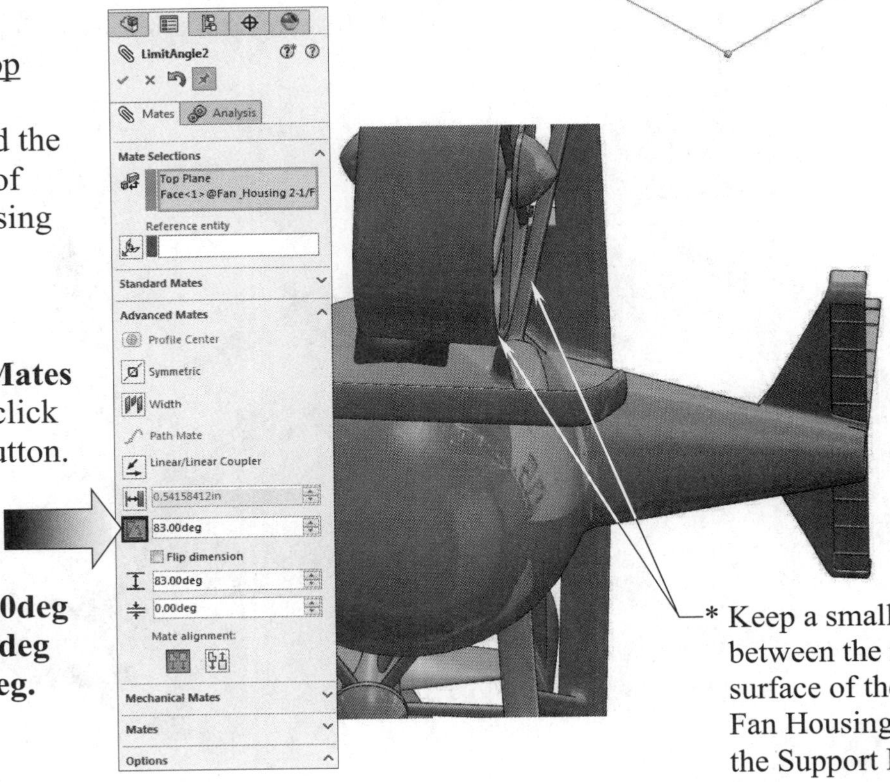

* Keep a small gap between the rear surface of the Fan Housing and the Support Rod

- Drag the Fan Housing up and down to test its limits.

- When moving upward it should stop at zero degrees; and when moving downward it should stop right before it hits the Support Rod.

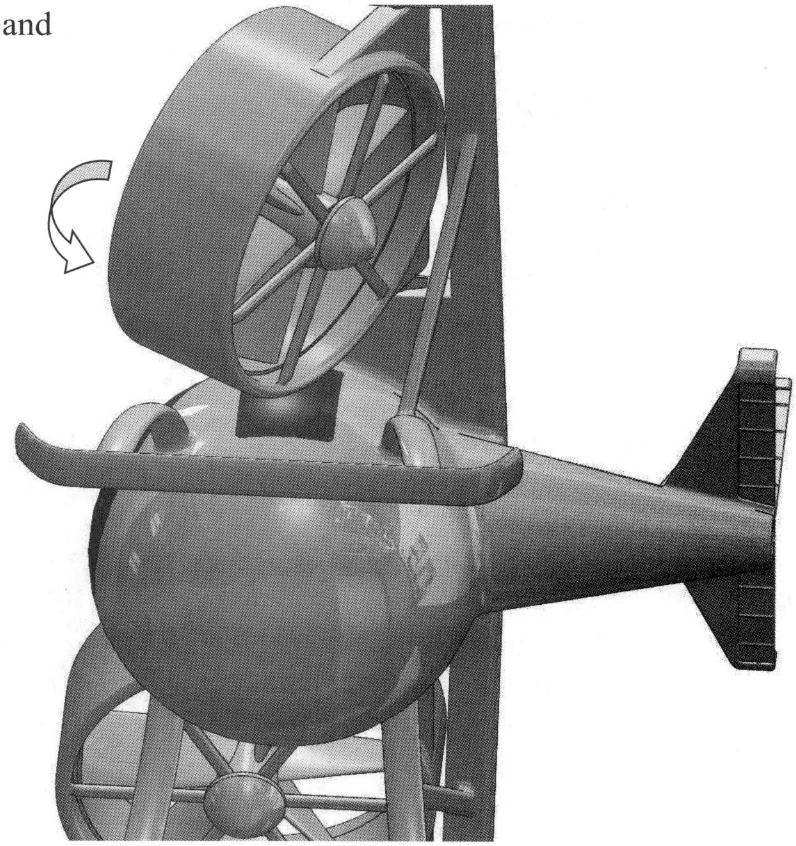

7. Adding a Parallel mate:

- Switch back to the **Standard Mates** section.

- Select the <u>2 planar faces</u> of the 2 Fan Housings as indicated.

- Click the **Parallel** button.

- Click **OK**. Drag one of the Fan Housings up and down to check its motions.

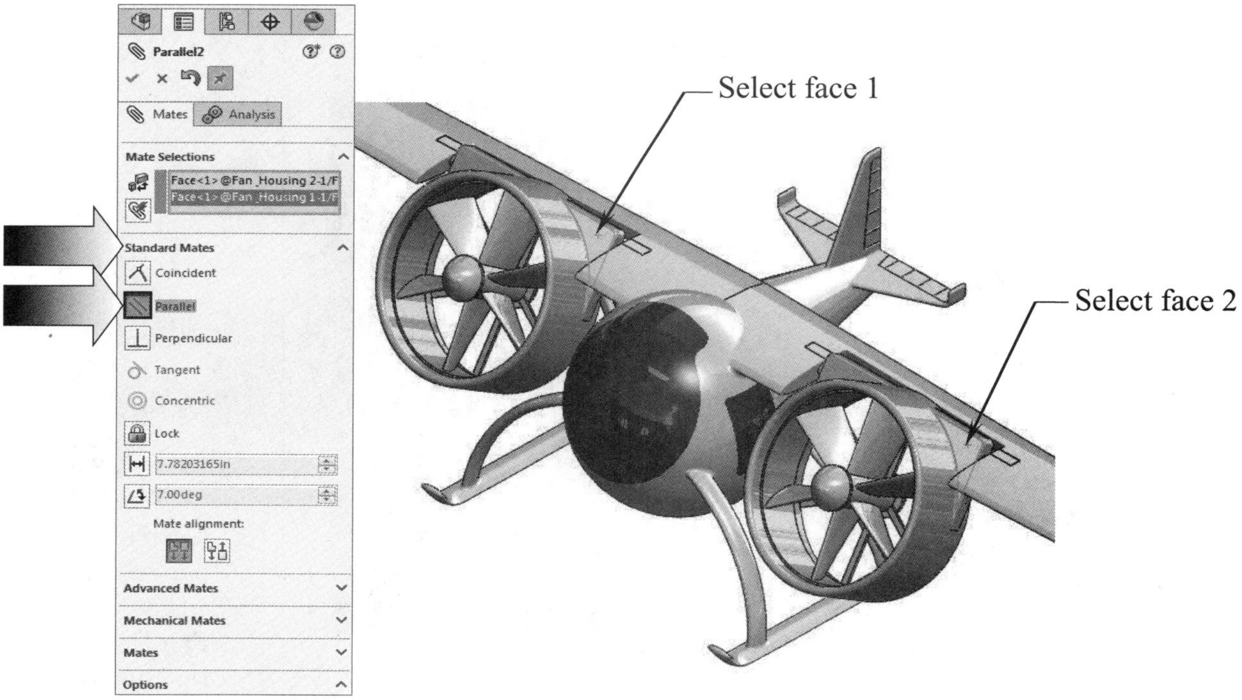

8. Adding a Gear mate:

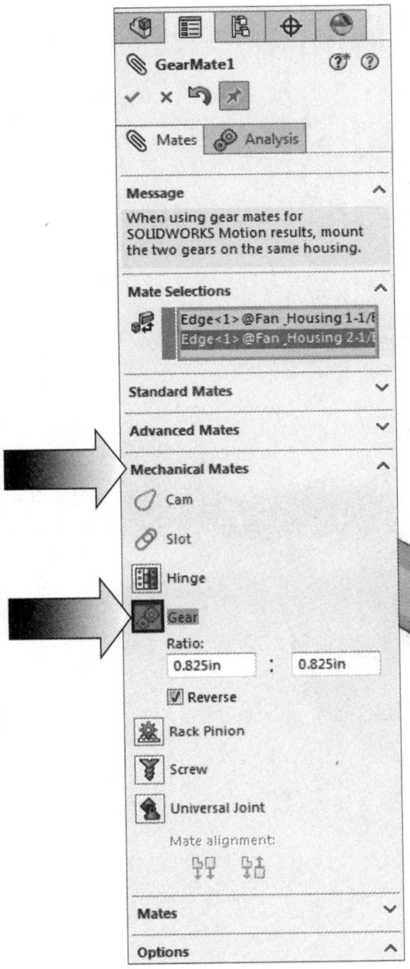

- A Gear mate forces two components to rotate relative to one another about selected axes.

- Switch to the **Mechanical Mates** section (arrow).

- Click the **Gear** button and select the <u>circular edges</u> of the 2 Blades as noted below.

- The **Ratio** of the 2 selected edges should be the same (0.825in X 0.825in).

- Click the **Reverse** checkbox if necessary.

- Click **OK** to exit the Mate command.

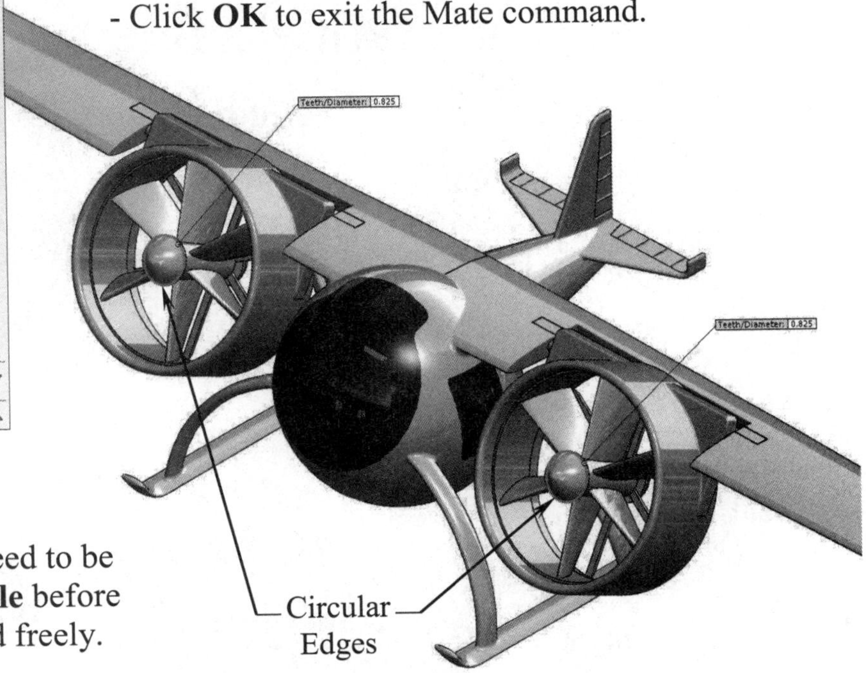

- The Blades still need to be changed to **Flexible** before they can be rotated freely.

- Click on the sub-assembly icon and select the option: **Make Sub Assembly Flexible** (arrow).

- Make both sub-assemblies flexible.

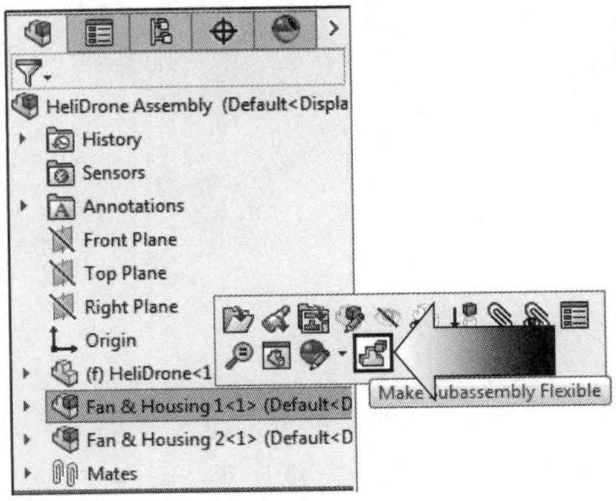

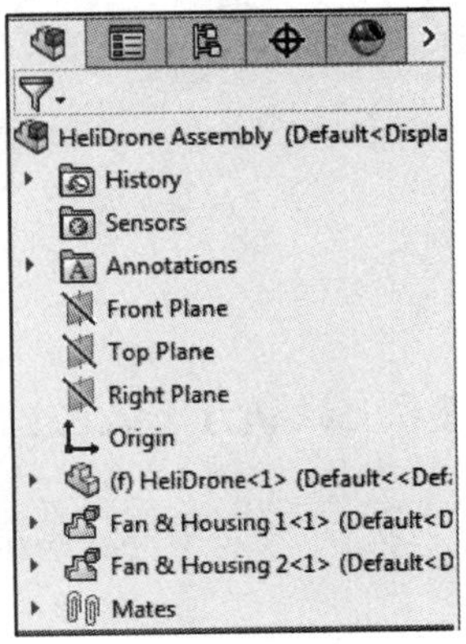

9. Testing the assembly motions:

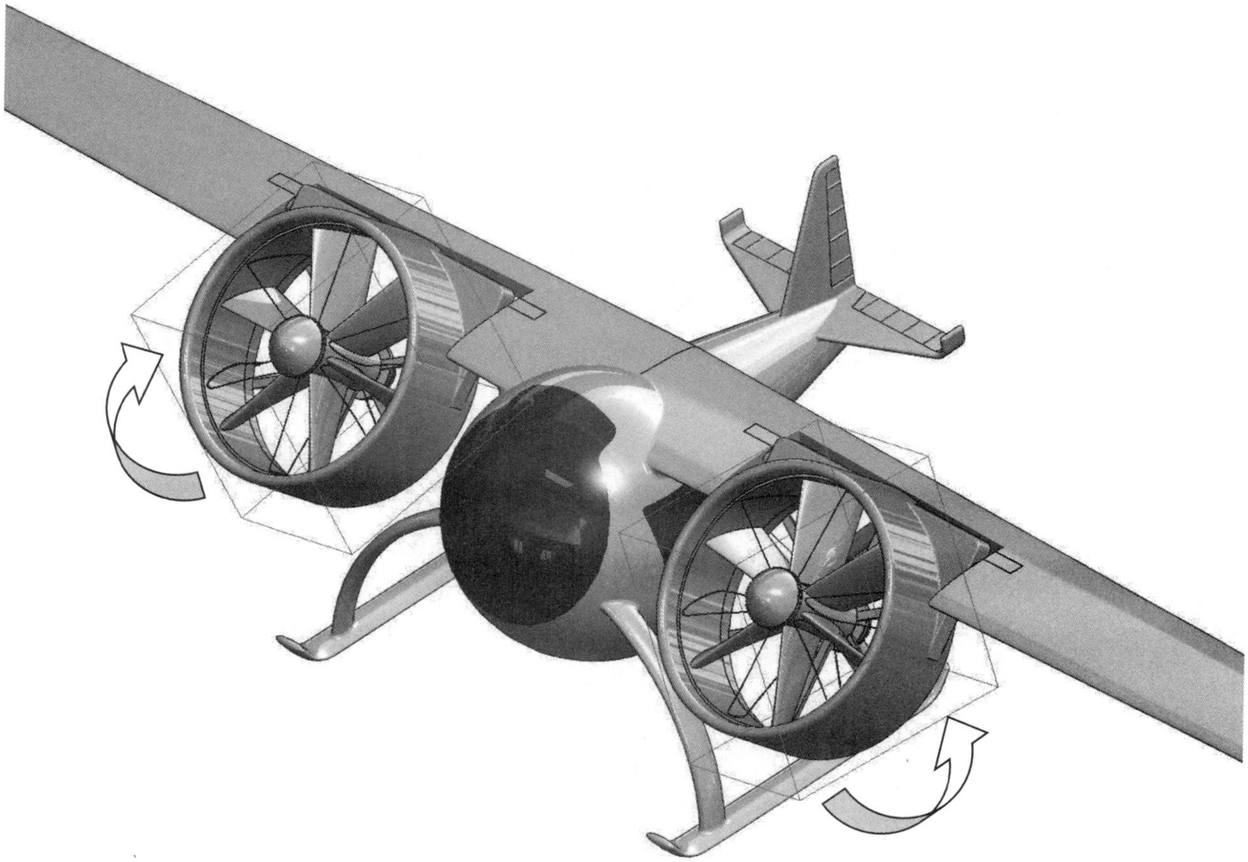

10. Saving your work:

- Press **Save** (or Control + S) and click **Yes** to overwrite the existing assembly document with your completed one.

Radial Explode

Radial Explode was added to SOLIDWORKS 2015 which allows you to explode components aligned cylindrically about an axis in one step.

You can explode components aligned radially or cylindrically about an axis. The radial explode steps are saved in the assembly. In the animation the steps play back, showing the components rotating around their center axis. When you open an eDrawings file and click explode, the exploded view appears.

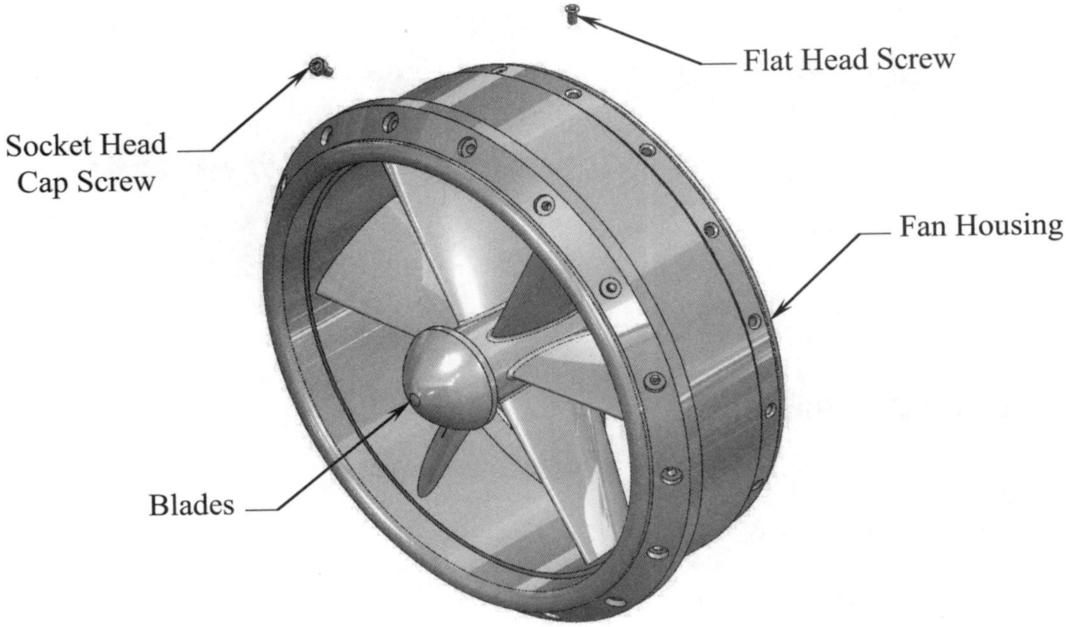

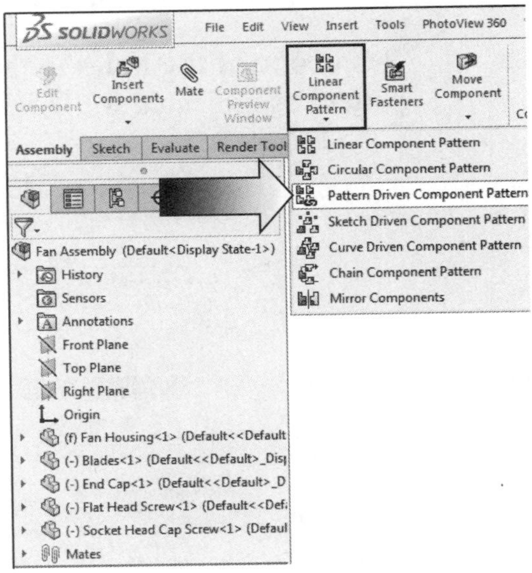

1. Opening an existing assembly:

- Browse to the Training Files and open an assembly document named: **Fan Assembly.sldasm**

2. Creating the 1st Pattern Driven:

- Select **Pattern Driven Component Pattern** from the Linear Component drop down (arrow).

- Expand the FeatureManager tree and select the **Flat Head Screw** to use as the Component-To-Pattern.

- For Driving Feature or Component, select **one of the holes** in the existing pattern as noted.

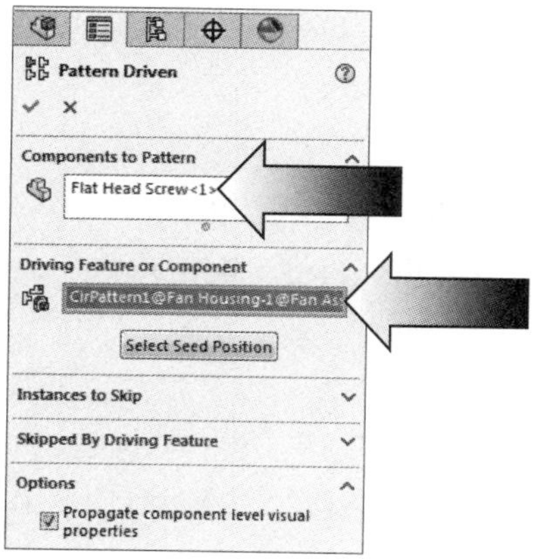

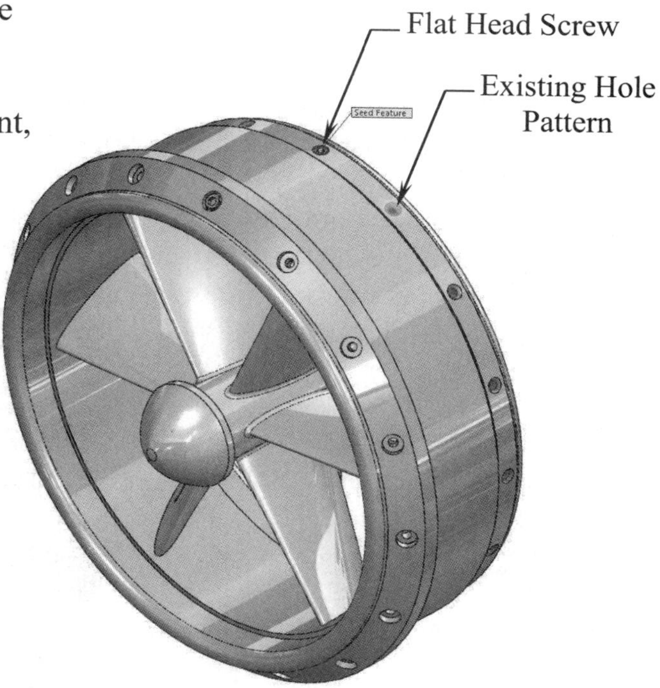

- Click **OK**.

3. Creating the 2nd Pattern Driven:

- Select the **Driven Component Pattern** option once again.

- Select the **Socket Head Cap Screw** for Component to Pattern.

- Select **one of the holes** in the existing pattern as indicated for Driving Feature.

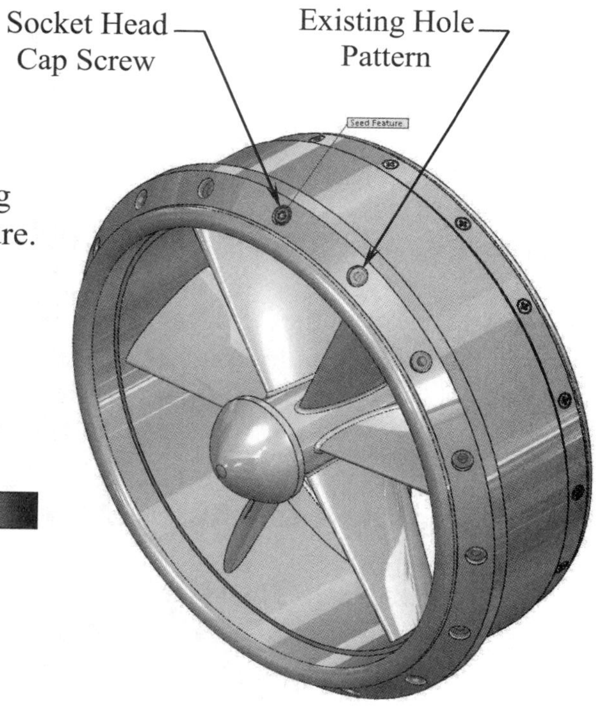

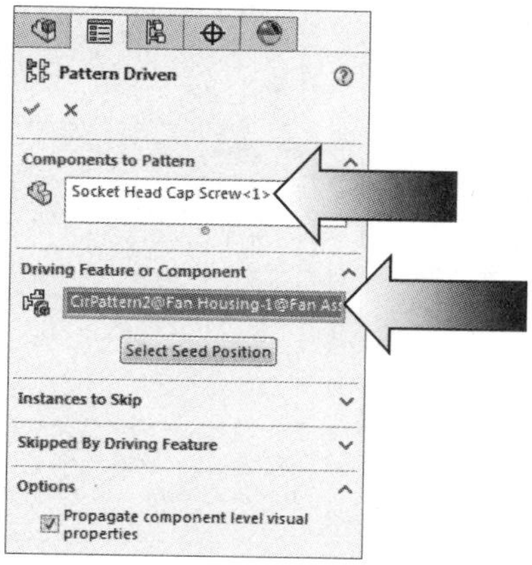

- Click **OK**.

4. Creating the 1st radial exploded view:

Drag the arrow head outward

- From the Assembly toolbar, click: **Exploded View**.

- Select the **Radial Step** option (arrow).

- Select the **Flat Head Screw** and all **15 Instances**.

- Drag the **Direction-Arrow** outward to approximately **.700in**.

- The Flat Head Screws are exploded radially.

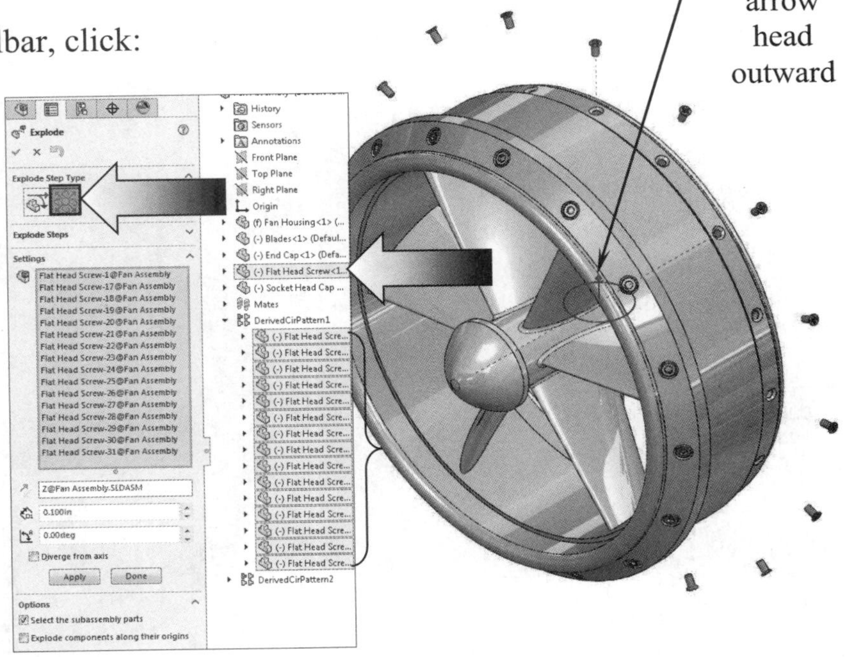

- Do not click OK just yet; we will need to explode the Socket Head Cap Screws as the next explode step.

5. Creating the 2nd radial exploded view:

Drag the arrow head outward

- The Radial Step option should be selected already.

- Select the **Socket Head Cap Screw** and its **15 Instances**.

- Drag the **Direction-Arrow** outward to approximately **1.250in**.

- The Socket Head Cap Screws are exploded radially.

- Click **OK** to exit the exploded view mode.

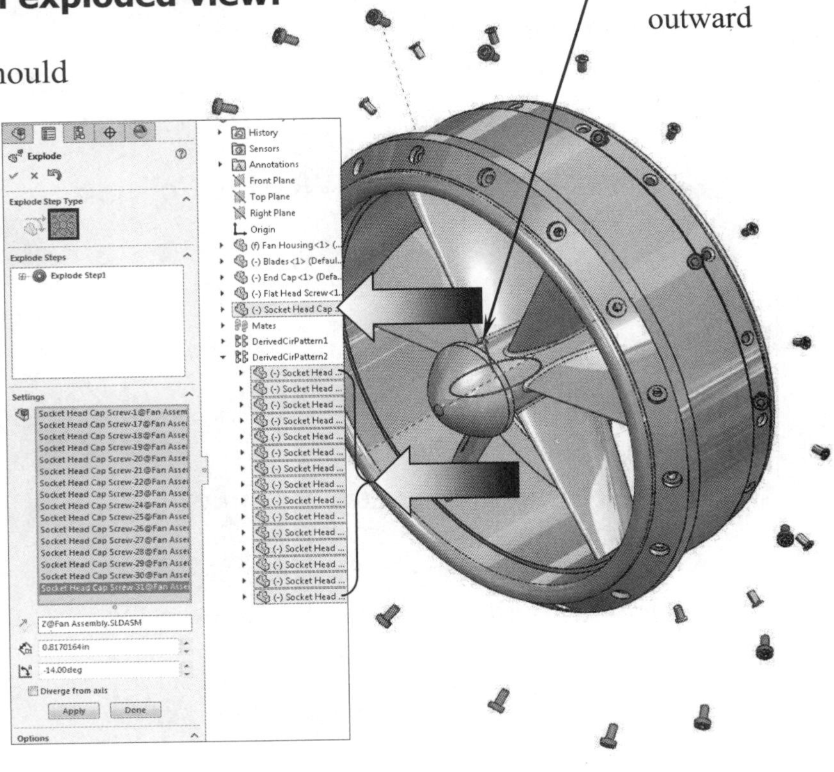

6. Verifying the exploded view:

- Change to the **Front** orientation (Control + 1).

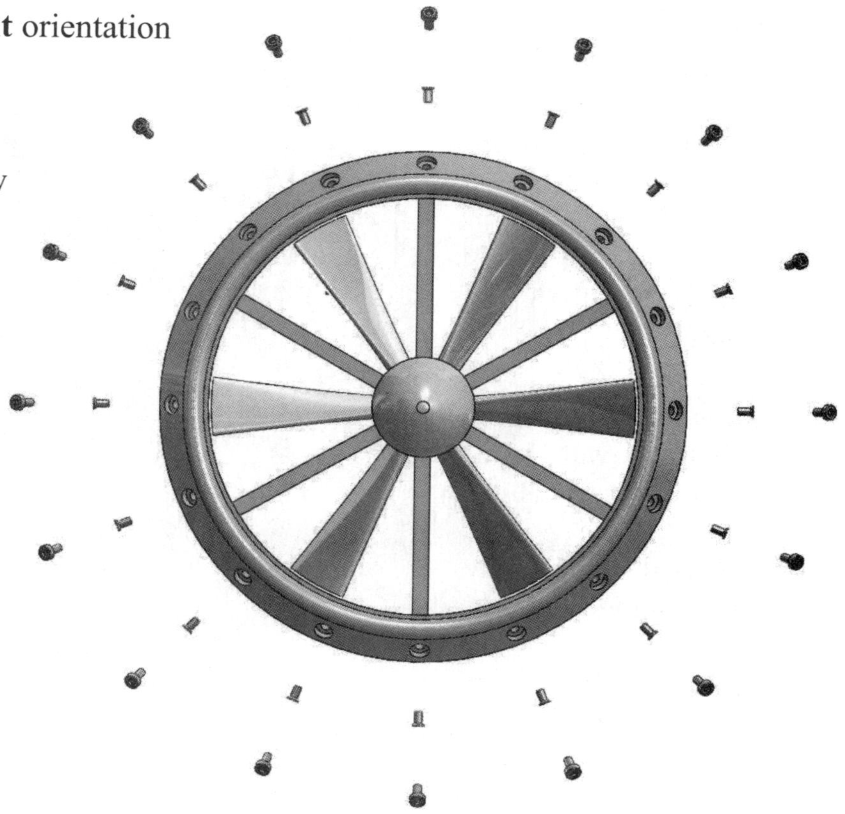

- Your exploded view should look similar to the image shown on the right.

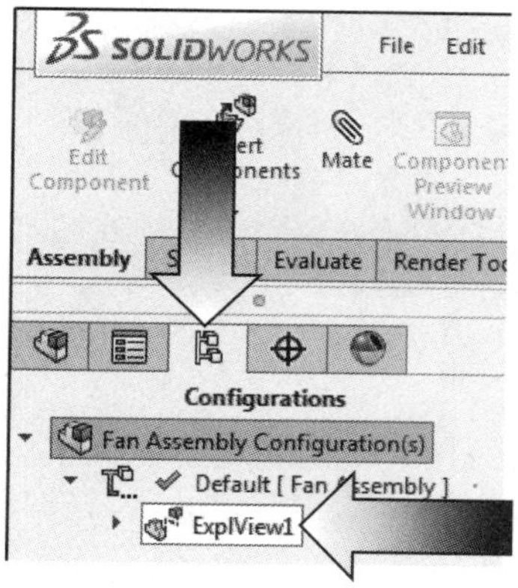

- Switch to the **Configuration Manager** tree (arrow) and expand the **Default** configuration to see or to edit the Exploded View (arrow).

- Double click on the **ExplView1** to Collapse or to Explode the assembly.

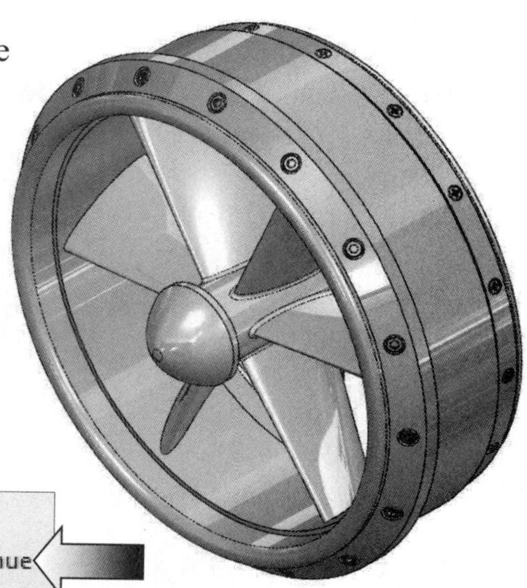

7. Saving your work:

- Click **File / Save As**.

- Enter **Radial Explode** for the name of the document.

- Select the option: **Save As Copy and Continue**, and click **Save**.

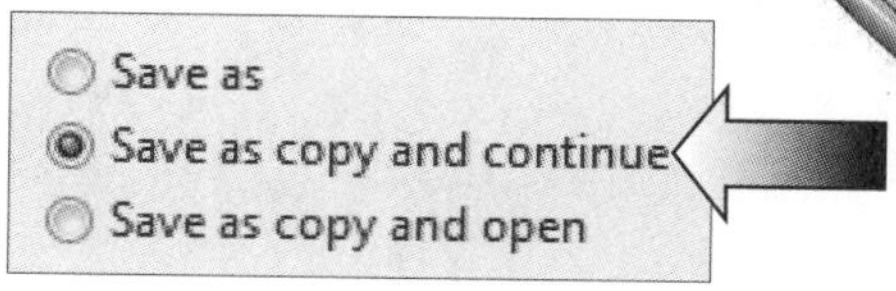

CHAPTER 12

Using Smart-Mates

Fixture Assembly
Using Smart-Mates

- Beside the standard mates such as Concentric, Coincident, Tangent, Angle, etc., which must be done one by one, SOLIDWORKS offers an alternative option that is much more robust called Smart-Mates.

- There are many advantages for using Smart-Mates. It can create several mates at the same time, depending on the type of entity selected. For example, if you drag a circular edge of a hole and drop it on a circular edge of another hole, SOLIDWORKS will automatically create two mates, a concentric mate between the two cylindrical faces of the holes and a coincident mate between the two planar faces.

- Using Smart-Mates, you do not have to select the Mate command every time. Simply hold the ALT key and drag an entity of a component to its destination, a smart-mate symbol will appear to confirm the types of mates it is going to add. At the same time, a mate toolbar will also pop up offering some additional options such as Flip Mate Alignment, change to a different mate type, or simply undo the selection.

- Using the Alt + Drag option, the Tab key is used to flip the mate alignments, this is done by releasing the Alt key and pressing the Tab key, while the mouse button is still pressed. This option works well even if your assembly is set to lightweight.

- In addition to the Alt + Drag, if you hold the Control key and Drag a component, SOLIDWORKS will create an instance of the selected component and apply the Smart-Mates to it at the same time. Using this option you will have to click the Flip Mate Alignment button on the pop-up toolbar to reverse the direction of the mate, the Tab key does not work.

- This lesson will guide you through the use of the Smart-Mate options, and in some of the steps, use the standards mate options as well.

Fixture Assembly
Using Smart-Mates

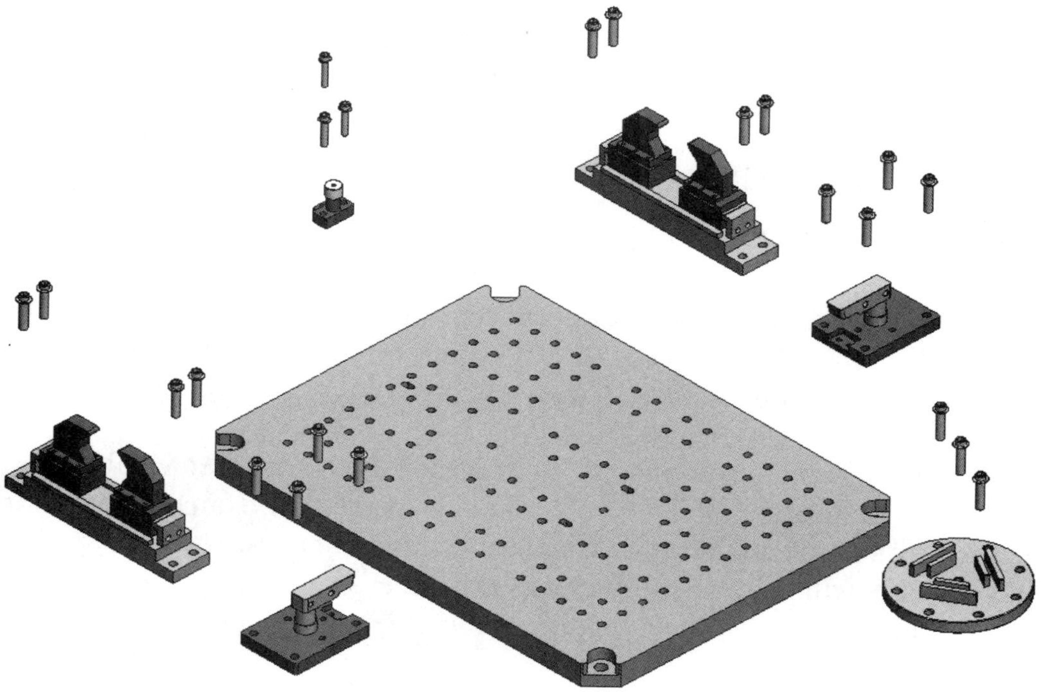

View Orientation Hot Keys:

Ctrl + 1 = Front View
Ctrl + 2 = Back View
Ctrl + 3 = Left View
Ctrl + 4 = Right View
Ctrl + 5 = Top View
Ctrl + 6 = Bottom View
Ctrl + 7 = Isometric View
Ctrl + 8 = Normal To Selection

Dimensioning Standards: **ANSI**

Units: **INCHES** – 3 Decimals

Tools Needed:

Concentric & Coincident	Concentric two cylindrical faces	Coincident two edges
Coincident two planar faces	Coincident two vertices	Coincident two origins

1. Opening an existing assembly document:

- Select **File / Open**.

- Browse to the Training Files folder, locate and open the document named: **Fixture Assembly**.

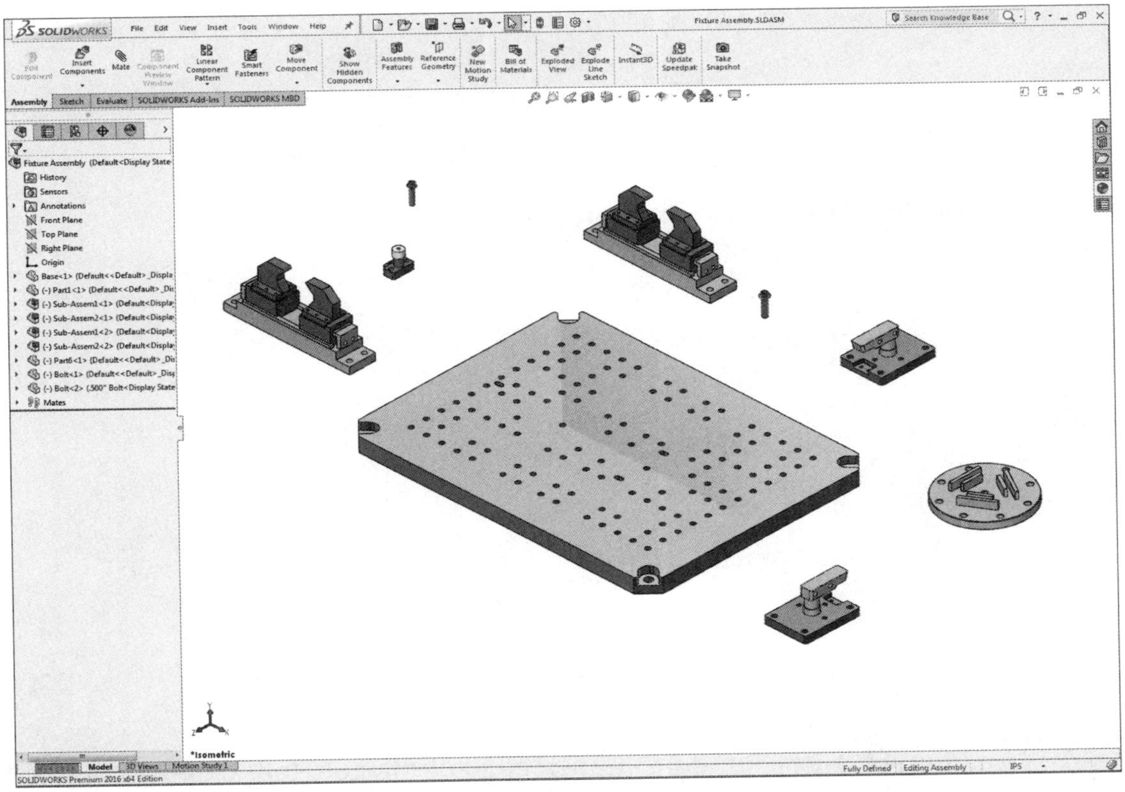

2. Enabling the Selection options:

- Go to **Tools / Options / Display / Selection** and enable the two checkboxes:
  * Allow Selection in Wireframe...
  * Allow selection in HLR and...

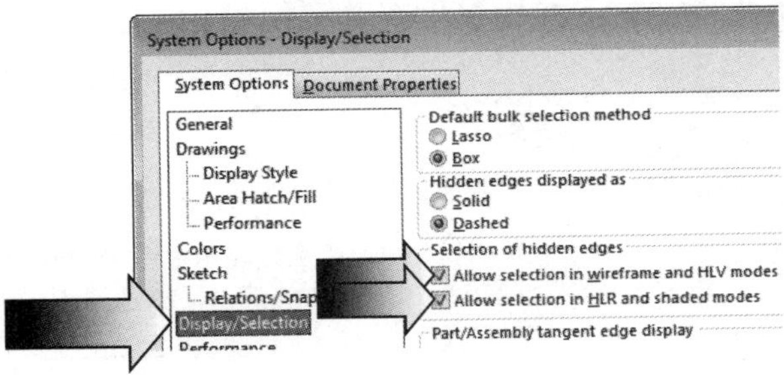

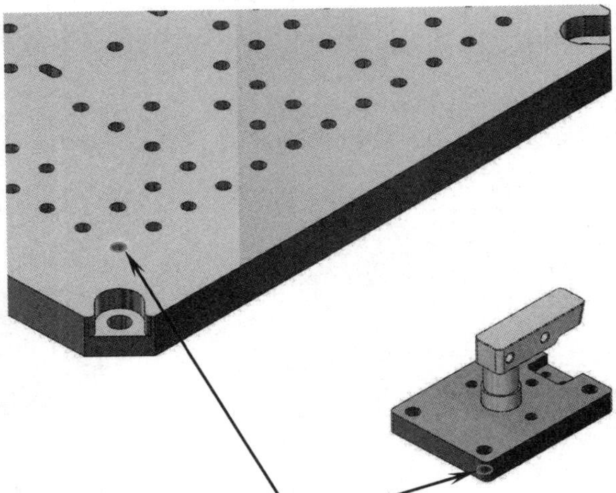

Locate the bottom edge and the upper edge of the 2 holes

3. Exploring the Smart-Mate options:

- Some types of Smart-Mates can be created in an assembly by dragging and dropping one entity to another.

- Depending on the entity that you drag, you will get different mate result. Use either a linear or circular edge of the model, a planar or cylindrical face, or a vertex to drag with Smart-Mates.

 Concentric & Coincident 2 circular edges

 Concentric 2 cylindrical faces

 Coincident 2 linear edges

 Coincident 2 planar faces

 Coincident 2 vertices

 Coincident 2 origins or coordinate systems

Start Here - Hold the **ALT** key, drag the hidden edge of the hole to the upper edge of the mating hole but do not release the mouse. Hover the cursor over the edge of the hole until the Smart-Mate symbol appears, then release the mouse button.

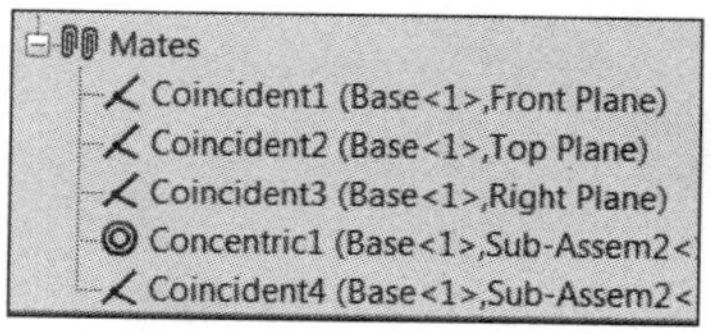

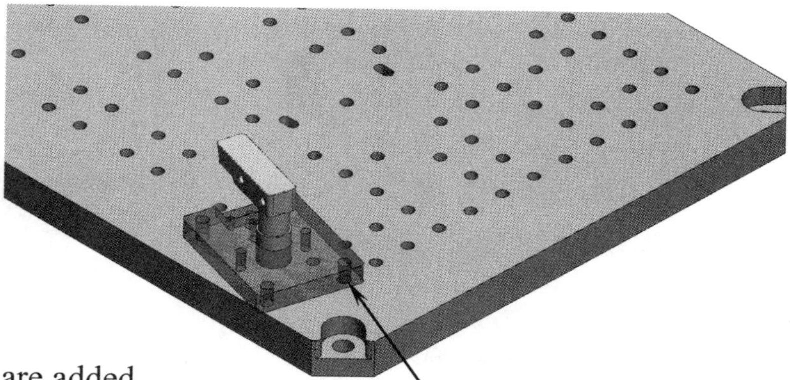

- Two new mates are added automatically. Expand the Mates folder to see them.

 Smart-Mate symbol for Concentric & Coincident

4. Using Smart-Mate Concentric:

- The concentric mate is created when two cylindrical surfaces are dragged and dropped onto one another.

- Hold the **ALT** key, drag the cylindrical face of the 1st hole and drop on the cylindrical face of the 2nd hole. The mouse cursor must be stopped on an entity and must not be moving in order for the Smart-Mate symbol to appear.

- Release the mouse cursor when the concentric symbol pops up, click **OK** on the pop-up toolbar to accept the concentric mate.

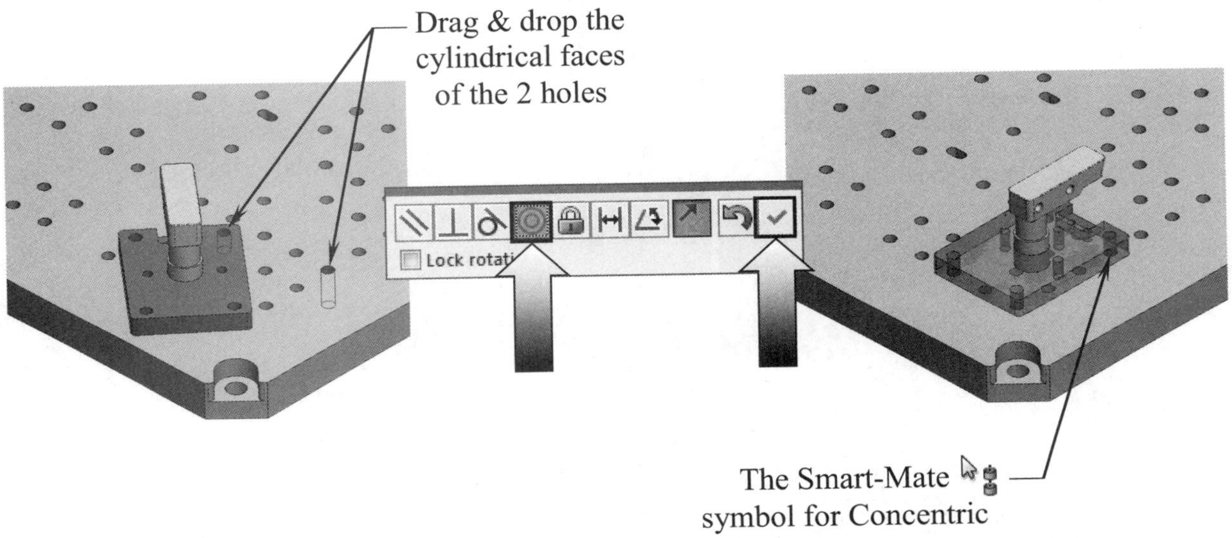

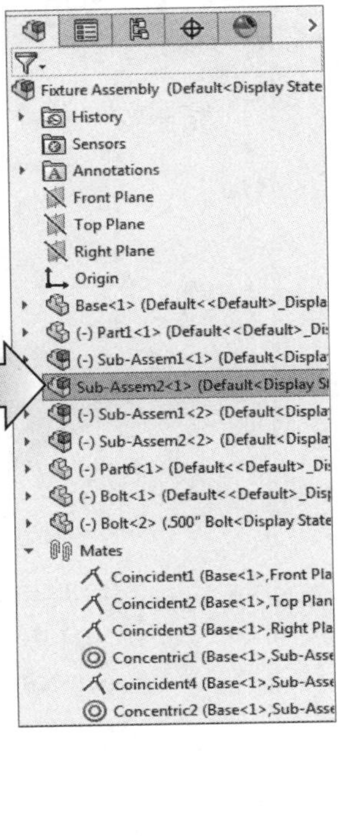

- The sub assembly becomes fully defined. There is no minus sign (-) before the name Sub-Assem2.

- The Base component is considered the parent part, it was previously mated to the 3 planes of the assembly, therefore it is also fully defined. It does not have the minus sign before its name.

- The rest of the components and sub-assemblies are still under defined, they still have 6 degrees of freedom to move or rotate about any direction.

- We are going to explore the Smart-Mates some more and assemble the entire assembly using this dynamic mate options.

5. Creating a Smart-Mate Concentric & Coincident:

- Zoom in closer between the two components that will get mated next.

- Hold the **ALT** key, drag and drop the hidden edge of the hole1 onto the upper edge of the hole2 as noted.

- Keep the mouse cursor steady until the Smart-Mates symbol appears, and then release the mouse button.

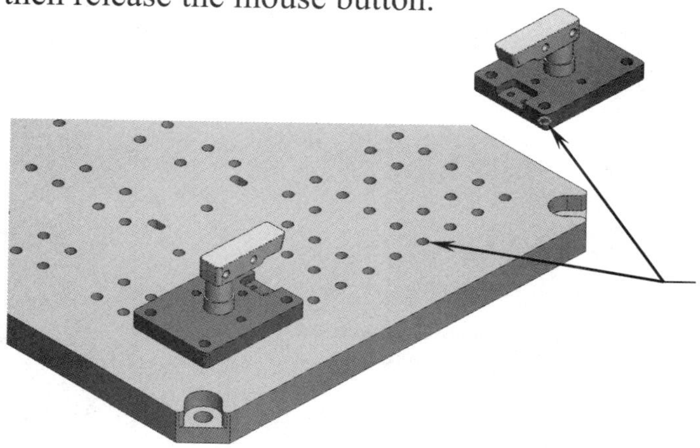

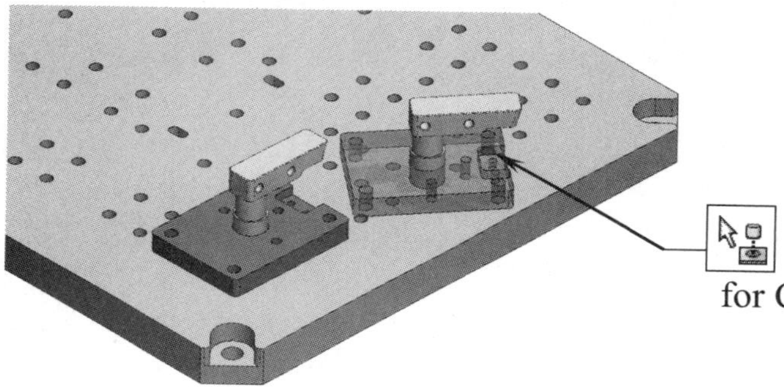

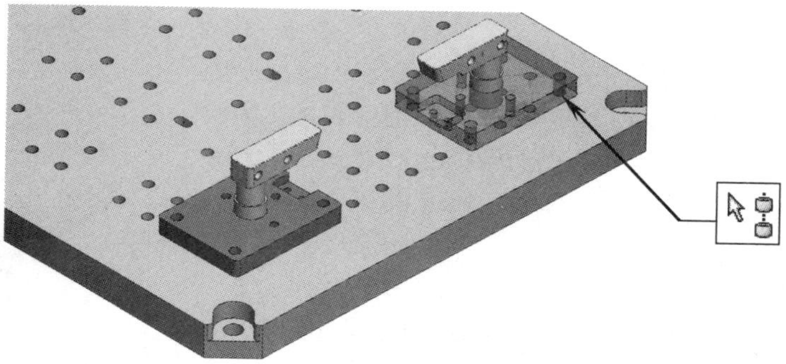

- Next, drag and drop the cylindrical face of hole1 to the cylindrical face of hole2, wait for the Smart-Mate Concentric symbol to appear, then click the check mark to accept it.

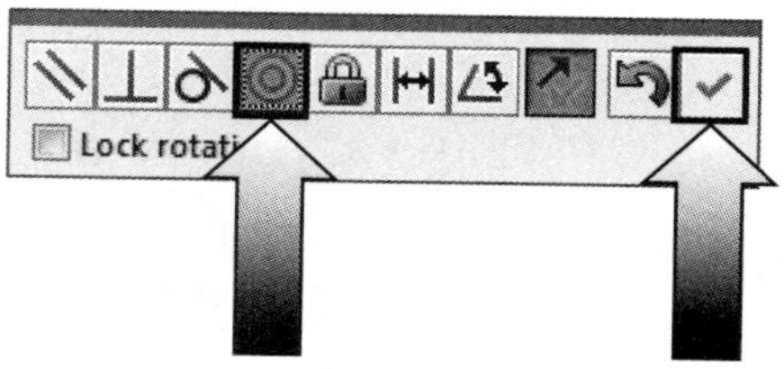

6. Repeating the previous Mate:

- Move the cylindrical part above the base as shown.

- We are going to use the same mate techniques to assemble this part.

- The Explode Lines are added for clarity only, you do not have to add them.

- Hold the **ALT** key, drag & drop the hidden edge of the hole in the cylindrical part onto the upper edge of the mating hole in the base.

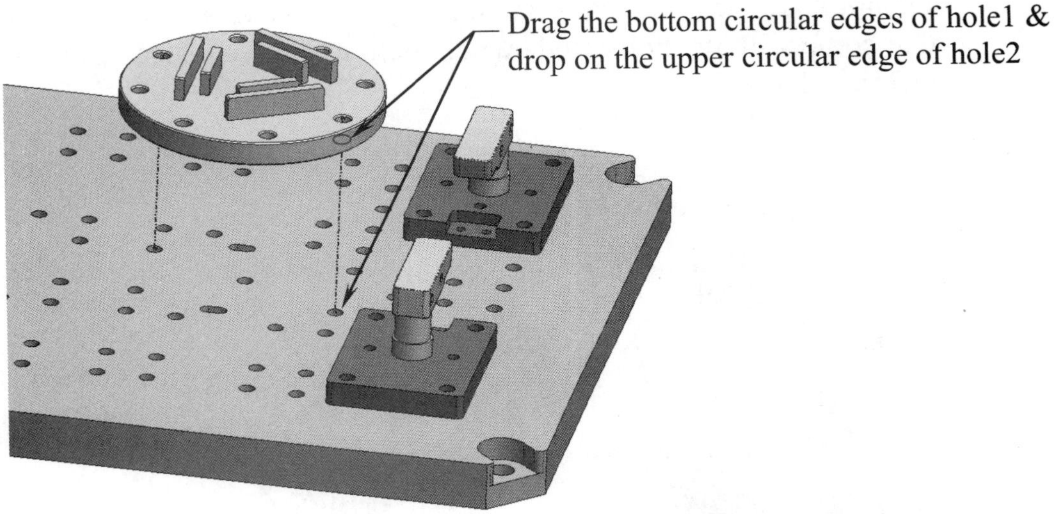

- If done properly, there should be two mates added to the selected entities already. Check the Mates group and look for the new Concentric and Coincident mates.

- Repeat the same step and mate one other hole of the same components, to fully define their positions.

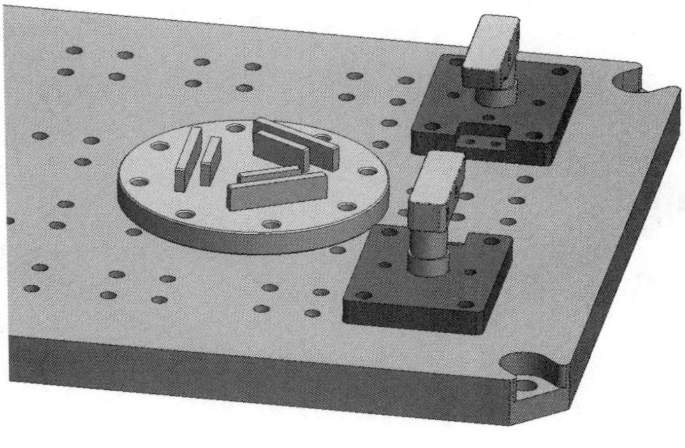

7. Mating other components:

- Since the holes in the components were patterned and have the exact same diameters, two mates per component would be enough to fully define them.

- The Explode Lines are added for clarity again, you do not need to add them.

- Use the same techniques and add the Smart-Mates to the other components, use the explode lines for reference locations, and only create two mates for each component.

- Do not mate the bolts just yet, we are going to take a look at the configurations that come with the bolts, and switch them to different sizes and use them in different locations.

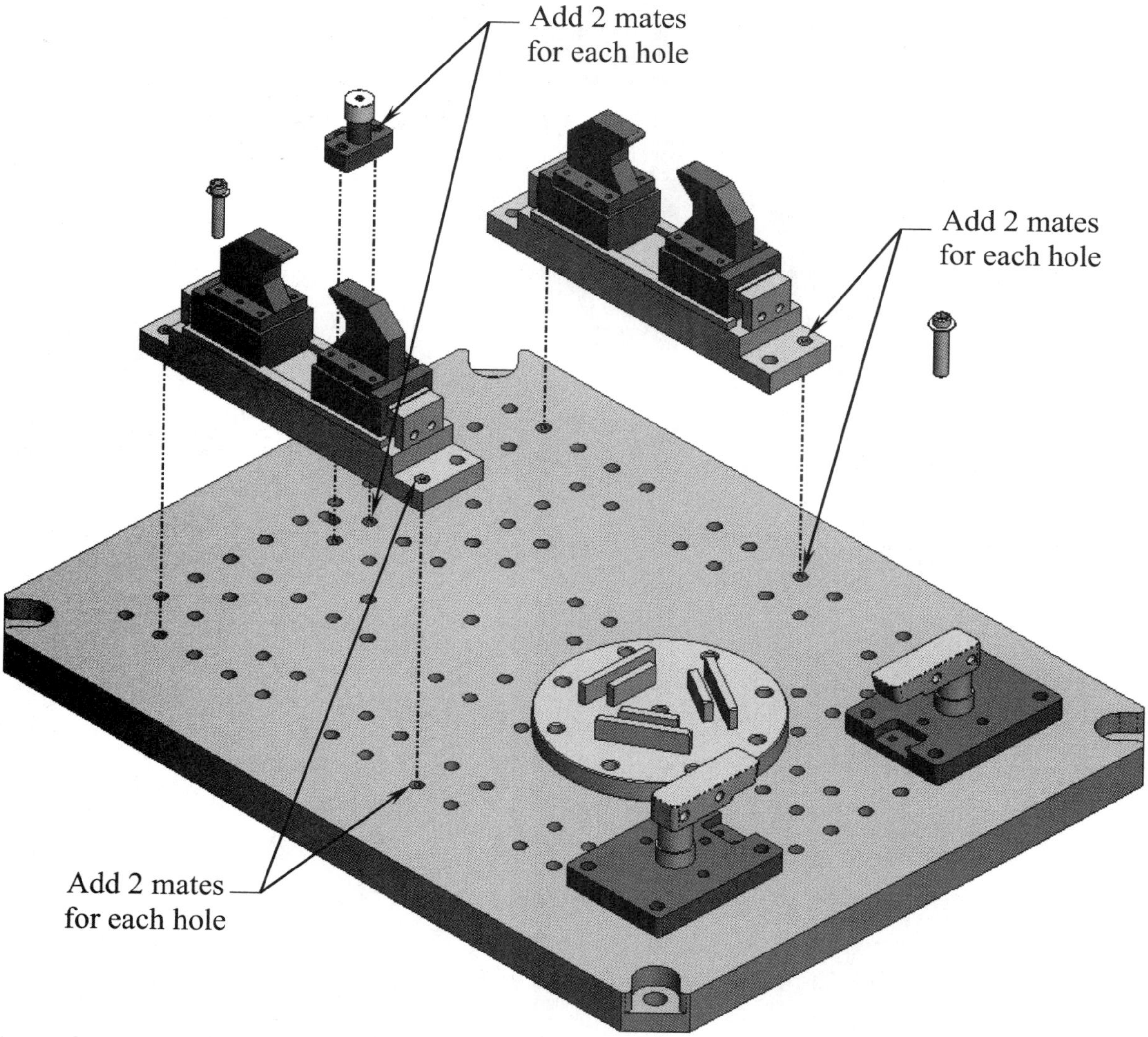

8. Checking the status of the components:

- After adding two mates to each component, the FeatureManager updates and shows only the minus signs (-) before the bolts.

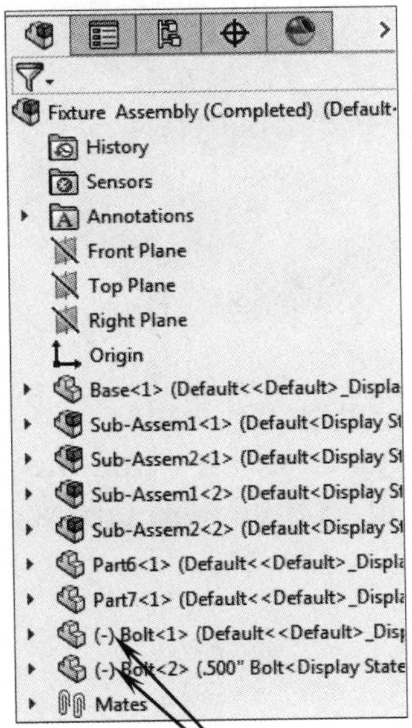

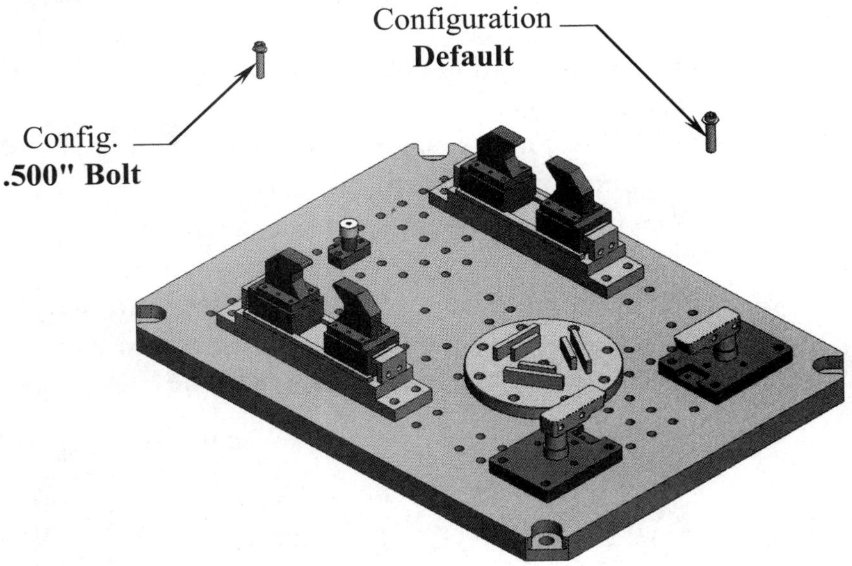

The minus sign (-) appears before the parts that still free move or rotate...

9. Switching Configuration:

- The Bolt has 2 configurations, the **Default** and the **.500"**.

- We have been using the Default size for most of the components, we now need 2 of the .500" for the next part.

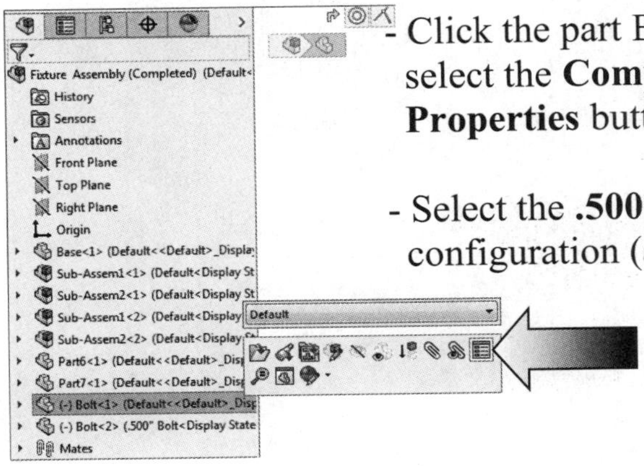

- Click the part Bolt and select the **Component-Properties** button (arrow).

- Select the **.500"** configuration (arrow).

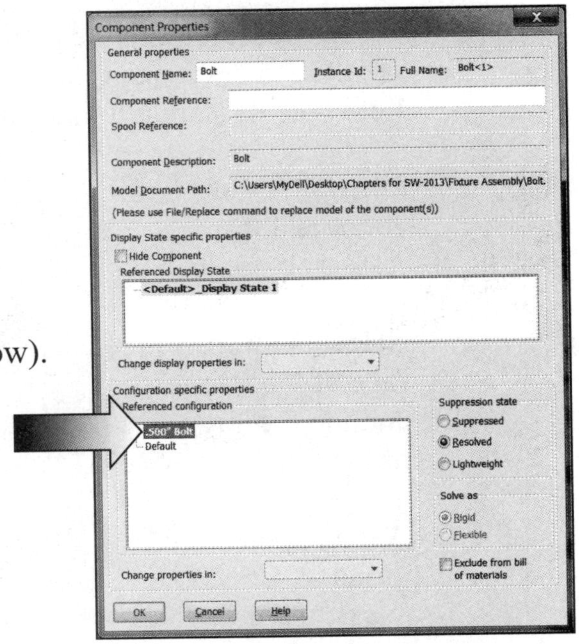

10. Creating an instance of the .500" bolt:

An instance of the bolt is mated to the hole

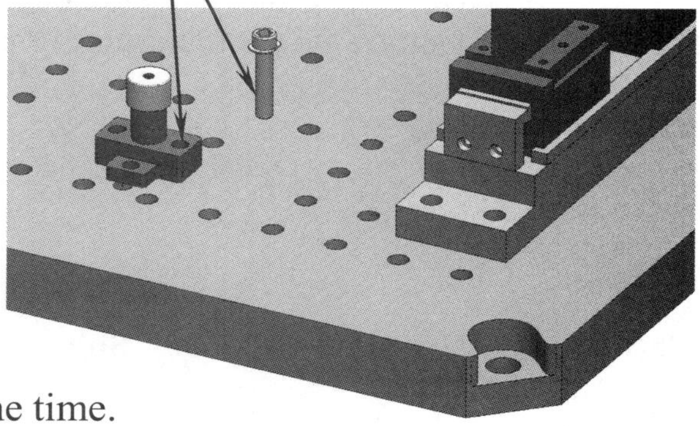

- When holding the Alt key and dragging a component the smart-mate is activated for mating the 2 components.

- But if you hold the Control key and drag a component, SOLIDWORKS makes a copy of the component and smart-mates it to the other component at the same time.

- <u>Hold</u> the **Control** key, drag and drop (the shaft body) <u>an instance</u> of the bolt to the mating hole as pictured below. Release the mouse button when the smart-mate symbol appears. Click the Flip Alignment button if needed (arrow).

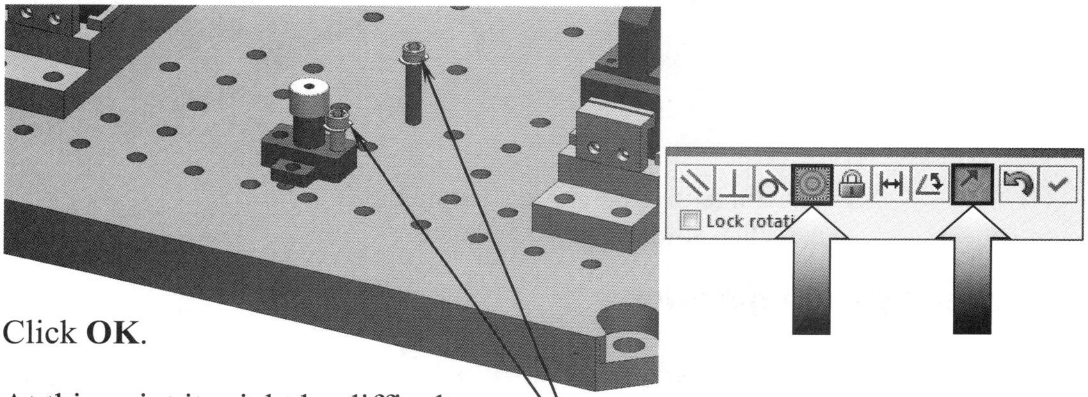

- Click **OK**.

- At this point it might be difficult to see the 2 faces to apply the next mate. Let's use the standard mates instead.

Hold the Control key and drag & drop a copy of the bolt to the hole

- Click the **Mate**  command from the Assembly toolbar.

- Select the **bottom face** of the flange and the **top face** of the Part6.

- A coincident mate is added. Click **OK** to exit the mate.

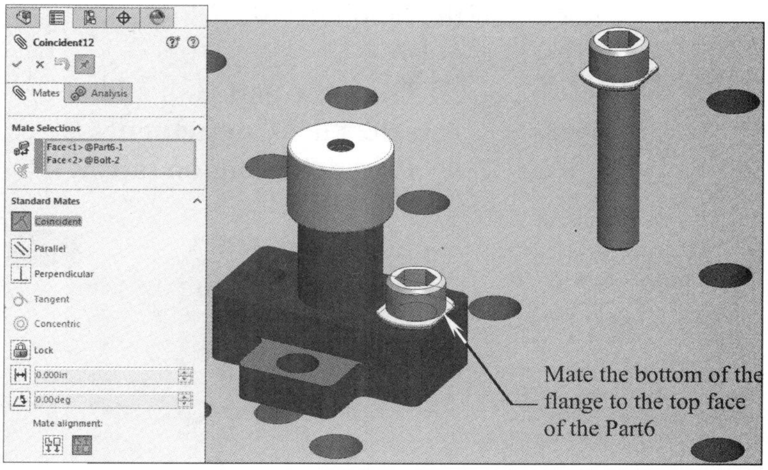

11. Creating another instance of the bolt:

- Move the Default-Bolt closer to the Sub-Assembly1 on the right as noted.

- Hold the **Control** key, drag and drop an instance of the (default) bolt to the mating hole as noted. Look for the smart-mate symbol before releasing the mouse button.

- Click the Flip Mate Alignment button if needed (arrow).

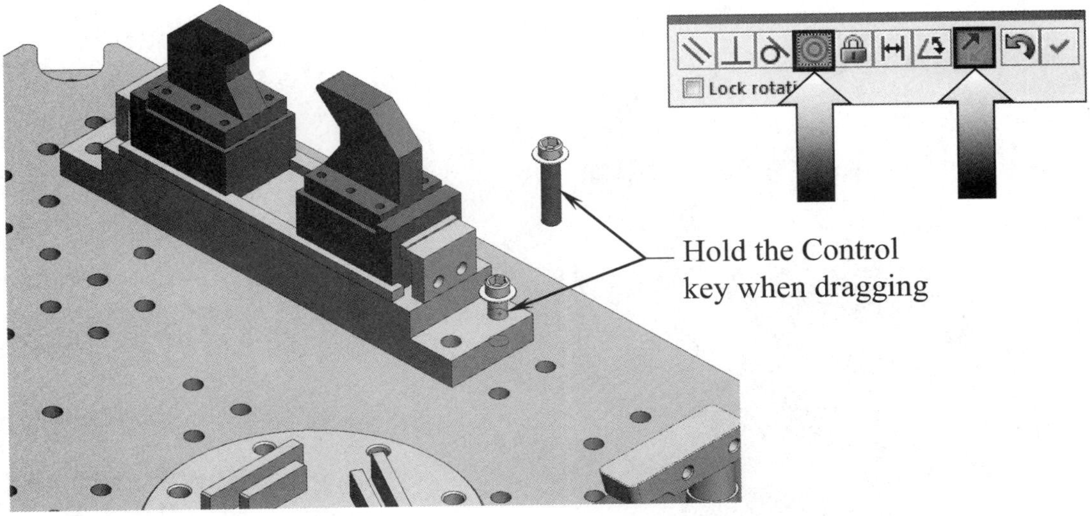

- Click **OK** to close the mate toolbar.

- It would be easier to use the standard mates again for the next mate.

- Click the **Mate** command  from the assembly toolbar.

- Select the **bottom face** of the flange and the **top face** of the Part2 as noted.

- A **coincident** mate is added automatically.

- Click **OK**.

- The bolt still has one degree of freedom left.

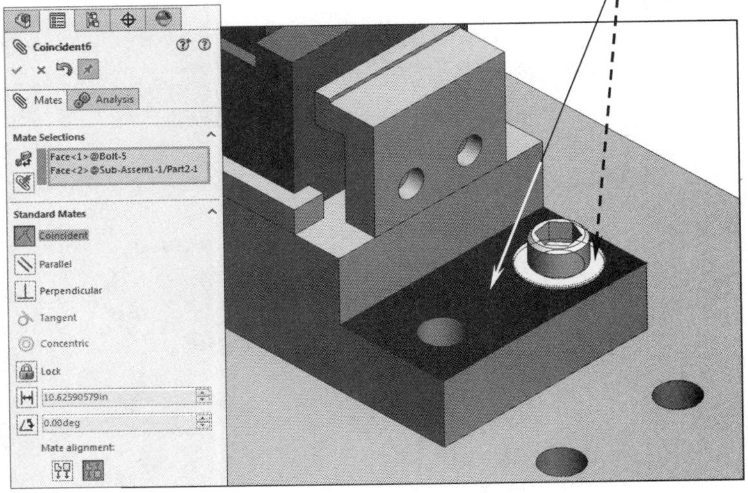

12. Adding more bolts:

- Rotate around to the other side of the sub-assembly1.

- <u>Hold</u> the <u>CONTROL</u> key and drag the default-bolt to make a copy and place it on the right of the Part2.

- Hold the Control key again, drag the copy of the default bolt to the mating hole as indicated. Look for the smart-mate symbol before releasing the mouse button. Click the Flip Mate Alignment if needed (arrow).

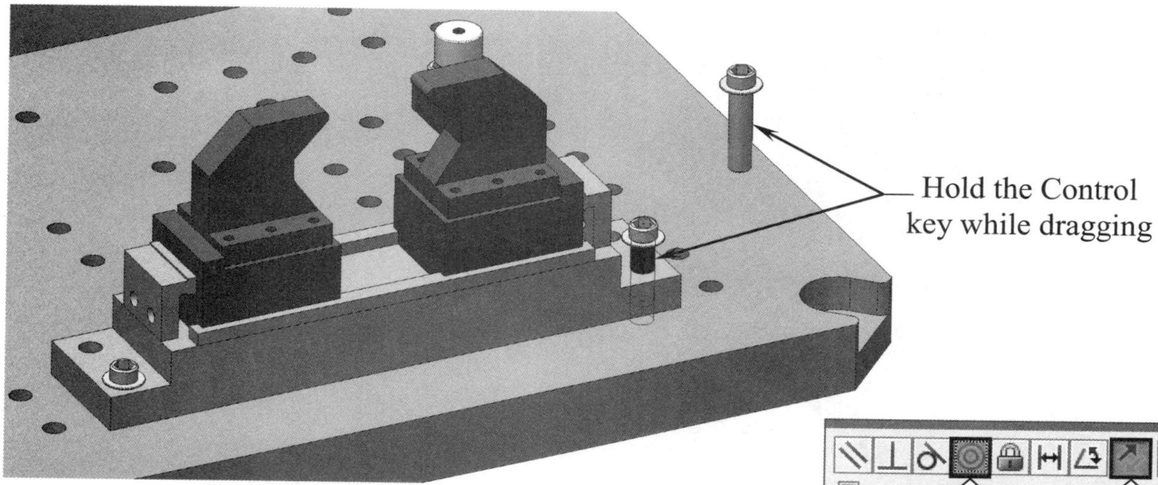

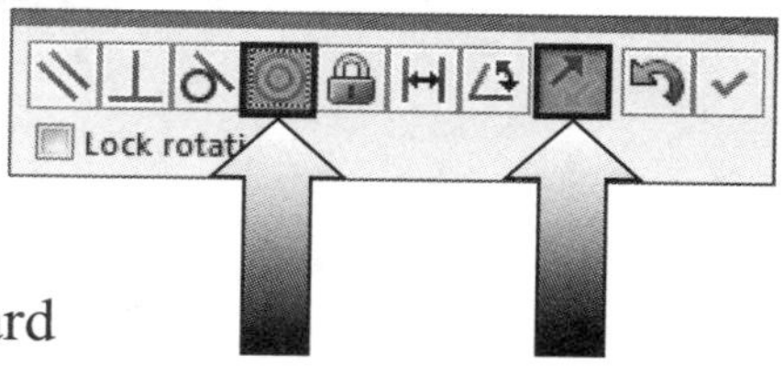

- Once again, it would be easier to use the standard mates for the next step, since we cannot really see the two mating faces very well.

- Click **Mate** .

- Select the **bottom face** of the flange and the **top face** of the Part2.

- Another **coincident** mate is added.

- Click **OK** to exit the mate mode.

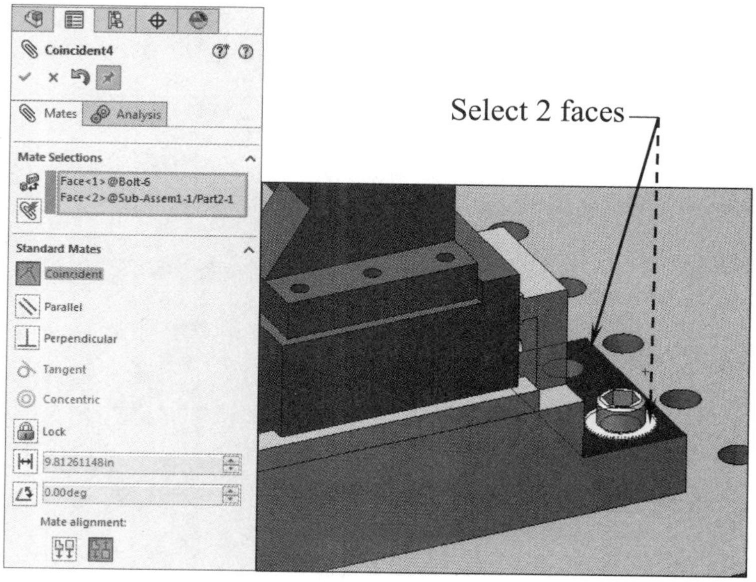

13. Repeating:

- For practice purposes, we are going to add more instances of the bolts to the other components.

- Keep in mind that fasteners do not have to be fully defined. Each bolt only needs two mates, and even though they still rotate, the assembly will not be effected at all.

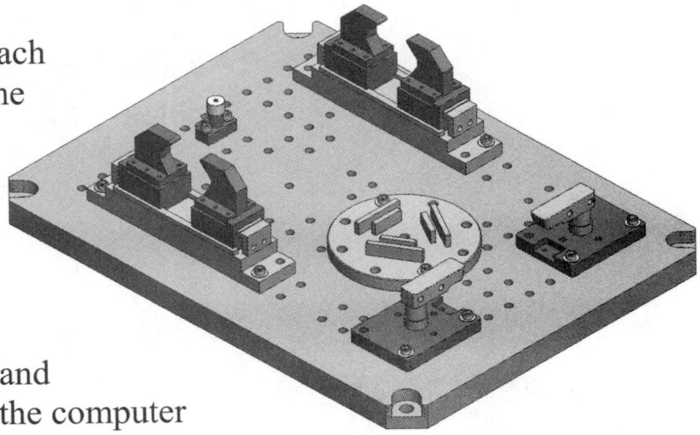

- By using one less mate for each component you can reduce the file size of this assembly by about 10%. It will also helps reduce the time that it takes to rebuild the assembly every time a change is applied. In other words, the less mates (and less components), the faster the computer performance.

14. Saving your work:

- Save your work as **Fixture Assemly.sldasm** and overwrite the existing file when prompted.

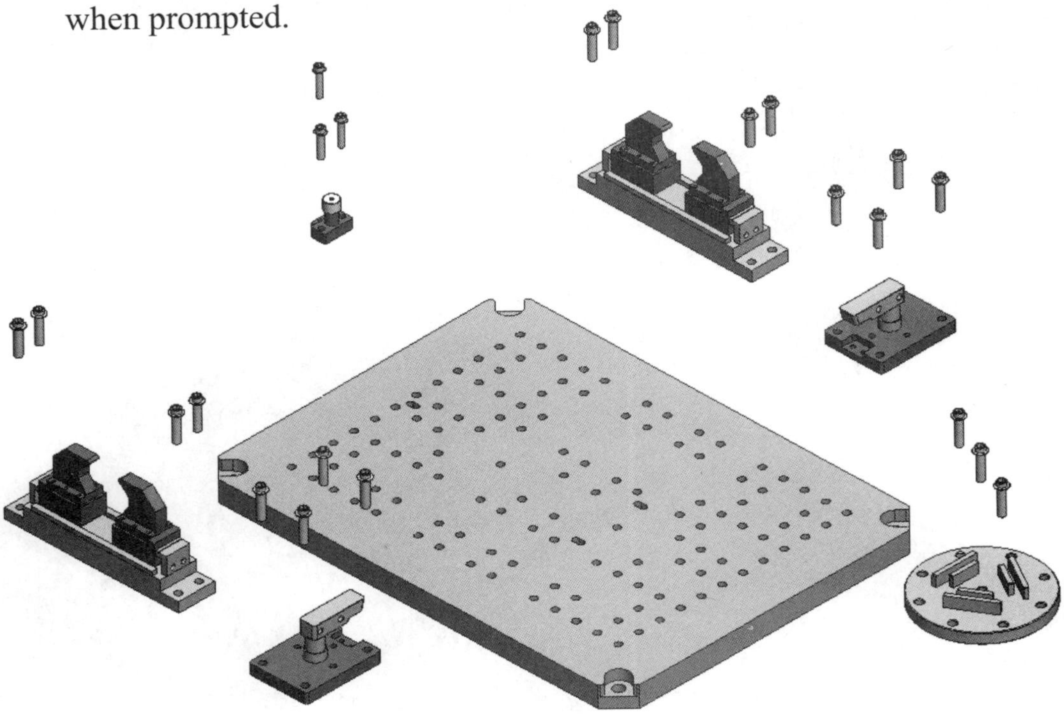

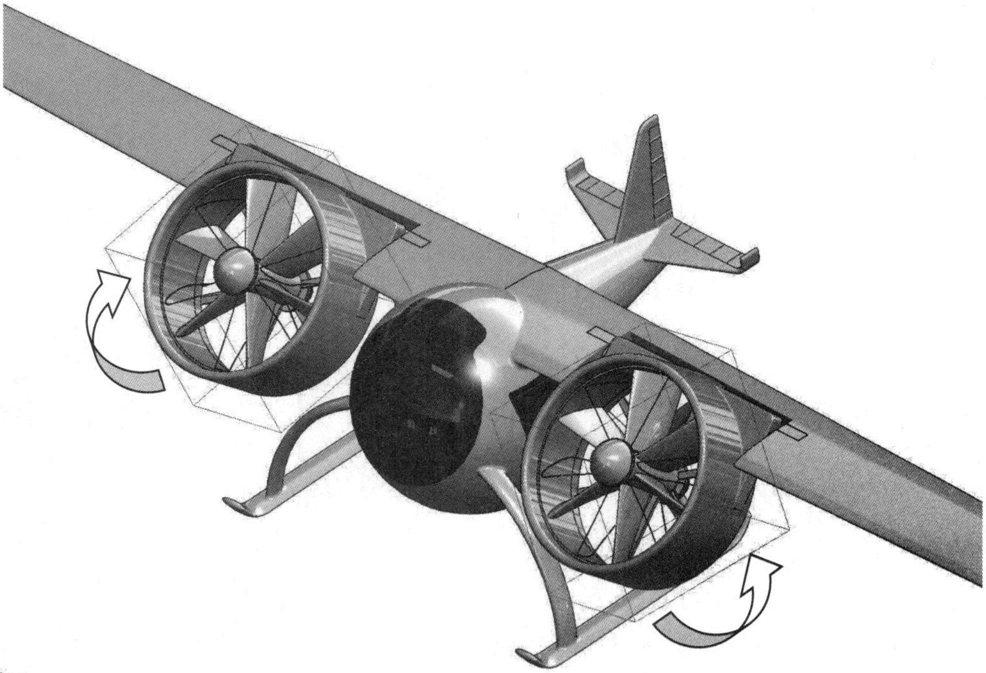

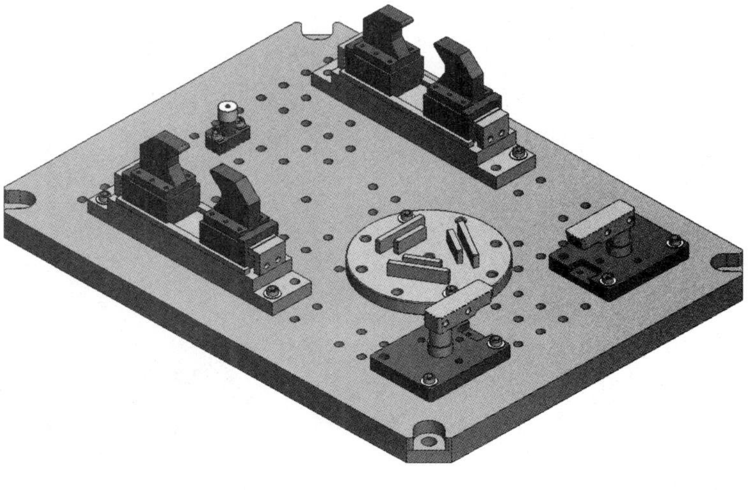

CHAPTER 13

Top-Down Assembly

Top-Down Assembly
Car Remote Control Housing

Top Down Assembly drives multiple part designs using a single "parent" part and creates in-context features. Top Down approach allows the SOLIDWORKS user to quickly put together the parametric models without much effort and time.

For example, you can build a shaft in the context of an assembly. Then if a new plate with a mating hole to the shaft is required, the mating hole can be built by referencing the edge (diameter) of a shaft. Thus, it establishes the parent and child relationship of the shaft and the mating hole. And if the shaft diameter changes, it will automatically change the corresponding mating hole diameter as well.

There are three methods in Top Down Assembly mode:

- Individual features can be designed top down by referencing other parts in the assembly, as in the case of the shaft and hole described above.
- Complete parts can be built with top down methods by creating new components within the context of the assembly. The component you build is actually mated to another existing component in the assembly.
- An entire assembly can be designed from the top down as well, by first building a layout sketch that defines component locations, key dimensions, etc. Then build 3D parts using one of the methods above, so the 3D parts follow the sketch for their size and location.

Whenever you create a part or feature using top down techniques, external references are created to the geometry you referenced. These references can be locked, broken, or deleted if needed.

Top-Down Assembly
Car Remote Control Housing

View Orientation Hot Keys:

Ctrl + 1 = Front View
Ctrl + 2 = Back View
Ctrl + 3 = Left View
Ctrl + 4 = Right View
Ctrl + 5 = Top View
Ctrl + 6 = Bottom View
Ctrl + 7 = Isometric View
Ctrl + 8 = Normal To Selection

Dimensioning Standards: **ANSI**

Units: **INCHES** – 3 Decimals

Tools Needed:

Make Assembly	New Part	Convert Entities
Extruded Boss/Base	Shell	Fillet
Offset Entities	Explode View	Section View

1. Opening a part document:

- Browse to the training folder and open the part document named: **Square Remote Top.sldprt**

- Individual features can be designed by referencing other parts in the assembly. These external references are created when one document is dependent on another document for its solution. If the referenced document changes, the dependent document changes also.

2. Making an assembly from part:

- The construction of the new part will be done in the context of an assembly. The existing geometry of the Remote Bottom will be used to create the features for the Remote Bottom.

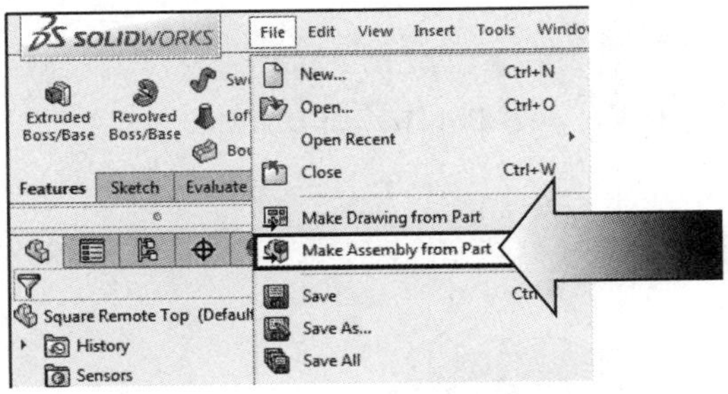

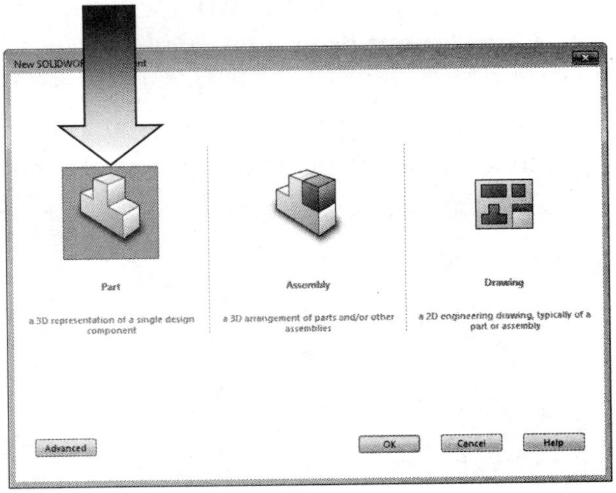

- Select **File / Make Assembly from Part** (arrow).

- Select the **Part Template** (arrow) if prompted.

3. Placing the 1st component:

- If the Origin is not shown in the new assembly document click: **View, Hide/Show, Origins**.

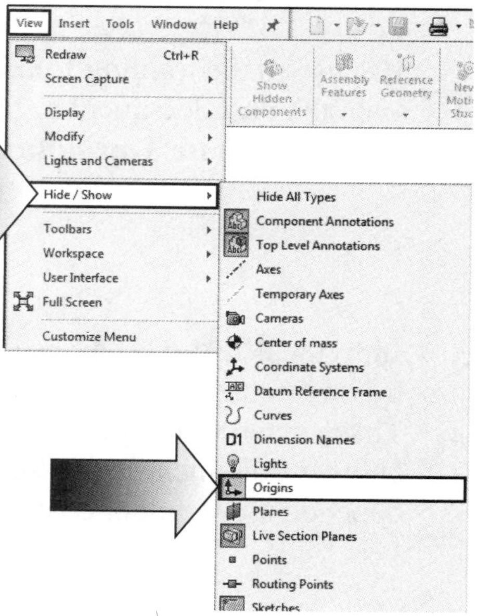

- Hover the cursor over the origin, look for the Inference Origin symbol (the double arrows symbol) and place the 1st part there.

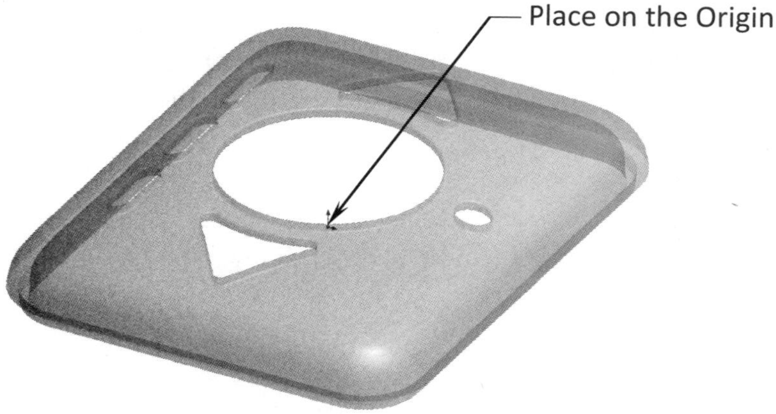

4. Creating a new part:

- Change to the **Assembly** tool tab and select **<u>New Part</u>** under the **Insert-Component** drop down.

- Select the **<u>Top</u>** plane to reference the new part (arrow). A new InPlace mate is created under the Mates group (arrow).

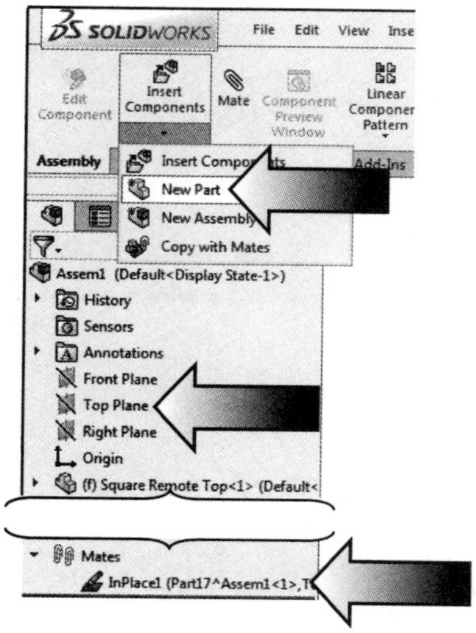

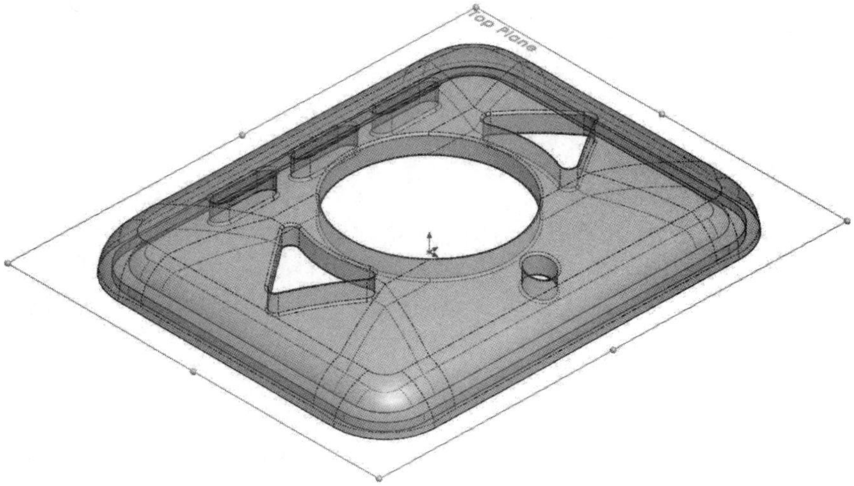

- The Edit Component command  is activated and a new sketch is also open on the Top plane.

- Change to the Bottom orientation (Ctrl+6).

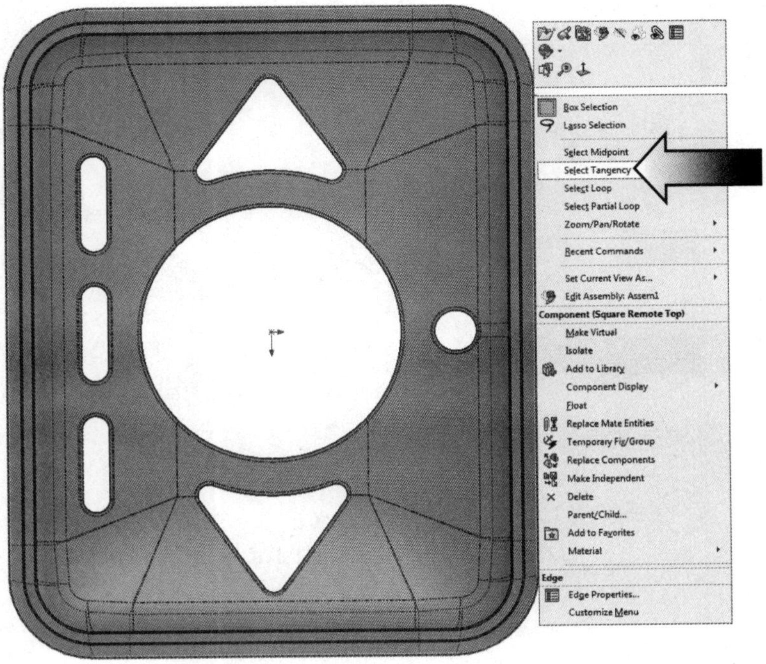

5. Converting the entities:

- One of the quick ways to create new sketch entities is to use the Convert Entities tool.

- Right click one of the outer edges of the Remote Top and pick: **Select Tangency**.

- All the edges that are tangent to each other are selected.

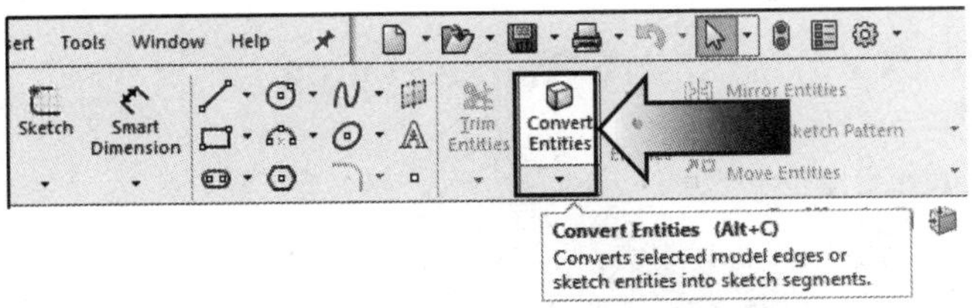

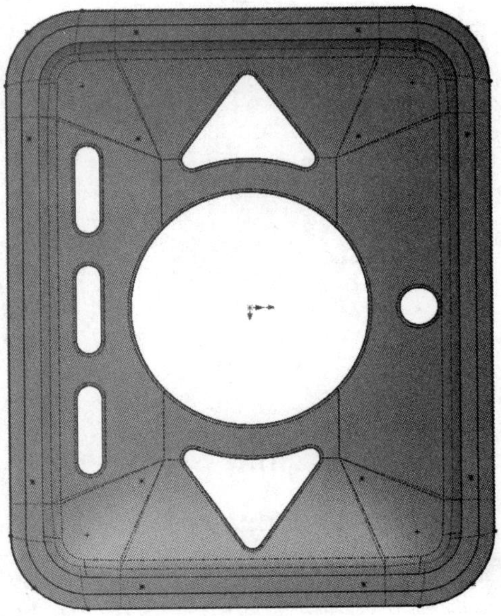

- Click the **Convert Entities** command .

- The selected edges are converted to sketch entities. An On Edge relation is added to each entity, and the sketch becomes fully defined automatically.

6. Extruding the sketch:

- Change to the **Features** tool tab and click **Extruded Boss/Base** .

- Use the default **Blind** type and click the **Reverse** button (arrow).

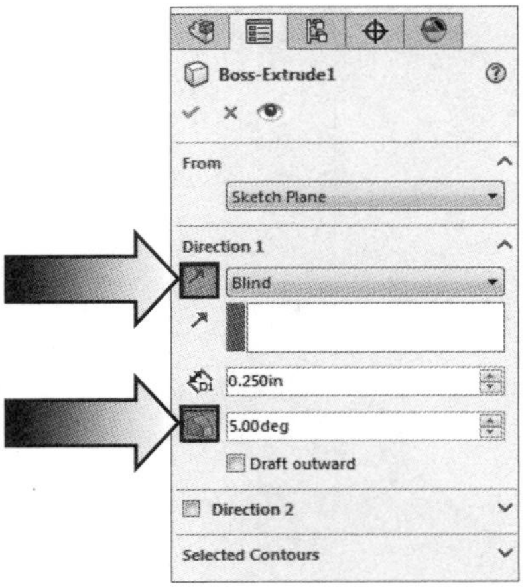

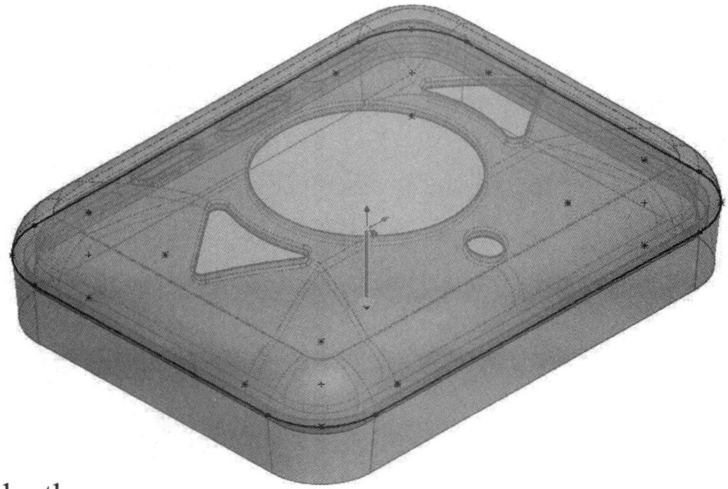

- Enter **.250in** for extrude depth.

- Enable the **Draft On/Off** button and enter **5.00deg** for draft angle.

- Click **OK**.

7. Adding the .1875in fillet:

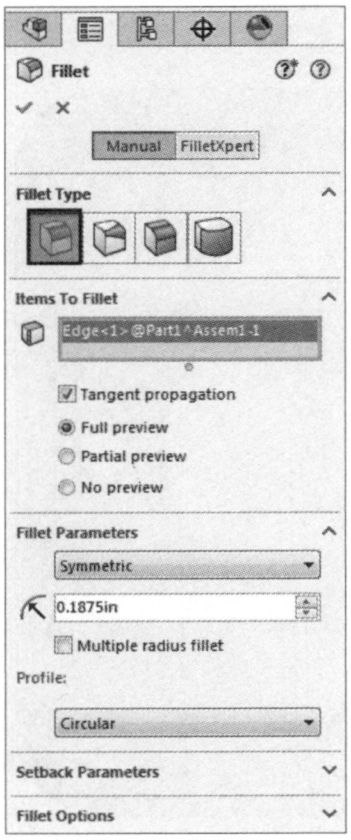

- Click the **Fillet** command and enter **.1875in** for radius.

- Use the default **Constant Size Radius** option.

- Select the **bottom edge** as noted.

- Click **OK**.

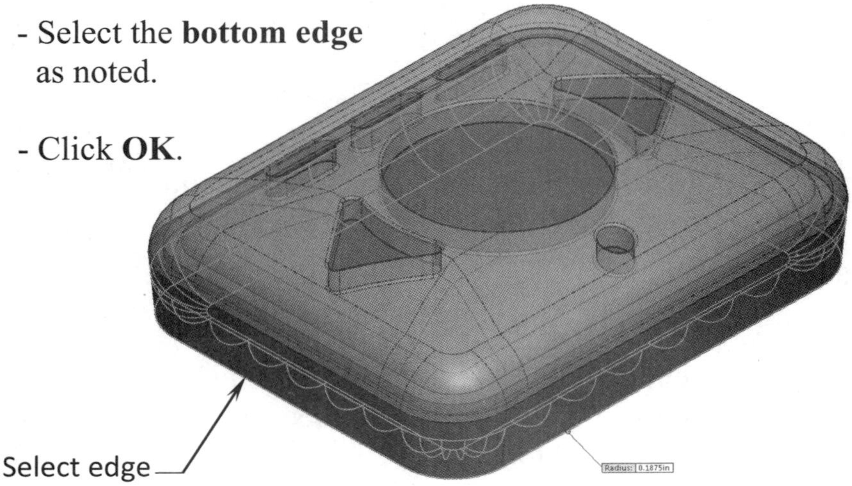

8. Shelling the part:

- The Shell command hollows out a part, but leaves open the selected faces, and creates thin-walled features on the remaining faces.

- Select the **Shell** command from the Features tool tab.

- For Wall Thickness, enter **.040in**.

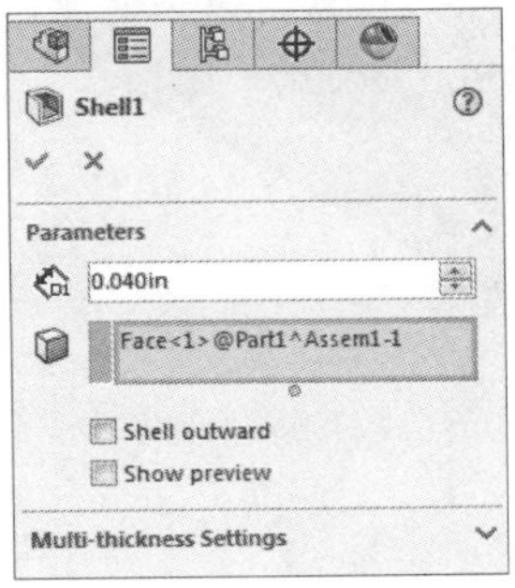

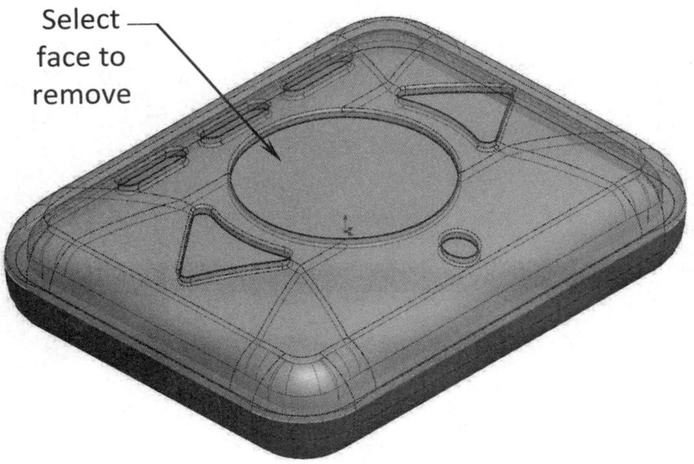

- For Faces to Remove, select the **top face** of the part.

- Click **OK**.

9. Hiding a component:

- Select the component **Square Remote Top** from the Feature tree and click: **Hide Component** (arrow).

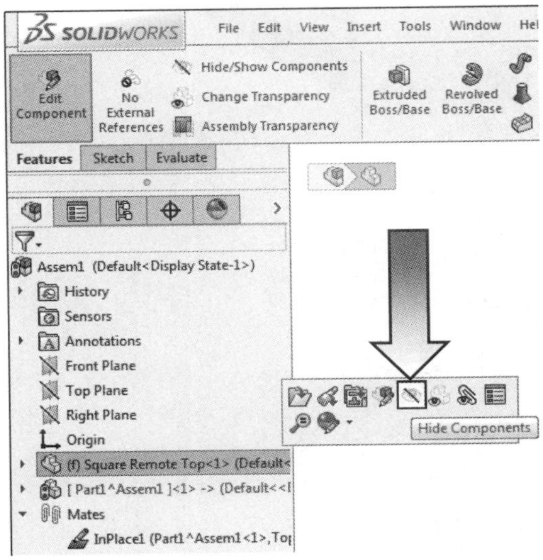

10. Adding features to the part:

- Select the **top face** of the part and open a new sketch.

- Right click one of the inner edges and pick: **Select Tangency** (arrow).

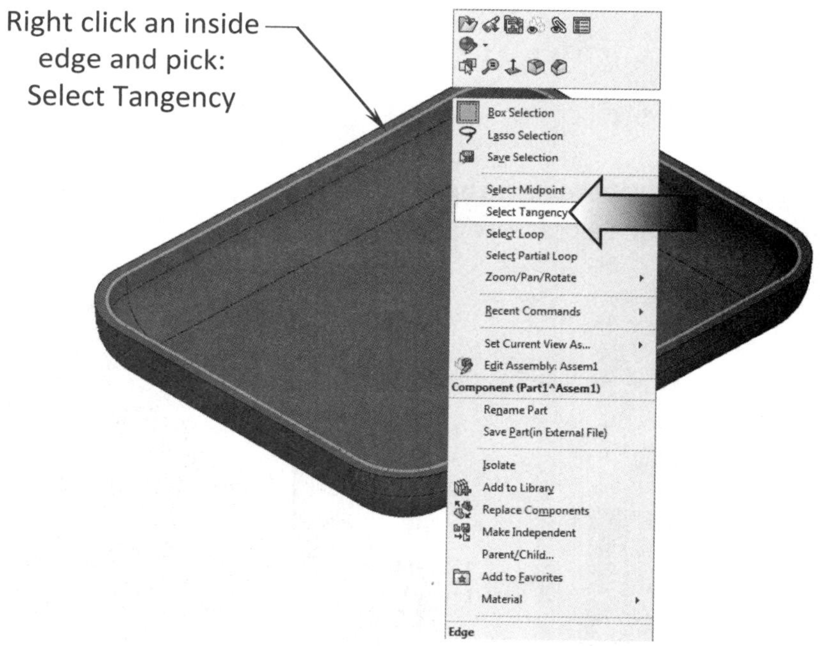

- All inside edges are selected. They will be converted to new sketch entities and used to create a boss feature on the inside of the part.

- Click the **Convert Entities** command  (arrow).

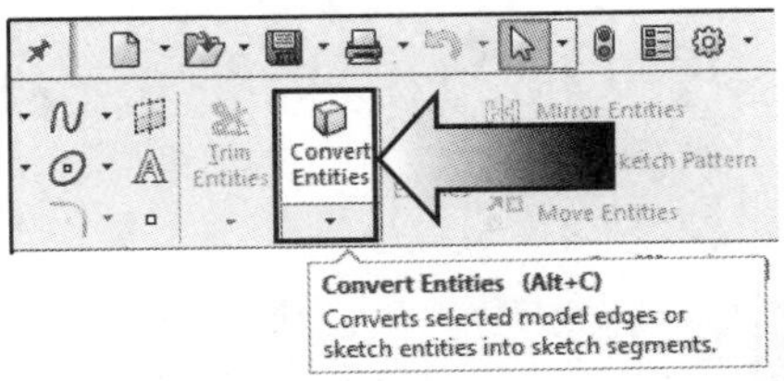

- The selected edges are converted to new sketch entities. The new entities are "tied" to the model where they were converted from. If an edge in the model is changed, the converted entity will also change.

11. Creating offset entities:

- To define the thickness of the feature an offset entity is needed.

- Right click one of the converted entities and pick: **Select Chain**. All connected entities are selected.

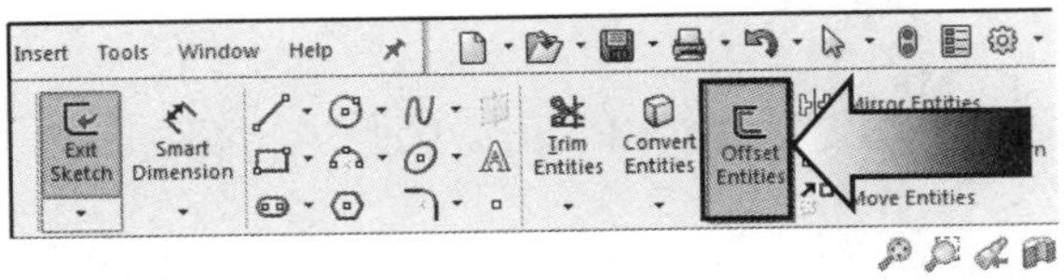

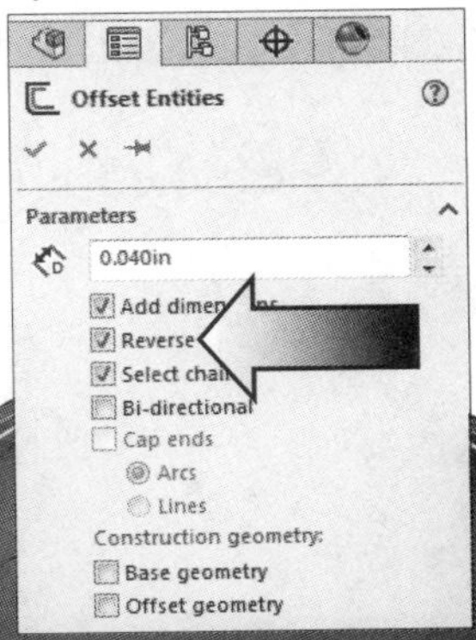

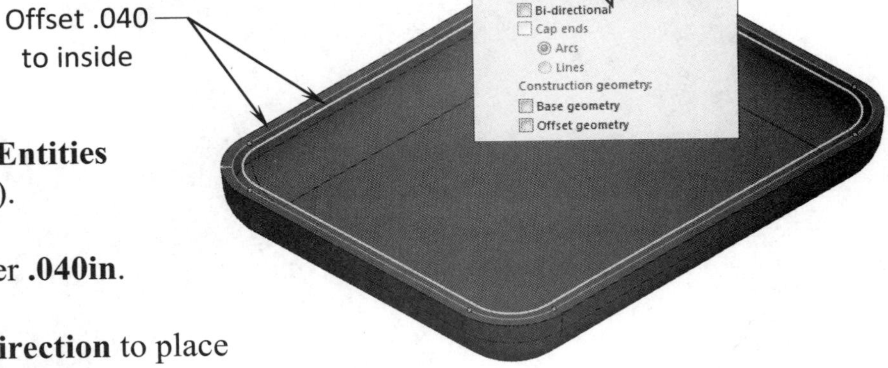

- Click the **Offset Entities** command (arrow).

- For distance, enter **.040in**.

- Click **Reverse Direction** to place the new entities on the inside.

- Click **OK**.

12. Extruding the sketch:

- Switch to the **Features** tool tab. Select the **Extruded Boss/Base** command .

- For <u>Extrude From</u>, select the **Offset** option and enter **.060in**. for distance (arrow).

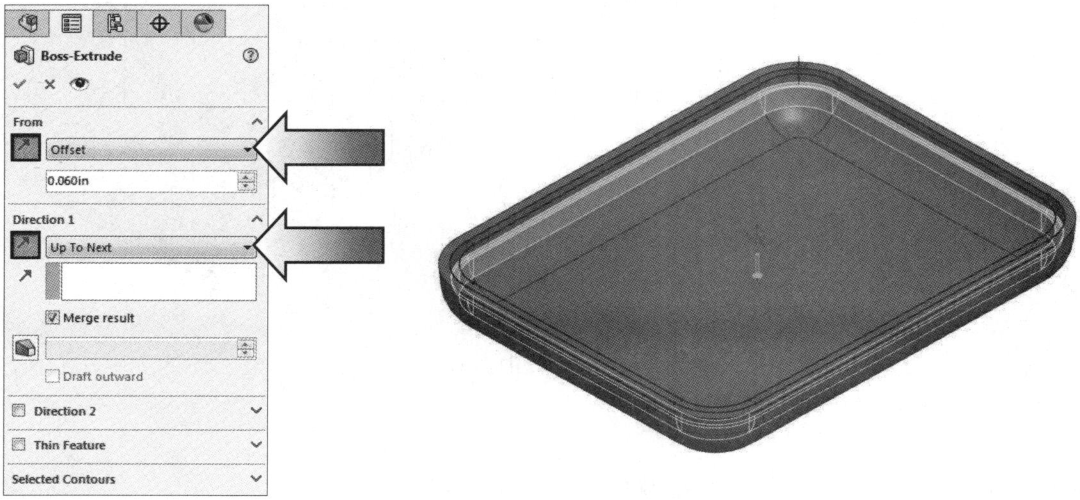

- For Direction 1, click the **Reverse** button <u>first</u> then select **Up-to-next** from the list.

- Click **OK**.

13. Adding the .125" fillet:

- Select the **Fillet** command  and enter **.125in.** for radius.

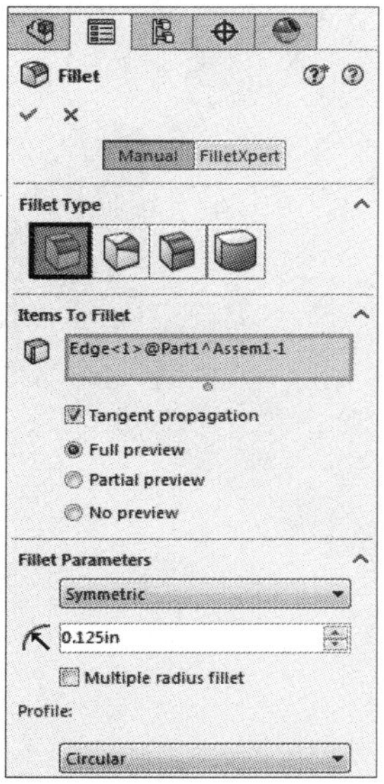

- Right click one of the edges on the inside of the part and pick: **Select Tangency**.

- The review graphics shows the fillet is being propagated to all connecting edges.

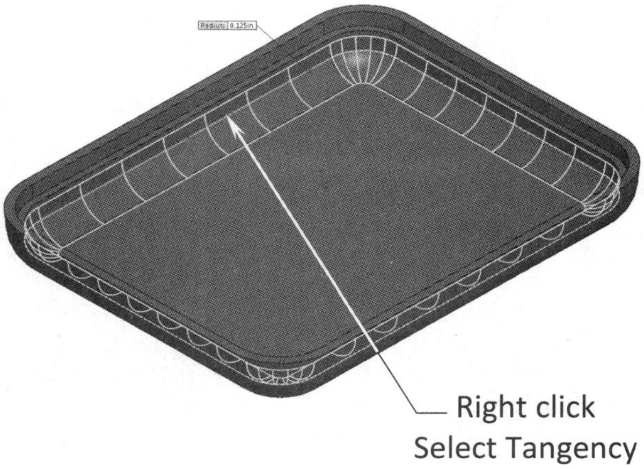

- Click **OK**.

14. Showing a component:

- Select the component **Square Remote Top** from the Feature tree and click: **Show Component** (arrow).

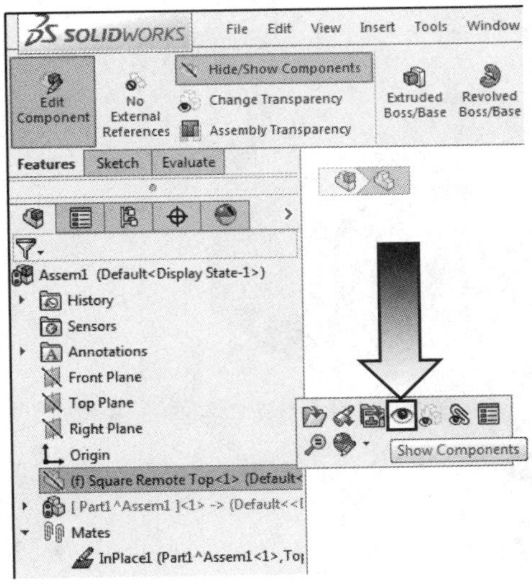

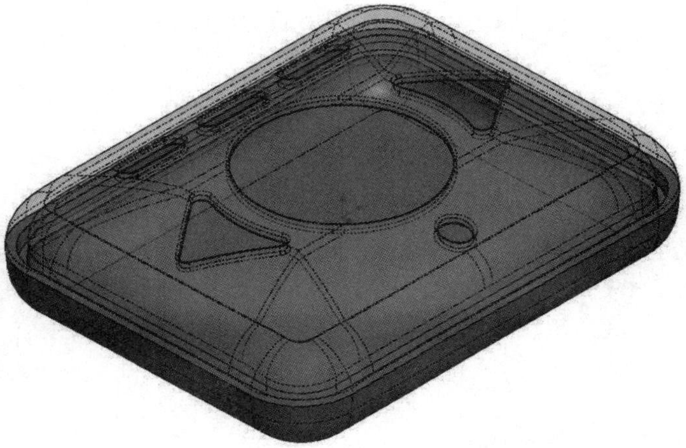

15. Creating a section view:

- Click the **Section View**  command from the **View Heads-Up** toolbar (arrow).

- For Section 1, select the **<u>Top</u>** plane as the cutting plane (arrow).

- Inspect the area where the lip meets the groove (circle).

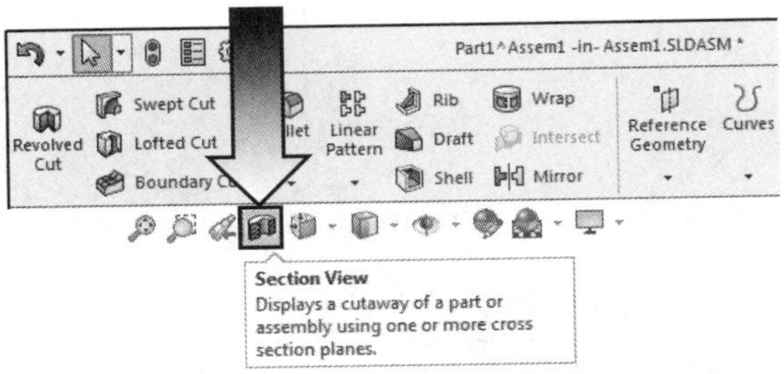

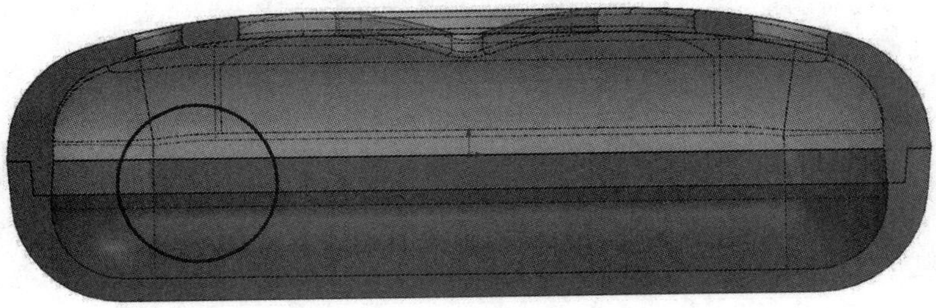

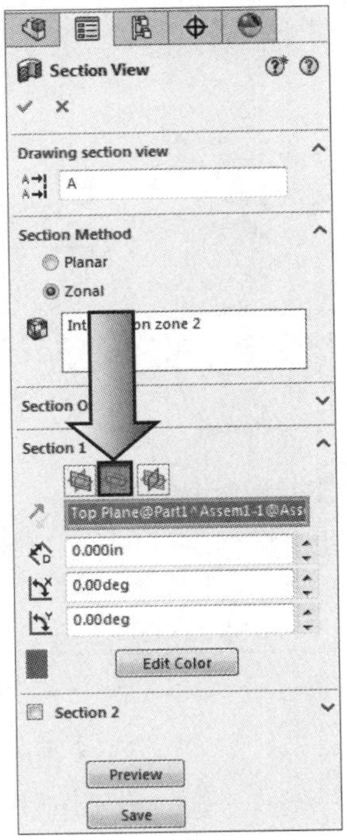

- Click off both the section  and the Edit Component commands .

16. Applying dimension changes:

- Click off the **Edit Component** button from the **Assembly** tool tab.

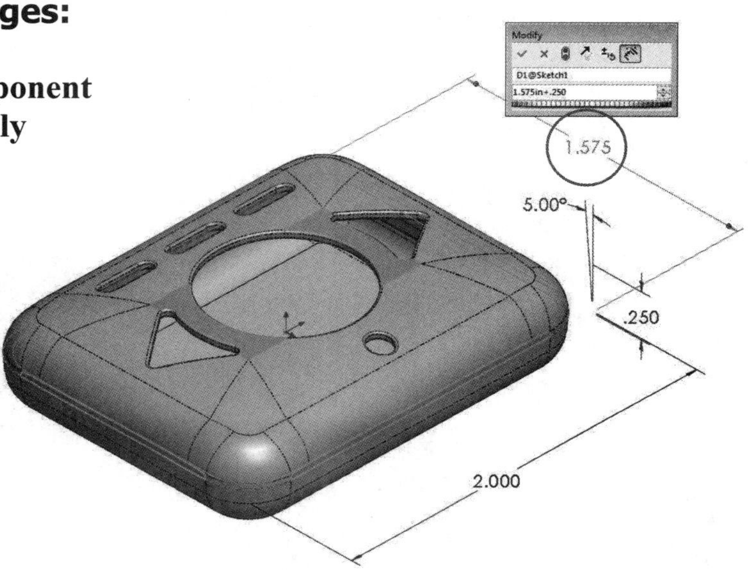

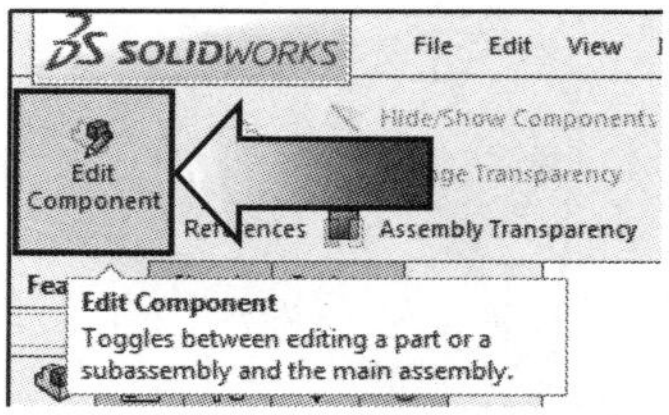

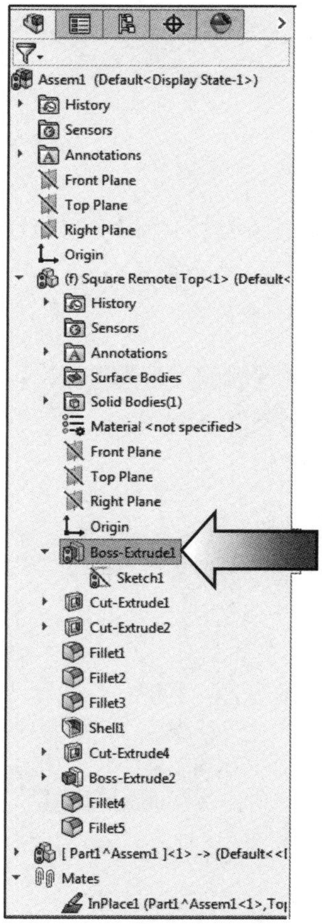

- Expand the component **Square Remote Top** from the Feature tree and double click the feature named: **Boss-Extrude1** to reveal its dimensions.

- Double click the dimension **1.575** (circle) and **add** **.250in** to it.

- Push the **Rebuild** button  (the green traffic light) to update.

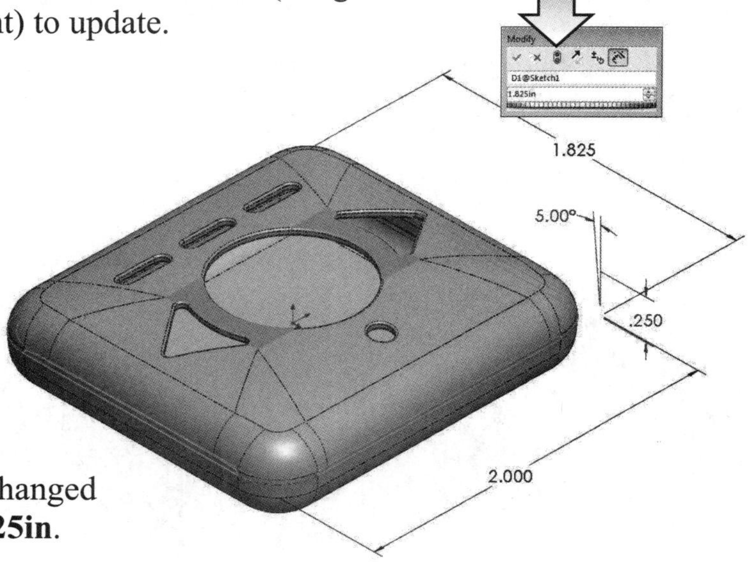

- The dimension is now changed to the new value of **1.825in**.

- Double click the dimension **2.000** and **<u>add</u>** **.250in** to it.

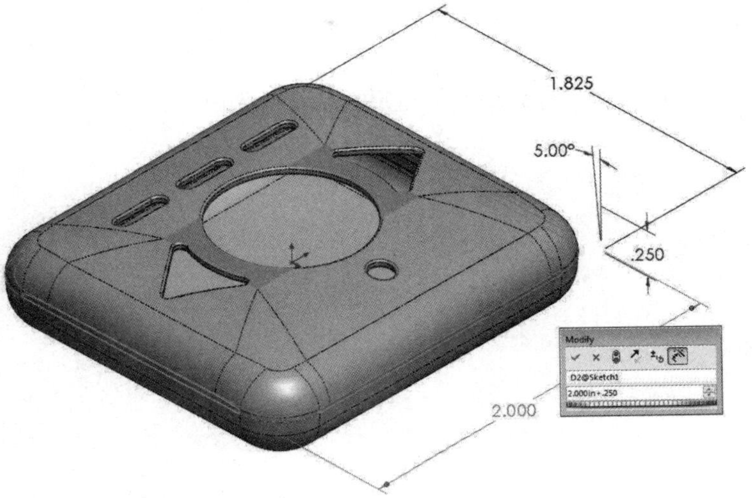

- Push the **Rebuild** button  to re-generate the change.

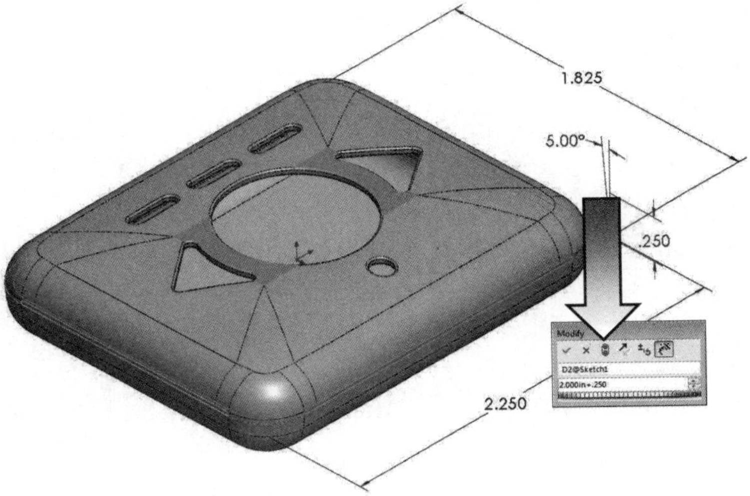

- The dimension is now changed to a new value of **2.250in**.

- Notice both components were updated? This is one of the benefits of designing new components in the context of an assembly. Any features that have external references will get updated at the same time when changes are done to them.

17. Creating an exploded view:

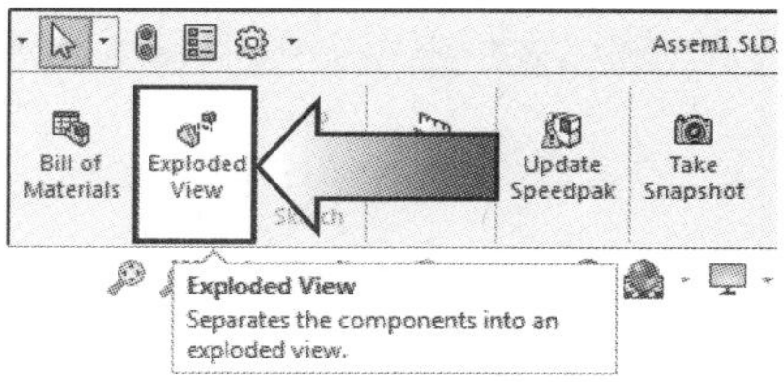

- Click **Exploded View** from the Assembly tool tab.

- Use the default Linear Explode Step option.

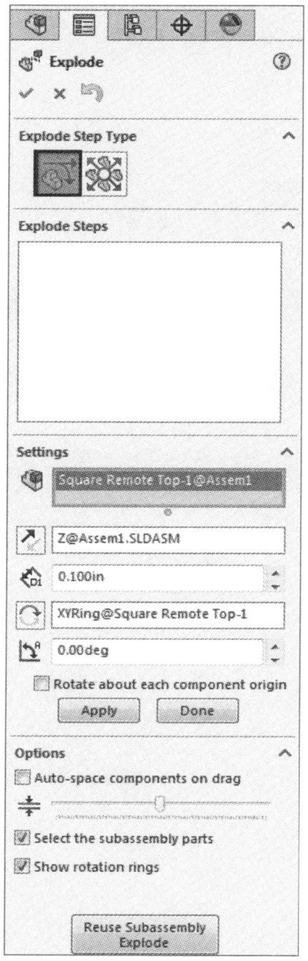

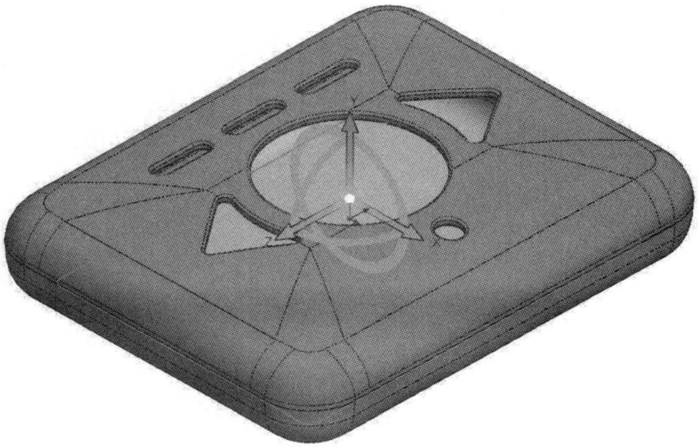

- Select the component **Square Remote Top** either in the graphics area or from the Feature tree.

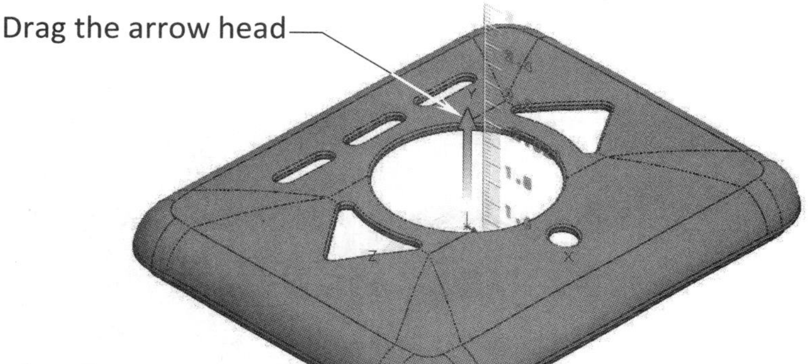

- The **Triad** appears showing the 3 direction arrows and a rotate ring.

- Hover the mouse cursor over the vertical arrow head and drag it upward.

- Click **OK**.

18. Playing the animation:

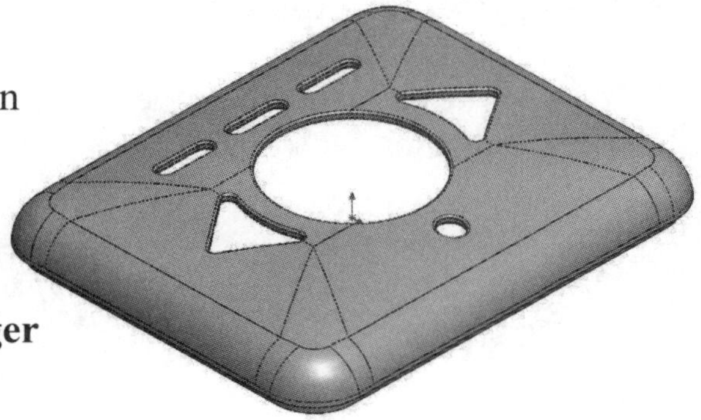

- SOLIDWORKS creates an animation for each exploded view and stores it in the Configuration Manager.

- Switch to the **ConfigurationManager** tree (arrow).

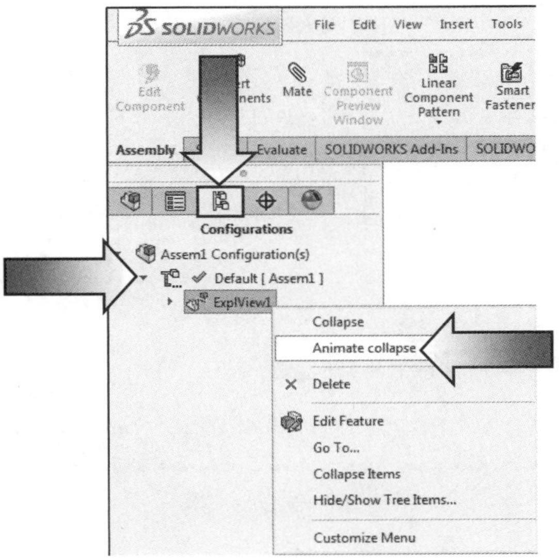

- Expand the **Default** Configuration (click the + sign).

- Right click on **ExpView1** and select: **Animate Collapse**.

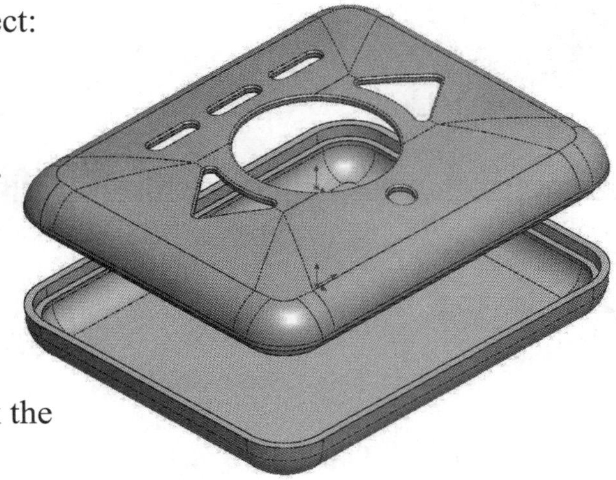

- Locate the **Animation Controller** toolbar and select the 2 options:
  * **Reciprocate**
  * **½ speed**

- Click the **Play** button to play back the animation simultaneously.

19. Changing the display mode:

- The appearance of the models can be improved using several methods, but in this lesson we will take a look at the option called **Tangent Edges Remove**.

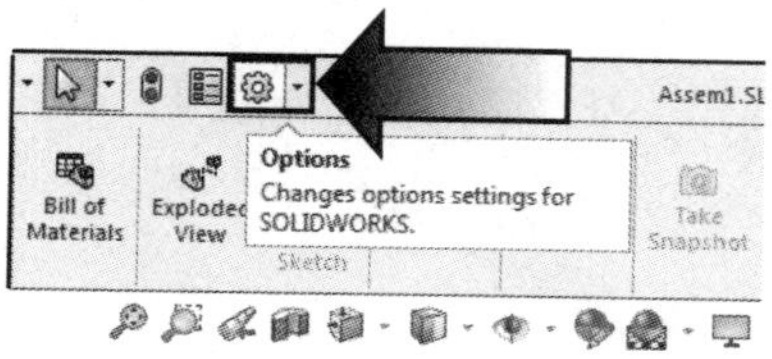

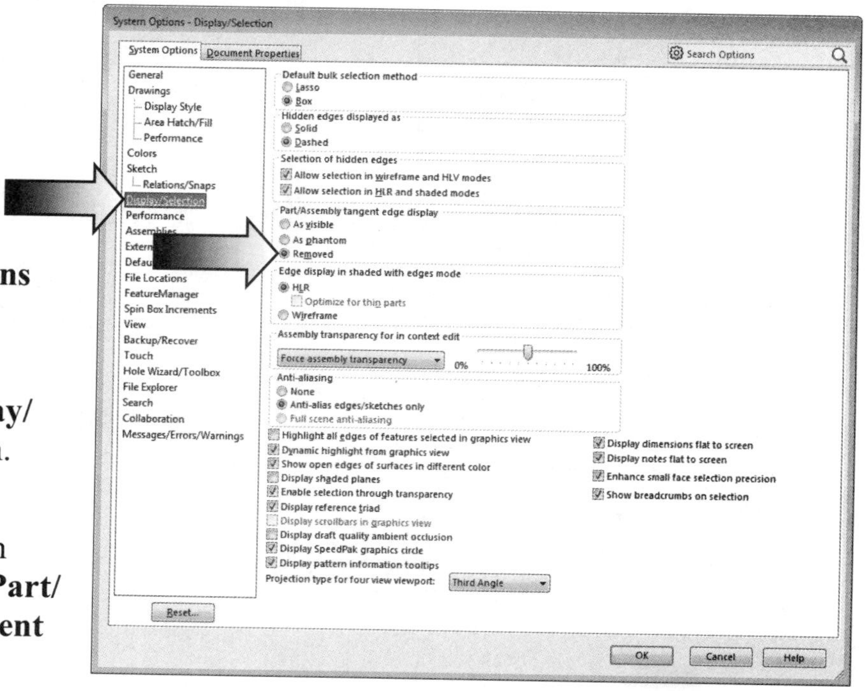

- Click the **Options** button (arrow).

- Click the **Display/ Selection** option.

- Select the option **Remove** under **Part/ Assembly Tangent Display**.

- Click **OK**.

<u>Shaded With Edges Visible</u>

<u>Shaded With Edges Visible</u>

<u>RealView Graphics Enabled</u>

20. Saving your work:

- Select **File / Save As**.

- Enter **Top Down Assembly.sldasm** for the name of the file and click **Save**.

CHAPTER 14

Using the Lip & Groove Option

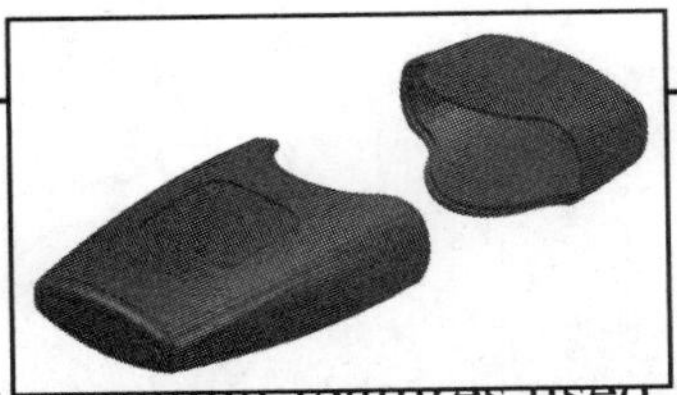

Using the Lip & Groove Option

The Fastening Features toolbar provides tools for creating fastening features used in mold and sheet metal products. They help streamline the creation of common features for plastic and sheet metal parts.

The available tools are: Lip / Groove, Mounting Boss, Snap Hook, Snap Hook Groove, and Vent.

This chapter discusses the use of the Lip / Groove and the Mounting Boss features.

- The Lip / Groove option creates fastening feature using two solid bodies where the lip is added to one body and the groove is created by subtracting material from the other body.

  For the groove, material is removed from the inside edges, but the lip gets material added to the outside edges.

  Clearance or gap and draft angle can be added to the lip / groove to help closing and opening the two solid bodies more easily.

- The Mounting Boss on the other hand, creates a tapered boss on each side of the two solid bodies, with or without the support ribs.

  A 3D sketch point is created to position the mounting boss. Relation and dimensions are used to precisely position the mounting boss.

  The options for the mounting boss are Hardware-Boss and Pin-Boss. The hardware-boss can accept a screw to fasten the two solid bodies while the pin-boss option uses a pin and aligns it to a hole.

Using the Lip & Groove Option

View Orientation Hot Keys:

Ctrl + 1 = Front View
Ctrl + 2 = Back View
Ctrl + 3 = Left View
Ctrl + 4 = Right View
Ctrl + 5 = Top View
Ctrl + 6 = Bottom View
Ctrl + 7 = Isometric View
Ctrl + 8 = Normal To Selection

Dimensioning Standards: **ANSI**

Units: **INCHES** – 3 Decimals

Tools Needed:

Edit Component	Mounting Boss
Lip / Groove	Section View

Top Down Assembly
Using the Lip & Groove Option

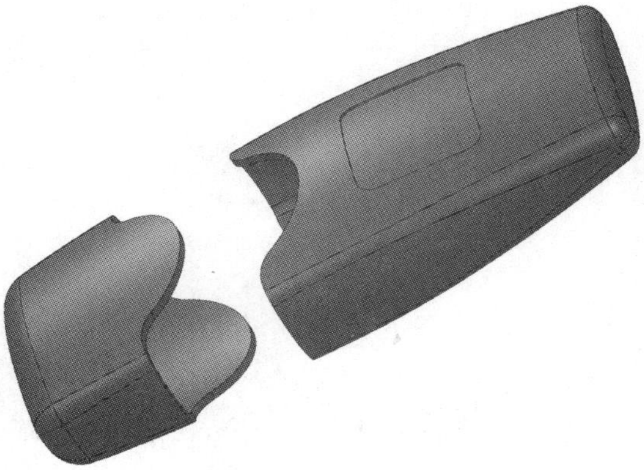

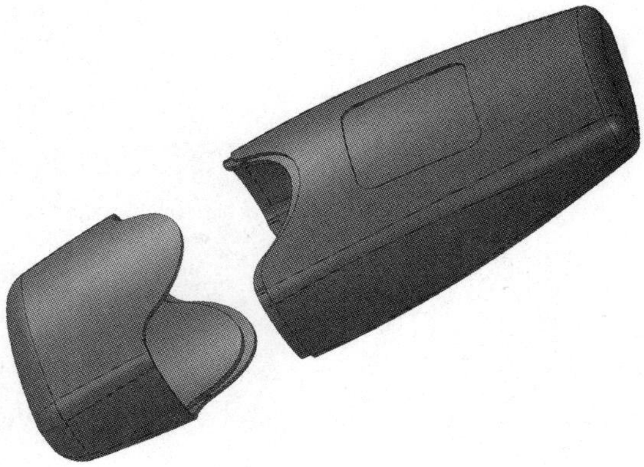

<u>Lip & Groove</u>

You can create lip and groove fastening features to align, mate, and hold together two plastic parts.

* The Lip option adds material to the part
* The Groove option removes material from the part

This session discusses the in-depth details of creating a set of Lip & Groove for the two plastic parts pictured above.

Fastening features streamline the creation of common features for plastic and sheet metal parts. You can create: **Lips and Grooves**. Align, mate, and hold together two plastic parts. Lip and groove features support multibodies and assemblies.	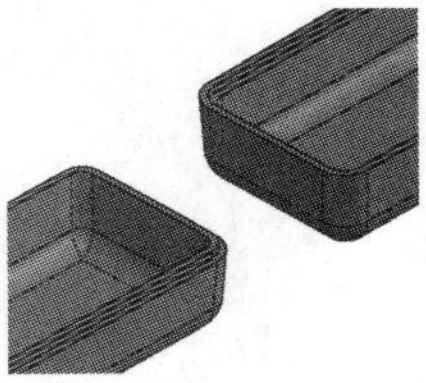
Mounting bosses. Create a variety of mounting bosses. Set the number of fins and choose a hole or a pin.	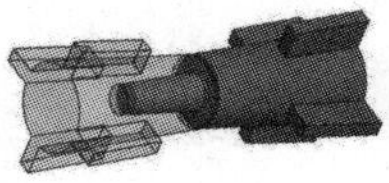
Snap hooks and **snap hook grooves**. Customize the snap hook and snap hook groove. You must first create a snap hook before you can create a snap hook groove.	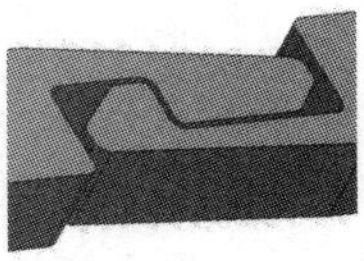
Vents. Create a variety of vents using a sketch you create. Set the number of ribs and spars. Flow area is calculated automatically.	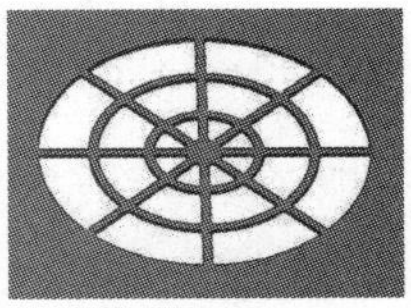

1. Opening the existing assembly:

- Select **File / Open**.

- Browse to the Training Folder and open an assembly document named: **Lip & Groove Assembly**.sldasm

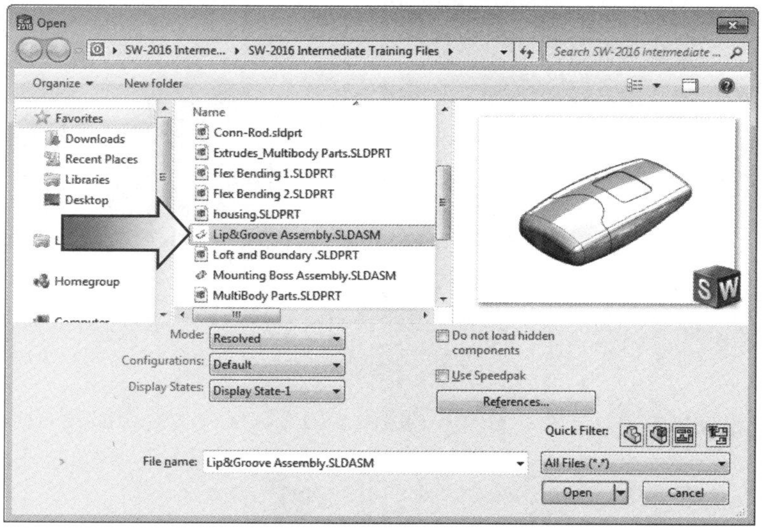

2. Editing the Housing:

- Select the component **<u>Housing</u>** and click **Edit Component** .

- From the **Insert** menu, select **Fastening Feature / Lip /Groove** .

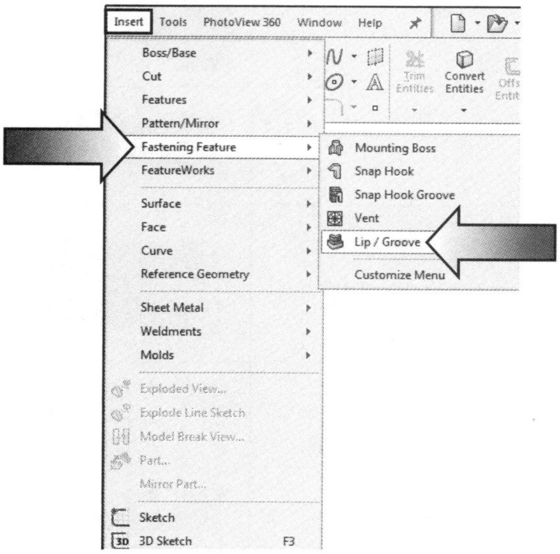

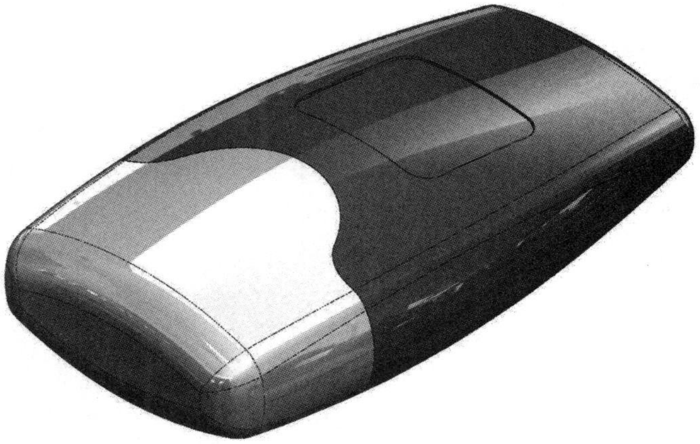

- Select the following from the FeatureManager tree:

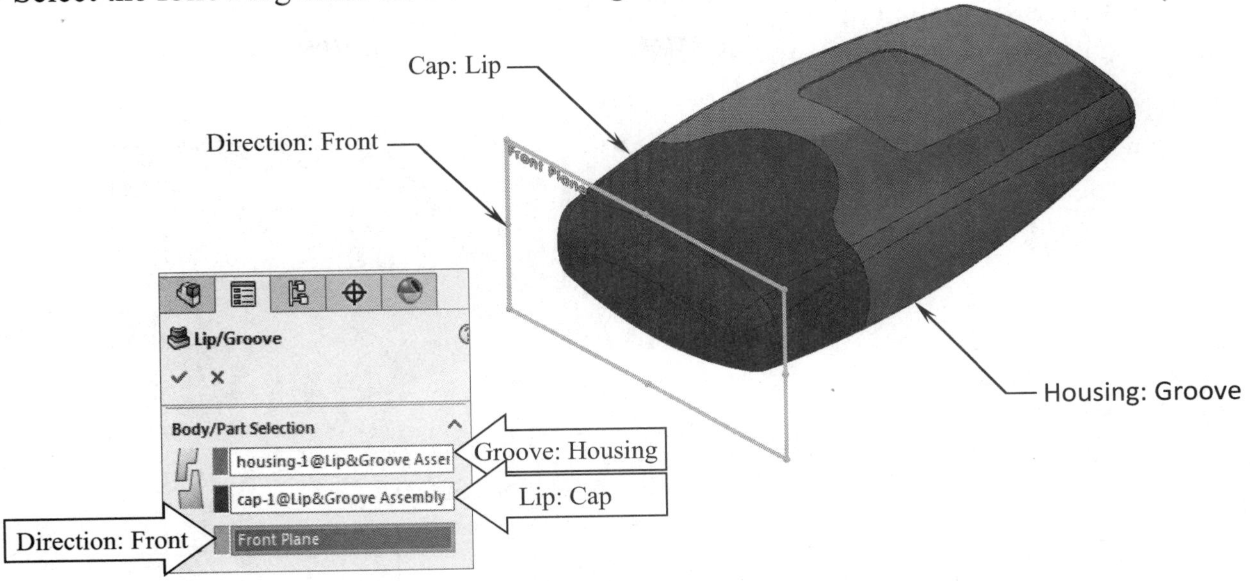

- For **Groove Selection**, right click and select **all faces** on the left-end of the part Housing as shown.

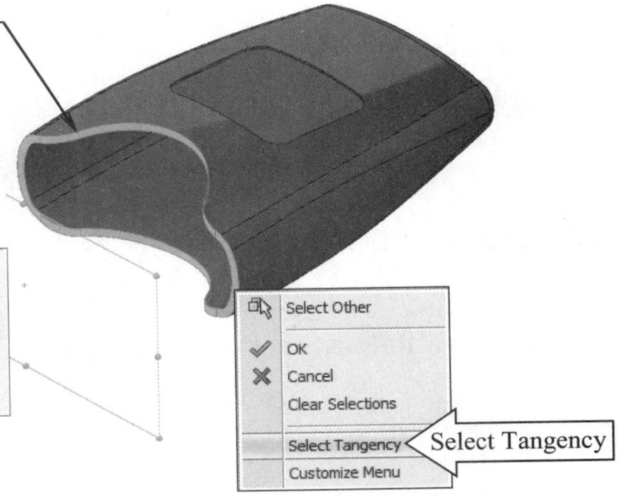

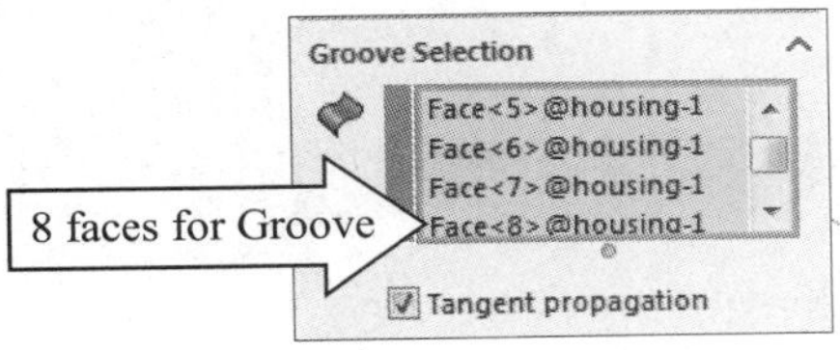

(Enable Select-Tangency checkbox.)

- For **Edges to remove**, select all **outer edges** on the left end of the same part.

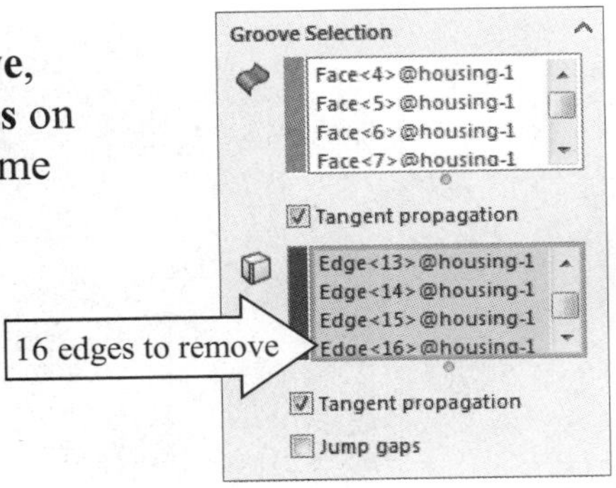

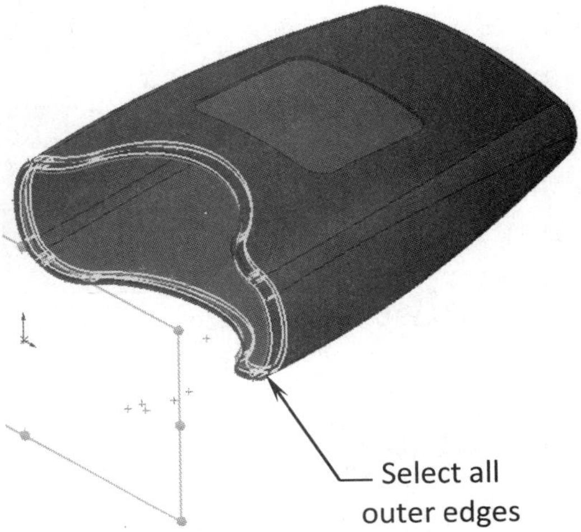

(Enable Select-Tangency checkbox.)

- For **Lips Selection**, right click and select **all faces** on the right-end of the part Cap as shown.

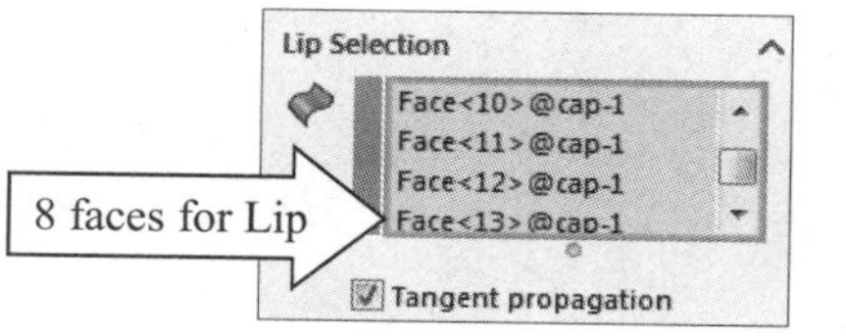

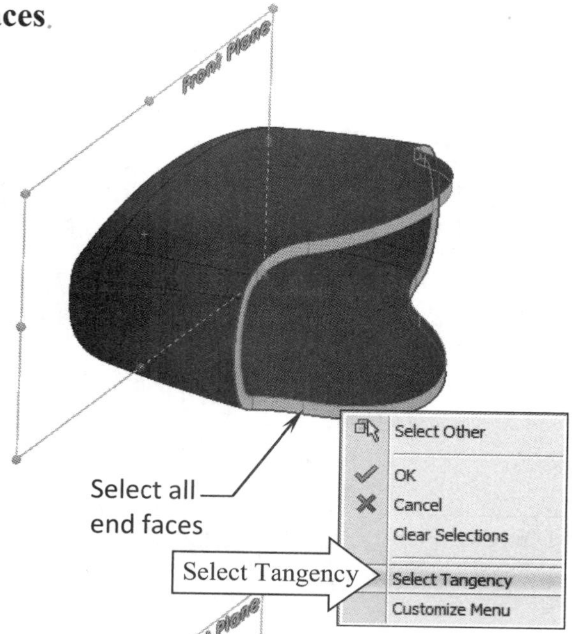

- For **Edges To Add Material**, select all **outer edges** on the right-end of the Cap.

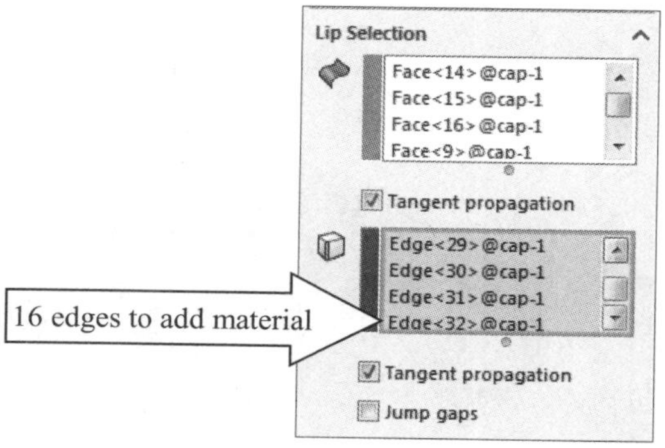

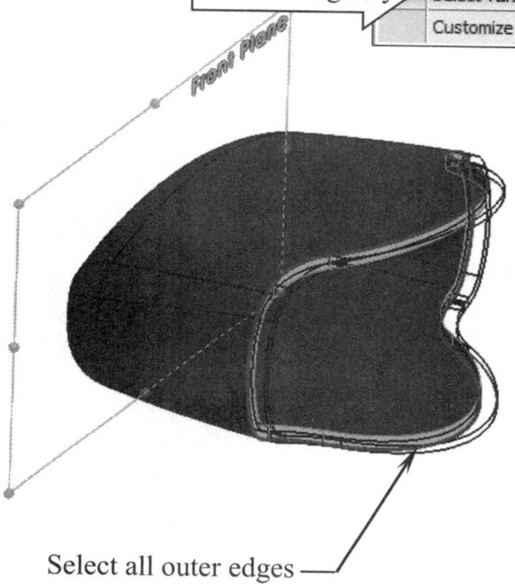

- Under **Parameters**, set the followings:

* Groove Width: **.031in**.

* Spacing: **0.005in**.

* Groove Draft: **3.00deg**.

* Upper Gap: **0.005in**.

* Lip Height: **.062in**.

* Lip Width: **.031in**.

* Lower Gap: **0.005in**.

- Click **OK** ✓.

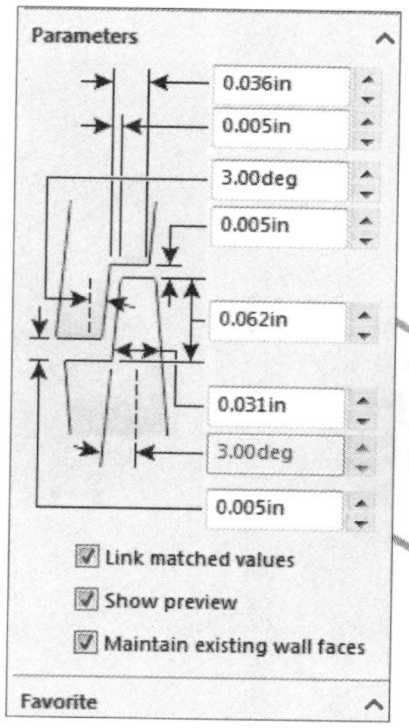

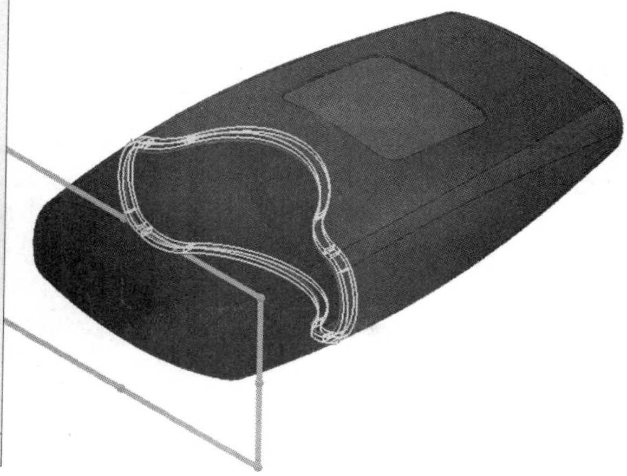

- Click off the Edit Component button .

3. Creating a section view:

- Create a Section View using the Right plane as the cutting plane.

- Zoom in on the Lips & Grooves details and verify the gaps between them.

- Click off the section view when finished.

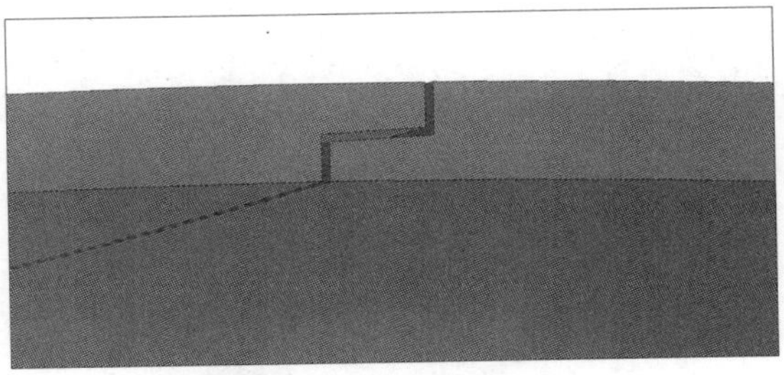

(Section View)

4. Saving your work:

- Select **File / Save As**.

- Use the same file name and overwrite the original document.

- Click **Save**.

Top Down Assembly
Using the Mounting Boss Option

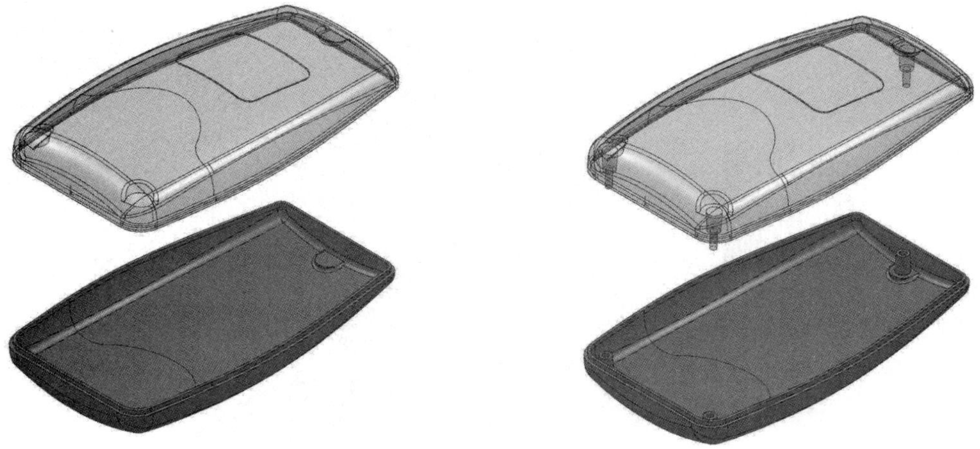

Mounting Boss

You can create common mounting features for plastic parts like Mounting Bosses, Snap Hooks, Snap Hook Grooves, Vents, and Lips/Grooves.

The mounting bosses come with a variety of options to help streamline the creation of common Fastening features.

Define/Position the Mounting Boss	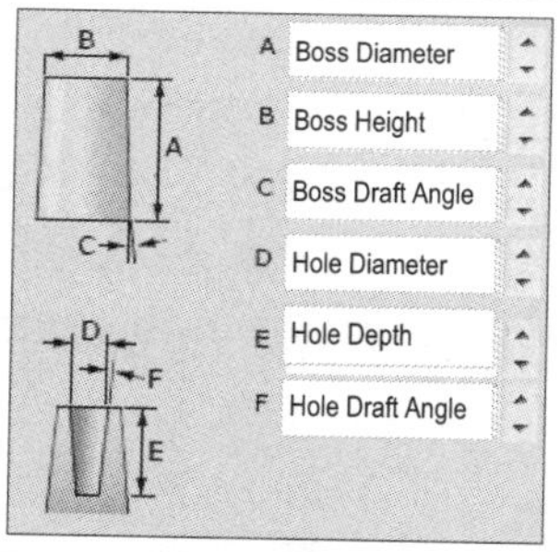	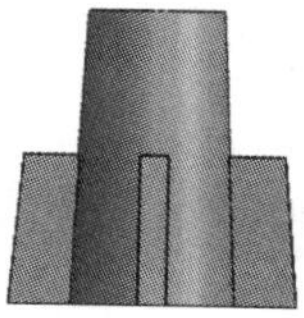	**Creates a mounting hole** 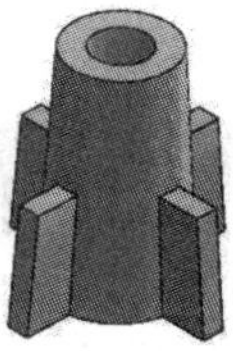
Define/Position the Fins	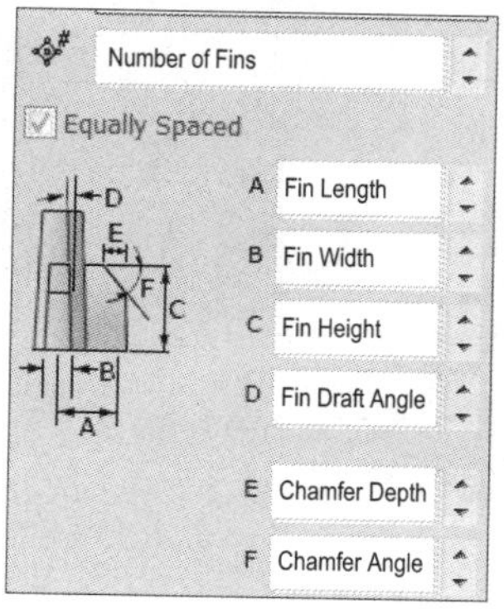	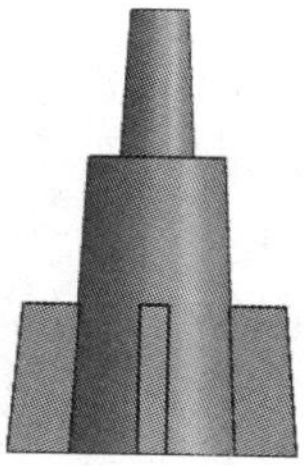	**Creates a mounting pin** 

Using the Mounting Boss option

1. Opening the existing assembly:

- Select **File / Open**.

- Browse to the Training Folder and open an assembly document named: **Mounting Boss Assembly**.sldasm

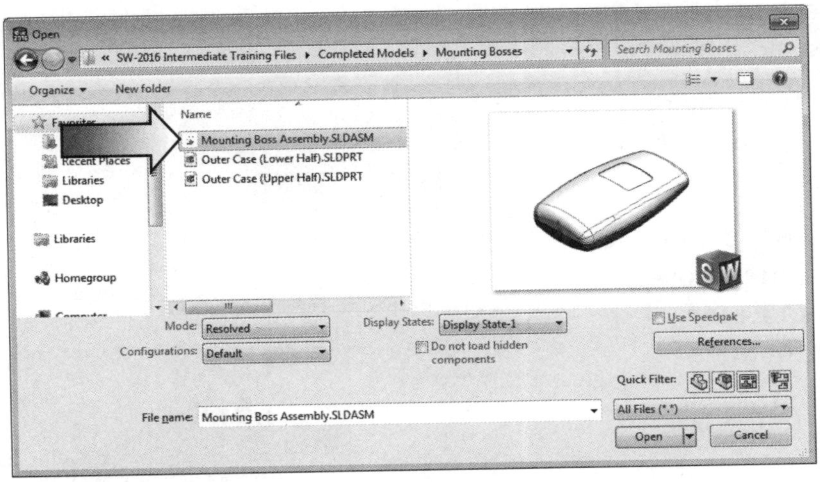

2. Editing Part: Select the part **Outer Case (Lower Half)** and click **Edit Component**.

- From the **Insert** menu, select **Fastening Feature / Mounting Boss** .

3. Setting the Parameters:

- The options to set the parameters for the mounting boss appear on the Feature tree.

- For **Position Face** to attach the mounting-boss, select the <u>**face**</u> as indicated.

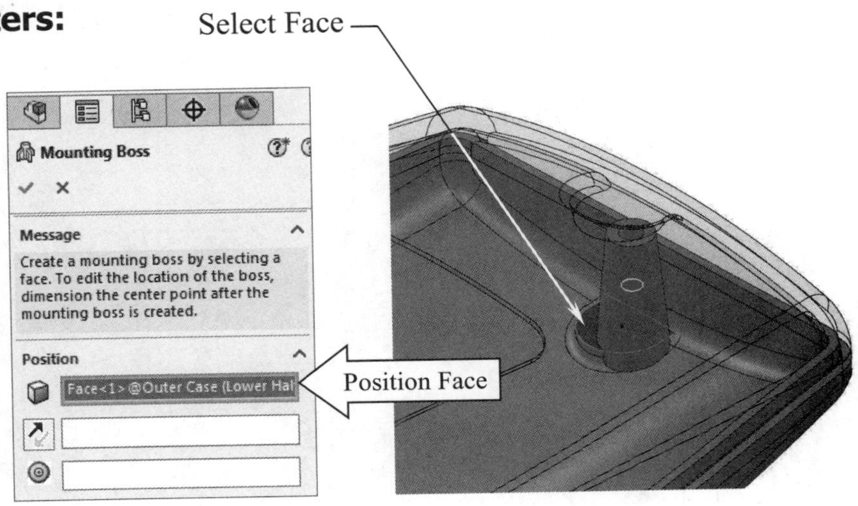

- For **Position Edge** to align the mounting boss, select the **circular edge** as noted.

(Use the Top plane here for direction only when required)

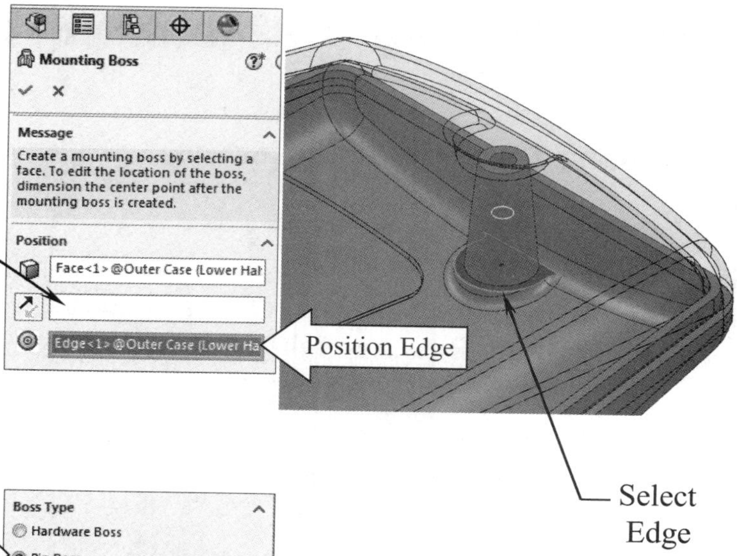

- For the **Boss Type** section, select the **Pin Boss** and the **Hole** option (arrow).

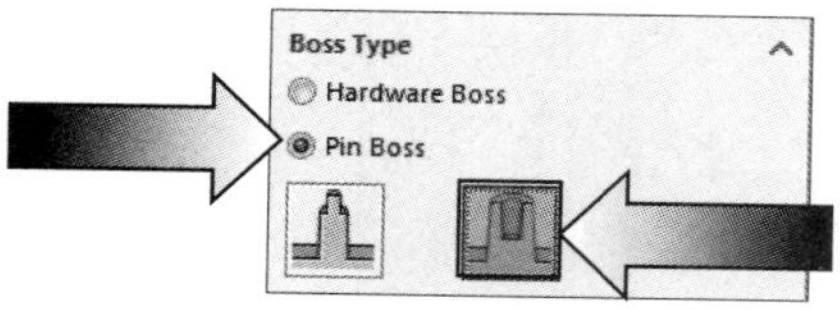

- For the Boss section, click the **Enter Boss Height** and **Enter Diameter** options.

- Enter the following dimensions:

  * **A = .200in.**
  * **B = .165in.**
  * **C = 5.00deg.**
  * **D = .093in.**
  * **E = .175in.**
  * **F = 2.00deg**
  * **Clearance = .005in.**

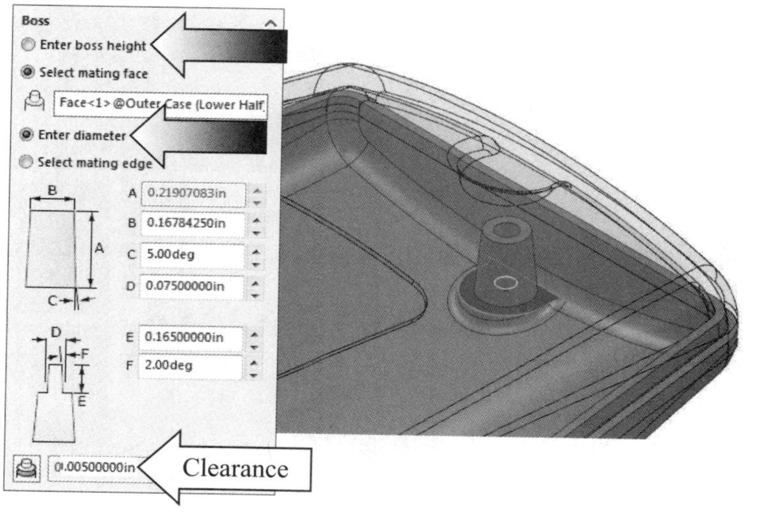

- In the **Fins** section, change the number of fins to **0** (zero).

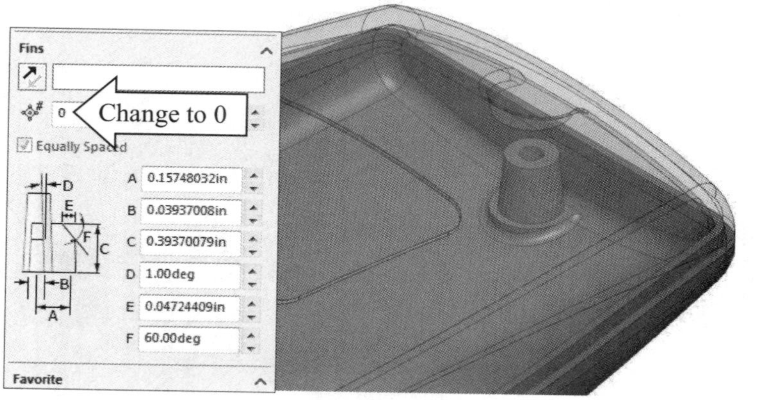

- Click **OK** ✔.

4. Adding two more mounting bosses:

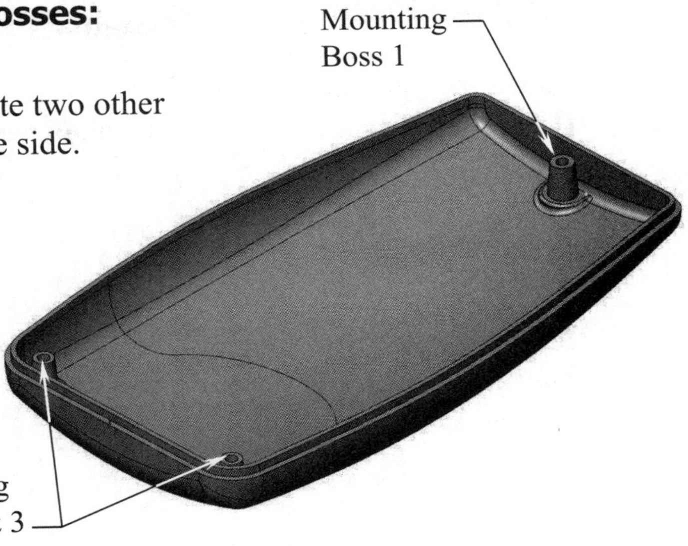

- Repeat the steps above and create two other mounting bosses on the opposite side.

- Exit the **Edit Component**  command when finished.

5. Toggling between the Explode and the Collapse views:

- Right click the name of the assembly and select **Explode***.

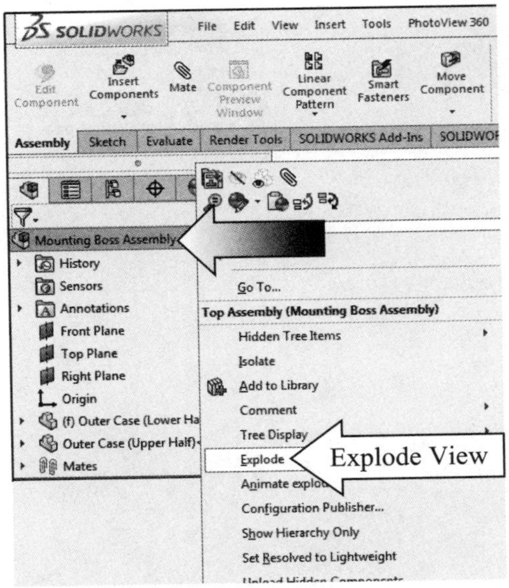

- Rotate the view to verify the details of the 3 mounting bosses.

* Remember to <u>**Collapse**</u> the assembly prior to editing the next component.

6. Creating the Mating Bosses:

- Select the part **Outer-Case (Upper Half)** and click the **Edit Component** command.

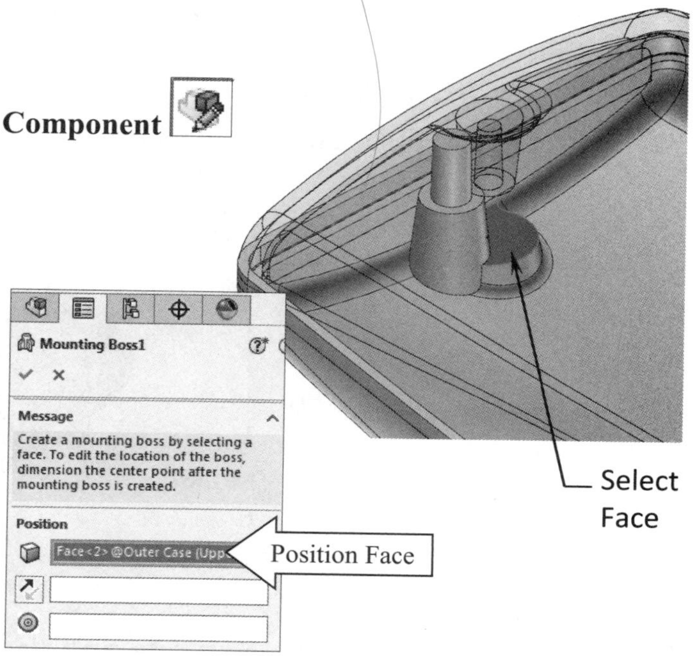

- Select **Insert/Fastening Feature/ Mounting Boss**.

- For **Position Face**, select the **Face** as indicated. (To select a hidden face, right click in the area where the face is under and pick **Select Other** then pick the face from the list.)

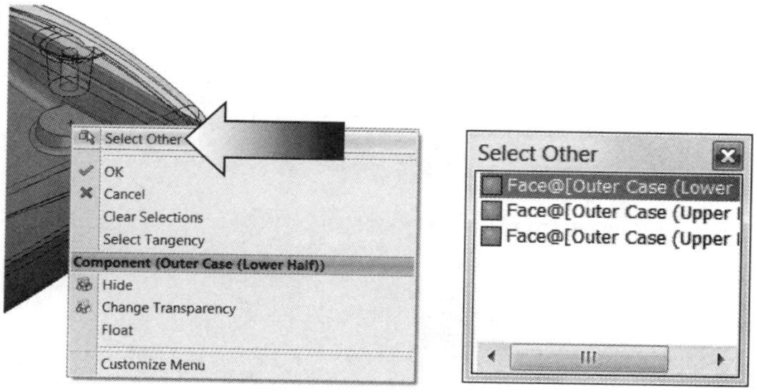

- For **Direction**, select the **Top** plane from the Feature tree (use only if required).

- For **Position Edge**, select the **Edge** as noted to align the center of the mounting boss to the center of the circular edge.

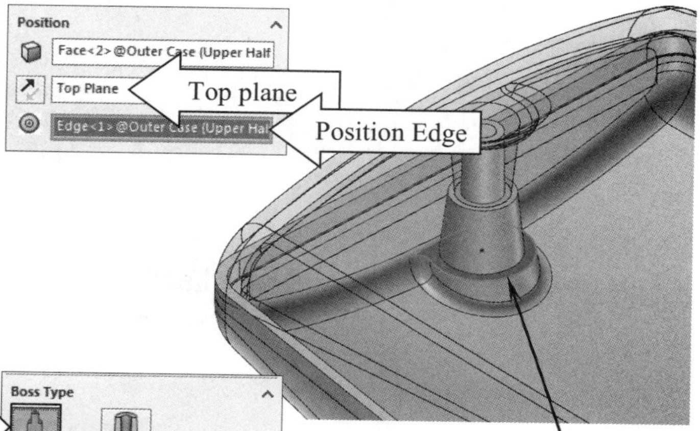

- For the **Boss Type** section, select the **Pin Boss** option.

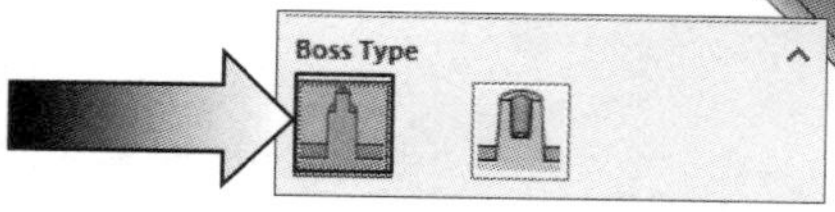

- Select the options **Select Mating Face** and **Enter Diameter**.

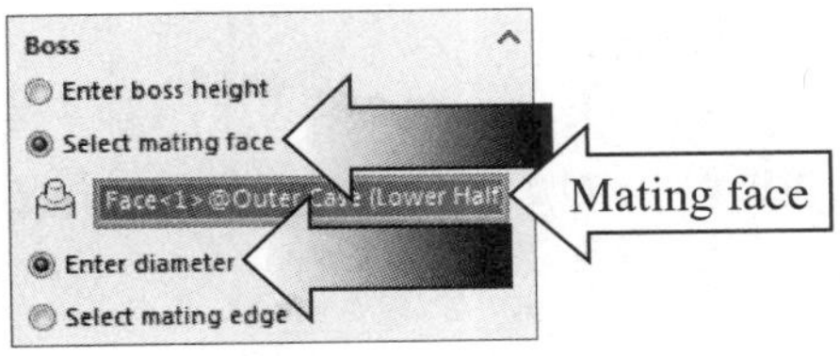

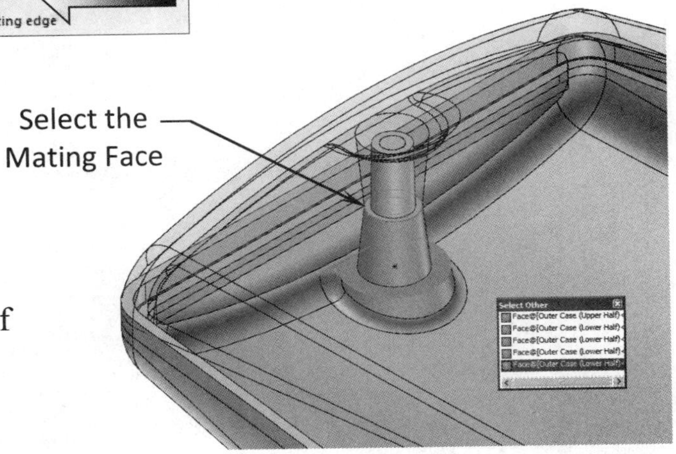

- Select the **upper surface** of the mounting boss of the Lower Half as noted.

- Enter the following dimensions:

  * **A = Defined by mating face.**

  * **B = .1678 in.**

  * **C = 5.00deg.**

  * **D = .075in.**

  * **E = .165in.**

  * **F = 2.00deg.**

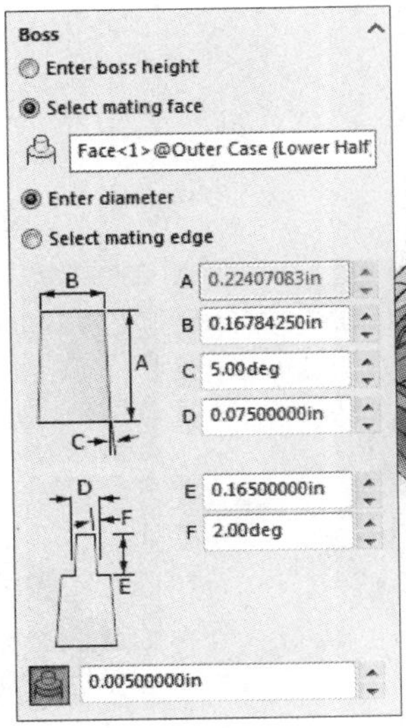

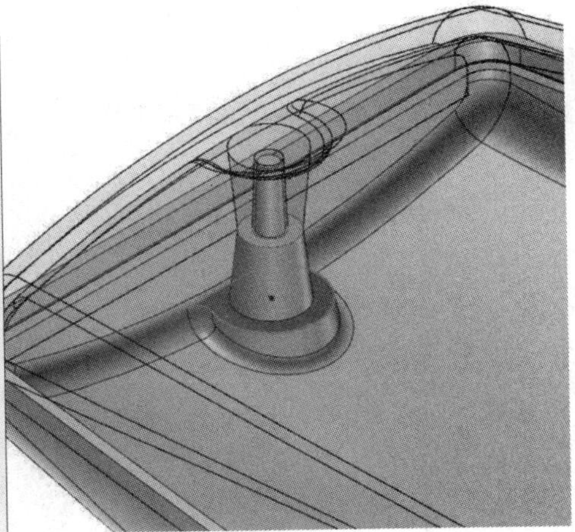

- Click **OK**.

- Click off the **Edit Component** button.

7. Creating a Section View:

- Create a section view using the Right plane and cutting plane.

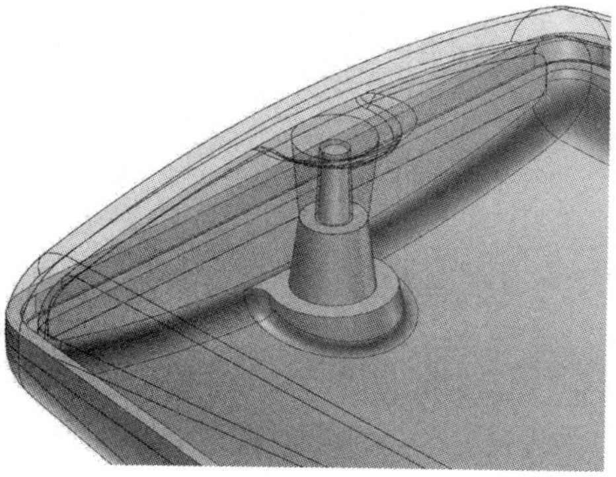

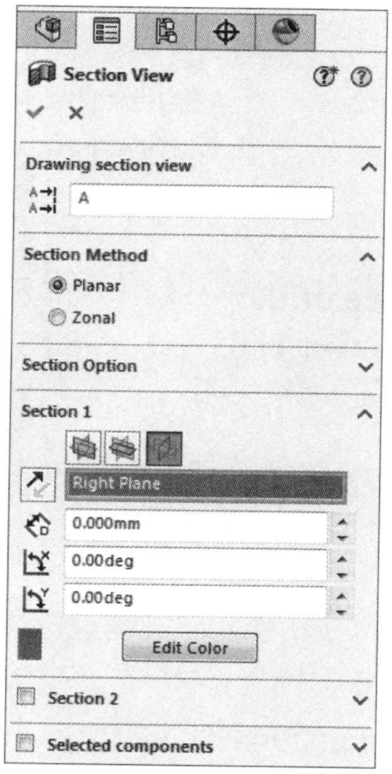

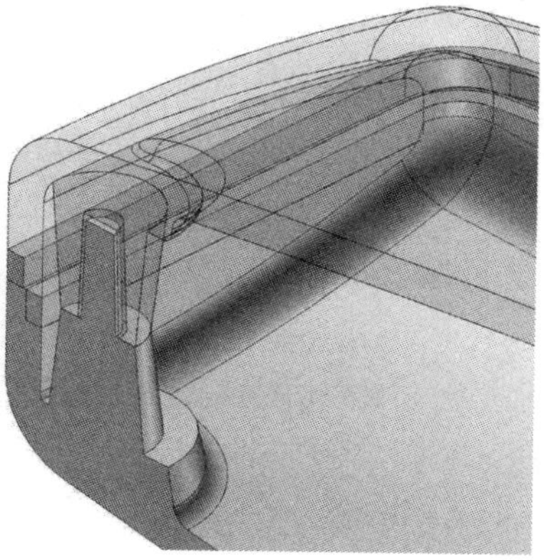

Section View

8. Repeating:

- Create two additional mounting bosses; use the same settings as the first one.

9. Saving your work as:

- Select **File / Save As**.

- Use the same file name and overwrite the original document when prompted.

- Click **Save**.

CHAPTER 15

Assembly Drawings & BOM

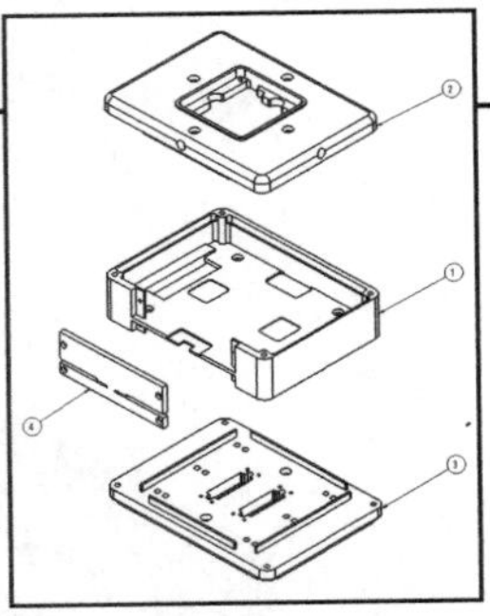

Assembly Drawings & BOM Overview

An assembly drawing normally consists of drawing views, balloons, and a bill of materials.

In a simple assembly that has only a few components, creating one exploded view to show all the components, and one isometric view to show how they are supposed to be assembled should be sufficient. But in a more complex assembly that has many components; other drawing views such as Section views and detail views are also added to enhance the clarity or details of the components.

If an assembly section view is created, the crosshatch pattern for each component should be altered so that they will have different angles to help differentiate the components. In addition, the pattern that represents the material for each component should also be applied to help eliminate any confusion (see example).

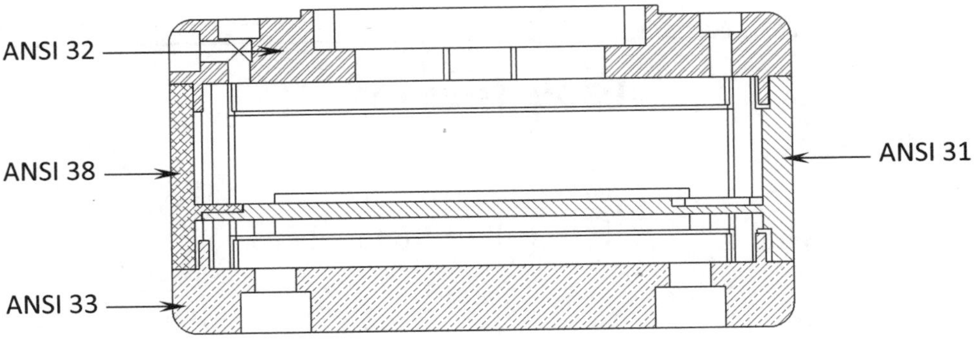

A Bill of Materials is added to show the item numbers, quantities, part numbers, and custom properties in assembly drawings.

Balloons will then be inserted into the drawing. The item numbers and quantities in the balloons correspond to the numbers in the Bill of Materials.

Aluminum Enclosure
Assembly Drawings & BOM

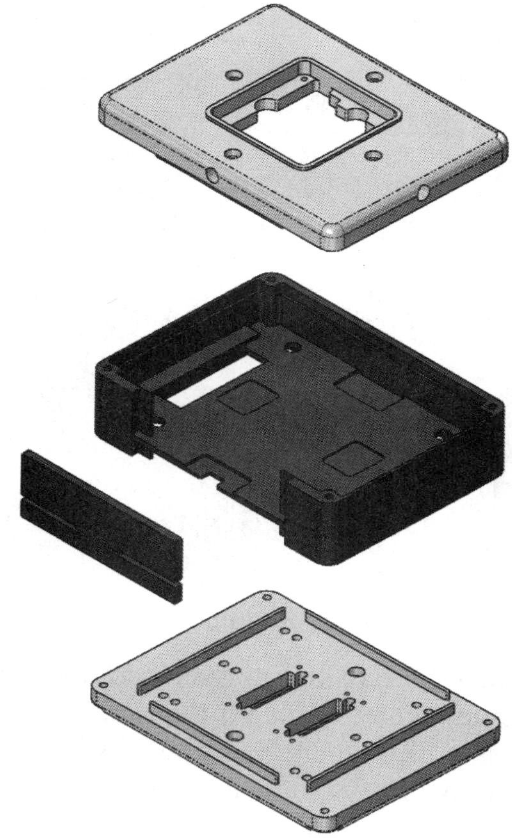

Dimensioning Standards: **ANSI**

Units: **INCHES** – 3 Decimals

Tools Needed:

New Drawing

Bill of Materials

Balloons

Magnetic Line

Link to Property

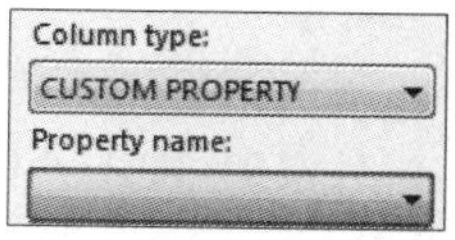

View Palette

1. Starting a new drawing document:

- Select **File / New / Drawing**.

- Select the Drawing Template (arrow) in the New SOLIDWORKS Document dialog box.

- Click **OK**.

- The default drawing template may have settings that are used with the ISO standards. We will need to change them to ANSI standards prior to making the drawings.

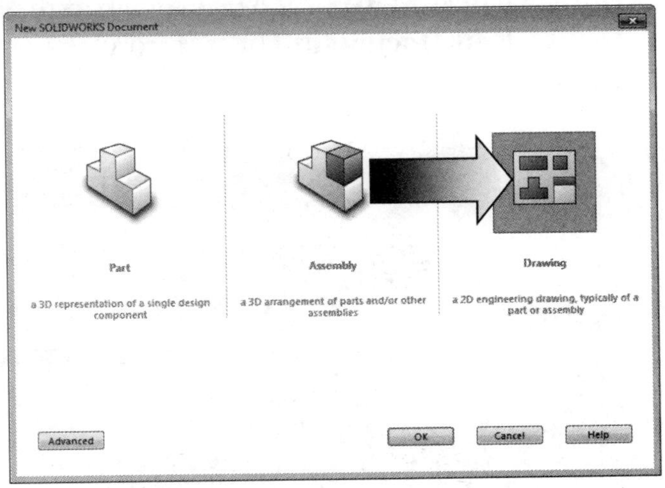

2. Selecting the ANSI standard sheet size:

- Push Escape if you do not see the option to select the drawing sheet size, similar to the dialog below.

- Right click inside the drawing and select **Properties** from the popup list (arrow).

- Select the **C (ANSI) Landscape** for the paper size (arrow).

- Select the **Third Angle Projection** option for the Type of Projection.

- Set the **Scale** to **1:1**.

- Enable the **Display Sheet Format** check box and click **OK**.

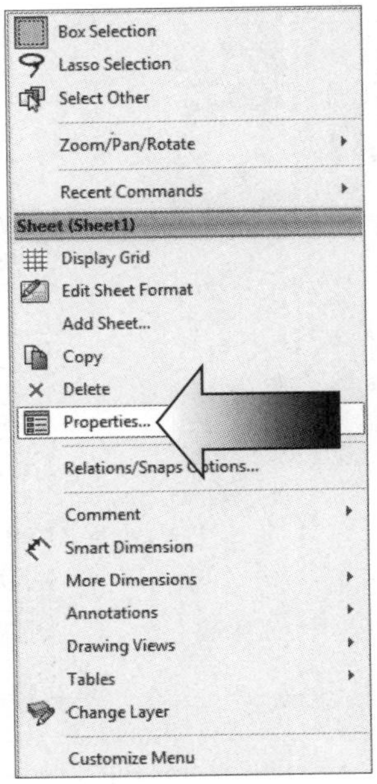

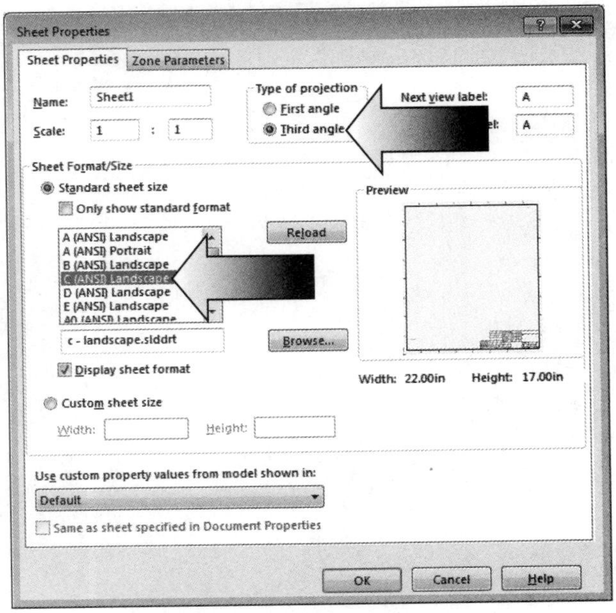

3. Switching to ANSI standards:

- Click the **IPS** (or MMGS) tab at the bottom right of the screen and select: **Edit Document Units** (arrow).

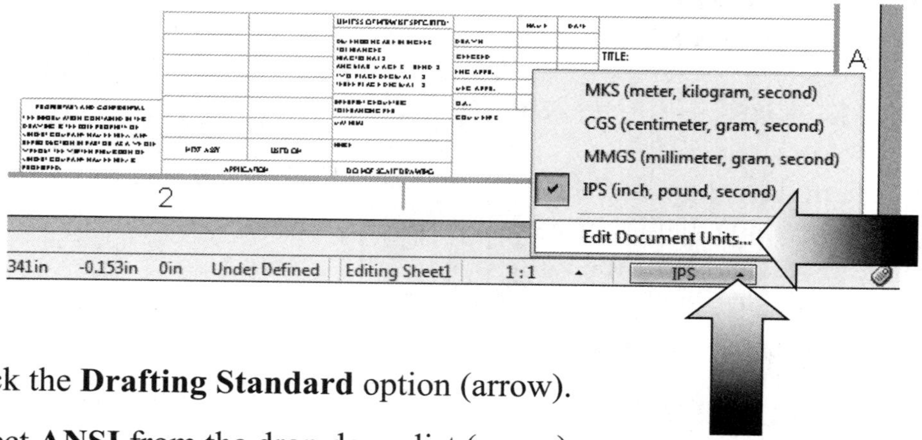

- Click the **Drafting Standard** option (arrow).
- Select **ANSI** from the drop down list (arrow).
- Click **OK**.

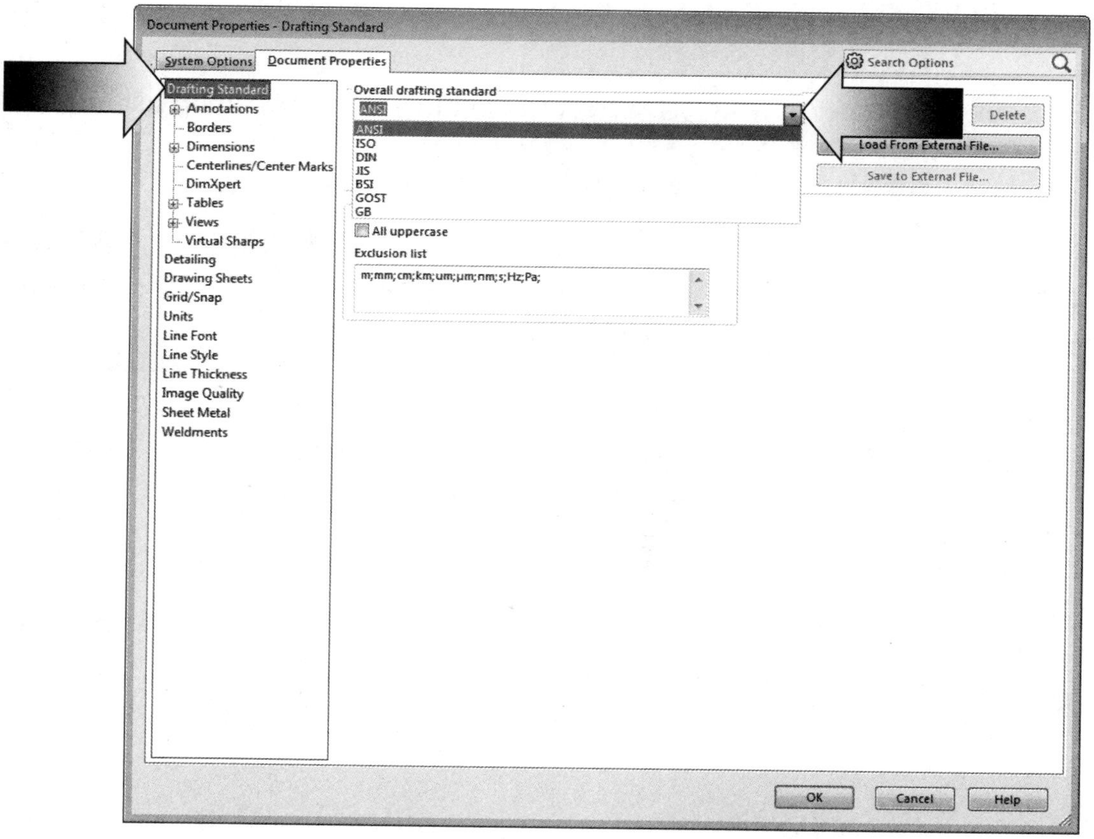

4. Using the View Palette:

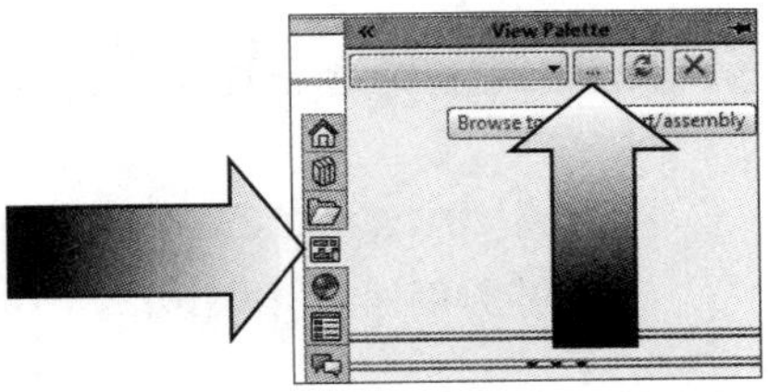

- Part and Assembly documents can be opened using the **View Palette**. Drawing views and Annotations can then be dragged and dropped into the drawing.

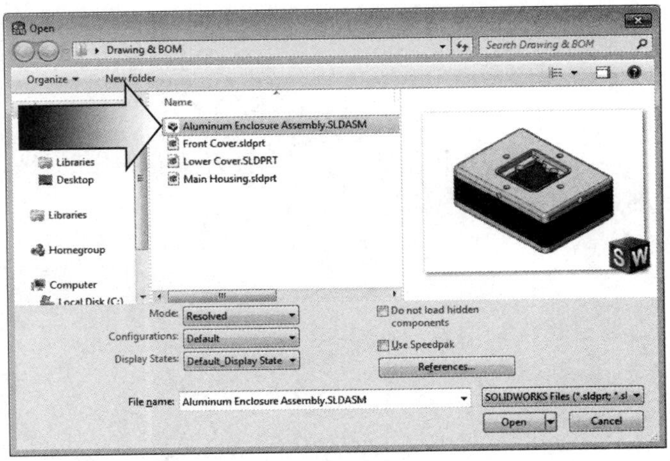

- Select the **View Palette** tab and click the **Browse** button (arrow).

- Open an assembly document named: **Aluminum Enclosure Assembly.sldasm**

- Drag and drop the Isometric Explode view onto the drawing as indicated and click **OK**.

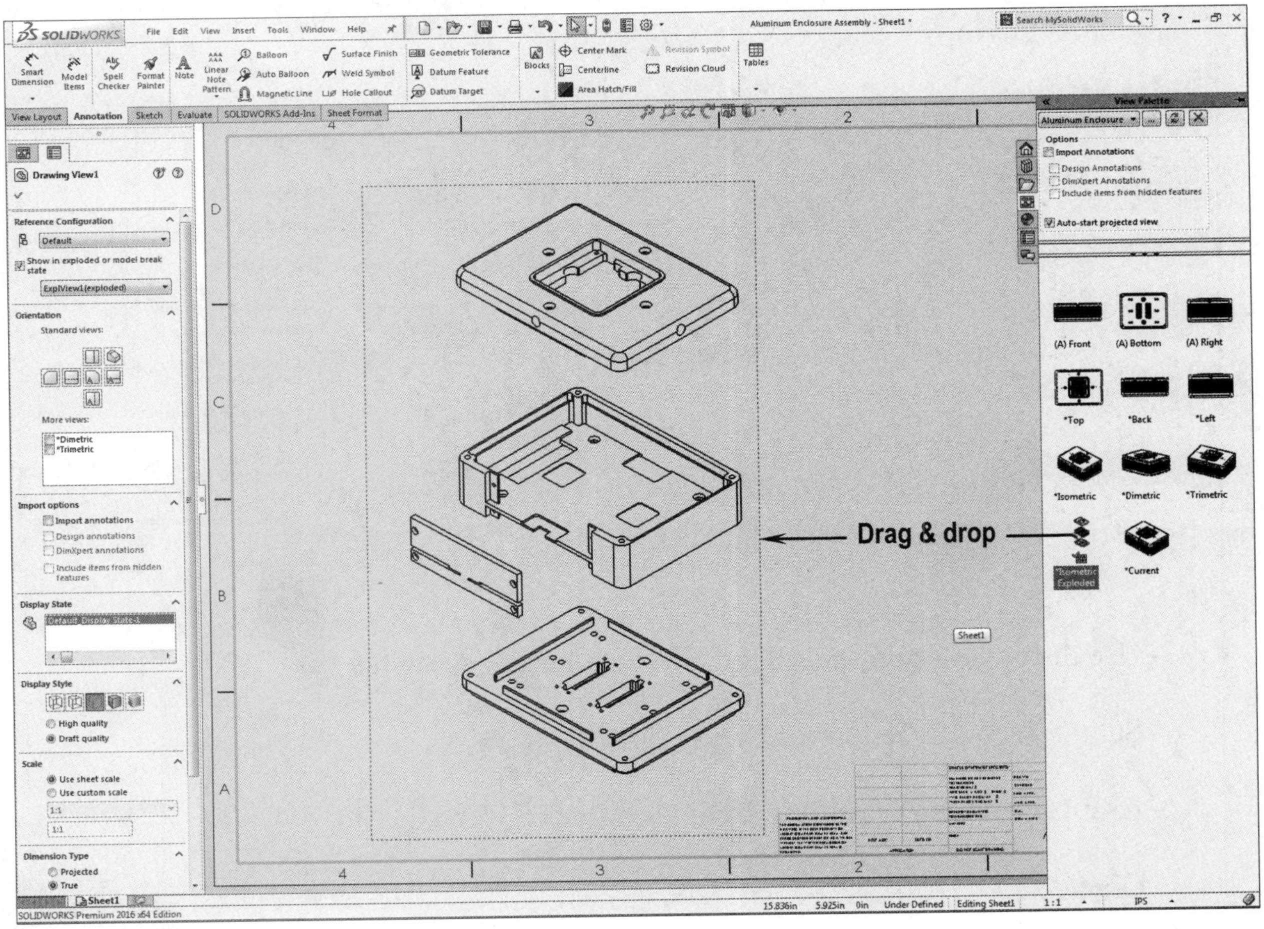

5. Inserting a Bill of Materials:

- A drawing can contain an Excel-based Bill of Materials or a table-based Bill of Materials, but not both. We will insert an Excel based BOM into the drawing.

- Select the dotted border of the drawing view and click the **Annotation** tab (arrow).

- Select the **Bill of Materials** option under the **Tables** drop down list (arrow).

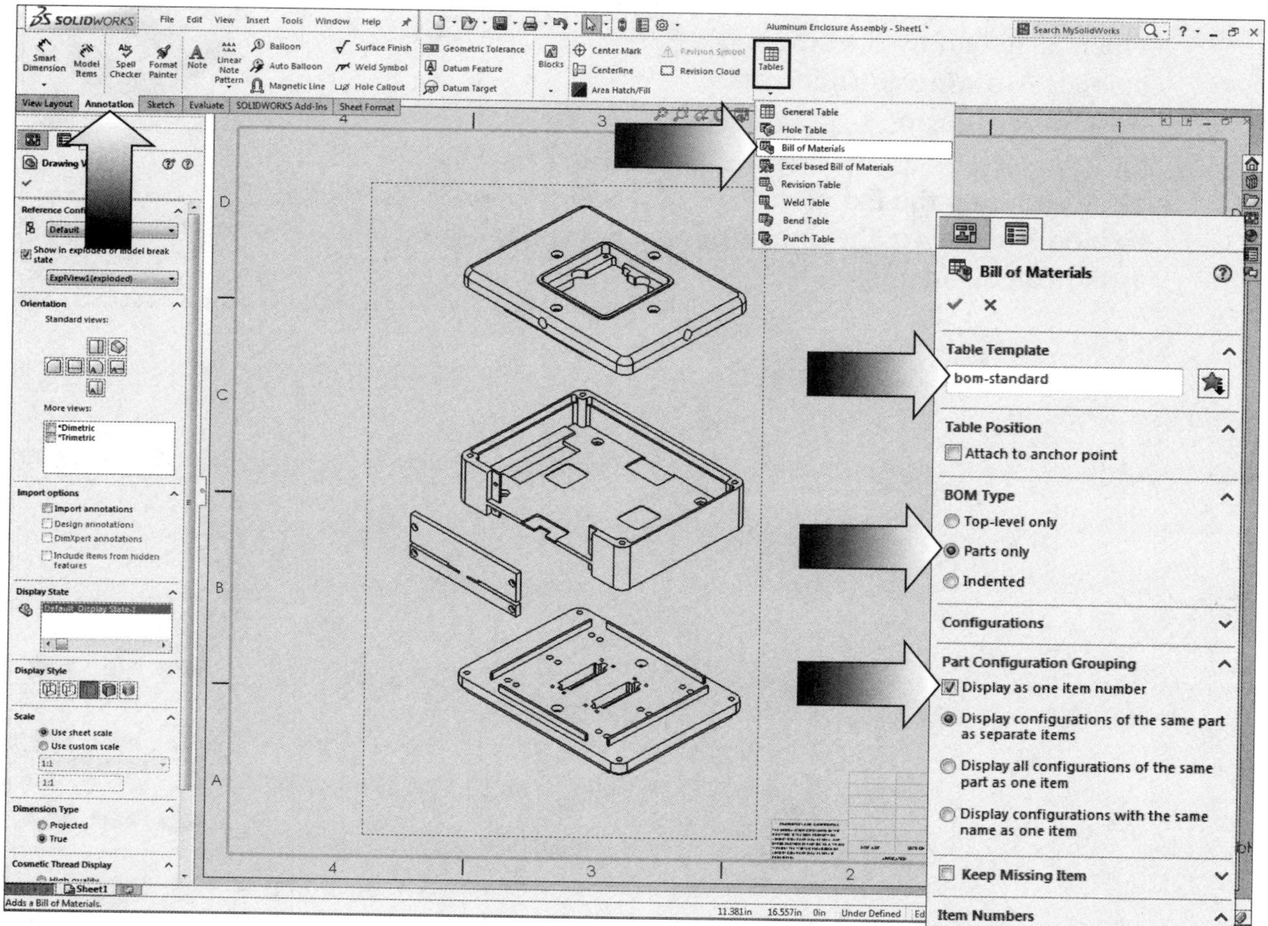

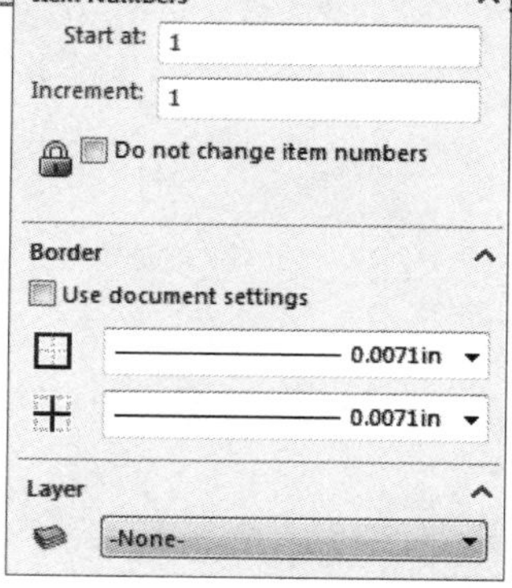

- Use the default **bom-standard** template for this drawing.

- Set the BOM Type to **Parts Only** (arrow).

- Enable the **Display as One Item Number** checkbox.

- Click **OK**.

- Place the BOM approximately as shown.

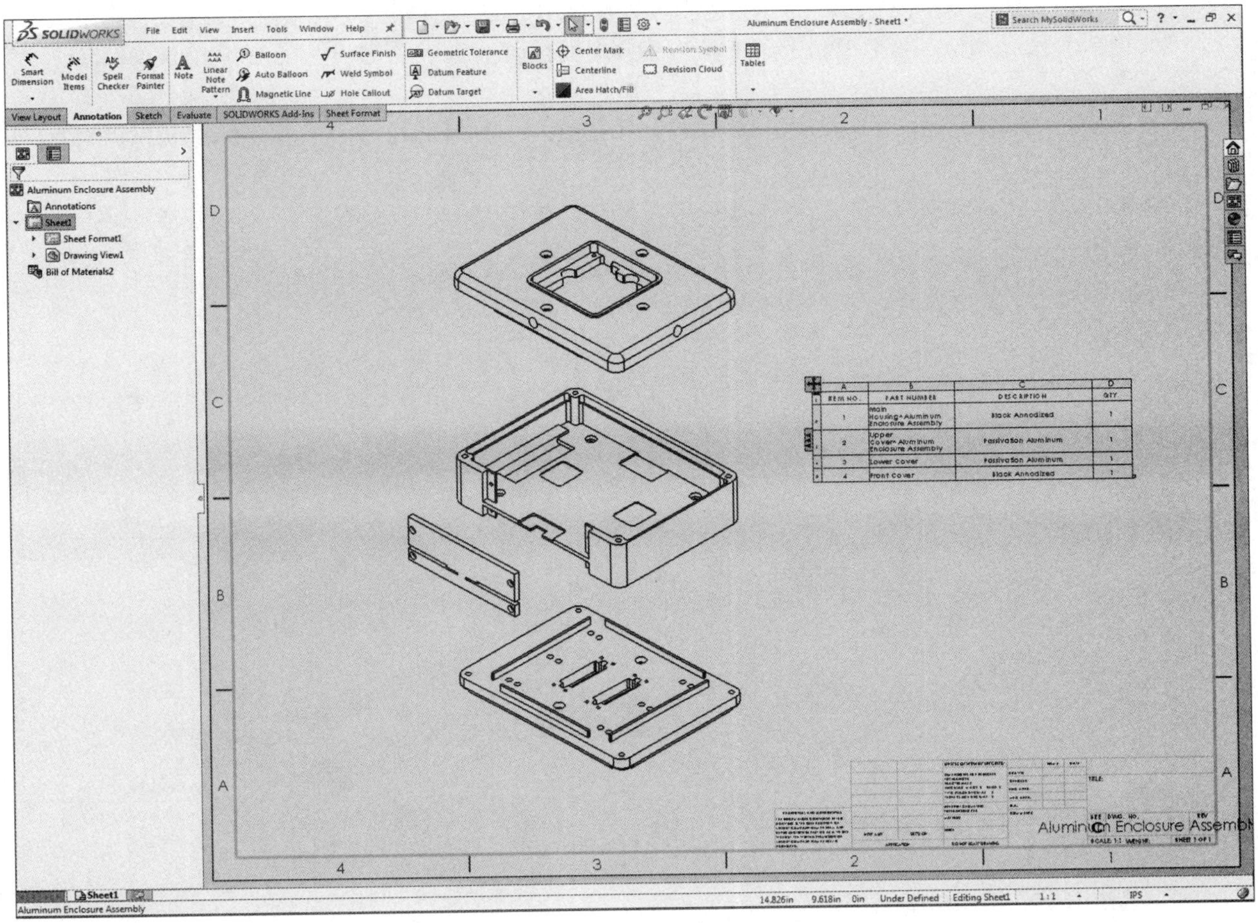

- Drag the '4-way' arrow to move the BOM (arrow).

- Click the **Use Document Font** button (arrow) to enable the formatting tools and modify the BOM content if needed.

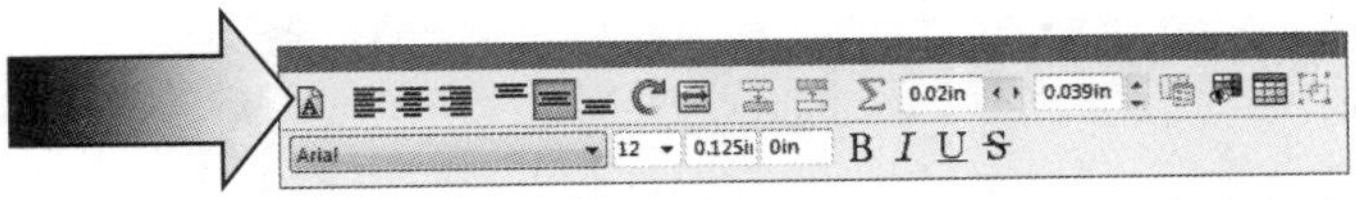

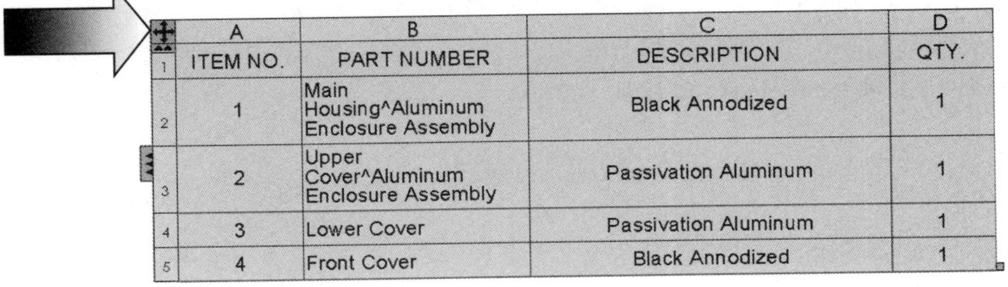

	A	B	C	D
1	ITEM NO.	PART NUMBER	DESCRIPTION	QTY.
2	1	Main Housing^Aluminum Enclosure Assembly	Black Annodized	1
3	2	Upper Cover^Aluminum Enclosure Assembly	Passivation Aluminum	1
4	3	Lower Cover	Passivation Aluminum	1
5	4	Front Cover	Black Annodized	1

6. Modifying the BOM's Row Height:

- Drag-Select from cell A1 to cell D4 to highlight all cells. Right click in one of the cells and select: **Formatting / Row Height**.

- Enter **.500in** for the height of the rows and click **OK**.

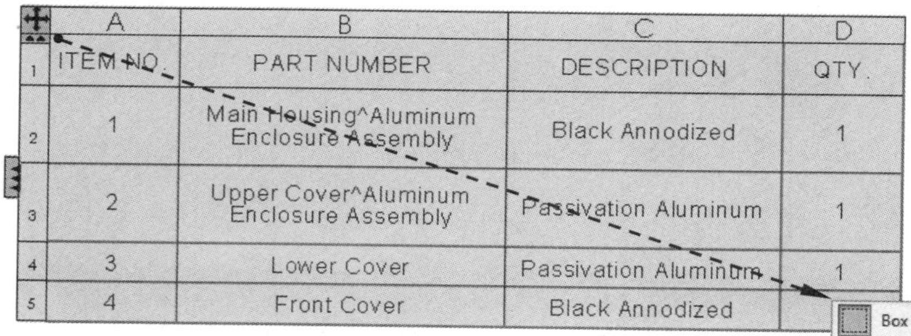

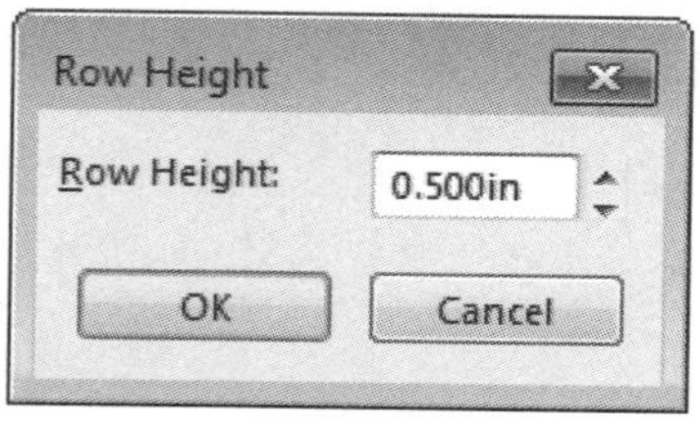

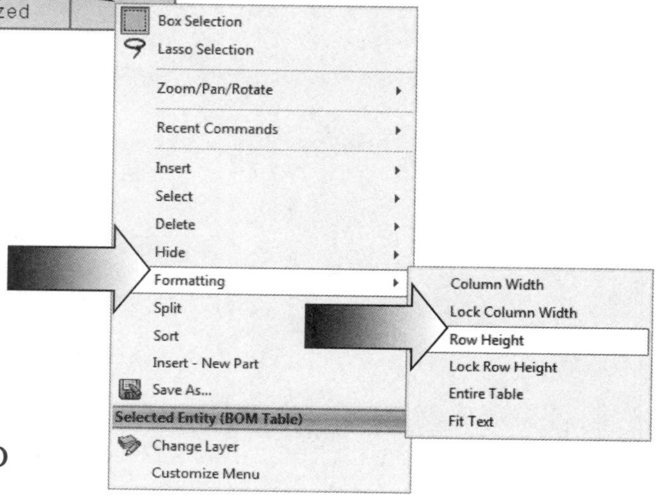

7. Adding a new column:

- Right click on the column header D and select **Insert / Column Right**.

- A new column E is added to the right side of column D.

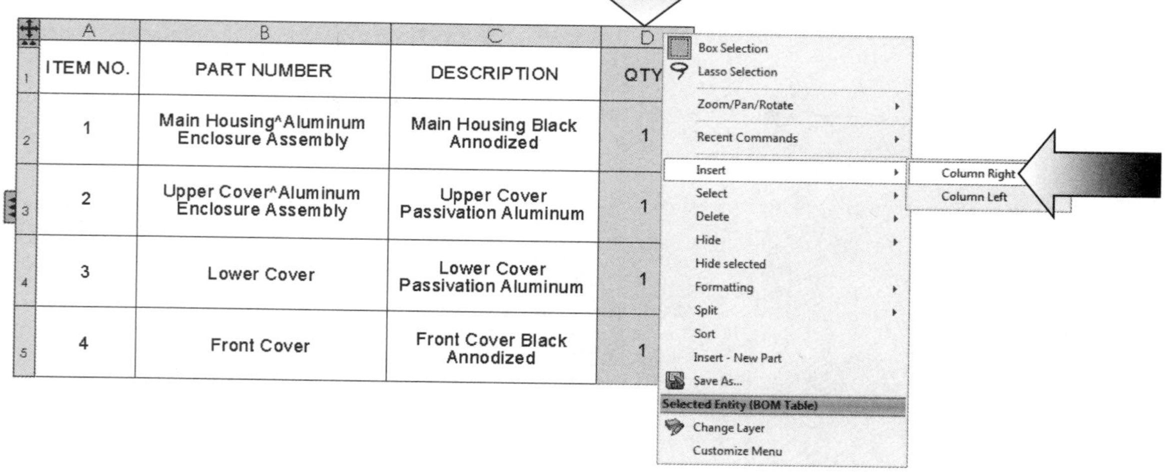

8. Customizing the new column:

- Double-click on the **column header E** and select:

* Column Type: **Custom Property**

* Property Name: **Finish**

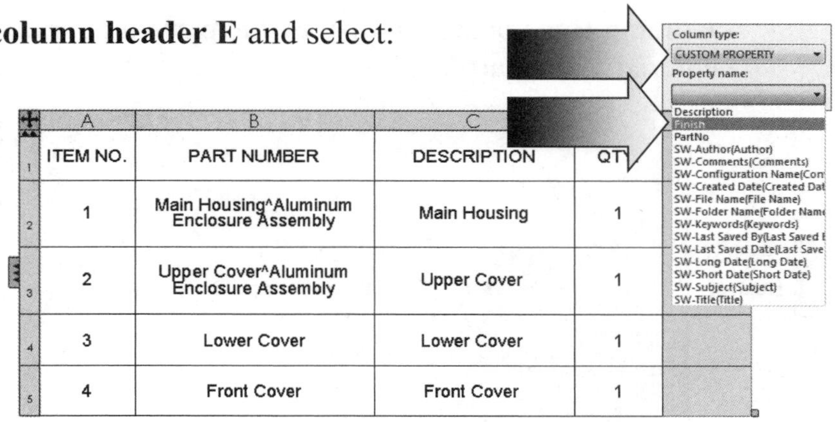

	A	B	C	
1	ITEM NO.	PART NUMBER	DESCRIPTION	QTY
2	1	Main Housing^Aluminum Enclosure Assembly	Main Housing	1
3	2	Upper Cover^Aluminum Enclosure Assembly	Upper Cover	1
4	3	Lower Cover	Lower Cover	1
5	4	Front Cover	Front Cover	1

- The finishes that were entered in the properties of each part are displayed in the new column.

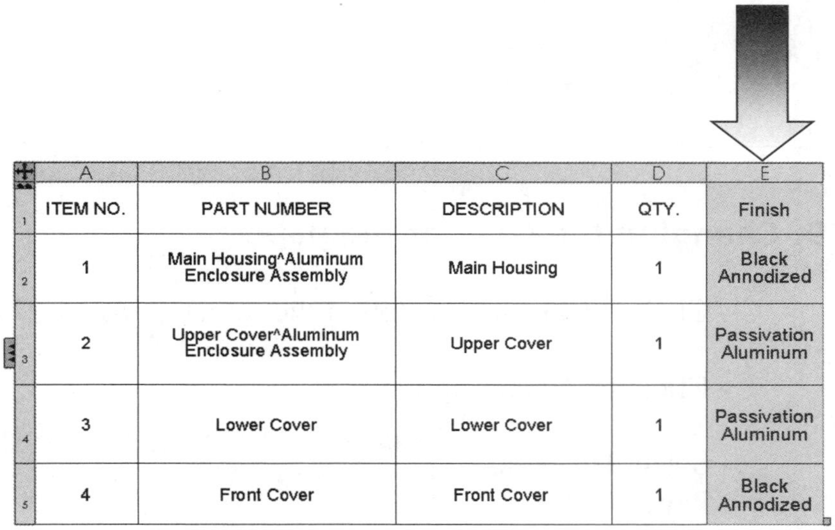

	A	B	C	D	E
1	ITEM NO.	PART NUMBER	DESCRIPTION	QTY.	Finish
2	1	Main Housing^Aluminum Enclosure Assembly	Main Housing	1	Black Annodized
3	2	Upper Cover^Aluminum Enclosure Assembly	Upper Cover	1	Passivation Aluminum
4	3	Lower Cover	Lower Cover	1	Passivation Aluminum
5	4	Front Cover	Front Cover	1	Black Annodized

- Double click on the **column header B** and change from Part Number to **Custom Property**.

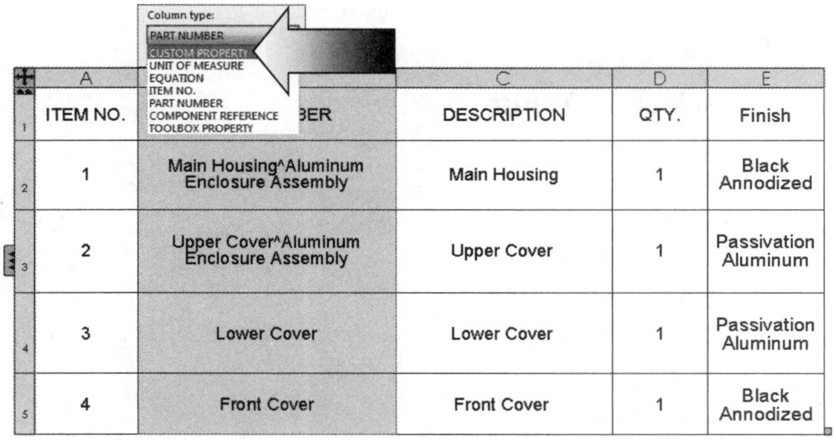

	A		C	D	E
1	ITEM NO.	BER	DESCRIPTION	QTY.	Finish
2	1	Main Housing^Aluminum Enclosure Assembly	Main Housing	1	Black Annodized
3	2	Upper Cover^Aluminum Enclosure Assembly	Upper Cover	1	Passivation Aluminum
4	3	Lower Cover	Lower Cover	1	Passivation Aluminum
5	4	Front Cover	Front Cover	1	Black Annodized

- Select the **PartNo** from the Property Name drop down list.

- Column B is updated to display the part numbers that were previously entered at the part level.

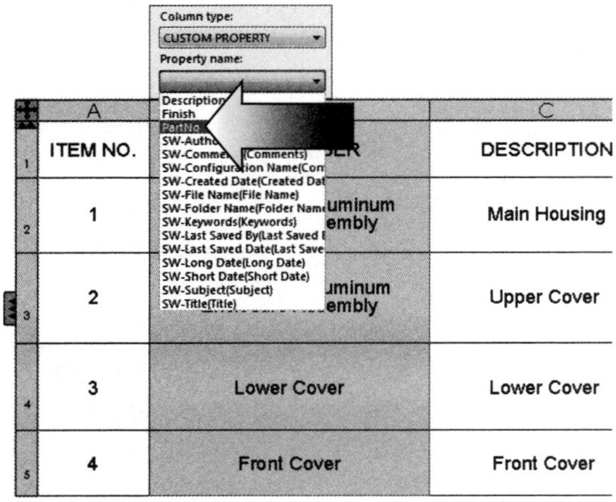

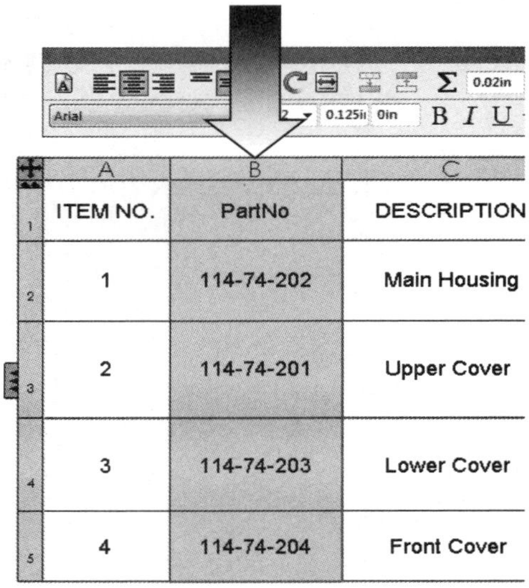

9. Changing the color of the paper:

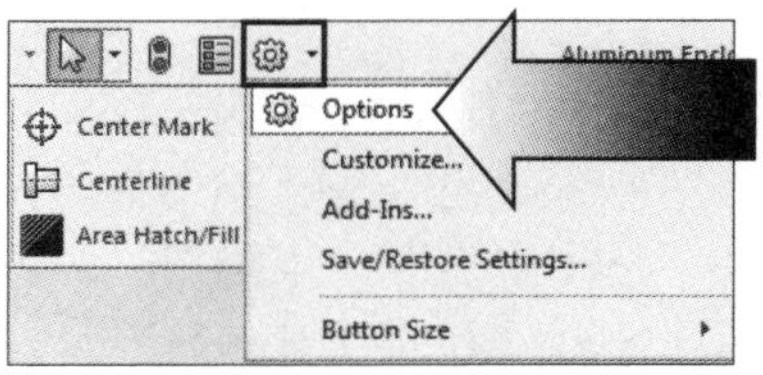

- Click **Options** on the top of the screen (arrow).

- Click the **Colors** option.

- Select **Drawing Paper Color** under Color Scheme Settings

- Click **Edit** and select the **White** color.

- Enable the check box for: **Use Specified Color For Drawings Paper Color** and click **OK**.

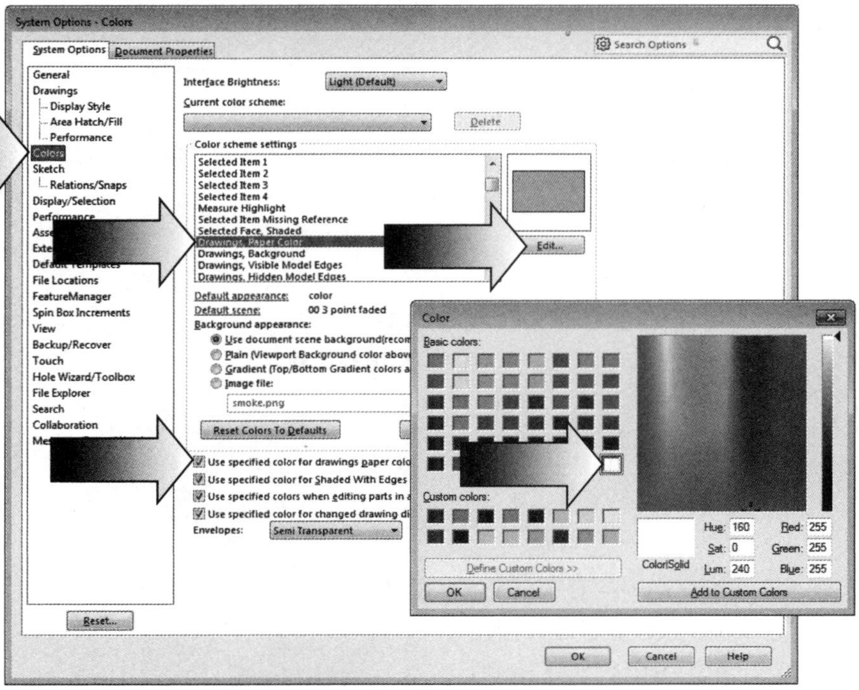

10. Adding balloons:

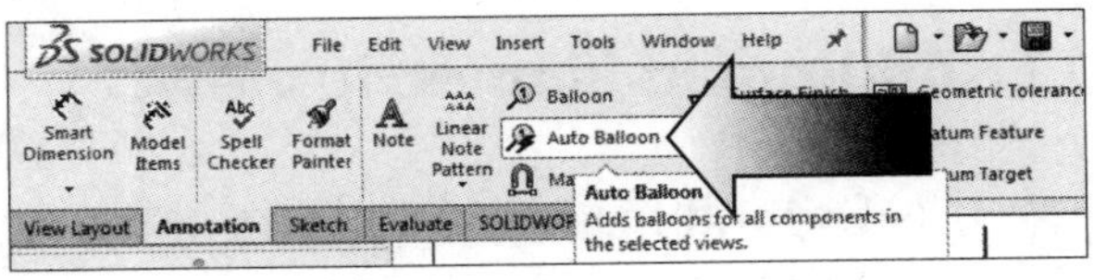

- Balloons are used to identify item numbers in the bills of materials.

- The balloon numbers are associated with the bill of materials as well as the order of the components displayed on the FeatureManager tree.

- Click **Auto Balloon** from the Annotation tab.

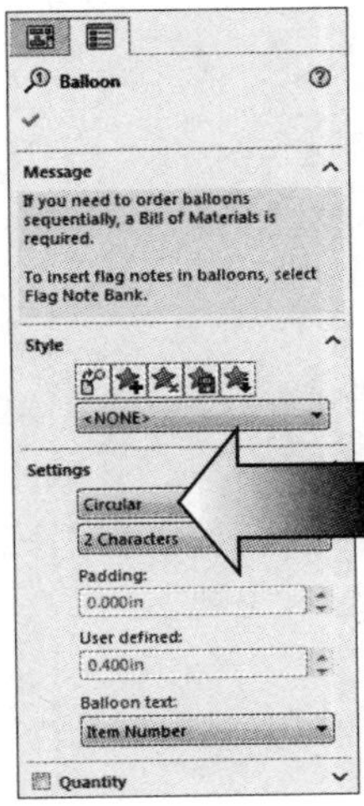

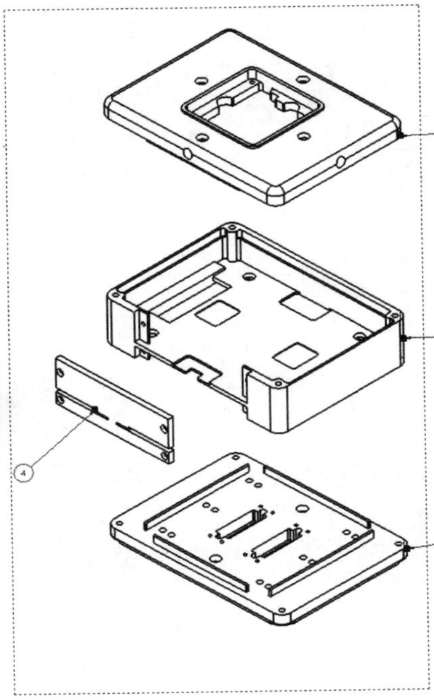

- The balloons are added to each unique component.

- Use the default **Circular** style.

- Click **OK**.

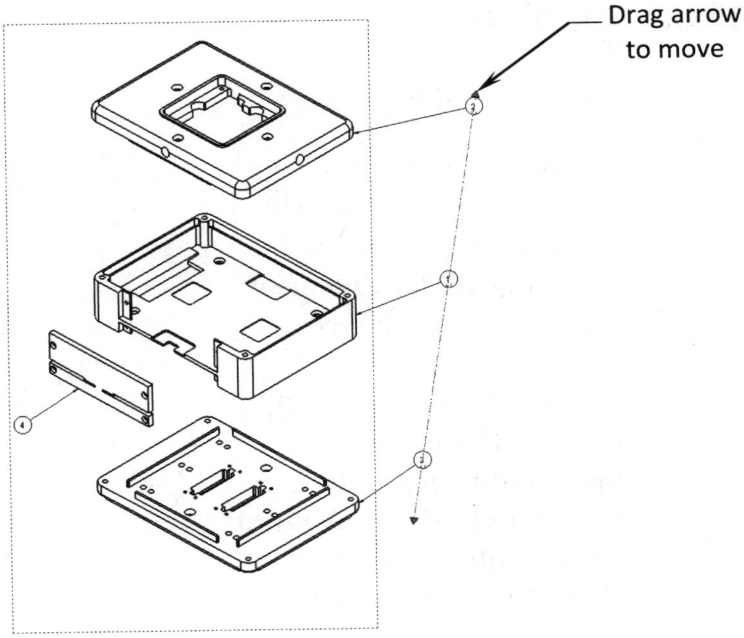

- The balloons are attached to the magnetic lines to align or to move them in groups.

- Drag one of the arrow heads to move the magnetic line and the balloons that are attached to it.

- Delete the magnetic lines and move the balloons individually if needed.

11. Adding an isometric view:

- Expand the **View Palette** and drag/drop the isometric view onto the drawing.

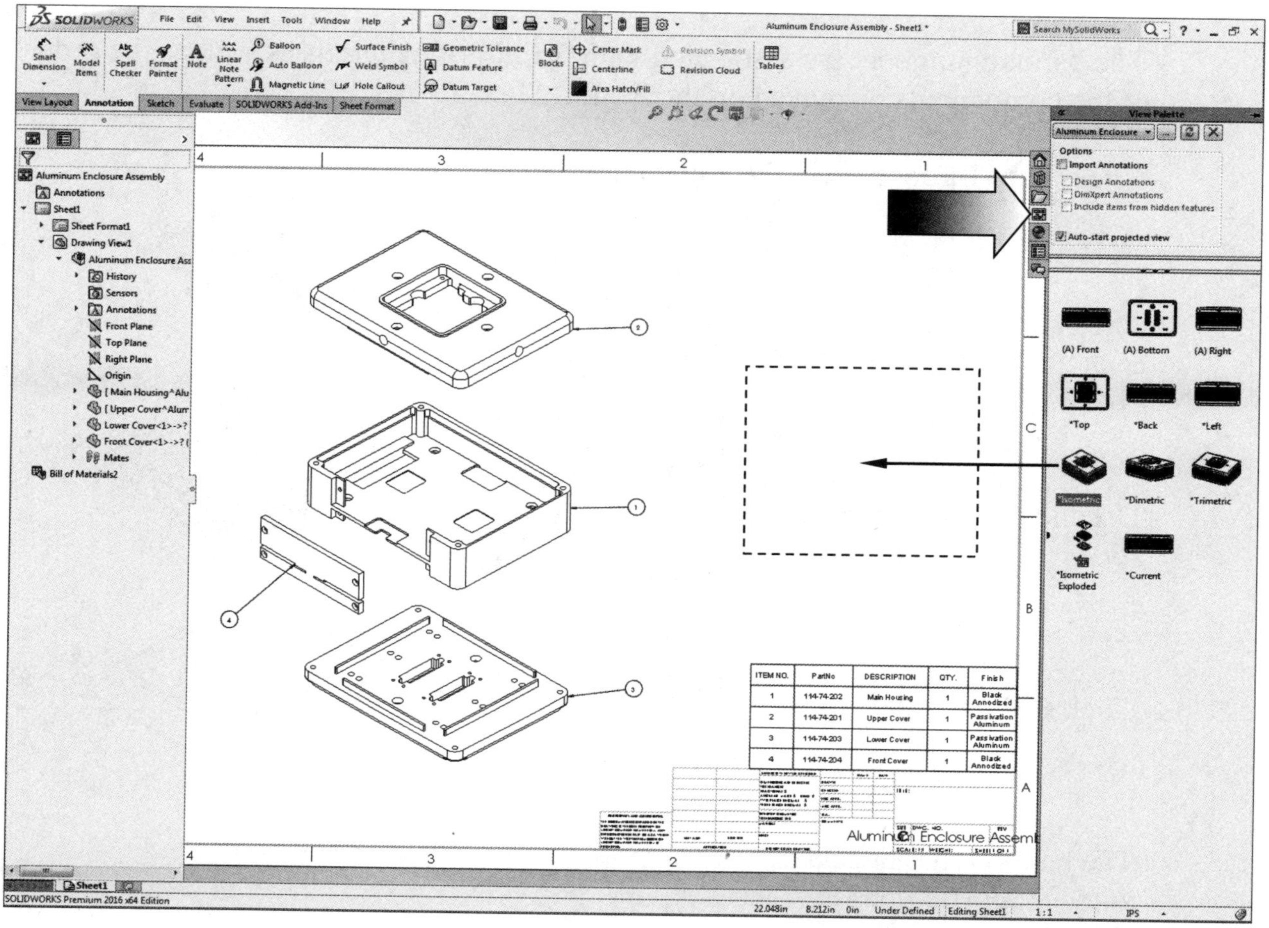

- The isometric view is aligned with the exploded view by default. We will need to break its alignment before it can be moved freely.

- Right click the dotted border of the isometric view and select: **Alignment / Break Alignment**.

- Move the isometric view to check its alignment.

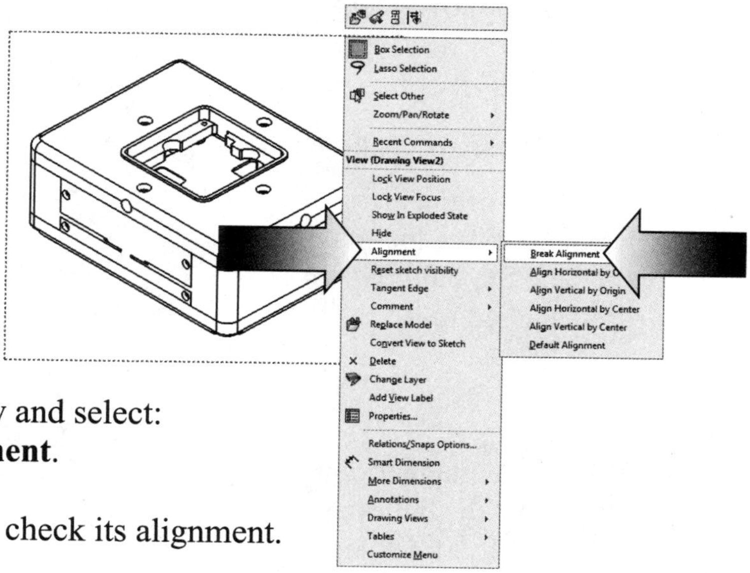

12. Changing the display of a drawing view:

- Click the dotted border of the isometric view and select the **Shaded With Edges** button from the properties tree (arrow).

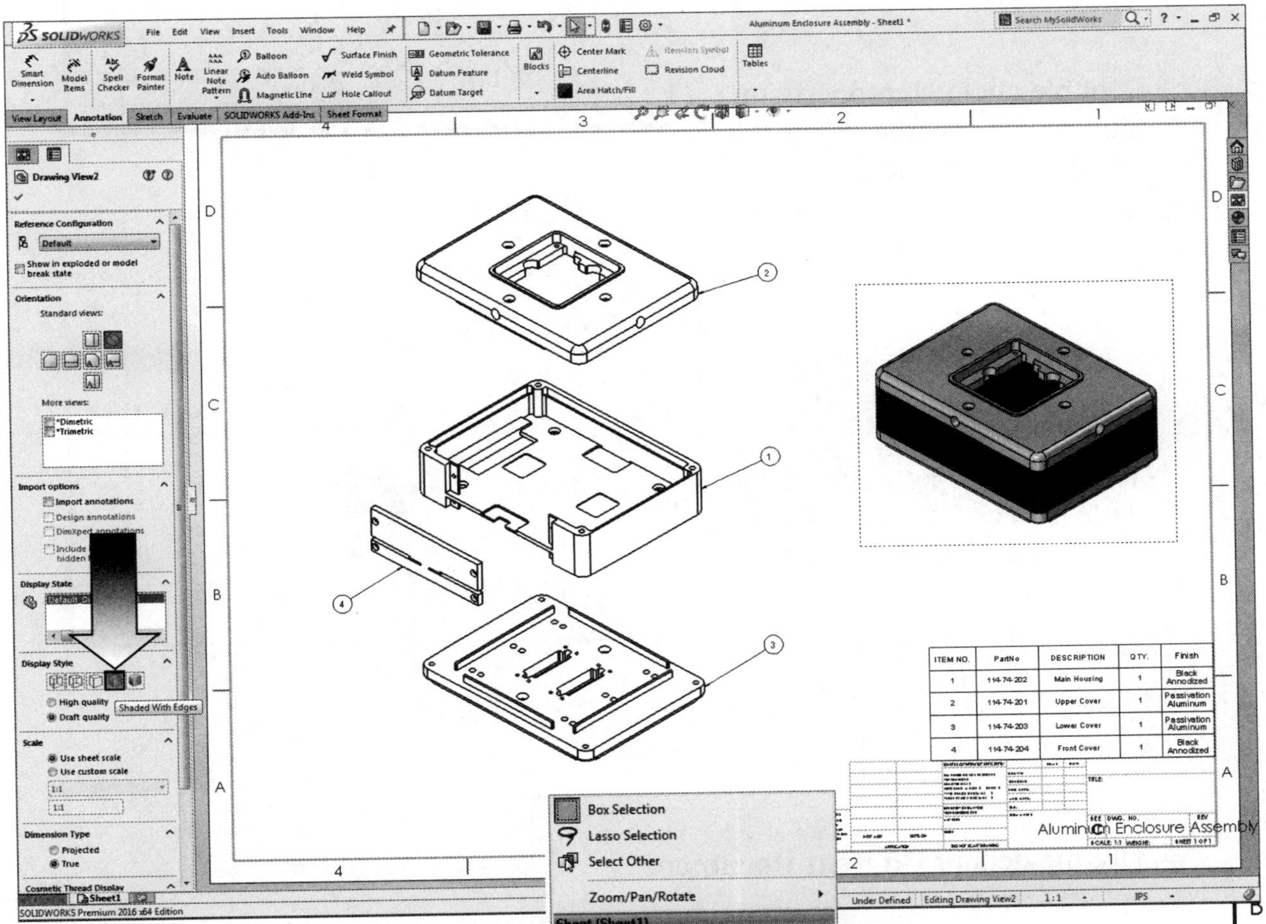

13. Editing the Sheet Format:

- The information in the Title Block is stored in the Sheet Format, which by default, is saved under the Sheet.

- Right click inside the drawing and select: **Edit Sheet Format**.

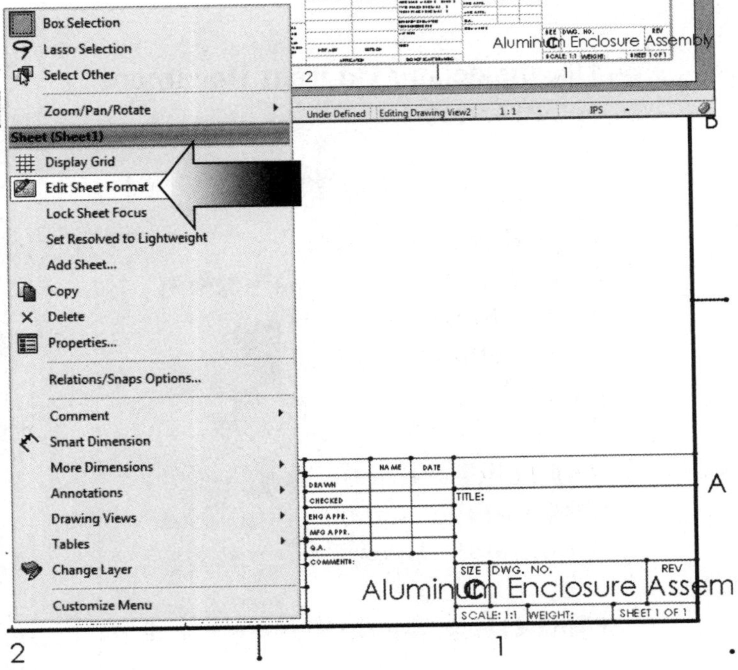

- Hover the cursor over the center of the company name field, look for the symbol "A" (note). The property link $PRP:"COMPANYNAME" appears.

- Double click the property link and enter the name of your company in this field.

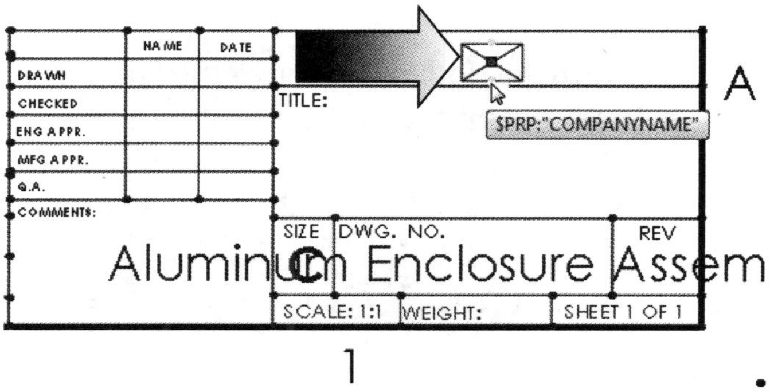

- Select the property link in the Title area and click the **Link To Property** button (arrow).

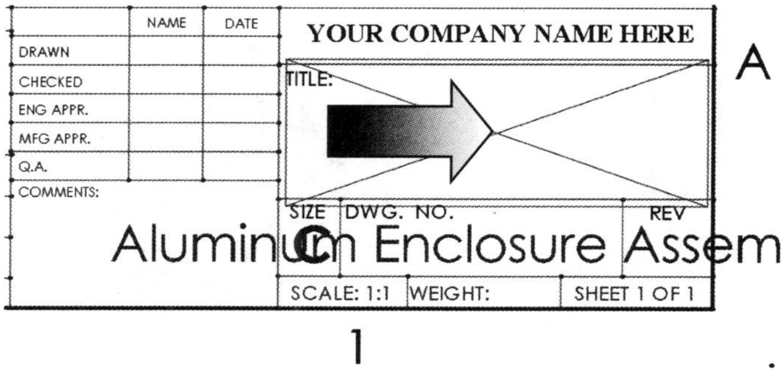

- Use the default **Current Document** option (arrow).

- Select the property: **SW-File Name (File Name)** under the Property Name drop down list (arrow).

- Click **OK**.

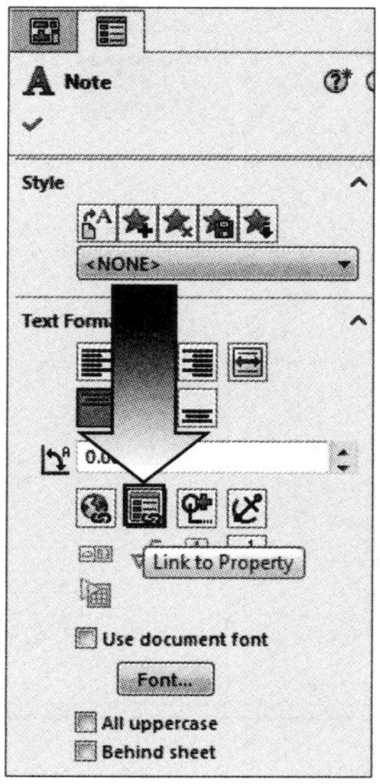

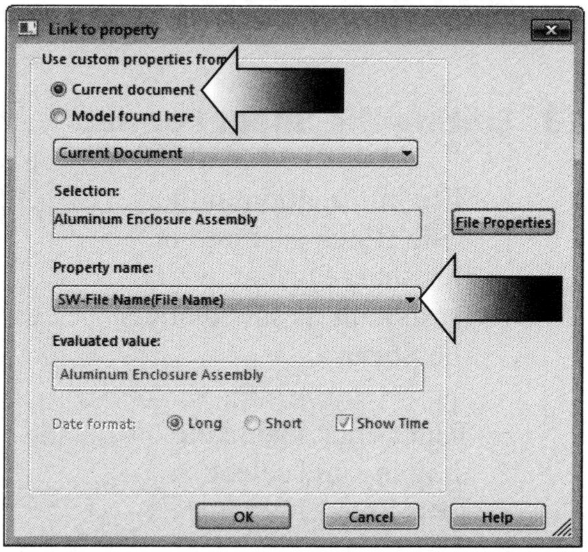

- The property links to the name of the document and displays it in the title field.

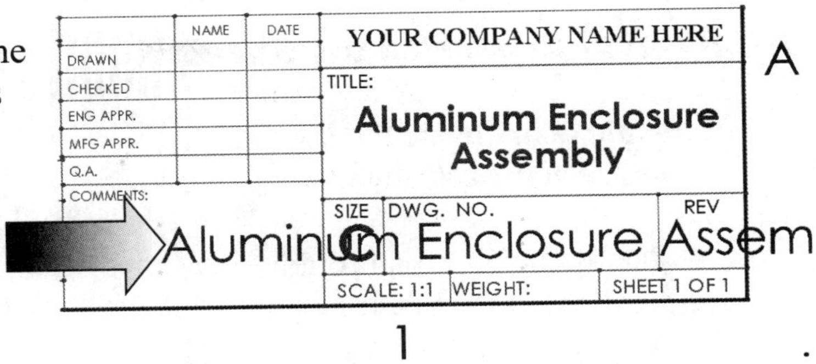

- Select the Drawing Number (Aluminum Enclosure Assembly) and click the **Link To Property** button.

- Use the default **Current Document** option.

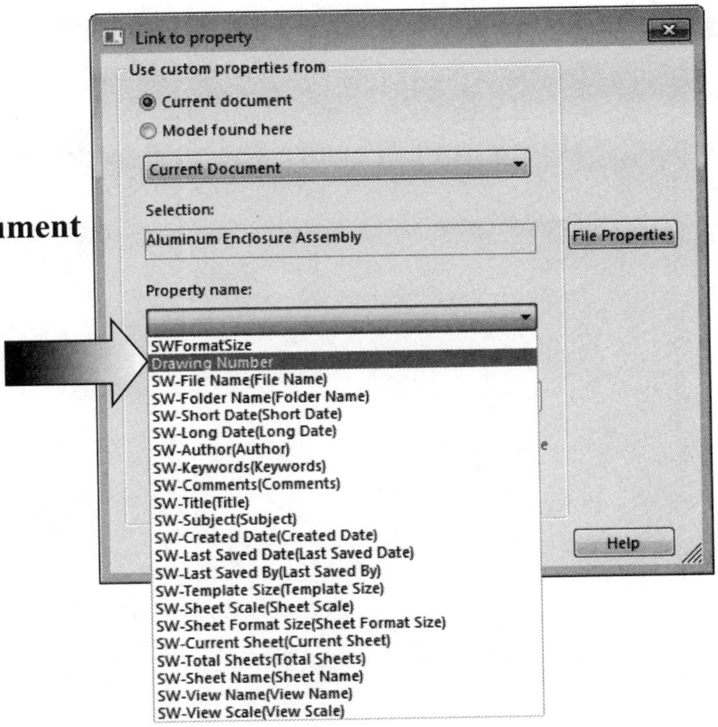

- Select the property: **Drawing Number** from Property name drop down list (arrow).

- Click **OK**.

- The Drawing Number is linked to the property that was previously entered in the part and is now displayed in the field.

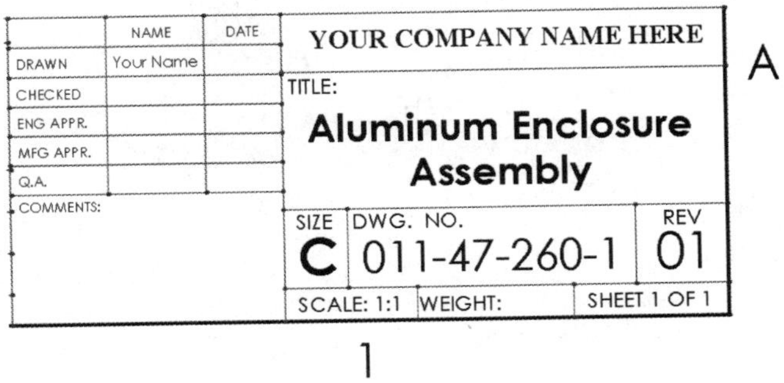

14. Switching back to the Sheet:

- Right click inside the drawing and select: **Edit Sheet**.

- The Sheet Layer is brought to the top and the Sheet Format layer is put to the back.

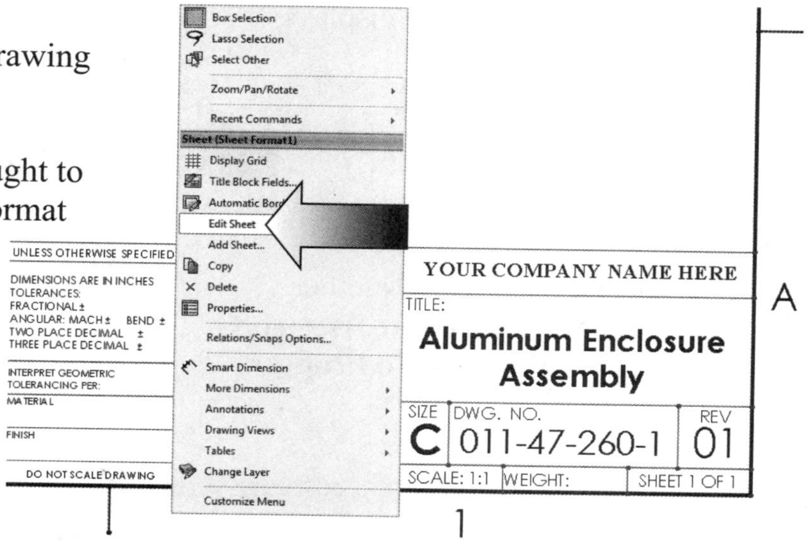

15. Saving your work:

- Click **File / Save As**.

- Use the default name **Aluminum Enclosure Assembly.slddrw**

- Press **Save**.

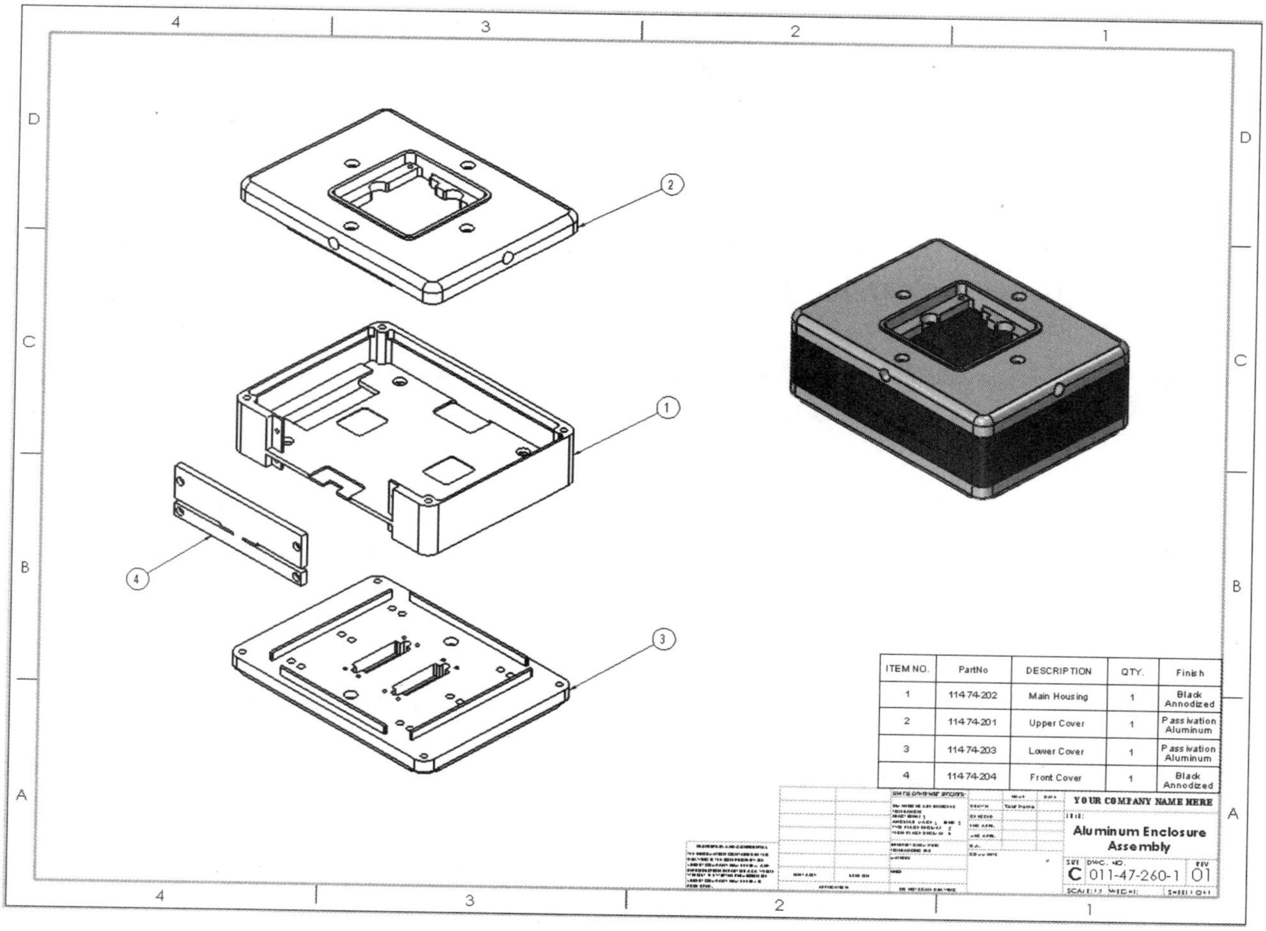

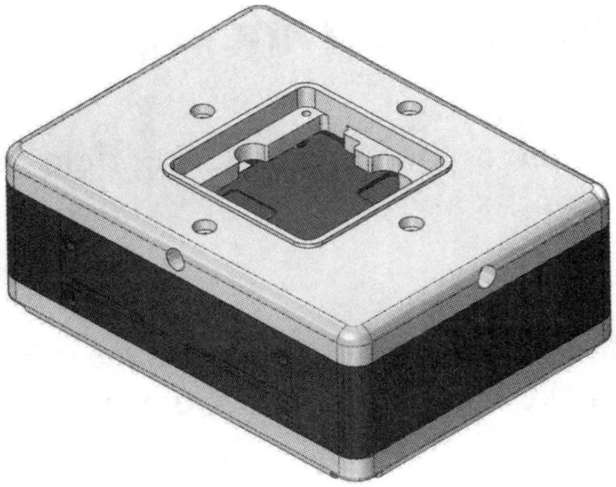

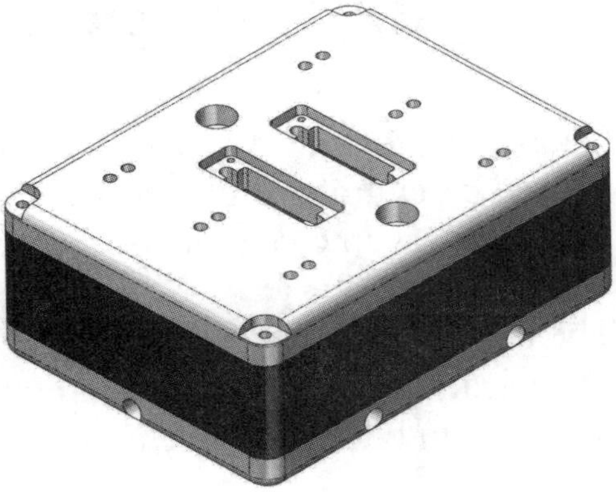

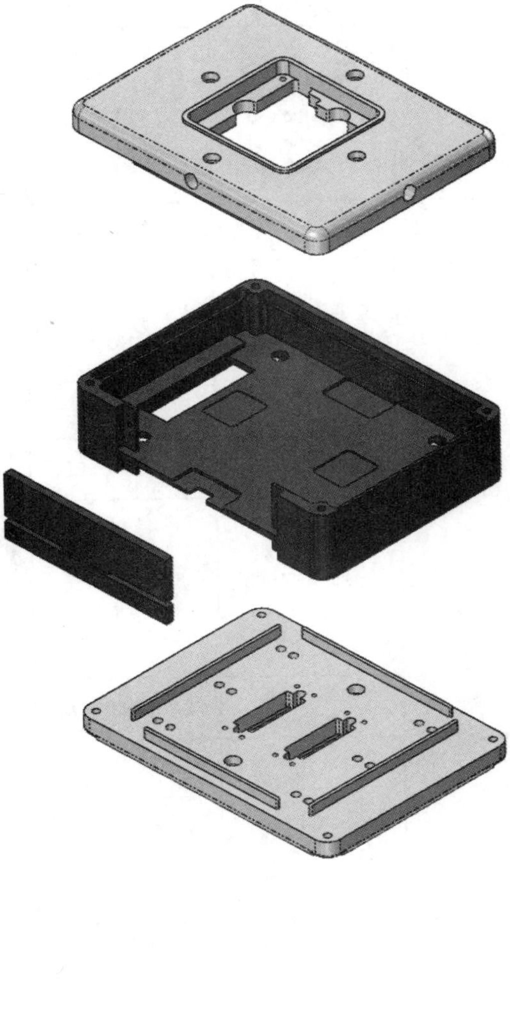

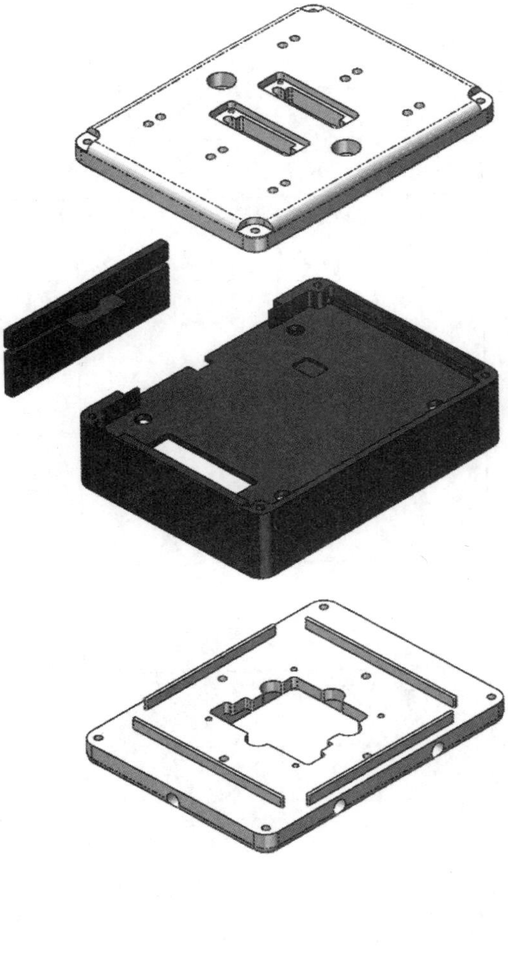

Reference Reading:
GD&T – Geometric Dimensioning & Tolerancing

Geometric Dimensioning & Tolerancing provides a vital link in the manufacturing field. It is used by engineers, designers, drafters, inspectors, machinists and anyone involved in turning ideas into satisfactory products.

The engineer and designer can use geometric and position tolerances to communicate specifications clearly and accurately to the people who make the parts and to the inspector who will in turn check the parts against the designer's drawings.

When properly applied, the process of proper tolerancing will help eliminate or reduce problems which may occur later, and products can be produced more accurately.

FORM Examples

		MMC – LMC or RFS	DATUM USED
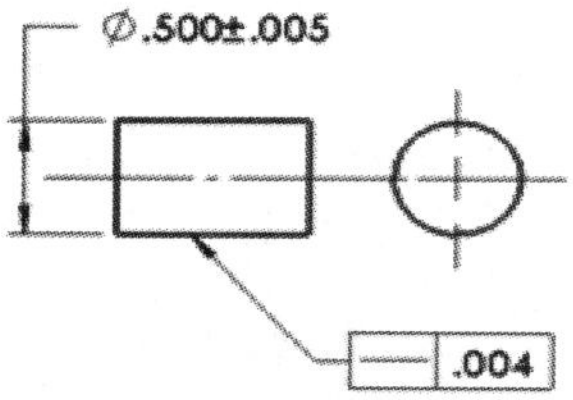	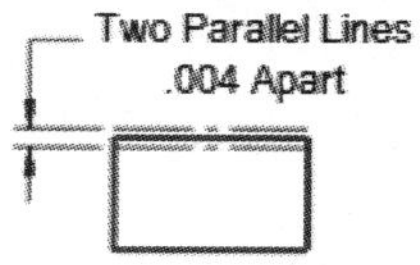	Ⓜ or Ⓛ Can apply to a Feature of Size	No
		MMC – LMC or RFS	DATUM USED
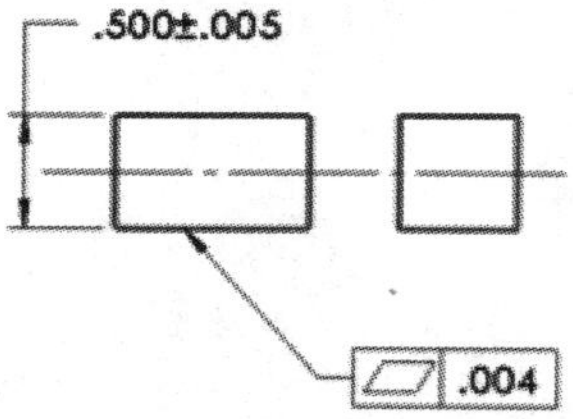	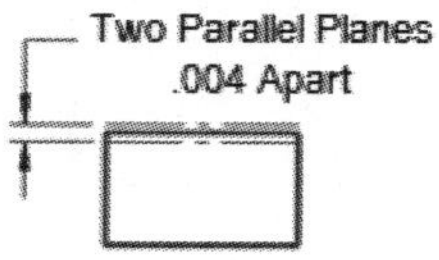	Does Not Apply	No
		MMC – LMC or RFS	DATUM USED
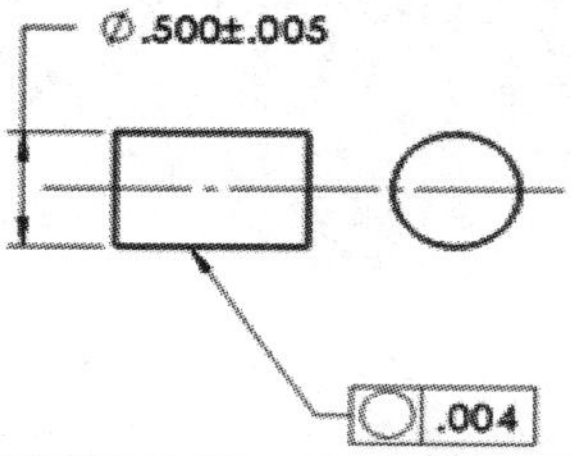	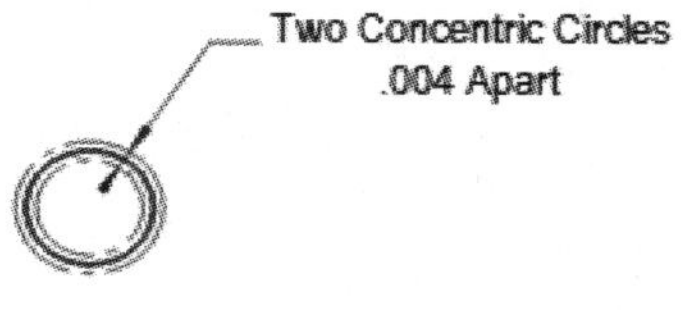	Does Not Apply	No
		MMC – LMC or RFS	DATUM USED
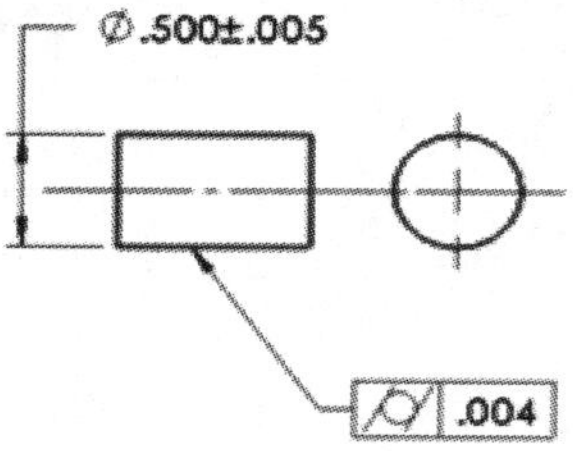	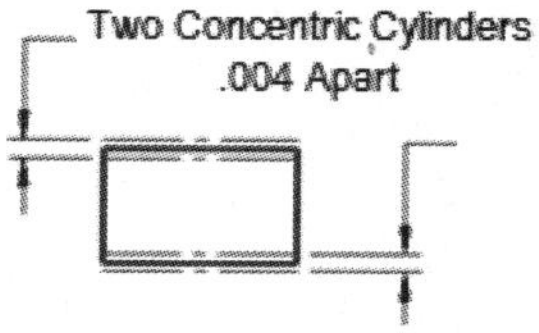	Does Not Apply	No

ORIENTATION Examples

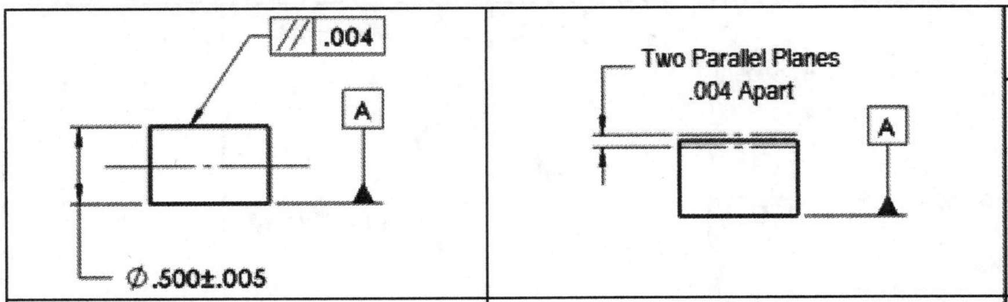

MMC – LMC or RFS	DATUM USED
(M) or (L) Can apply to a Feature of Size	Yes

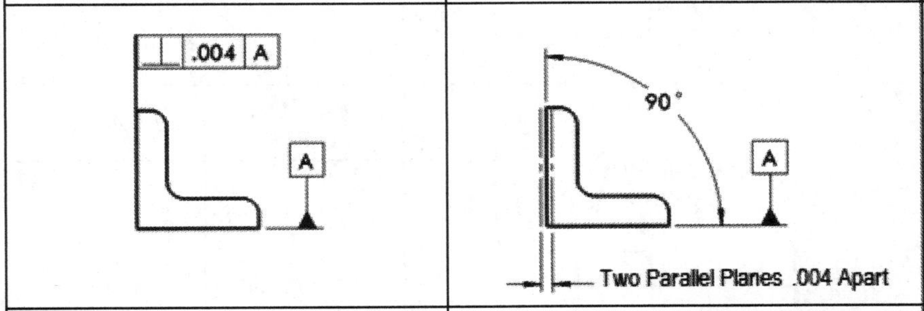

MMC – LMC or RFS	DATUM USED
(M) or (L) Can apply to a Feature of Size	Yes

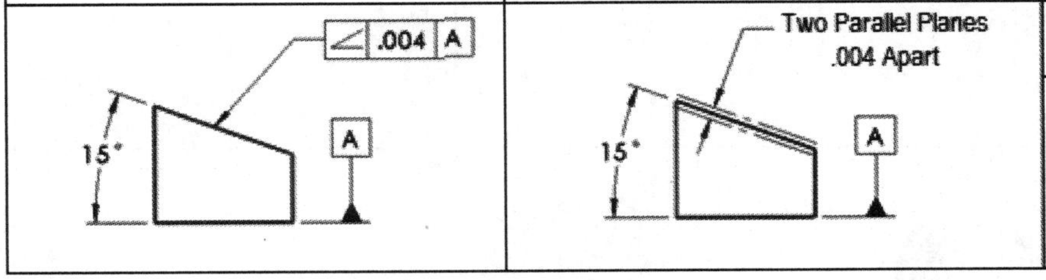

MMC – LMC or RFS	DATUM USED
(M) or (L) Can apply to a Feature of Size	Maybe Used or Not

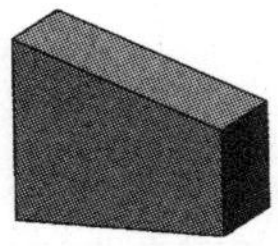

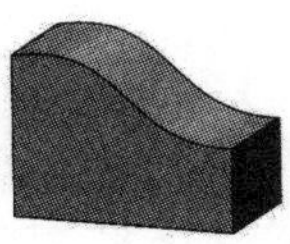

PROFILE Examples

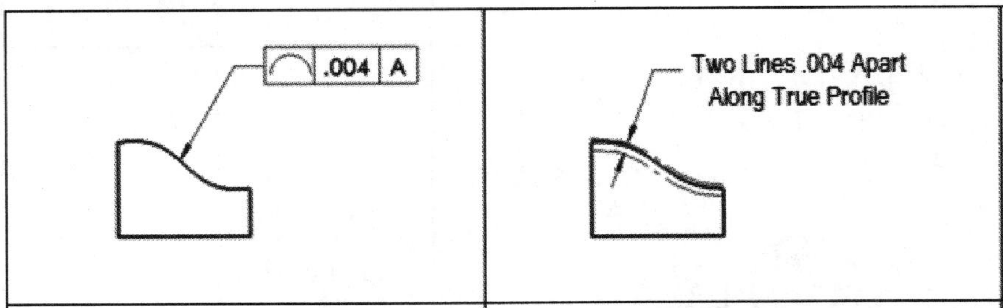

MMC – LMC or RFS	DATUM USED
Does Not Apply	Maybe Used or Not

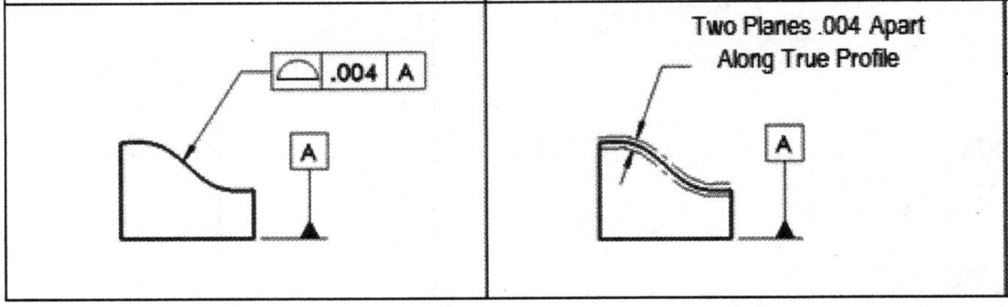

MMC – LMC or RFS	DATUM USED
Does Not Apply	Maybe Used or Not

RUNOUT Examples

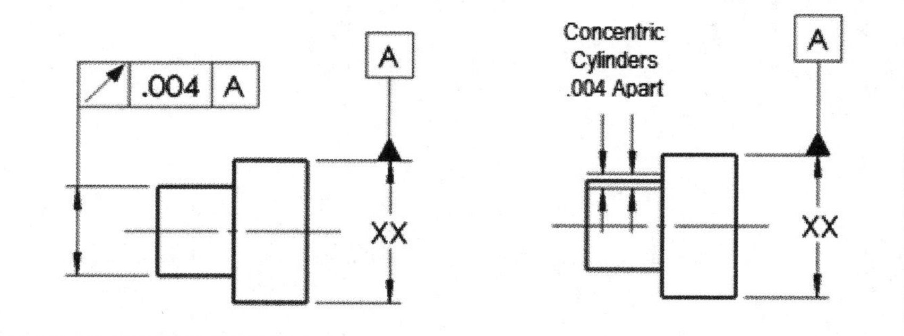

MMC – LMC or RFS	DATUM USED
RFS Always	Yes

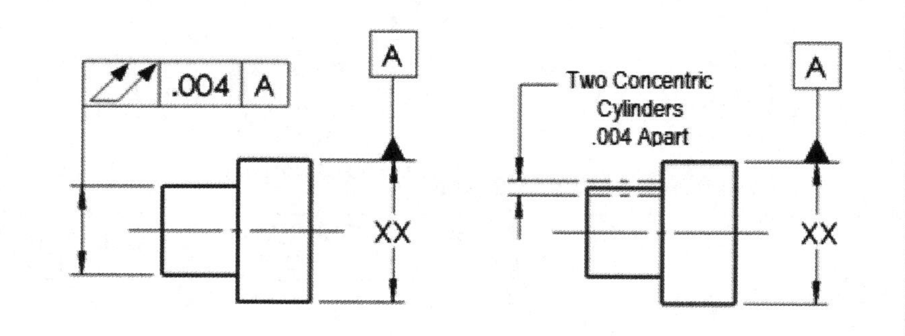

MMC – LMC or RFS	DATUM USED
RFS Always	Yes

LOCATION Examples

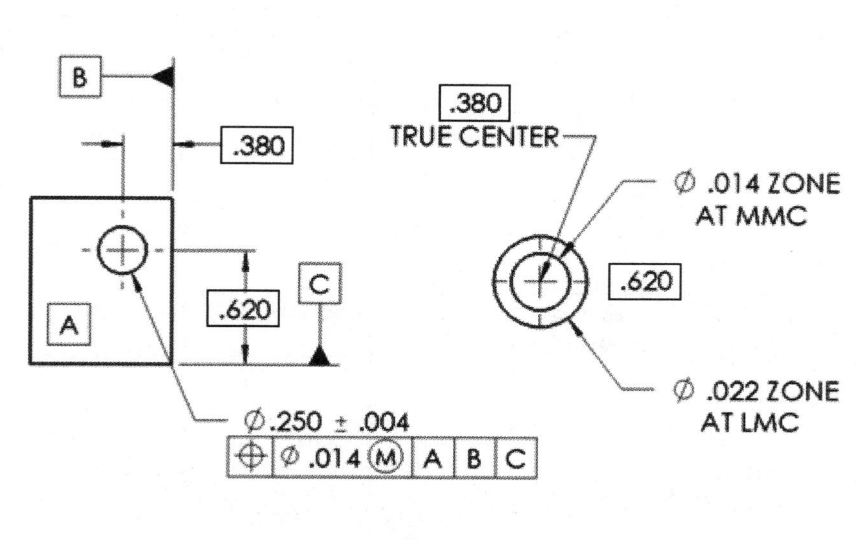

MMC – LMC or RFS	DATUM USED
(M) Or (L) Can apply to a Feature of Size	Yes

LOCATION Examples (cont.)

	MMC – LMC or RFS	DATUM USED
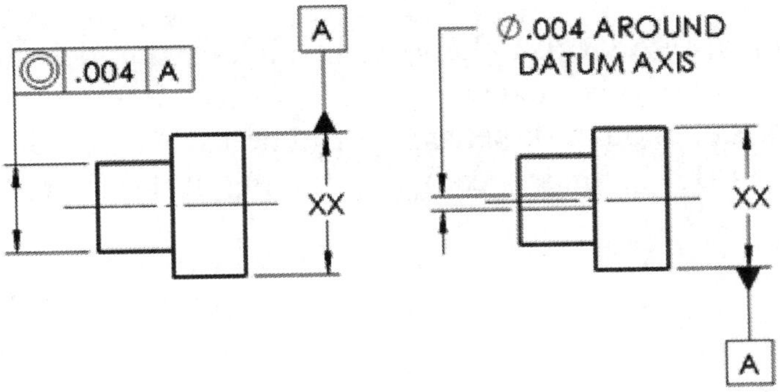	Ⓜ Or Ⓛ Can apply to a Feature of Size	Yes
	MMC – LMC or RFS	DATUM USED
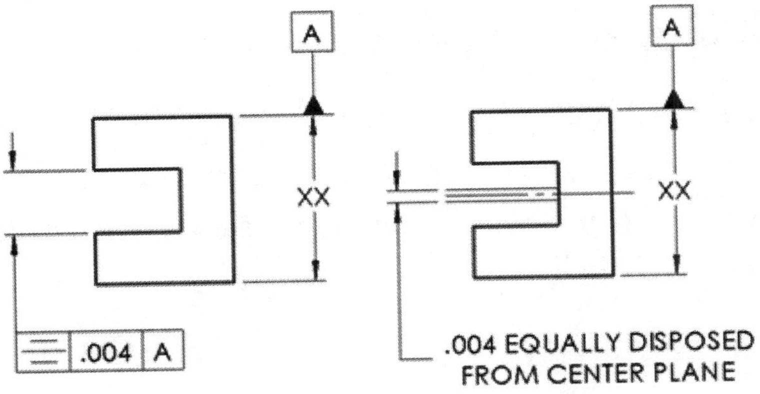	Ⓜ Or Ⓛ Can apply to a Feature of Size	Yes

- Geometric Dimensioning & Tolerancing plays an important role in the advancement of design and production technology. It is a cost saver and an eliminator of confusion.

- Geometric and Position Tolerances can be used at all levels. It is important to learn what they are, what they do, and what their applications are.

ASME (American Society for Mechanical Engineering)

ANSI Y14.5M (American National Standards Institute)

Symbols Description

ANGULARITY: ∠

The condition of a surface or line, which is at a specified angle (other than 90°) from the datum plane or axis.

BASIC DIMENSION: 1.00

A dimension specified on a drawing as BASIC is a theoretical value used to describe the exact size, shape, or location of a feature. It is used as a basic from which permissible variations are established by tolerance on other dimensions or in notes. A basic dimension can be identified by the abbreviation BSC or more readily by boxing in the dimension.

CIRCULARITY (ROUNDNESS): ○

A tolerance zone bounded by two concentric circles within which each circular element of the surface must lie.

CONCENTRICITY: ◎

The condition in which the axis of all cross-sectional elements of a feature's surface of revolution are common.

CYLINDRICITY: ⌭

The condition of a surface of revolution in which all points of the surface are equidistant from a common axis, or for a perfect cylinder.

DATUM: 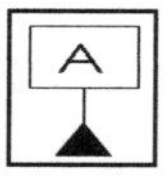

A point, line, plane, cylinder, etc., assumed to be exact for purposes of computation from which the location or geometric relationship of other features of a part may be established. A datum identification symbol contains a letter (except I, O and Q) placed inside a rectangular box.

DATUM TARGET: 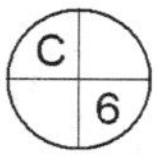

The datum target symbol is a circle divided into four quadrants. The letter placed in the upper left quadrant identifies its associated datum feature. The numeral placed in the lower right quadrant identifies the target; the dashed leader line indicates the target on far side.

FLATNESS: ⏥

The condition of a surface having all elements in one plane. A flatness tolerance specifies a tolerance zone confined by two parallel planes within which the surface must lie.

MAXIMUM MATERIAL CONDITION: Ⓜ

The condition of a part feature when it contains the maximum amount of material.

LEAST MATERIAL CONDITION: Ⓛ

The condition of a part feature when it contains the least amount of material. The term is opposite from maximum material condition.

REGARDLESS OF FEATURE SIZE: RFS

This is the default condition for all Geometric Tolerance. This means that the feature's nominal center is to be inspected to the datum's nominal center, regardless of the size or shape of either the feature or datum.

PARALLELISM: //

The condition of a surface or axis which is equidistant at all points from a datum plane or axis.

PERPENDICULARITY: ⊥

The condition of a surface, line, or axis, which is at a right angle (90°) from a datum plane or datum axis.

PROFILE OF ANY LINE: ⌒

The condition limiting the amount of profile variation along a line element of a feature.

PROFILE OF ANY SURFACE: ⌓

Similar to profile of any line, but this condition relates to the entire surface.

PROJECTED TOLERANCE ZONE: Ⓟ

A zone applied to a hole in which a pin, stud, screw, etc. is to be inserted. It controls the perpendicularity of any hole, which controls the fastener's position; this will allow the adjoining parts to be assembled.

REGARDLESS OF FEATURE SIZE: Ⓢ

A condition in which the tolerance of form or condition must be met, regardless of where the feature is within its size tolerance.

RUNOUT: ↗

The maximum permissible surface variation during one complete revolution of the part about the datum axis. This is usually detected with a dial indicator.

STRAIGHTNESS: —

The condition in which a feature of a part must be a straight line.

SYMMETRY: ⌯

A condition wherein a part or feature has the same contour and sides of a central plane.

TRUE POSITION: ⌖

This term denotes the theoretical exact position of a feature.

FREE STATE: Ⓕ

This symbol indicates the part must not be restricted during inspection.

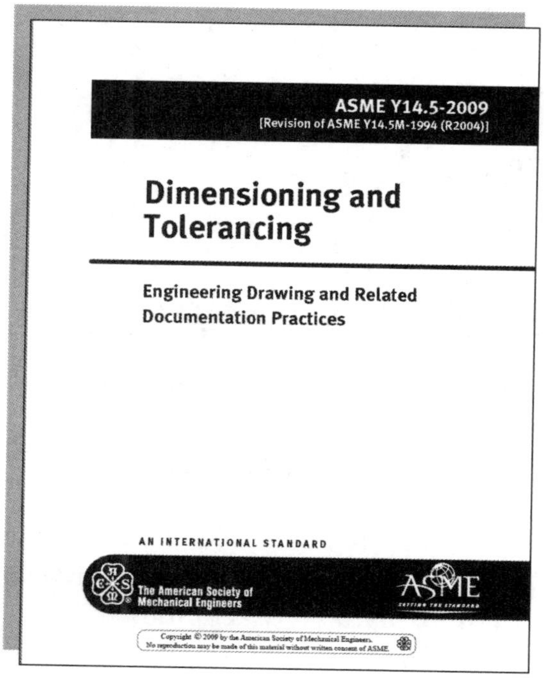

ASME Y14.5-2009
[Revision of ASME Y14.5M-1994 (R2004)]

Dimensioning and Tolerancing

Engineering Drawing and Related Documentation Practices

AN INTERNATIONAL STANDARD

The American Society of Mechanical Engineers

ASME

References:

https://www.asme.org/products/codes-standards/y145-2009-dimensioning-and-tolerancing

http://www.etinews.com/asme-y145-2009.html

FEATURE CONTROL FRAMES

- A feature control frame symbolizes the tolerance requirements for a feature of a part. It can be added to a drawing note for a feature tolerance, or can be specified by running a leader line from the feature control frame directly to the feature.

- The box may be attached to an extension line from the feature or it can be placed on a dimension line. A feature can have more than one feature control frame, depending on its requirements.

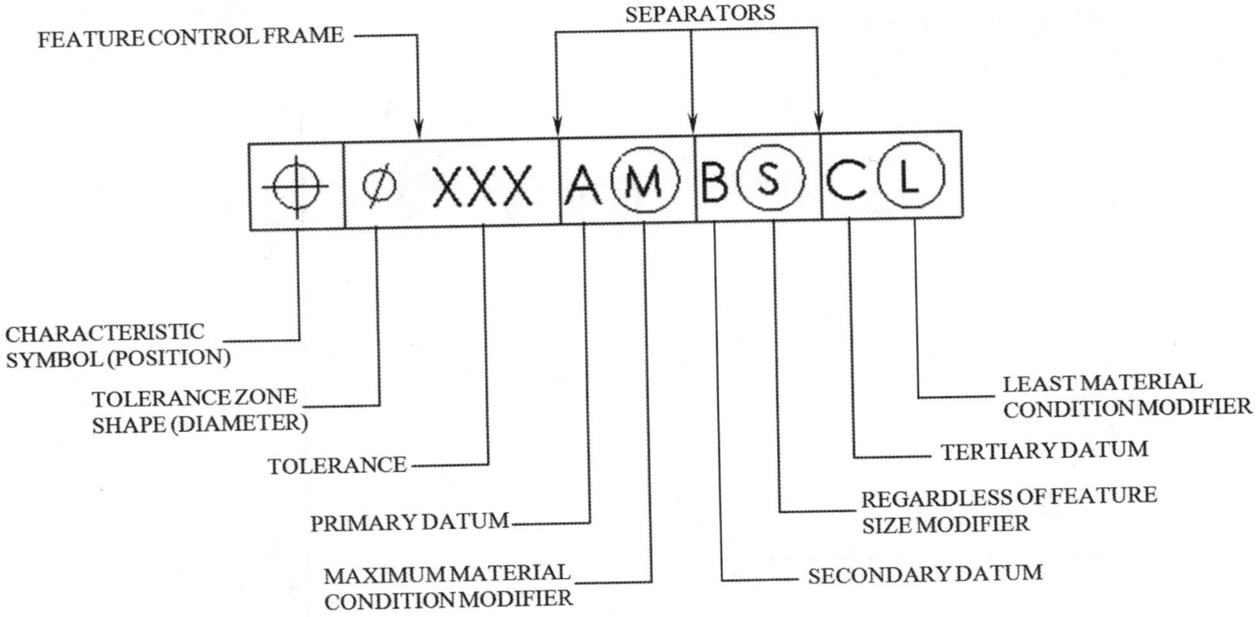

Placement of Feature Control Frame

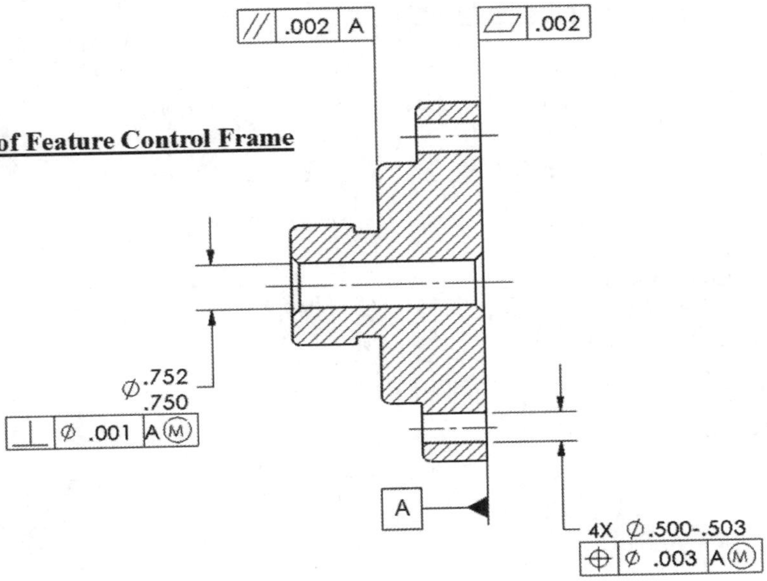

Size at MMC – Maximum Material Condition

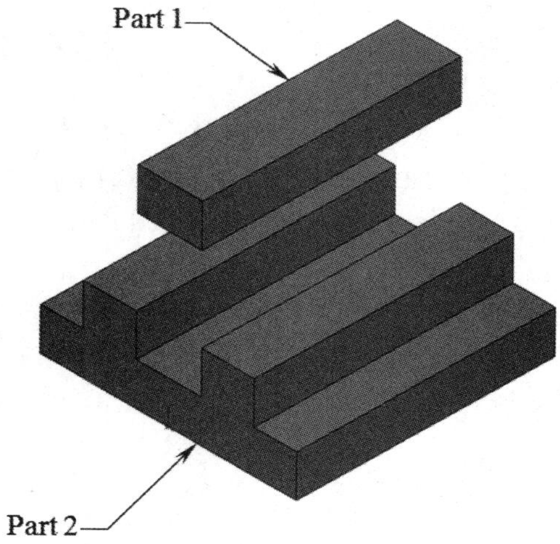

The 2 parts below are designed so that the Bar (part 1) will always fit into the slot of the Base (part 2), even when both are made at their most adverse condition of fit (MMC).

With the Bar (part 1), which is dimensioned at 1.500±.010, the MMC would be the largest within tolerance, or 1.510

With the Slot (part 2) at MMC, it would be 1.511, the smallest within tolerance.

It can safely be predicted that the Bar will always be assembled in the Slot, even if both parts are at their MMC.

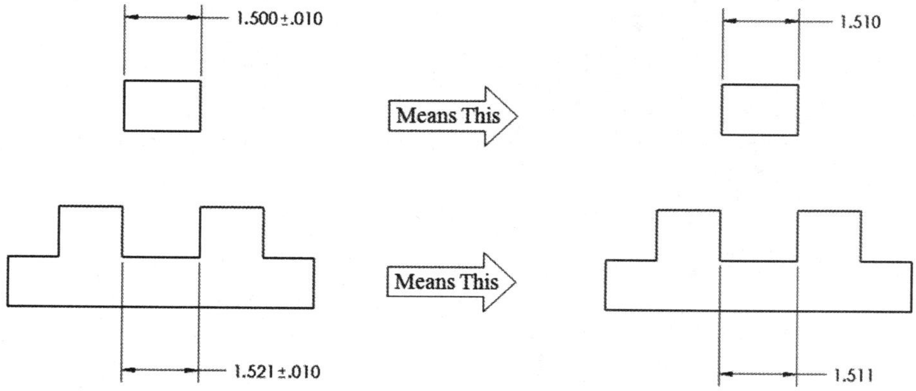

LMC – Least Material Condition

Least Material Condition is a provision that is the opposite of Maximum Material Condition. The abbreviation is LMC. Its symbol in a tolerance frame is an L within a circle (L)

Least Material Condition Specifies that the tolerance Applies when feature of size is made at its largest for an internal feature – or – at its smallest for an external feature.

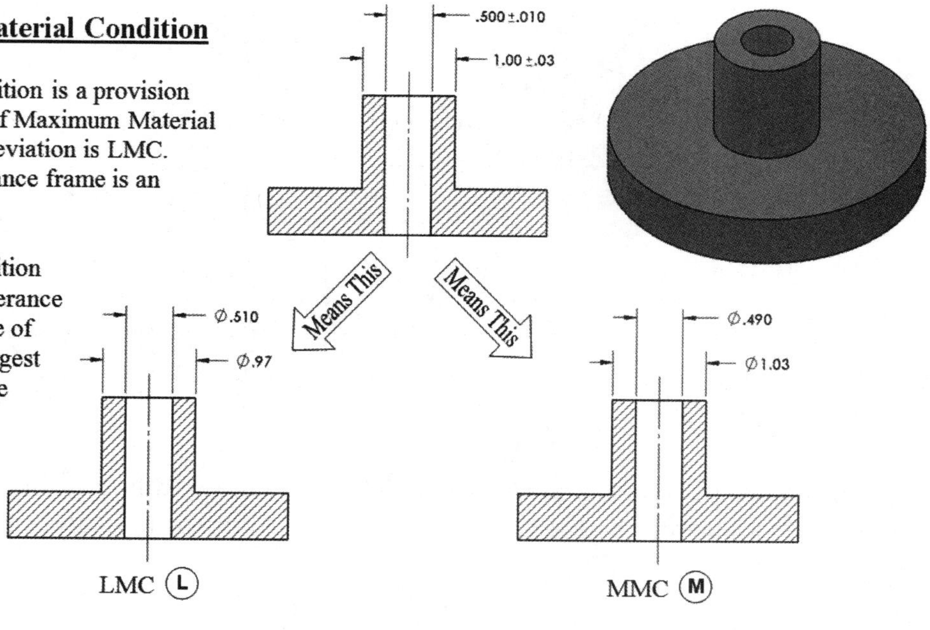

CHAPTER 16

Drawings & Detailing

Drawings & Detailing – Overview

Front Cover Plate

Detailed drawings can be generated in SOLIDWORKS the same method as any other 2D CAD systems. Using SOLIDWORKS, there are many advantages when creating the 3D models first and then generating the 2D drawings from those models after:

* Designing the 3D models are faster than creating lines.

* The drawings are created from the 3D models, so the process is more efficient.

* You can review models in 3D and check for correct geometry and design issues before generating the drawings, so the drawings are more likely to be free of design errors.

* You can insert dimensions and annotations from model sketches and features into the drawings automatically, so you do not have to create them manually in the drawings.

* Parameters and relations of models are retained in the drawings, so the drawings reflect the design intent of the model.

* Changes in models or in the drawings are reflected in their related documents, so making changes is easier and the drawings are more accurate.

In most cases, the orthographic drawings views will be created first and the dependent views such as section views, detail views, auxiliary views, broken views, and crops views are created after.

Dimensions, datums, tolerances, notes, and other annotations are then added to specify the precision and the clarity of the features in each drawings view.

Front Cover Plate
Drawings & Detailing

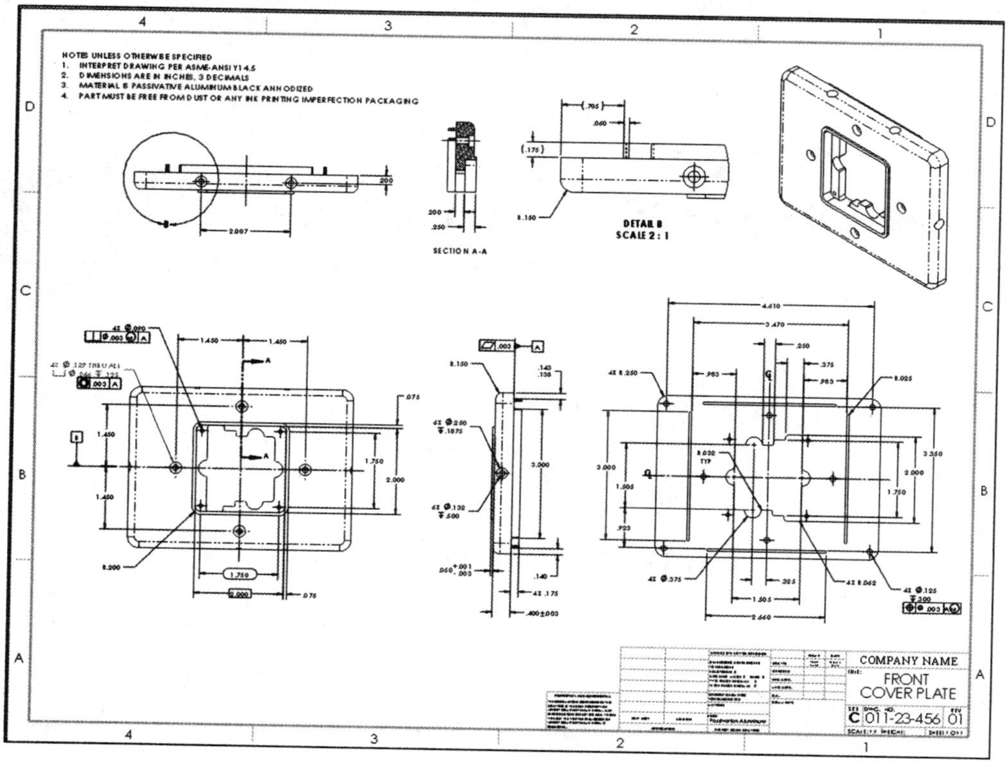

Dimensioning Standards: **ANSI**

Units: **INCHES** – 3 Decimals

Tools Needed:

Insert Sketch	View Palette	Projected View
Section View	Detail View	Notes
Model Items	Datum Feature	Geometric Tolerance

1. Opening a part document:

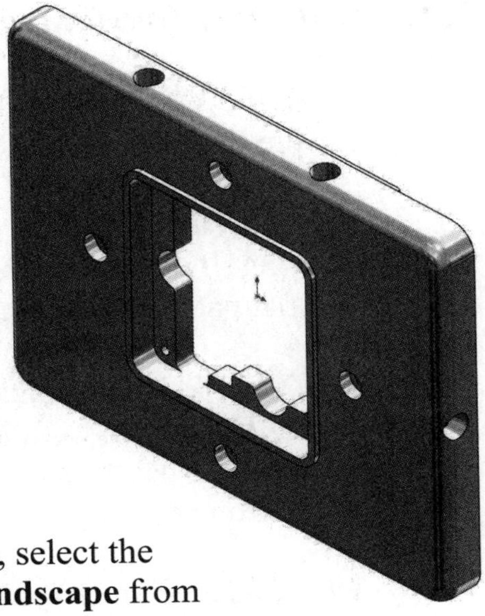

- Select **File / Open**.

- Browse to the part document named: **Front Cover Plate.sldprt** and open it.

- We will generate a detail drawing for this part.

- Select **Make Drawing From Part** from the **File** pull down menu (arrow).

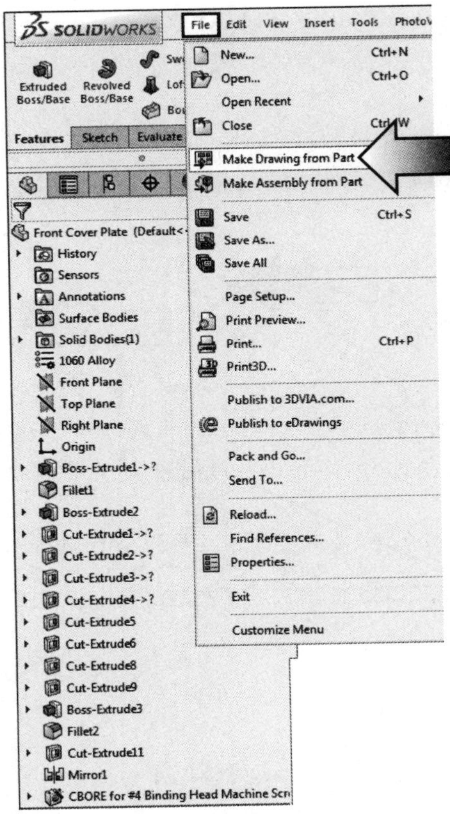

- For sheet size, select the **C (ANSI) Landscape** from the list (arrow).

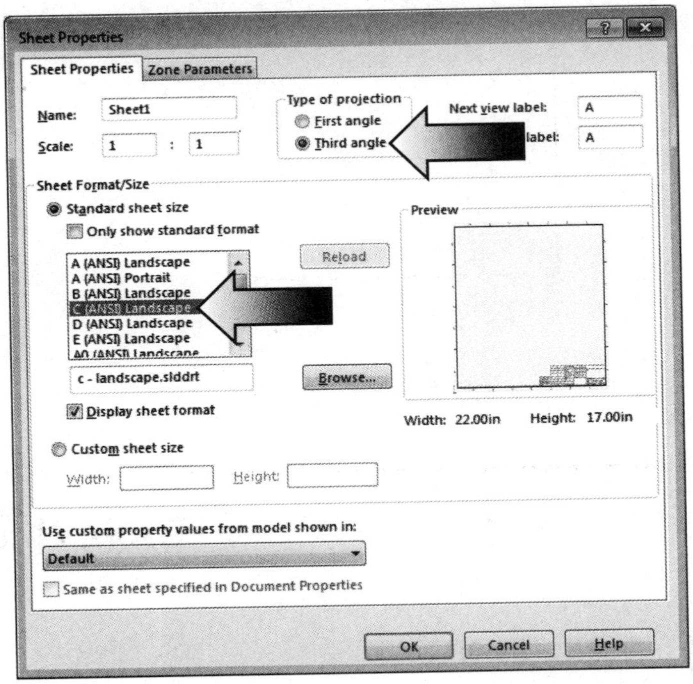

- Set the following parameters:

  * Scale: **1:1**
  * View & Datum Label: **A**
  * Type of Projection: **Third Angle**.
  * Display Sheet Format: **Enabled**.

- Click **OK**.

2. Creating the drawing views:

- Click the **View Palette** tab to expand it (arrow).
  Ensure that the option: **Auto Start Projected View** is checked (arrow).

- Use the View Palette to quickly insert one or more predefined views into the drawing. It contains images of standard views, annotation views, section views, and flat patterns (sheet metal parts) of the selected model.

- The View Palette orientations are based on the ten standard orientations (Front, Right, Top, Back, Left, Bottom, Current, and Isometric) and any custom views in the part or assembly. After you place the views, you can fold or project views from it.

- Drag and drop the **Front** view to the drawing approximately as shown.

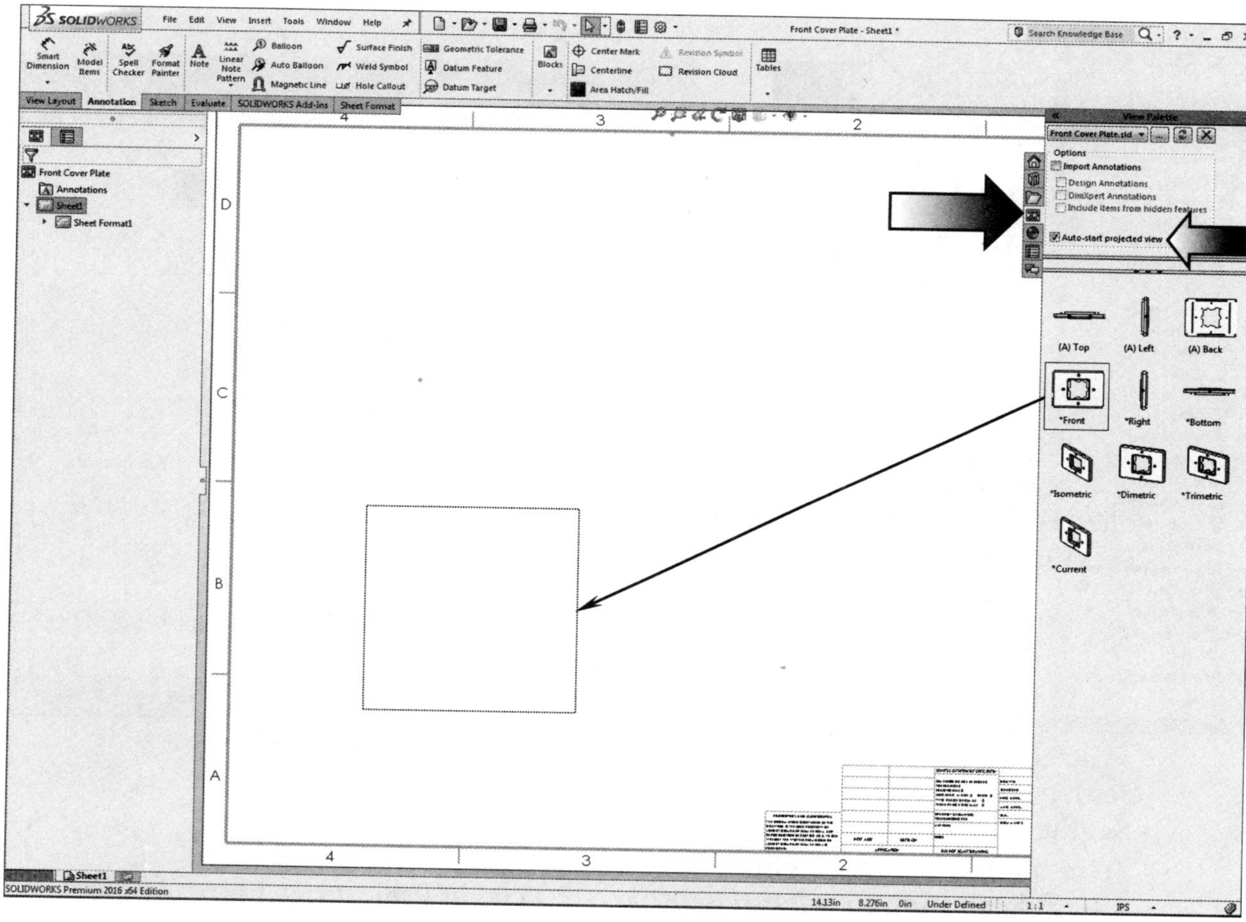

- The Projected View command is activated automatically, move the mouse cursor up and down to see the preview of the new drawing views.

- Create the **Front** view, **Top** view, **Right** view, and **Isometric** view and place them approximately as shown.

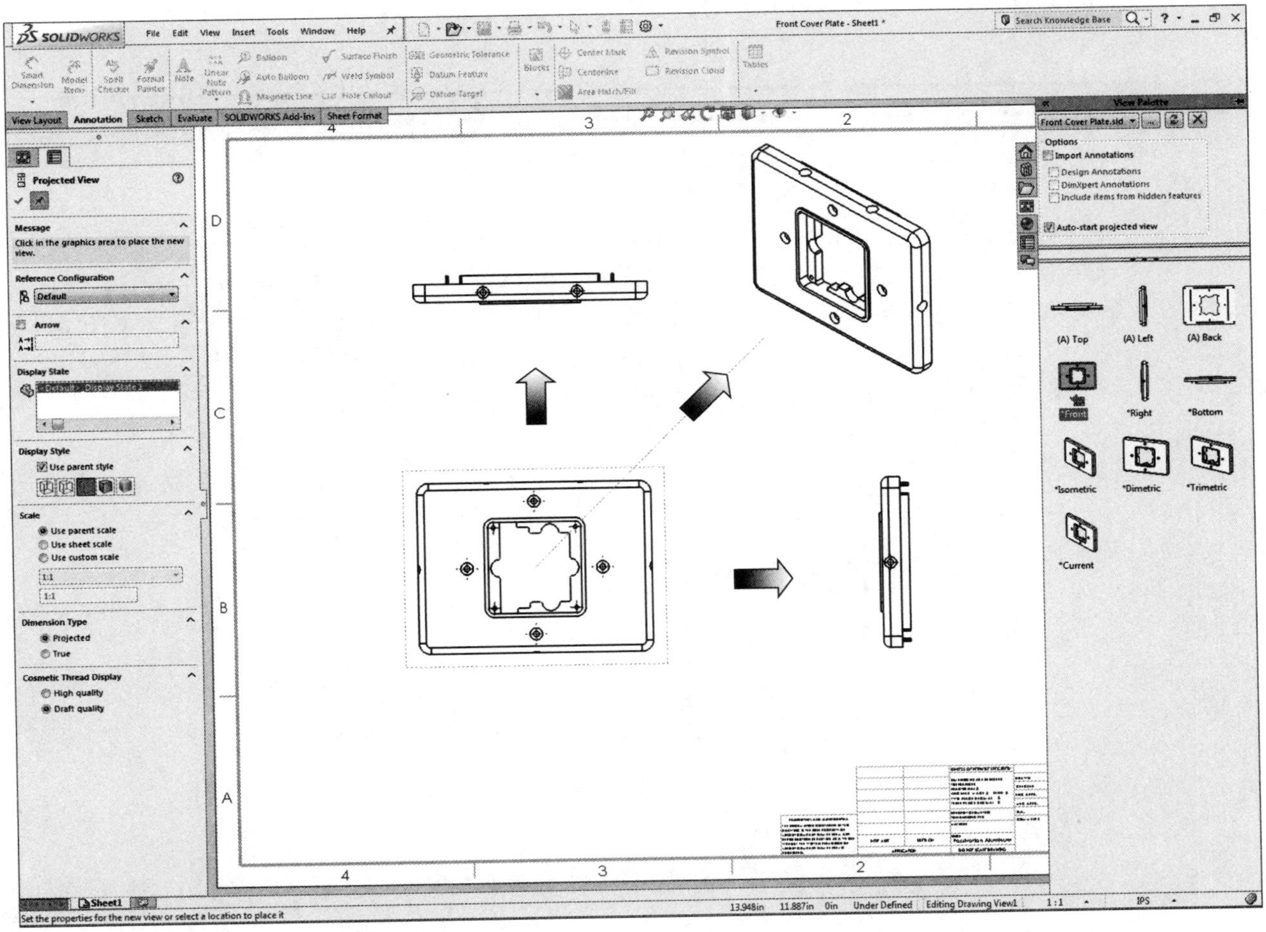

- The Front, Top, and Right views are aligned along the vertical and horizontal directions by default.

- The Top drawing view is not aligned with any view by default, it can be moved freely.

- To break the alignment of any of the views, right click their dotted drawing borders and select: **Alignment / Break Alignment**.

- To re-align the views, right click a drawing view's border and select: **Alignment / Default Alignment.**

- Drawing views can also be aligned manually to one another by using their origins or by the horizontal and vertical directions.

3. Changing to Phantom line style:

- The tangent edges in the drawing views should be displayed as Phantom lines instead of the default solid lines.

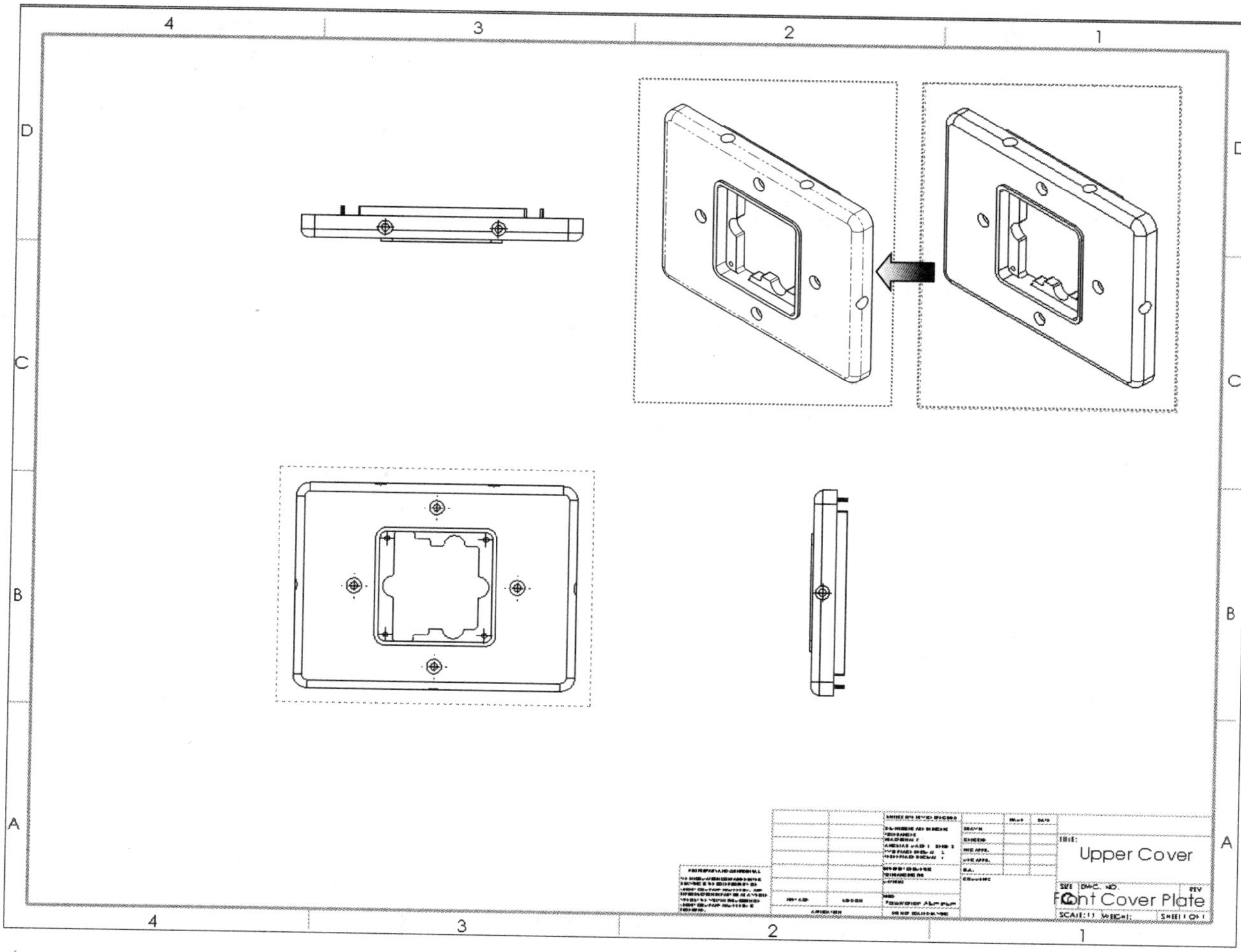

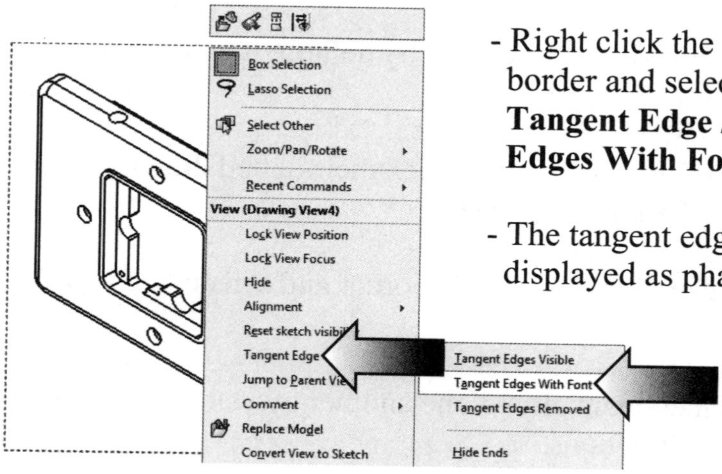

- Right click the Isometric's border and select: **Tangent Edge / Tangent Edges With Font** (Phantom).

- The tangent edges are now displayed as phantom lines.

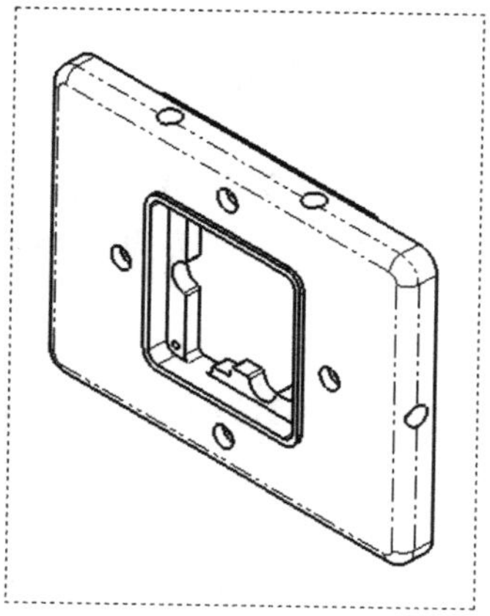

4. Creating a Partial Section view:

- Change to the **Sketch** tab and select the **Line** command. Zoom closer to the Top drawing view.

- Sketch a vertical line from the center of the view, approximately as shown.

> **Section View**
>
> Create a section view to show the interior part of an object as if it was cut in half or quartered

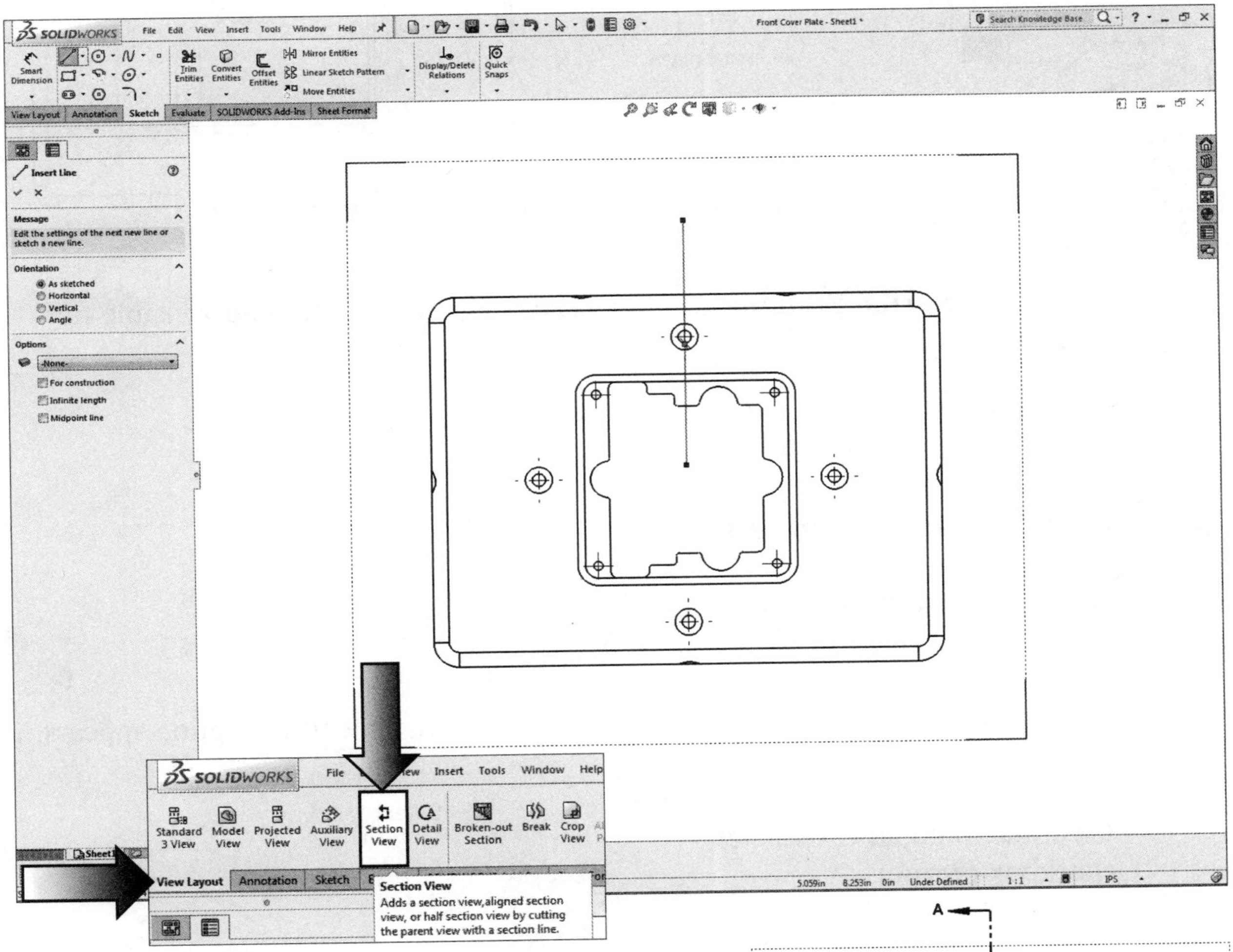

- Switch to the **View-Layout** tab and click the **Section View** command.

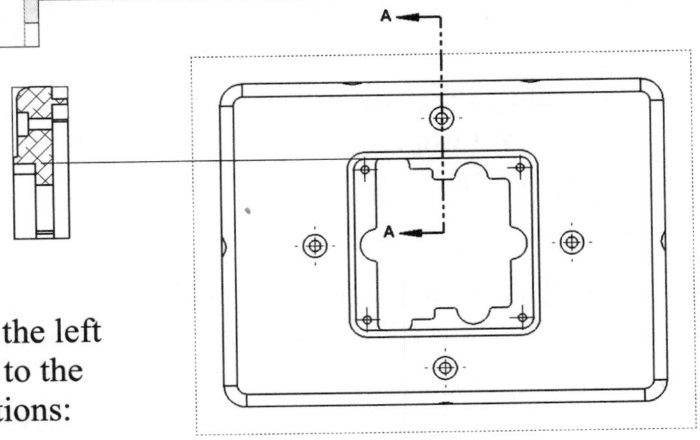

- Place the partial section view to the left side of the Top view. Look over to the feature tree for the following options:

- Click the **Flip Direction** button to flip the view and the section arrows.

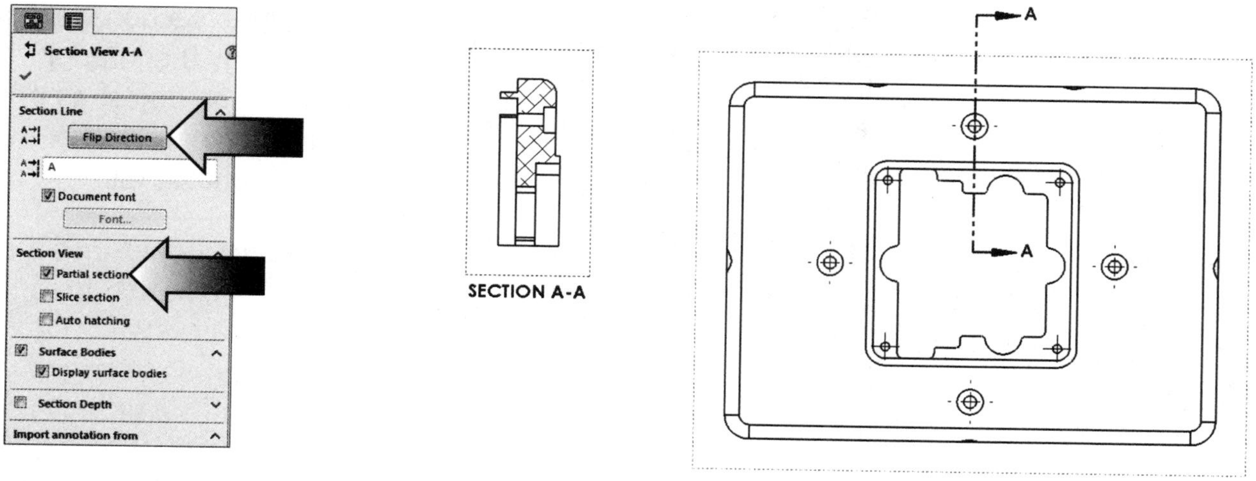

- Enable the **Partial Section** checkbox. The counterbore hole is now visible for detailing.

- Click **OK**.

5. Changing the hatch pattern:

- Zoom closer to the partial section view.

- Select one of the sectioned faces as noted. The Area Hatch/Fills option appears.

- Clear the Material Crosshatch checkbox (arrow).

- Select the pattern: **ANSI38-Aluminum** from the drop down list.

- Change the hatch scale to **3**.

- Click **OK**.

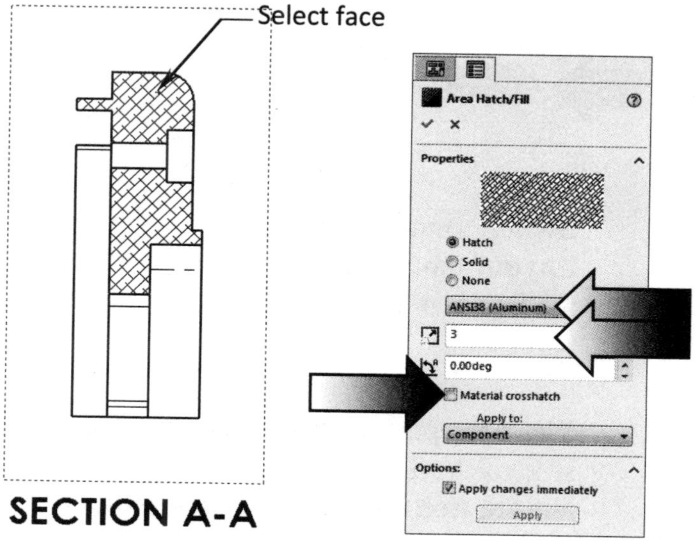

6. Creating a Detail view:

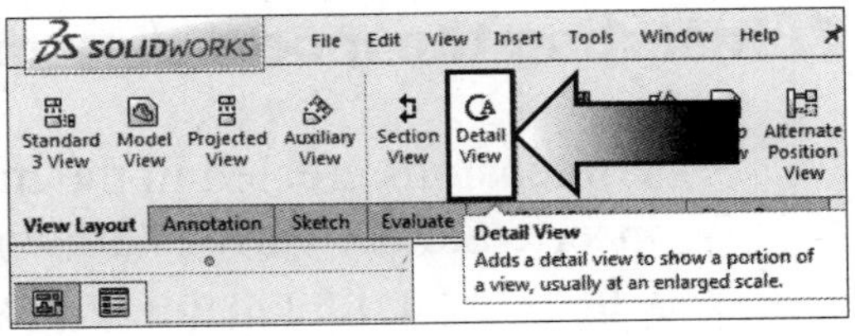

- Click the **Detail View** command from the View Layout tab. The mouse cursor changes to the Circle command.

- Zoom closer to the Right view.

- Sketch a **circle** approximately as shown to capture the features on the left side of the drawing view.

Detail View

Create a detail view in a drawing to show a portion of a view, at an enlarged scale of 2X or more

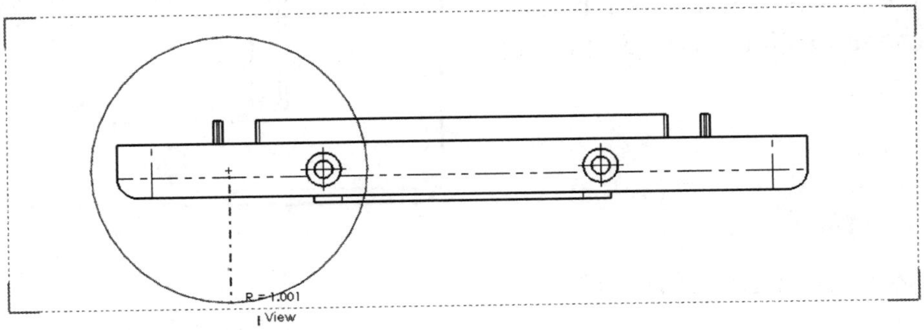

- Place the detail view on the right side as shown below.

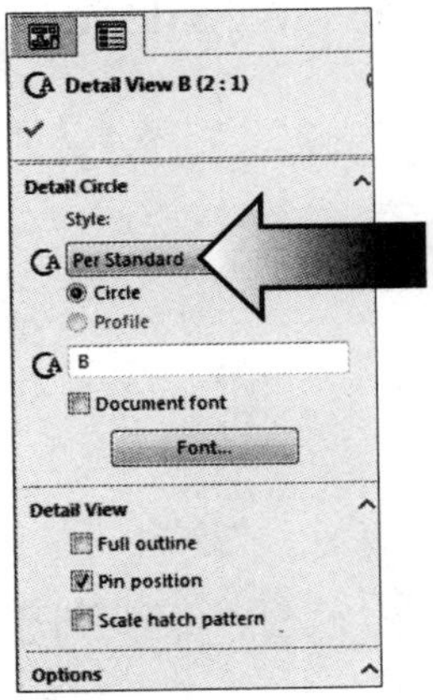

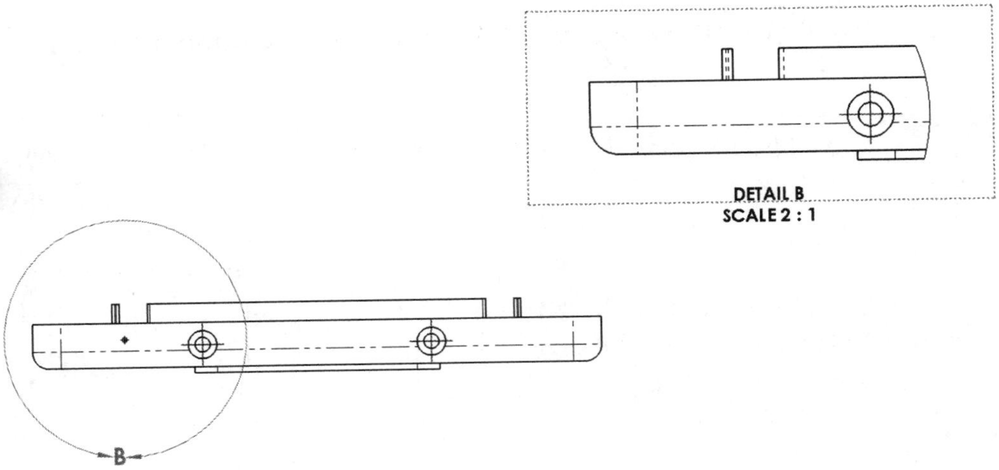

- The default style for the detail circle has been preset to **Per Standard**.

- Switch to different styles available. Change back to Per Standard when finished.

7. Inserting the model dimensions:

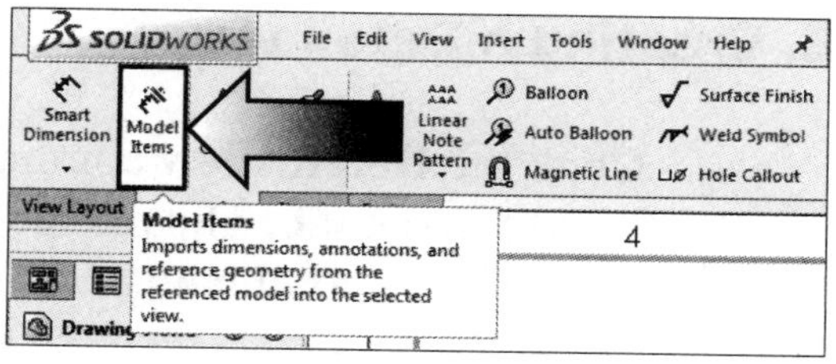

- Dimensions created in the model get inserted to the various drawing views. Changing a dimension in the model updates the drawing, and changing an inserted dimension in a drawing changes the model.

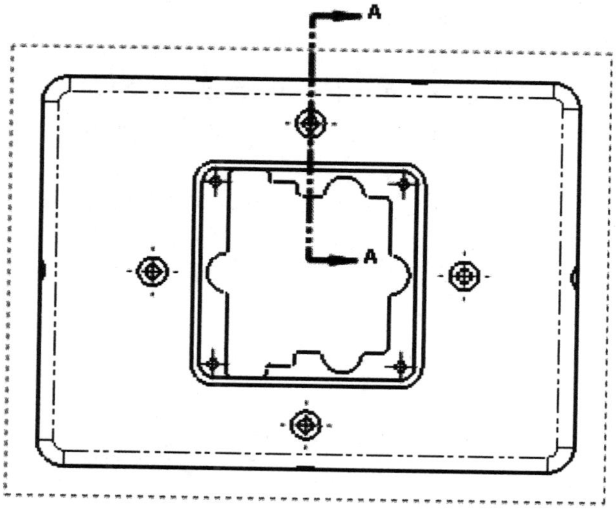

- Zoom to the **Top** drawing view and click its dotted border to activate it.

- Switch to the Annotation tab and select the **Model Item** command (arrow).

- For Source, select the option: **Entire Model**.

- For Dimensions, select: **Marked for Drawing** (default), **Hole Wizard Locations**, and **Hole Callouts**. Leave the other options at their default settings.

- Click **OK**. The dimensions are imported but some organizing needs to be done.

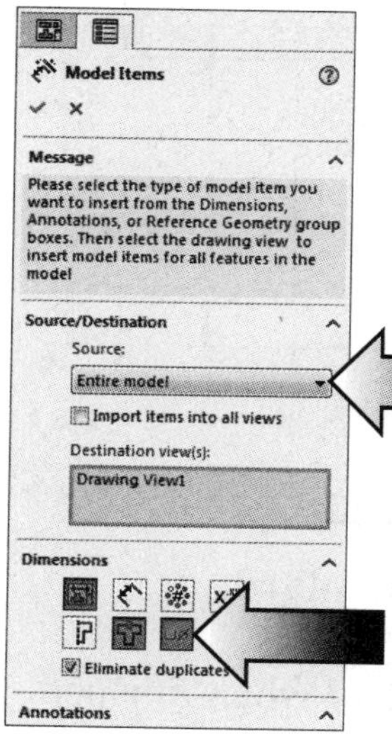

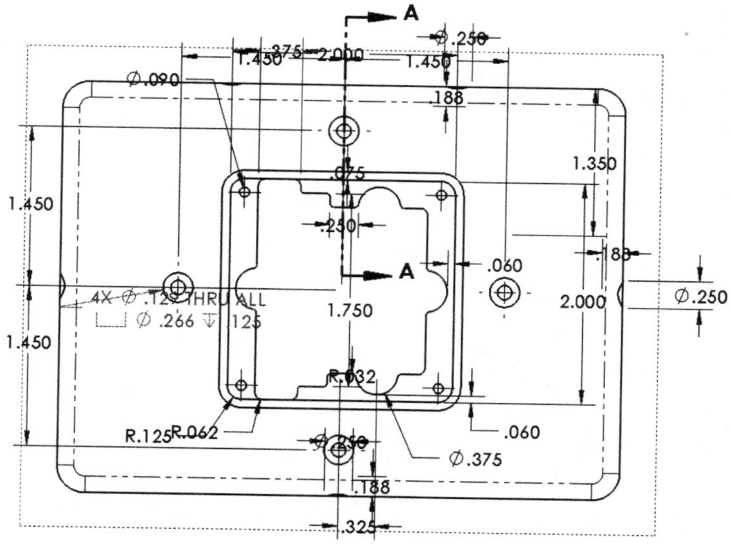

8. Cleaning up the dimensions:

- Keep the dimensions shown in the image below and delete the others.

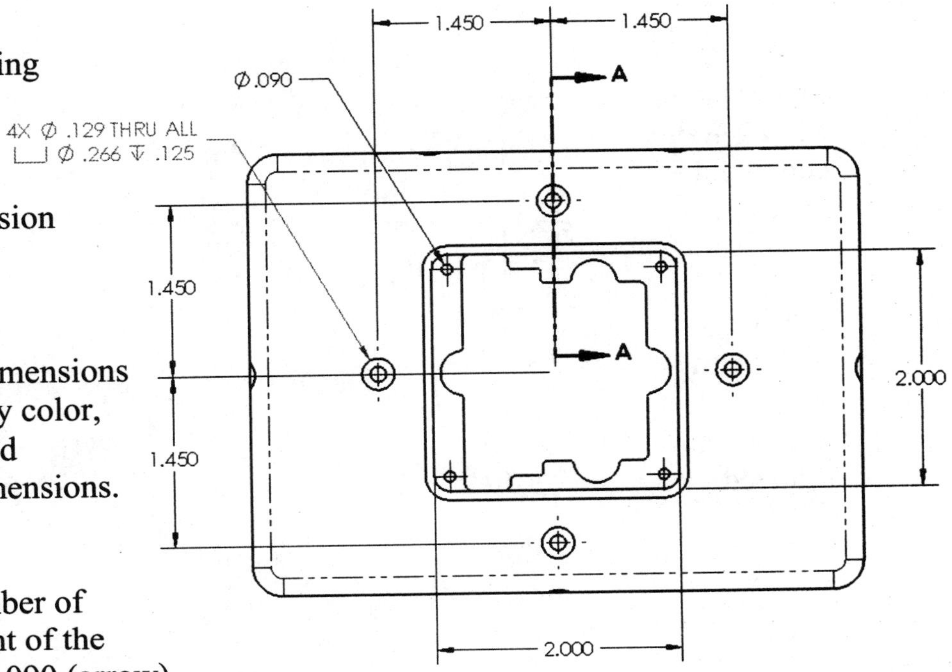

- Add the missing dimensions (circled) by using the Smart Dimension command.

- The added dimensions appear in gray color, they are called reference dimensions.

- Add the number of places in front of the dimension Ø.090 (arrow).

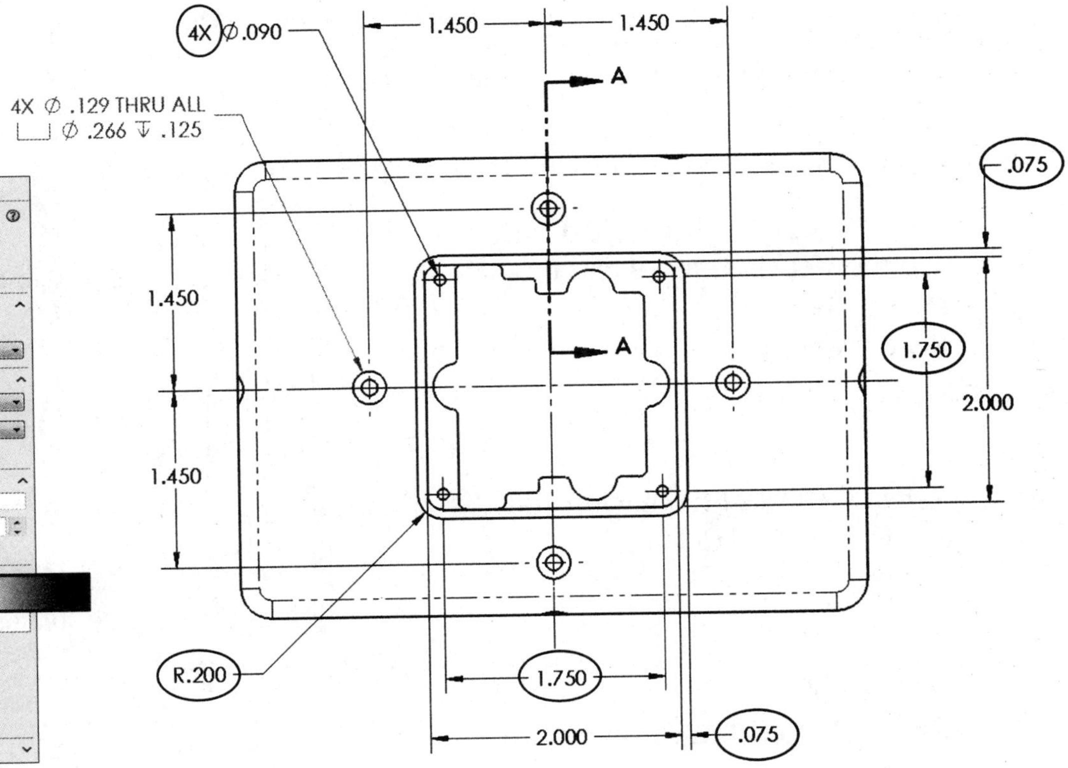

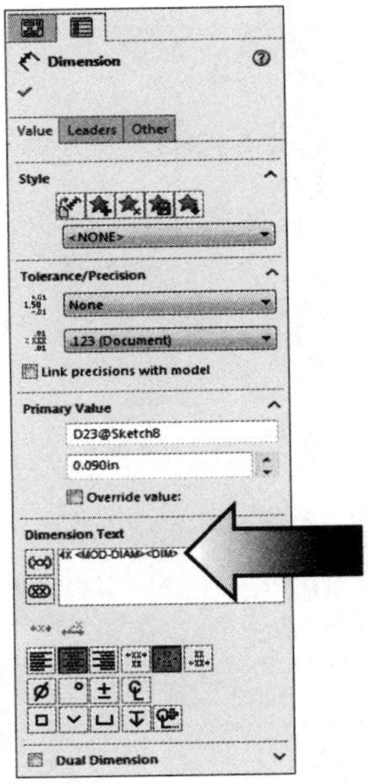

9. Inserting dimensions to another view:

- Click the dotted border of the **Right** view to activate it.

- Select the **Model Items** command once again.

- The settings from the last time are still selected.

- Click **OK**.

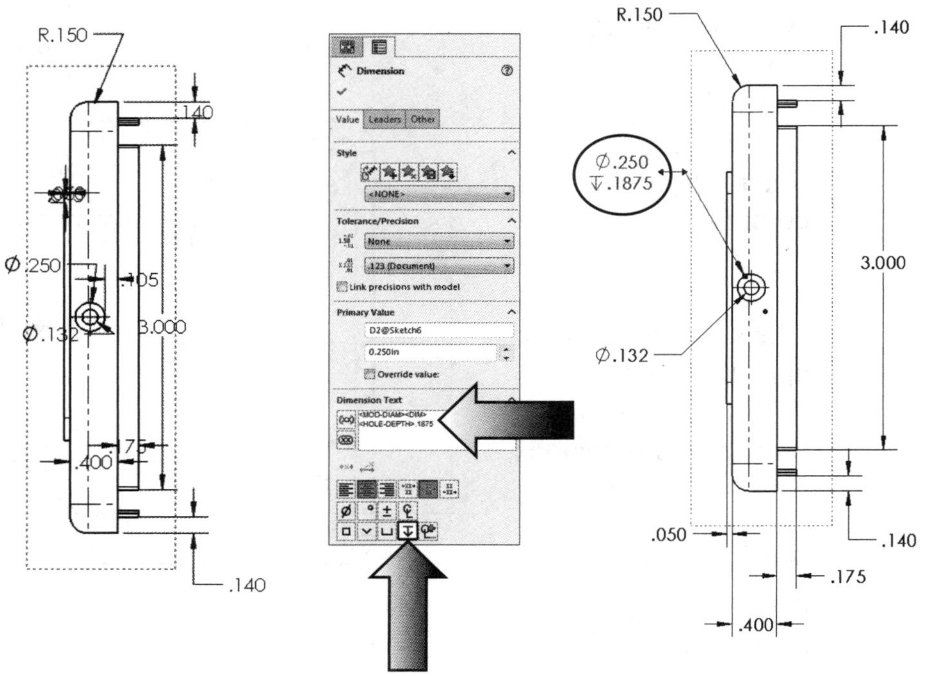

- Keep only the dimensions shown on the right image and delete the others.

- Select the dimension Ø.250 and add the **Depth Symbol** and the **Depth Dimension** from the PropertyManager tree (arrow).

- Select the Ø.132 dimension and add the word **THRU** under it (arrow).

- Click **OK** to exit the Property tree.

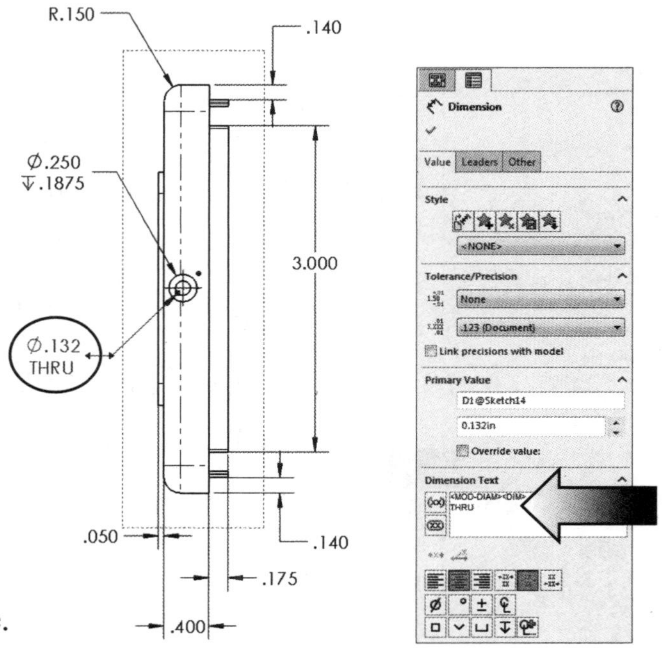

10. Breaking the view alignment:

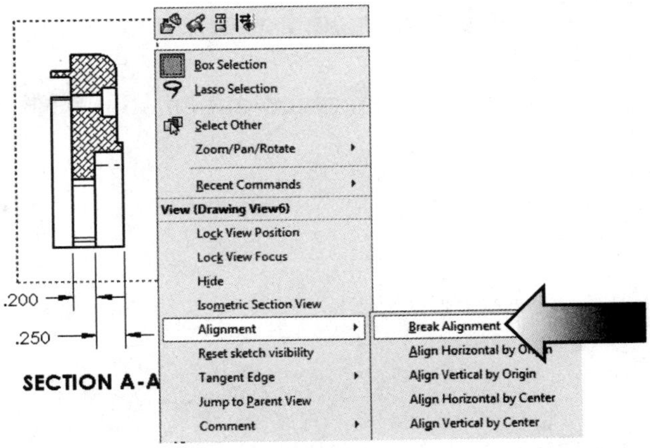

- Right click the Partial Section view's border and select: **Break Alignment** (arrow).

- Move the partial section view by dragging its dotted border to create some space and add the 2 dimensions shown.

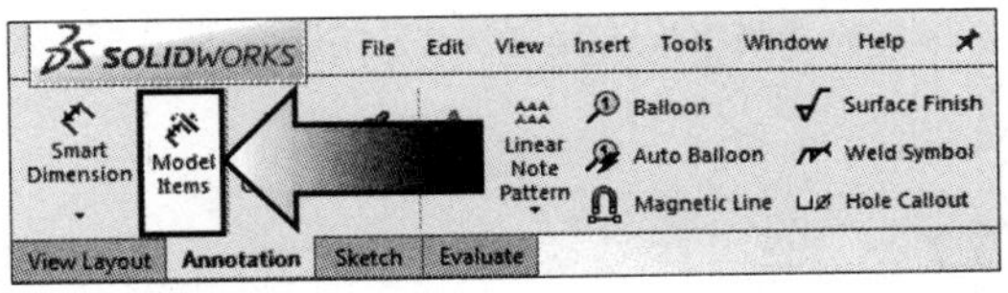

- Select the **Model Items** command.

- Insert the model dimensions into the **Top** view.

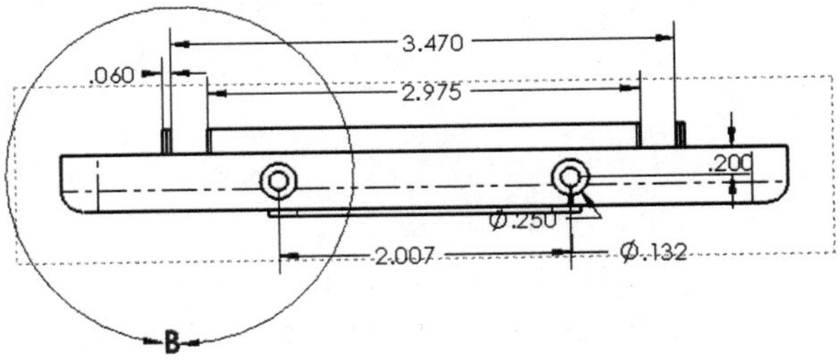

- Keep only the holes locating dimensions and delete the others.

- The dimensions that were deleted earlier will get re-inserted into other views later on.

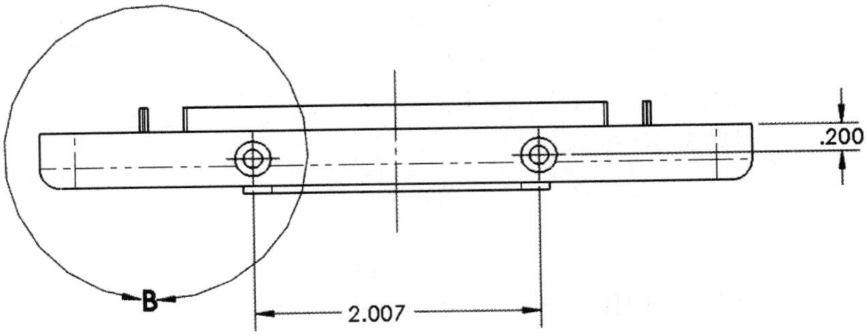

- Insert the model dimensions into the **Detail View B**.

- Add the reference dimensions and click the **Add Parenthesis** for each one (arrow).

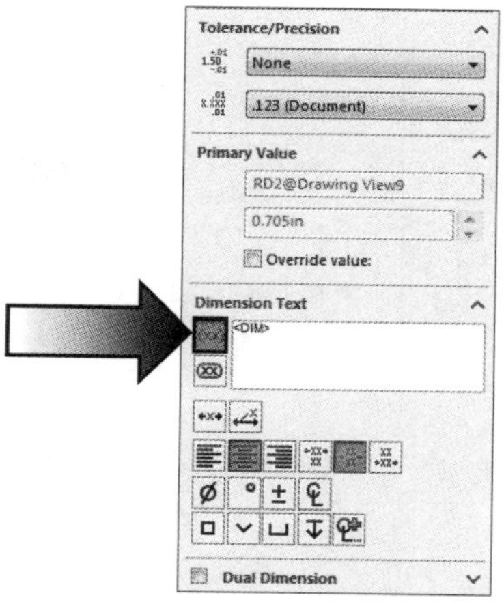

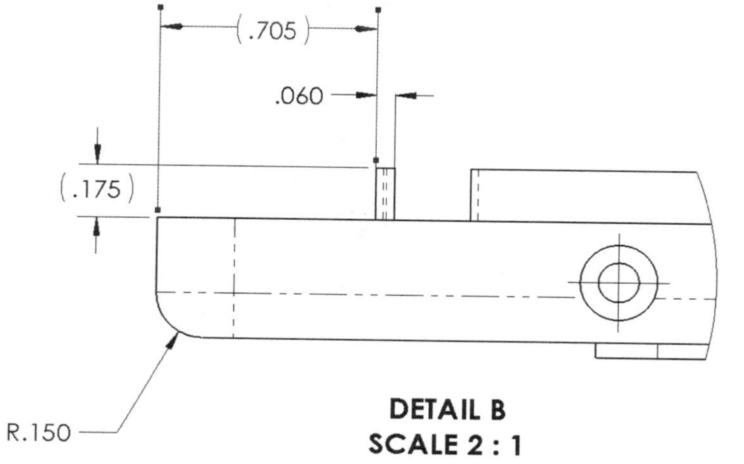

11. Creating a Projected View:

- A back view is needed to detail the features on the far side. There are several ways to add this view but we will try the Projected View command instead.

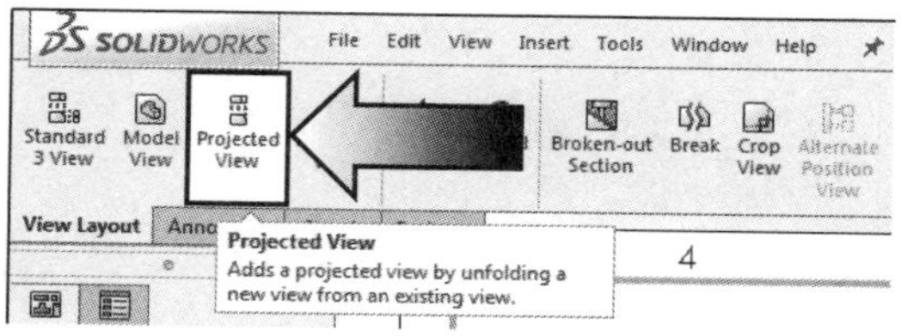

- Switch back to the View Layout tab and click the **Projected View** command (arrow).

- Move the cursor to the right to see the preview graphic of the back view.

- Place the back view approximately as shown.

- Click **OK**.

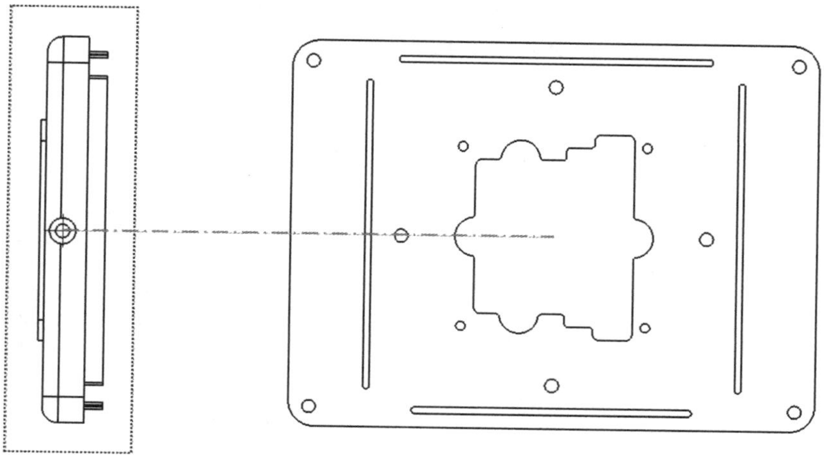

- Insert the model dimensions into the back view and add the dimensions shown.

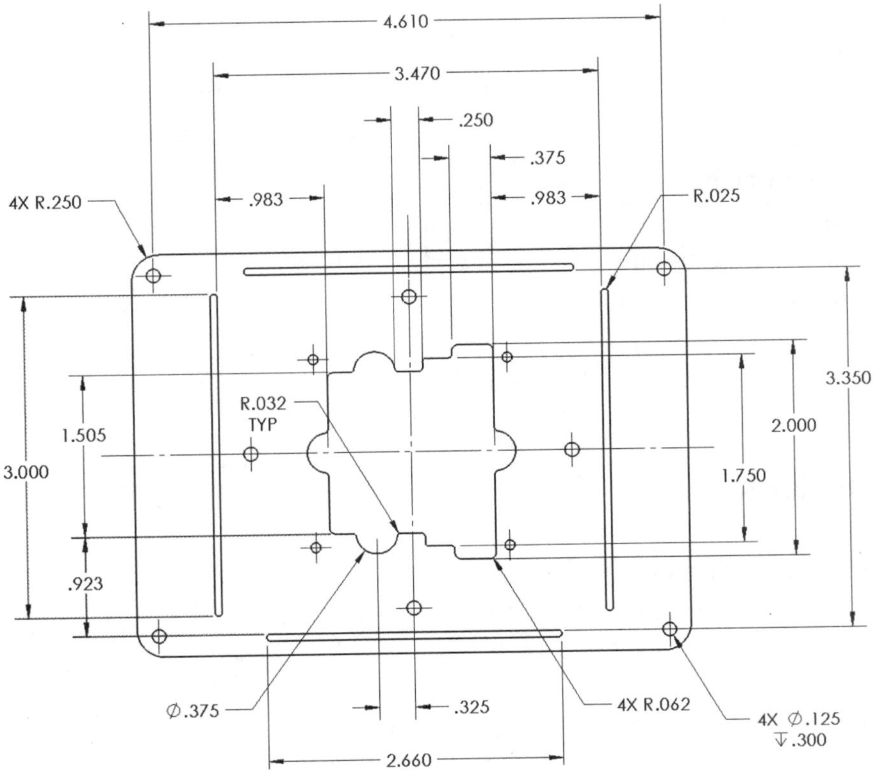

12. Adding the Centerline Symbol:

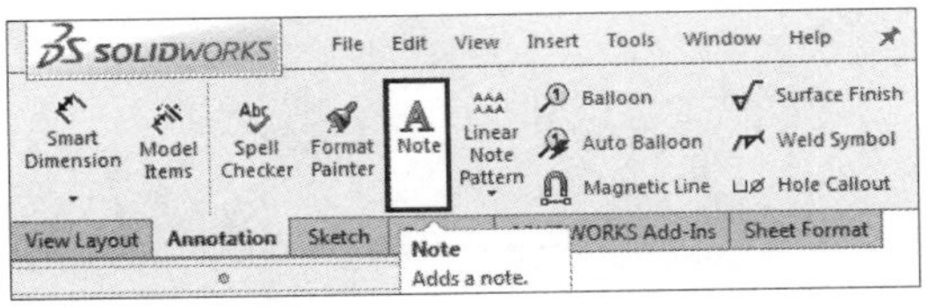

- A library of symbols such as degrees, depth, countersink, and so on is available. In the Dimension Value PropertyManager, click More Symbols under Dimension Text to access the library. Symbols libraries for various annotations, such as Notes, Geometric Tolerance Symbols, Surface Finish Symbols, Weld Symbols, and so on, are also available in the PropertyManagers.

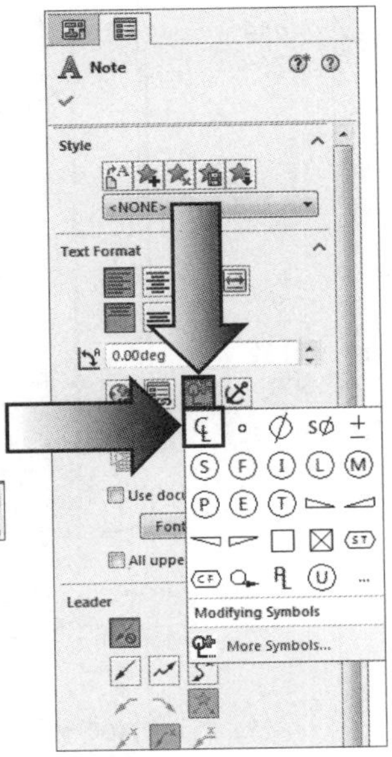

- Switch to the **Annotation** tab.

- Select the **Note** command, click the **Add Symbol** button  (arrow).

- Select the **Centerline** symbol  (arrow).

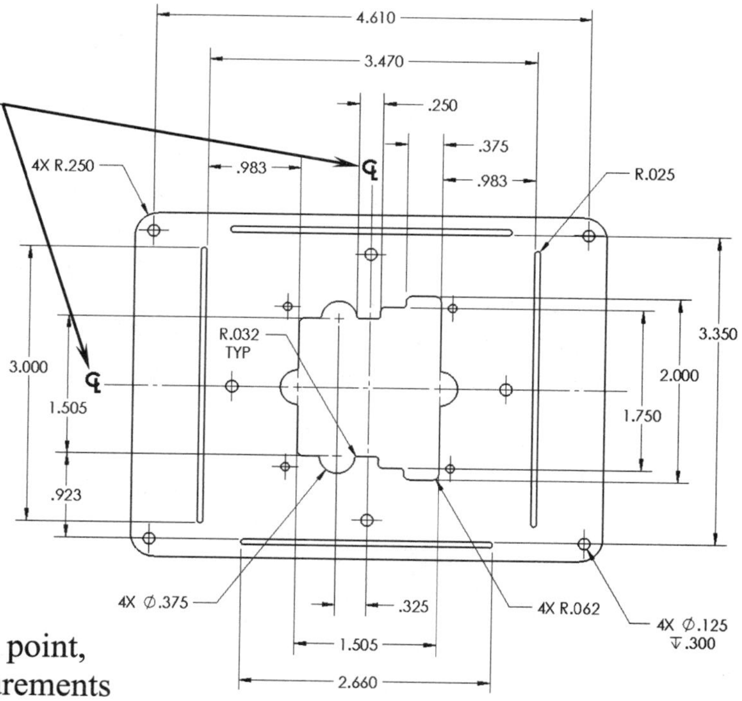

- Place the centerline symbol next to the horizontal and vertical centerlines approximately as shown.

13. Adding Datums:

- A datum is a reference (line, point, axis, etc.) from which measurements are taken.

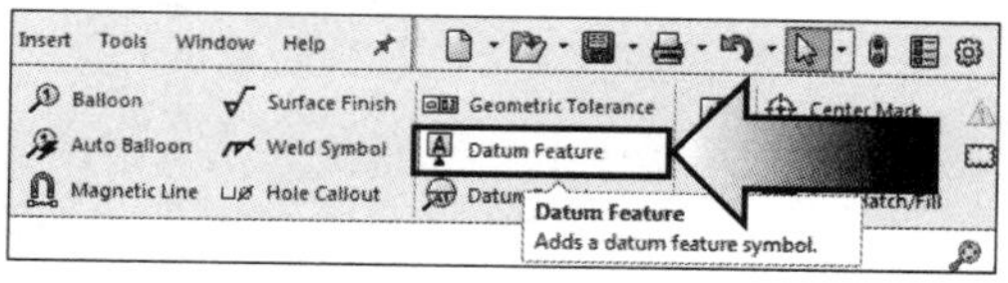

- It takes two clicks to create a datum. The 1st click is to identify where the datum will be attached, and the 2nd where it is placed.

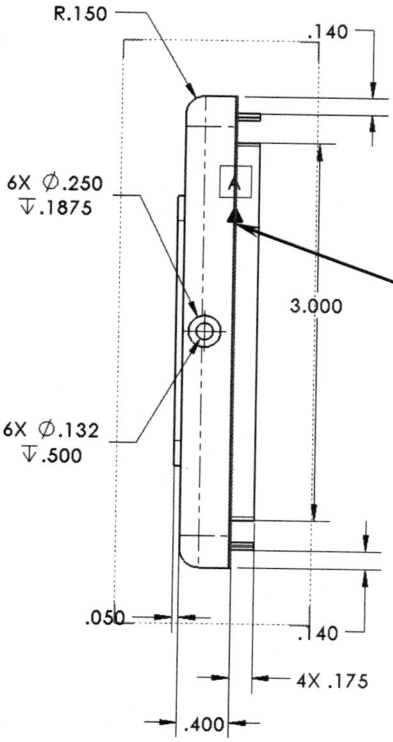

- From the **Annotation** tab, select the **Datum Feature** command.

- Select the vertical edge as noted to attach the datum.

- Place the **Datum A** above the drawing view as shown. The datum can be placed on the left or right side of the line.

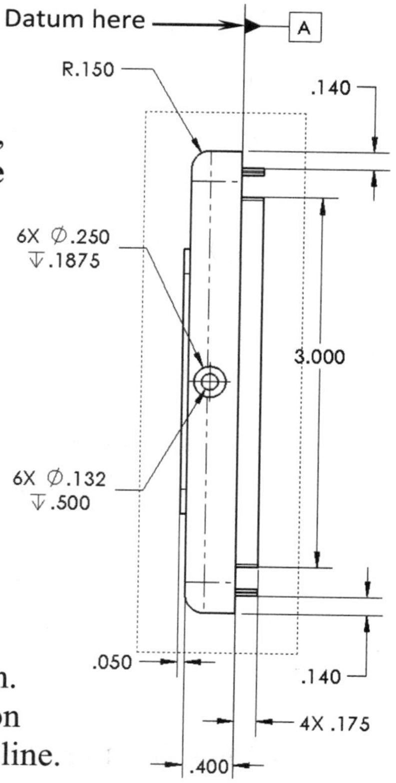

- Select the <u>horizontal centerline</u> as noted to attach Datum B.

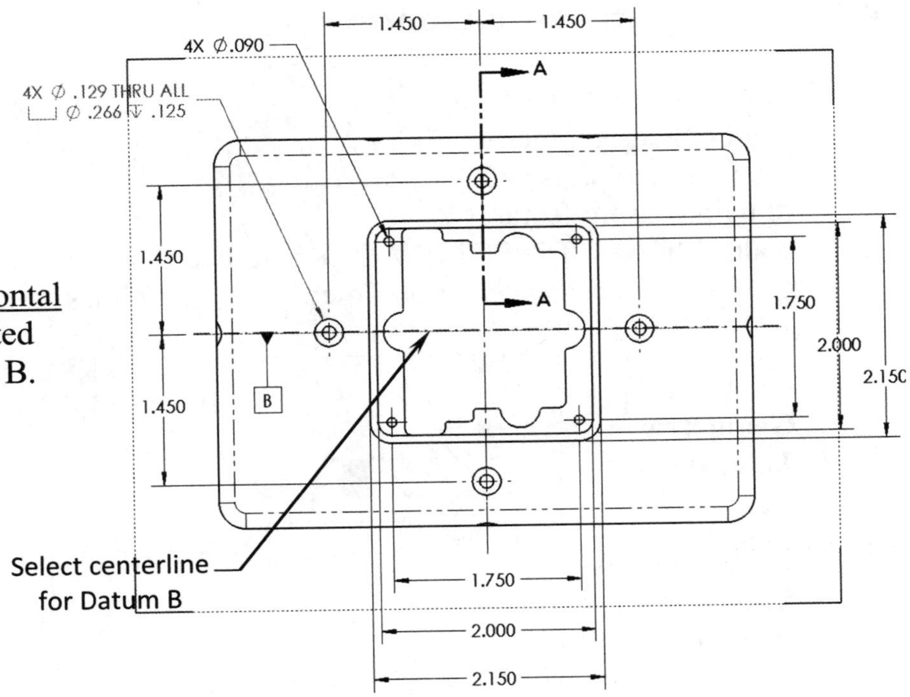

- Move the mouse cursor outward and place **Datum B** approximately as shown.

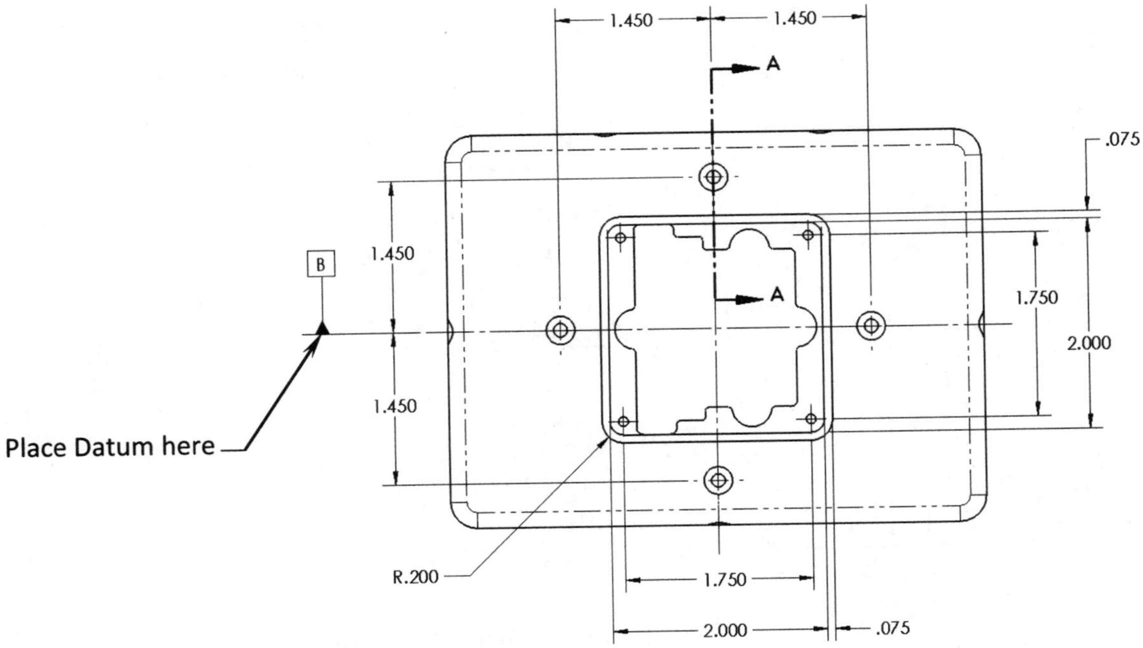

- Click **OK** to exit the Datum Feature command.

14. Adding a Flatness tolerance:

- The geometric tolerance symbol adds geometric tolerances to parts and drawings using feature control frames. The SOLIDWORKS software supports the ASME Y14.5-2009 Geometric and True Position Tolerancing guidelines.

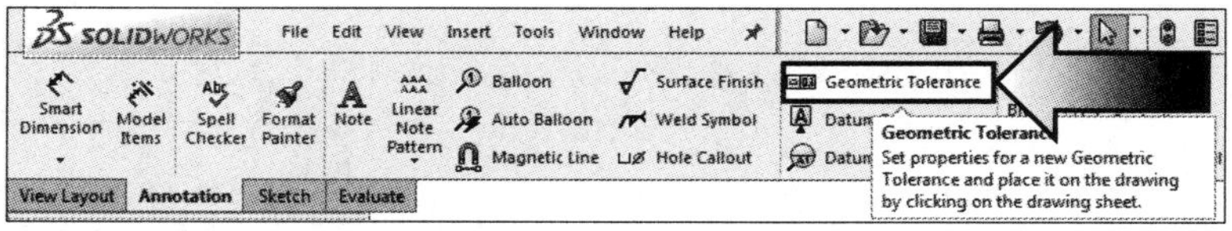

- Click the **Geometric Tolerance** Command.

- Select **Flatness** from the list.

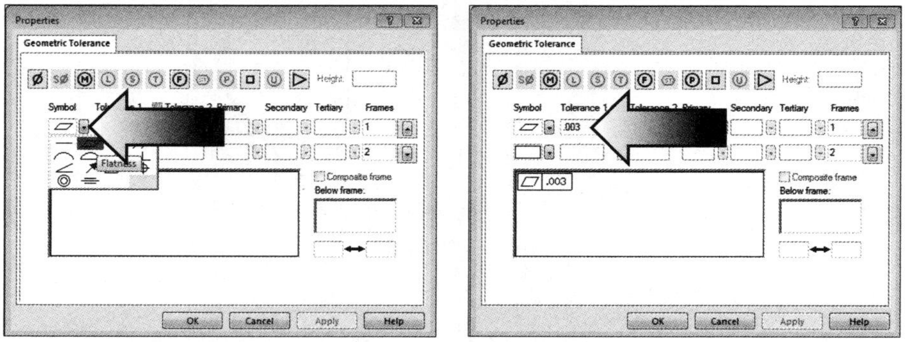

- Enter **.003** under Tolerance 1.

- Select the vertical edge as noted to attach the tolerance, and then move upward to align it next to Datum A. Click **OK**.

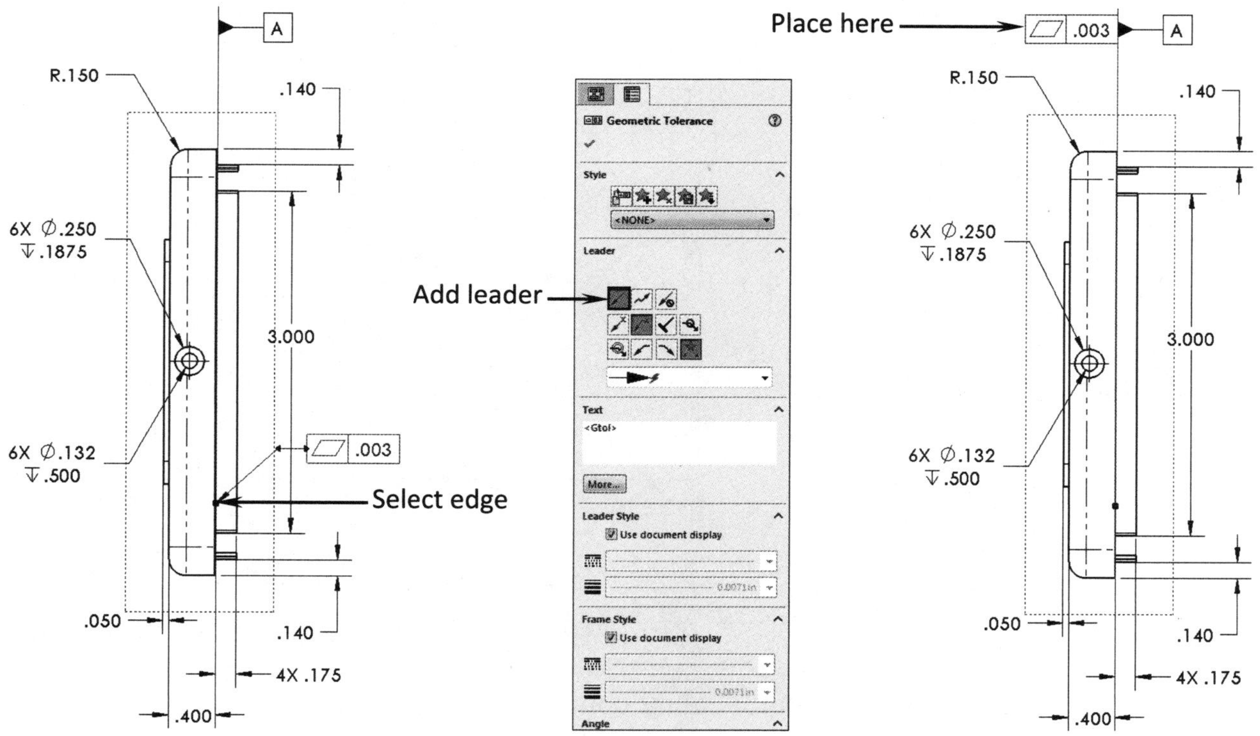

15. Adding a Perpendicular tolerance:

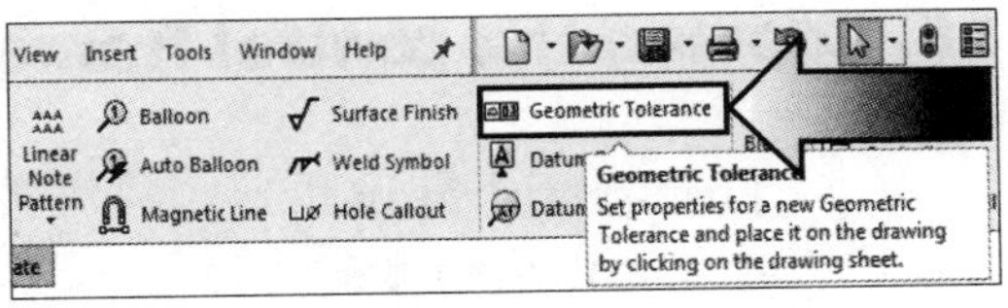

- Perpendicularity in GD&T can mean two different things depending which reference feature is called out.
The normal form or **Surface Perpendicularity** is a tolerance that controls Perpendicularity between two 90° *surfaces*, or features. Surface Perpendicularity is controlled with two parallel planes acting as its tolerance zone.
Axis Perpendicularity is a tolerance that controls how perpendicular a specific *axis* needs to be to a datum. Axis Perpendicularity is controlled by a cylinder around a theoretically perfect parallel axis.

- Select the dimension of the hole (circled).

- Click the **Geometric Tolerance** command.

- Select the **Perpendicular** symbol from the list.

- Enter **.003** under Tolerance 1.

- Click the **Maximum Material Condition** symbol Ⓜ.

- Enter **A** for Primary Datum.

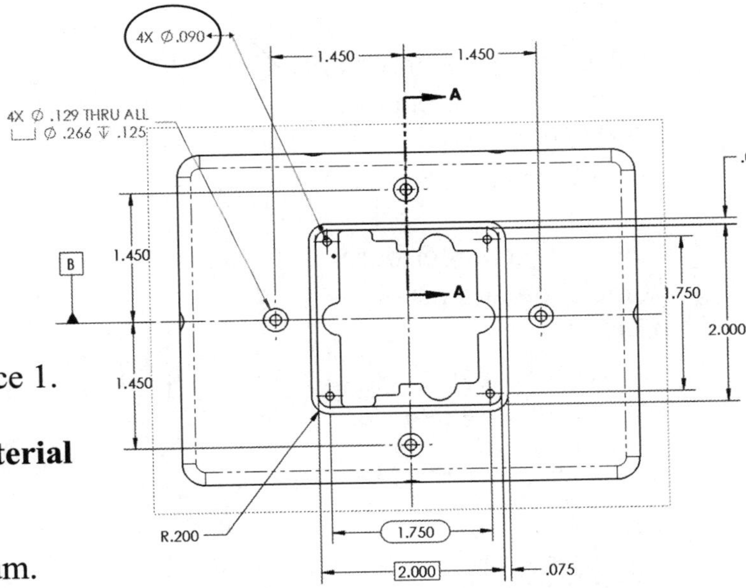

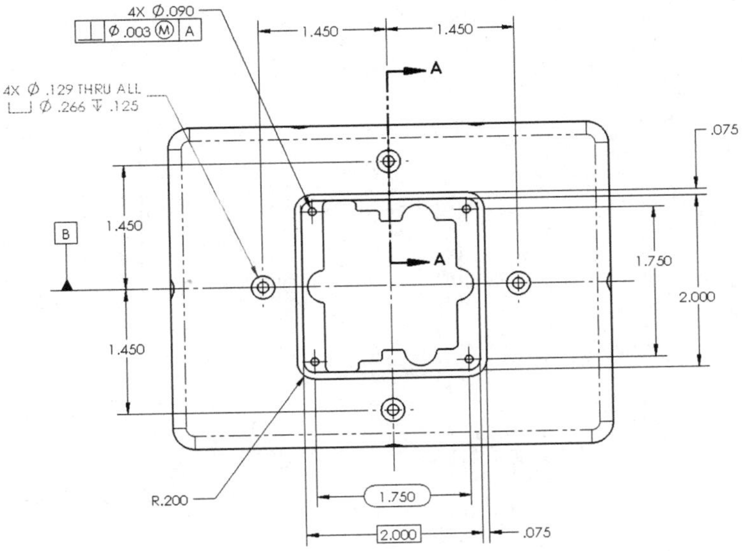

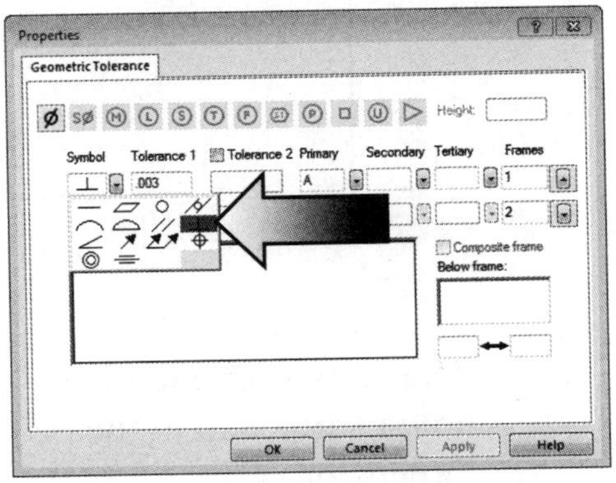

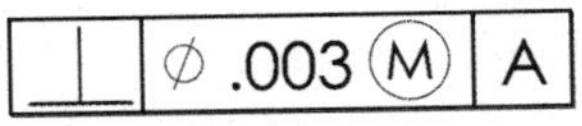

- The Perpendicular control frame.

- Click **OK**.

16. Copying the control frame:

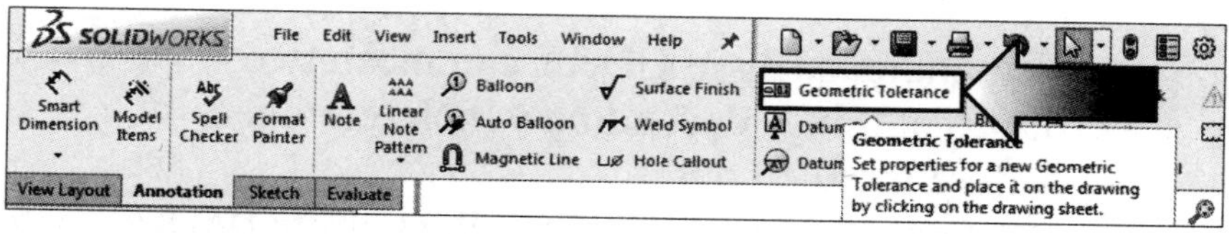

- True position in terms of the axis, point or plane defines how much variation a feature can have from a specified exact true location.

- This step demonstrates how to make a copy of a geometric tolerance and attach it to another dimension.

- Select the perpendicular control frame and press: **Ctrl+C**.

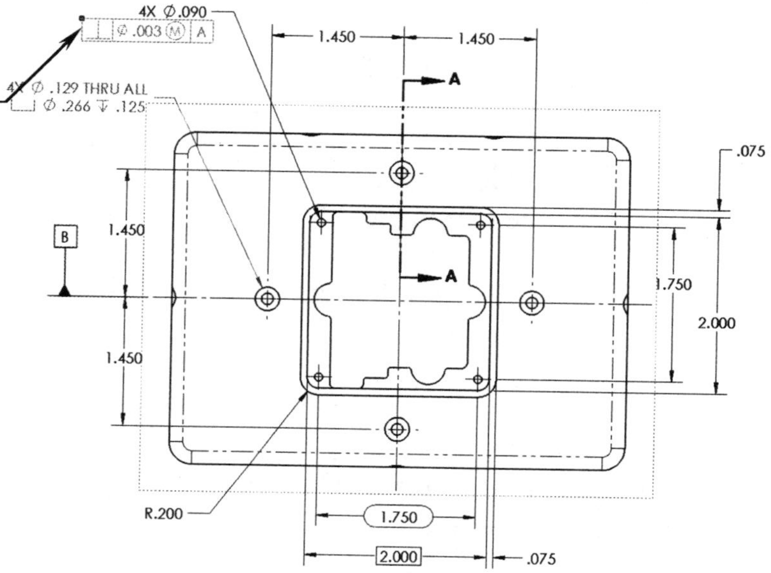

- Select the counter bore dimension and press: **Ctrl+V**.

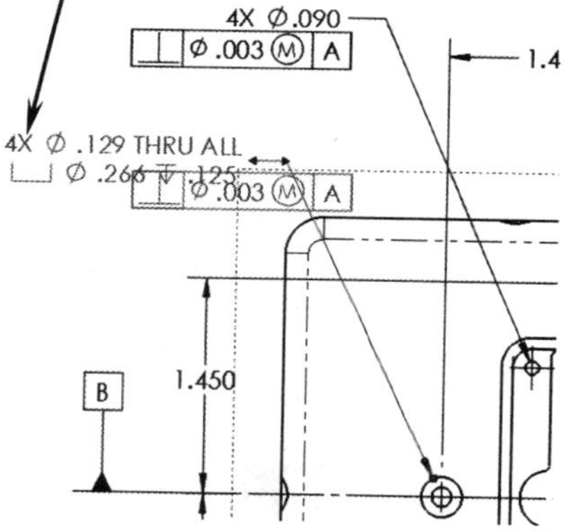

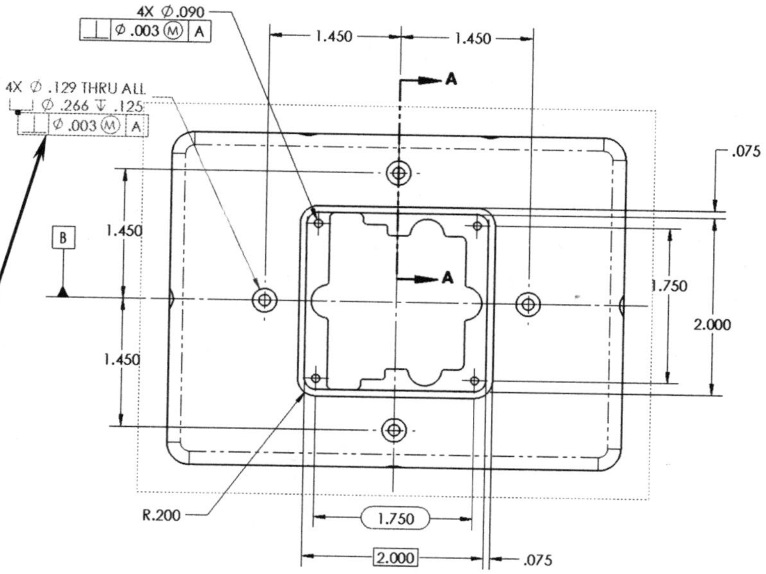

- The copy is created but not yet attached to the dimension.

- Drag the copy of the control frame and drop it on the counterbore dimension to attach it.

17. Modifying the geometric tolerance:

- For the counter bore feature we will change the symbol to Position, or also called True Position.

- True position in terms of the axis, point, or plane defines how much variation a feature can have from a specified exact true location.

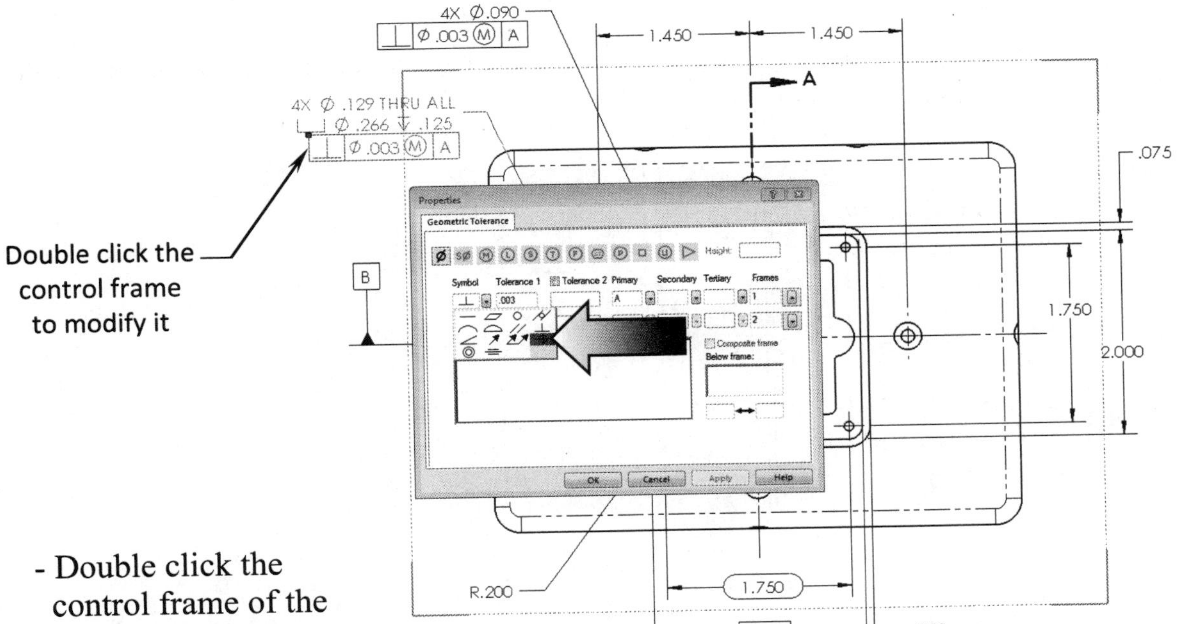

- Double click the control frame of the counterbore hole.

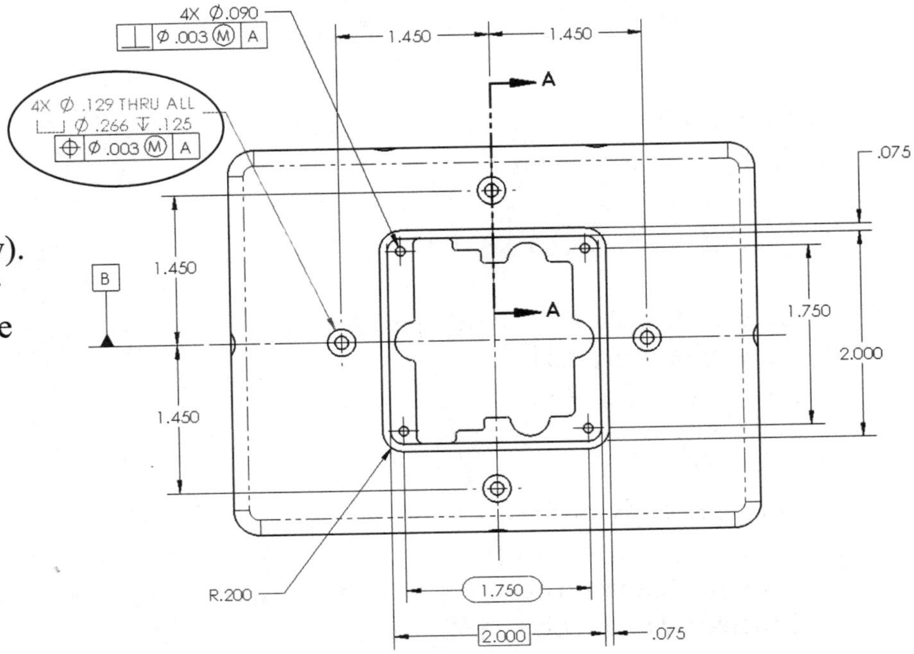

- Change the symbol to **Position** (arrow). Leave the other references at the same values.

- Click **OK**.

18. Adding another Position tolerance:

- Zoom in on the **Back** view and locate the small hole on the lower right corner.

- Select the dimension **4X Ø.125** and click the **Geometric Tolerance** command.

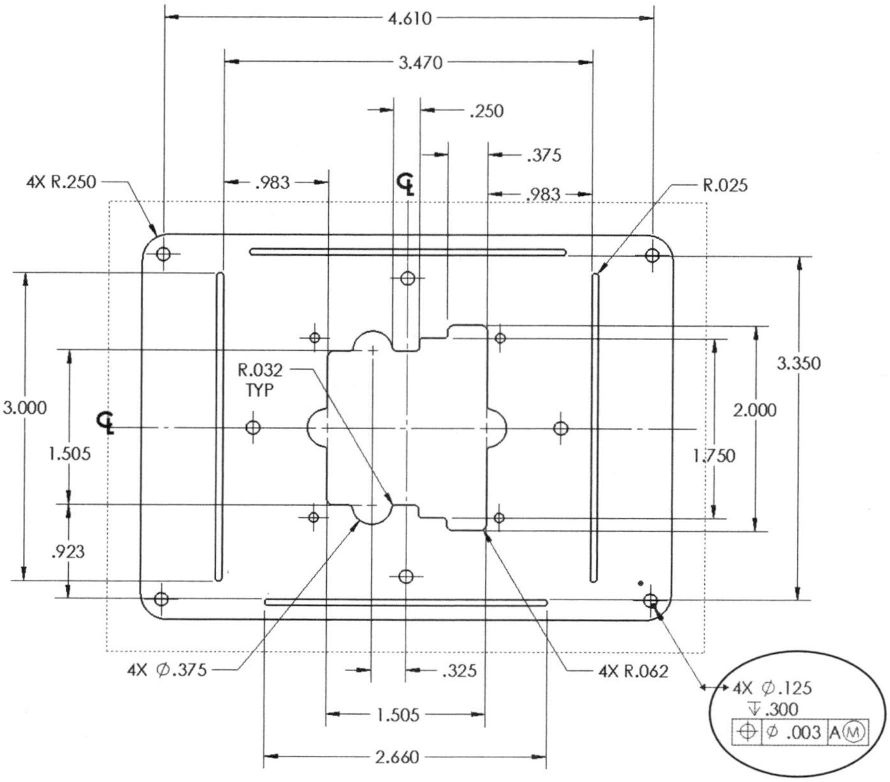

- Create a True Position tolerance that looks like the one shown below.

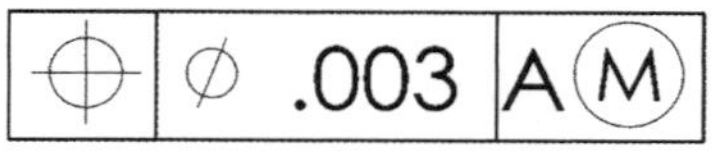

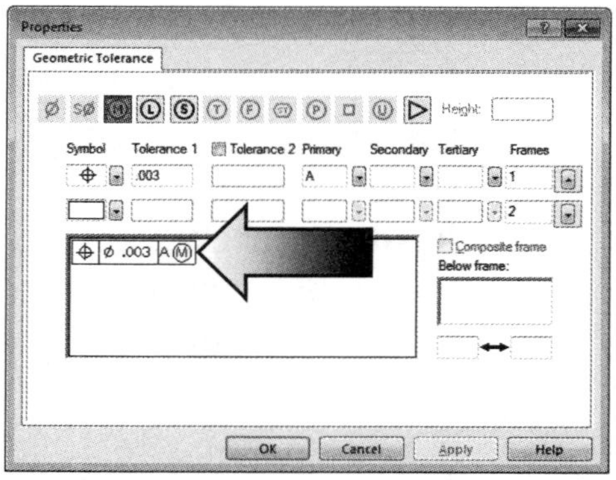

- Be sure to attach the control frame to the hole dimension (circled).

- Click **OK**.

- *For practice purposes, we will create some other tolerances such as: Symmetric, Bilateral, Limit, Basic, etc., in the next few steps.*

19. Adding a Symmetric tolerance:

- Zoom in on the Right view and select the **.400** dimension on the lower right side.

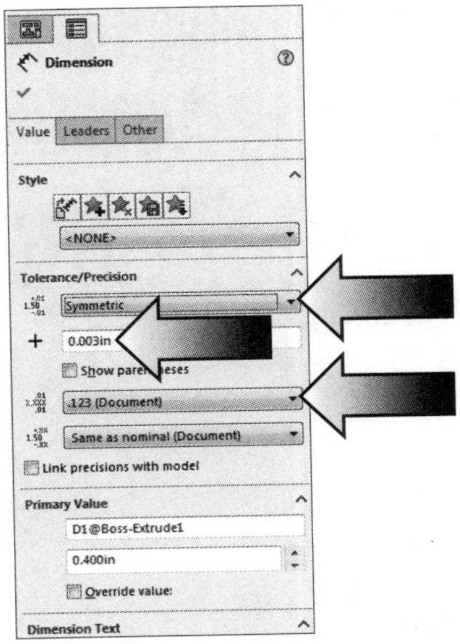

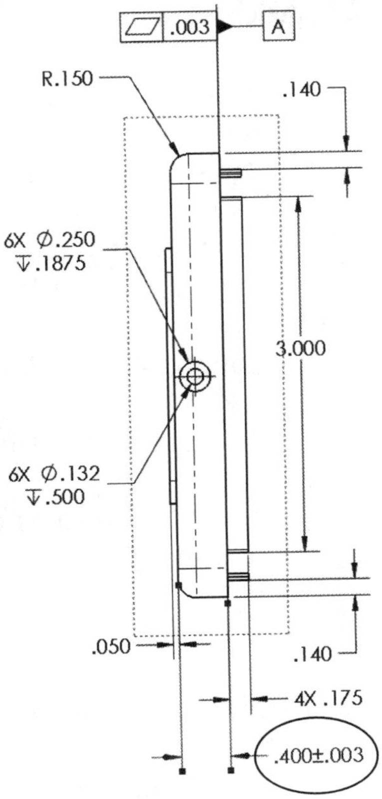

- Expand the **Tolerance/ Precision** section and select the **Symmetric** option.

- Enter **.003in** for Max-Variation.

- Change the number of decimals to **3** (arrow).

- Using Symmetric, only one dimension value is used (circled).

- Click **OK**.

20. Adding a Bilateral tolerance:

- Select the **.050** dimension in the same drawing view.

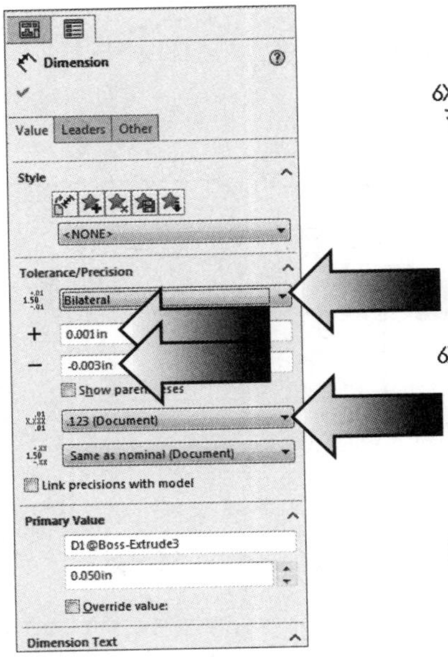

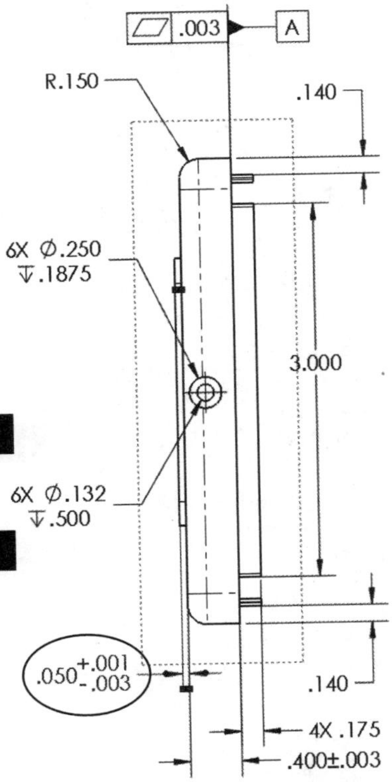

- Select the **Bilateral** option under the **Tolerance/Precision** section.

- Enter **.001in** for Max-Variation

- Enter **.003** for Min-Variation.

- Set the number of decimals to **3** places. Using Bilateral, two different values are used (circled).

- Click **OK**.

21. Adding a Limit tolerance:

- Use Limit Tolerance to specify a range or the total amount a dimension can vary.

- Click the dimension **.140** and select the **Limit** option.

- Enter **.003** for Max Variation.

- Enter **.002** for Min Variation.

- Set the number of decimal to **3** places.

- Click **OK**.

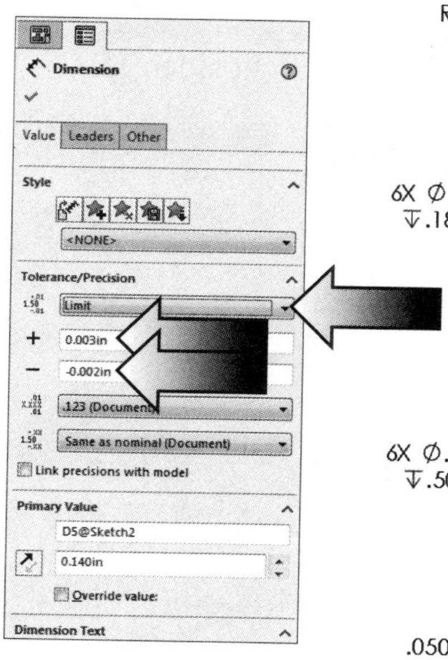

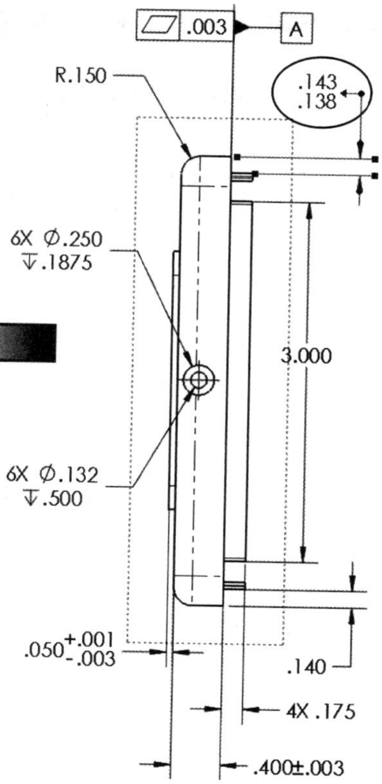

22. Adding a Basic tolerance:

- The Basic Dimension has a box around the dimension.
A basic dimension is a numerical value used to describe the theoretically exact size, profile, orientation, or location of a feature.

- Add a **Basic** tolerance to the dimension **2.000** (circled).

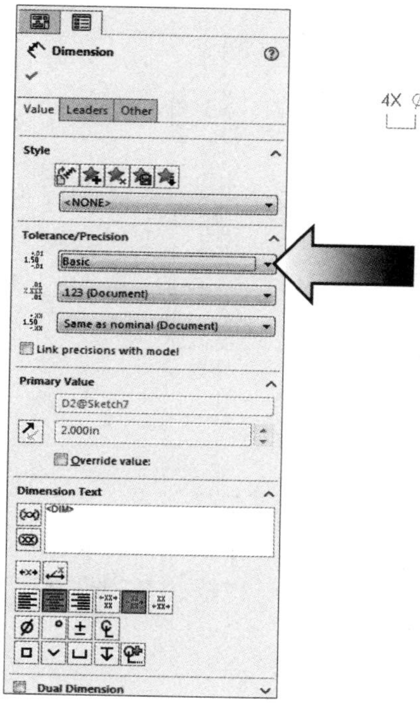

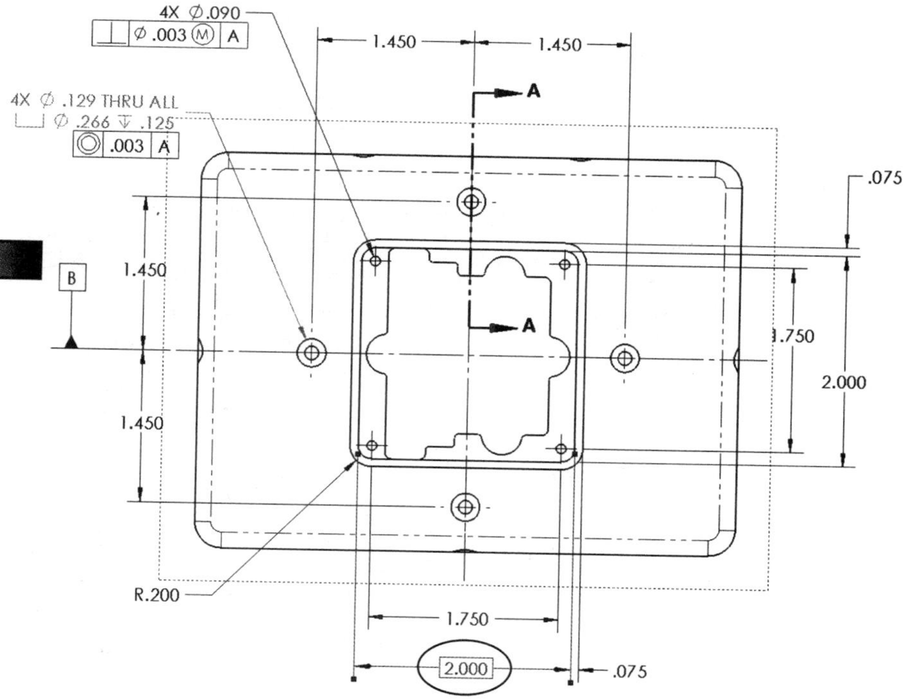

23. Adding General Notes:

- Zoom to the upper left area of the drawing.

- Switch to the Annotation tab and select the **Note** command (arrow).

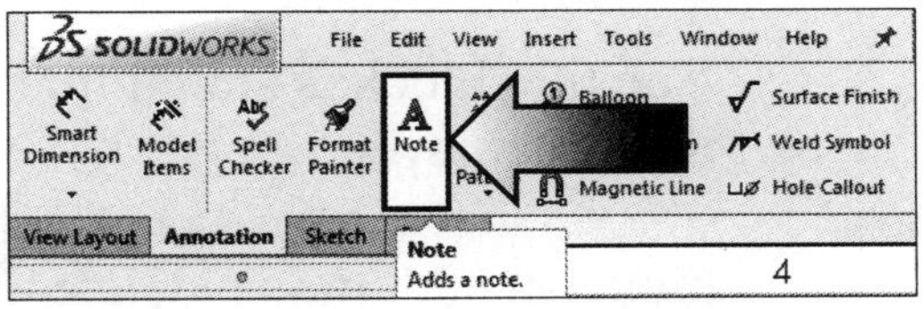

- Before typing, place the note near the upper left corner of the drawing (arrow).

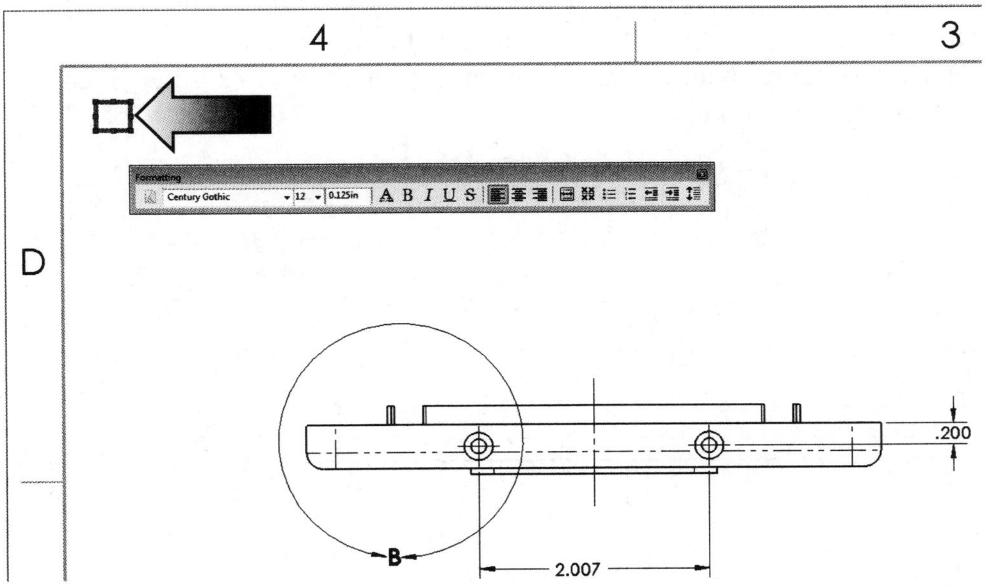

- Enter the notes shown below.

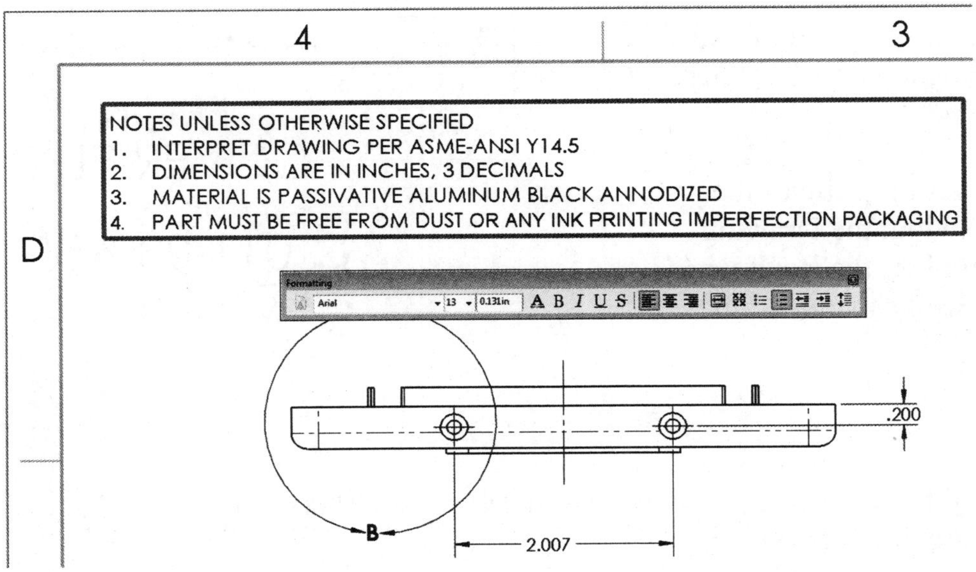

24. Filling out the Title Block:

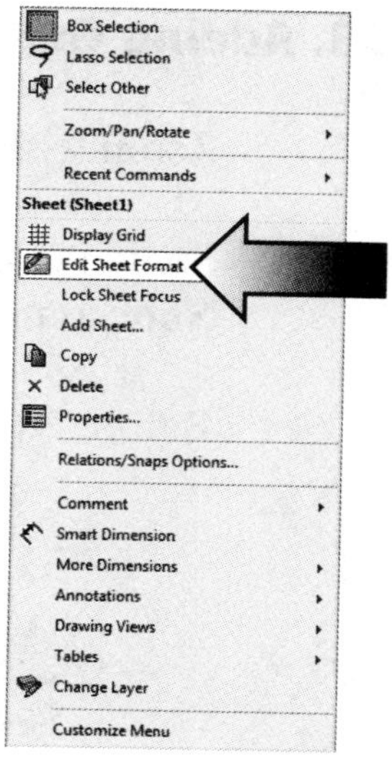

- The title block is stored in the Sheet Format, which is behind the Sheet layer.

- You can add, move, delete, or modify any lines or text in the title block.

- Using the default drawing template, there is a "blank note" already placed in the center of each field. These blank notes, or any new notes, can be linked to any custom properties such as: Company Name, Part Number, Description, Weight, Material, Revision, etc.

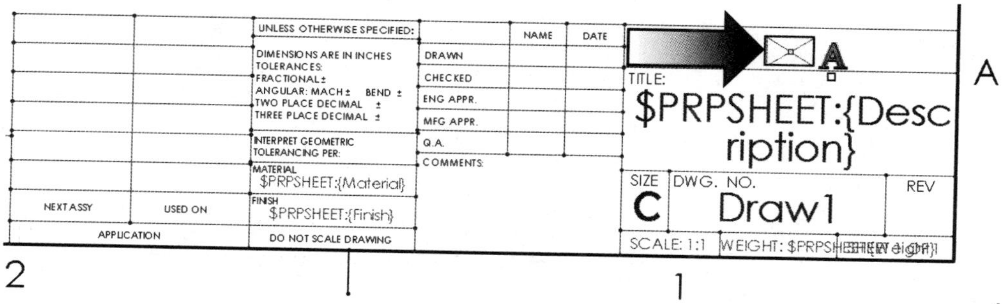

- Hover the mouse cursor over the center of the Company Name file (arrow). Double click the blank note when the note symbol appears.

- Enter the name of your company or school here.

- Enter the Title of the drawing, the Drawing Number, the Revision, as well as Your Name and Date in the fields as indicated.

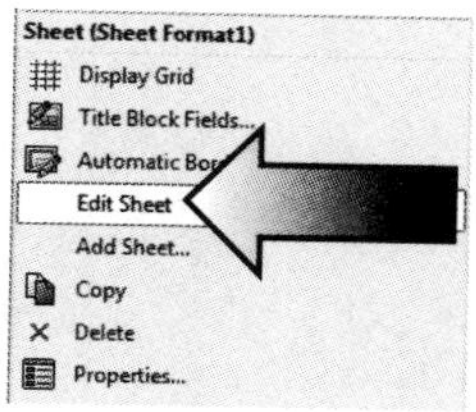

- Right click inside the drawing and select Edit Sheet to return to the drawing (arrow).

25. Saving your work:

- Select **File Save As**.

- Enter **Front Cover Plate.slddrw** for the name of the drawing.

- Click **Save**.

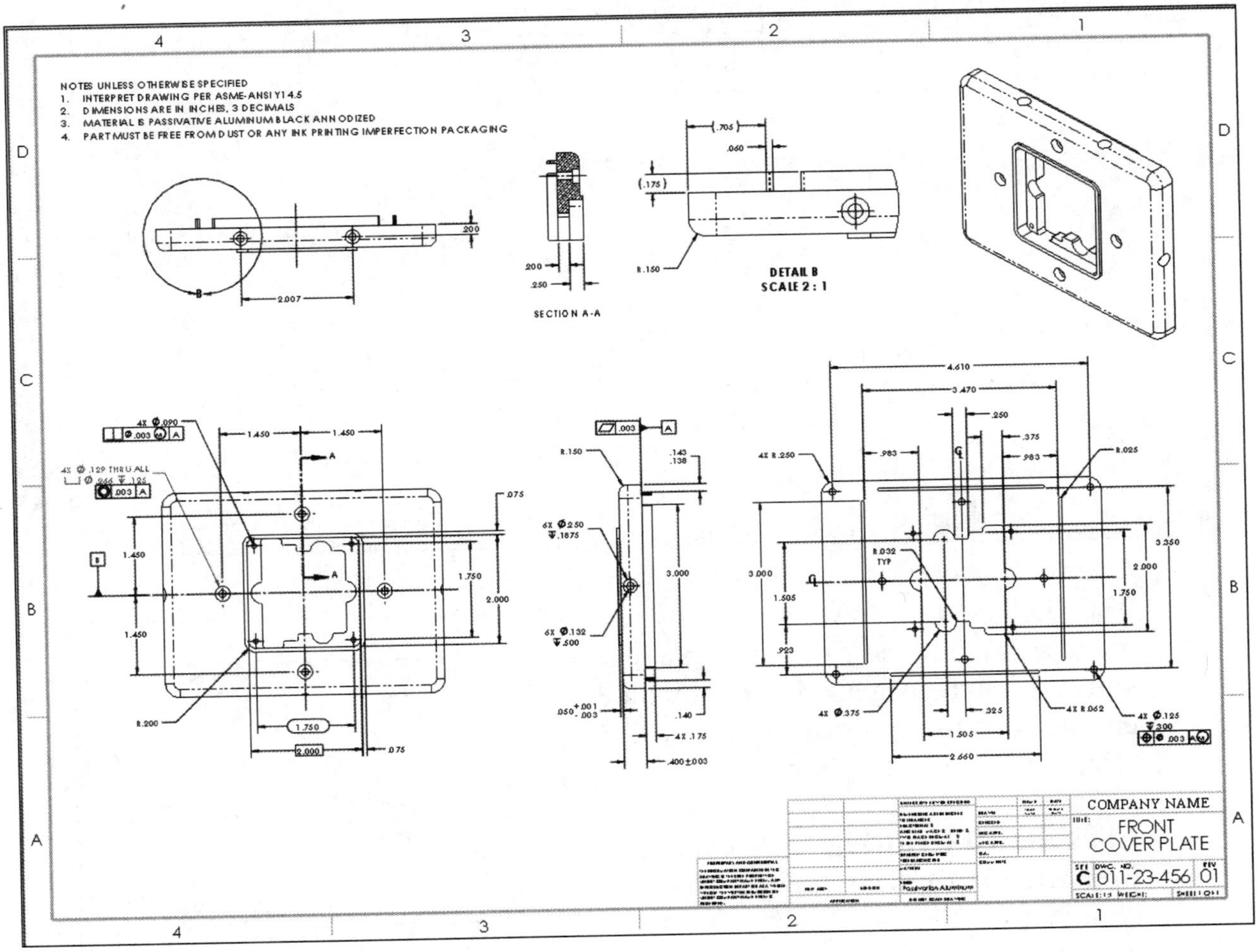

OPTIONAL:

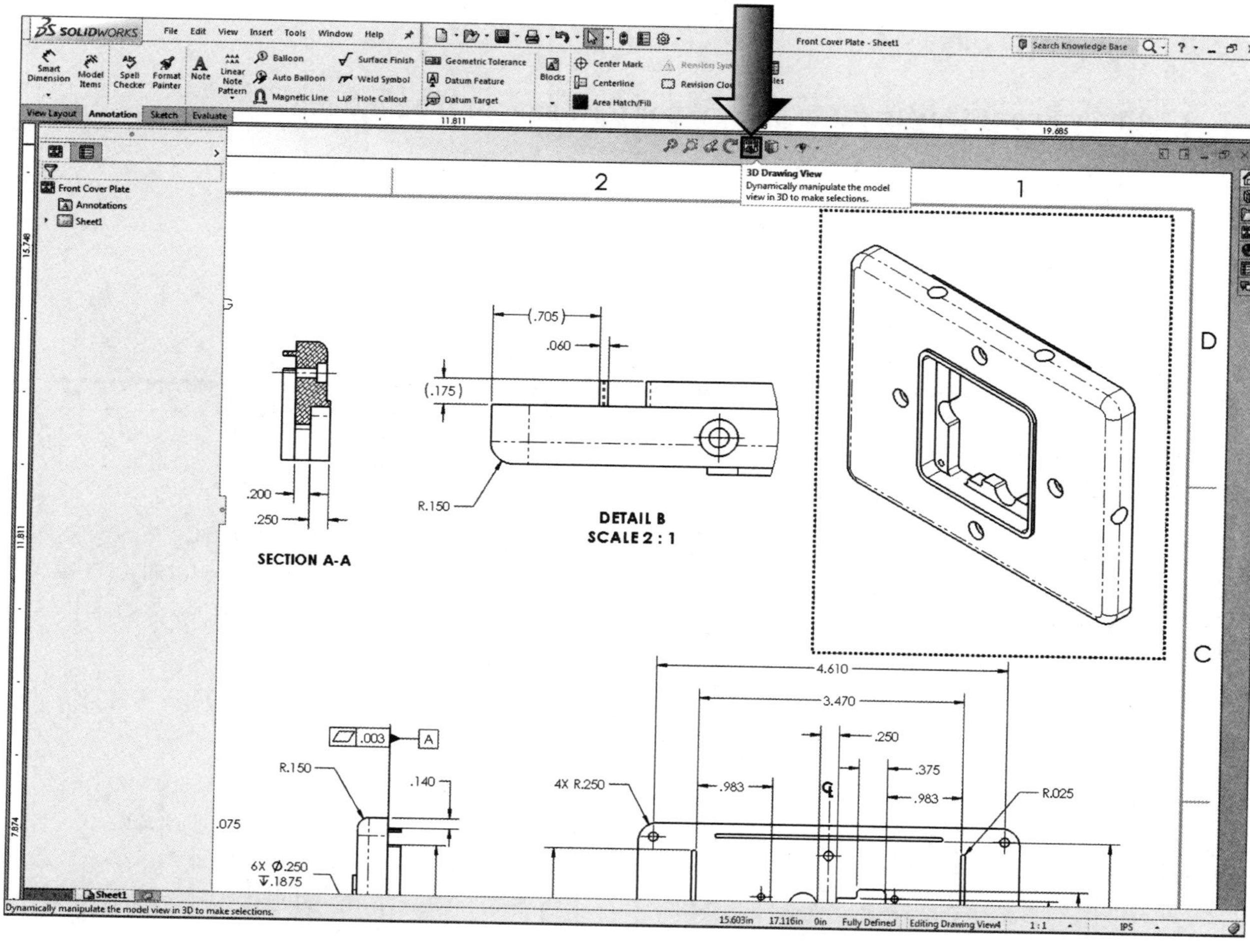

- The 3D Drawing View mode lets you rotate a drawing view out of its plane so you can see the edges obscured by other entities. It is used to make geometry selection in a drawing view easier.

- Click the **3D Drawing View** command from the View (Heads Up) tool bar.

- The Rotate command is the default tool, press and drag the left mouse button to rotate the view to different orientations.

- The new view can be saved for future use.

- Press **Esc** when finished.

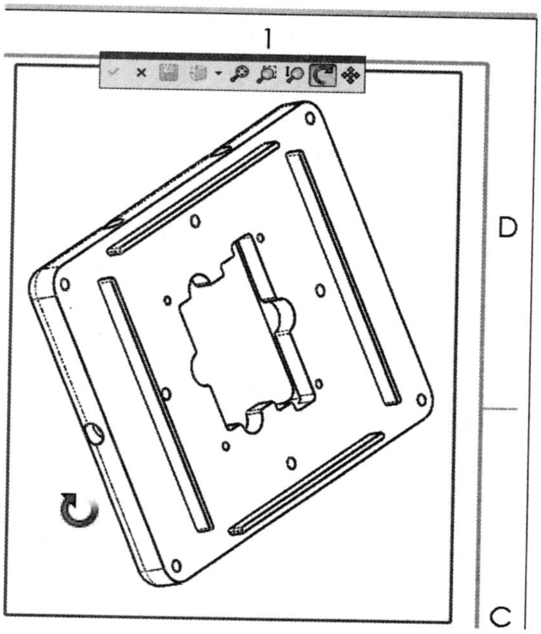

CHAPTER 17

Sheet Metal Parts

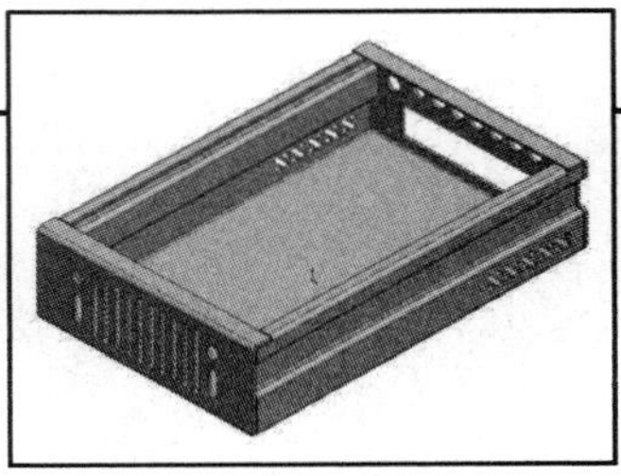

Sheet Metal Parts - Overview

Sheet metal parts are generally used as enclosures for components or to provide support to other components.

A sheet metal part can be created on its own without any references to the components it will enclose, or it can be designed in the context of an assembly that contains the enclosed components. It can also be designed within another part document in a multibody environment.

There are several approaches to designing a sheet metal part:

1. Design as sheet metal part from the very beginning: When you create a part initially out of sheet metal you can use the **Base Flange** tool with an open or closed profile sketch. The Edge Flange tool will add the other flanges to the base. This eliminates extra steps because you create a part as sheet metal from the initial design stage.

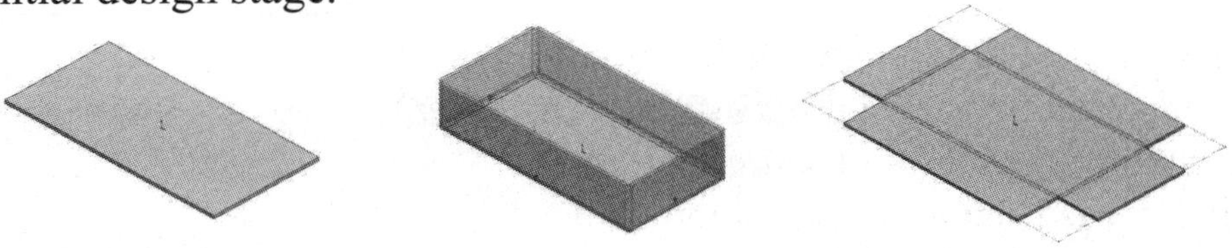

2. If you build a solid using non-sheet metal features, you need more features: **Base Extrude**, **Shell**, **Rip**, and **Insert Bends**. However, there are instances when it is preferable to build a part and then insert sheet metal bends. For example, conical bends are not supported by sheet metal features such as **Base Flange** and **Edge Flange**. Therefore, you must build the part using extrusions, revolves, and so on, and then add bends to the conical part.

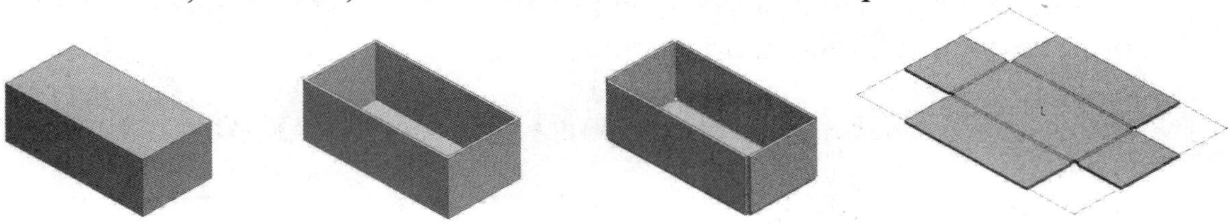

Hard Drive Enclosure
Sheet Metal Parts

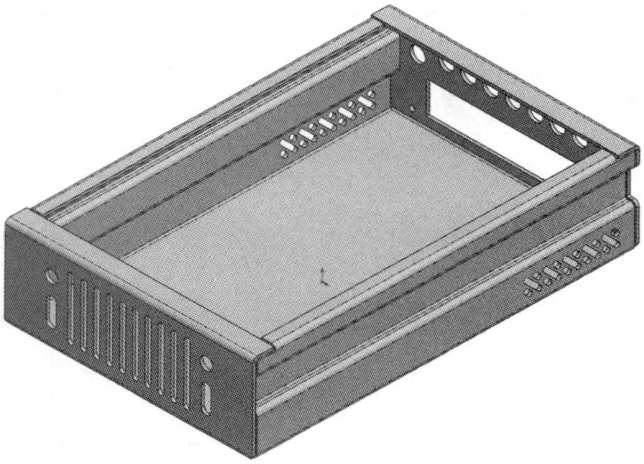

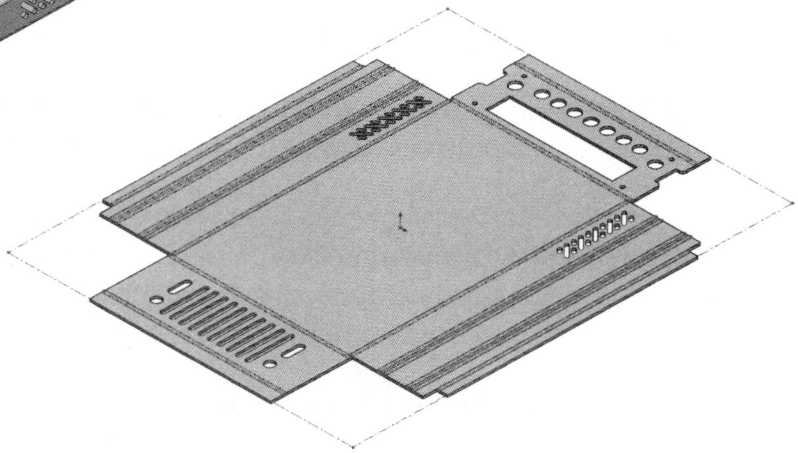

View Orientation Hot Keys:

Ctrl + 1 = Front View
Ctrl + 2 = Back View
Ctrl + 3 = Left View
Ctrl + 4 = Right View
Ctrl + 5 = Top View
Ctrl + 6 = Bottom View
Ctrl + 7 = Isometric View
Ctrl + 8 = Normal To Selection

Dimensioning Standards: **ANSI**

Units: **INCHES** – 3 Decimals

Tools Needed:

Insert Sketch	Line	Rectangle
Centerline	Convert Entities	Base Flange
Edge Flange	Extruded Cut	Library Features
Flat Pattern	Mirror Feature	Cut List

1. Starting a new part document:

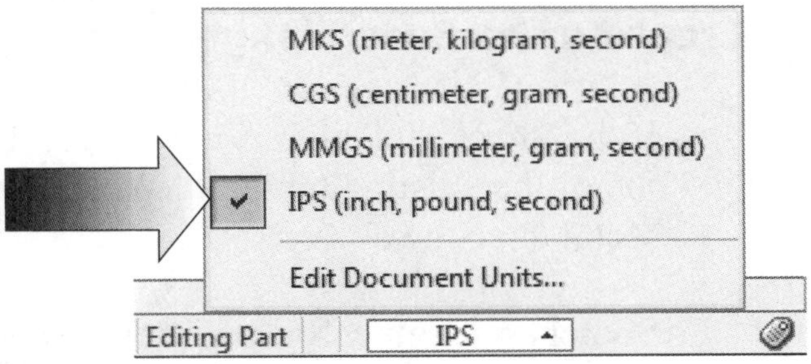

- Click **File / New / Part**.

- At the bottom right corner, set the Units to **IPS**.

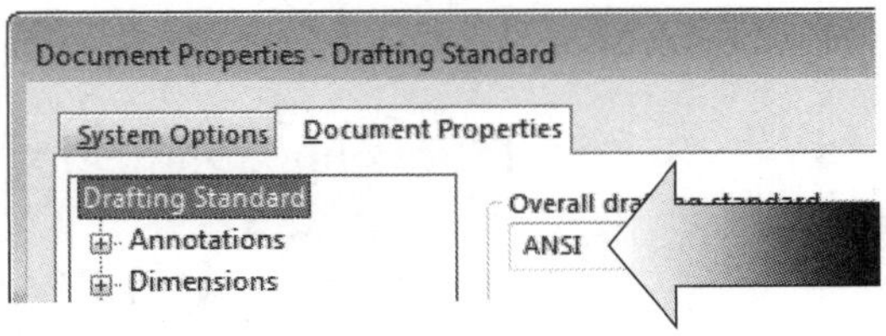

- Click **Edit Document Units** and select **ANSI** under the Drafting Standard option.

- Open a new sketch on the **Front** plane.

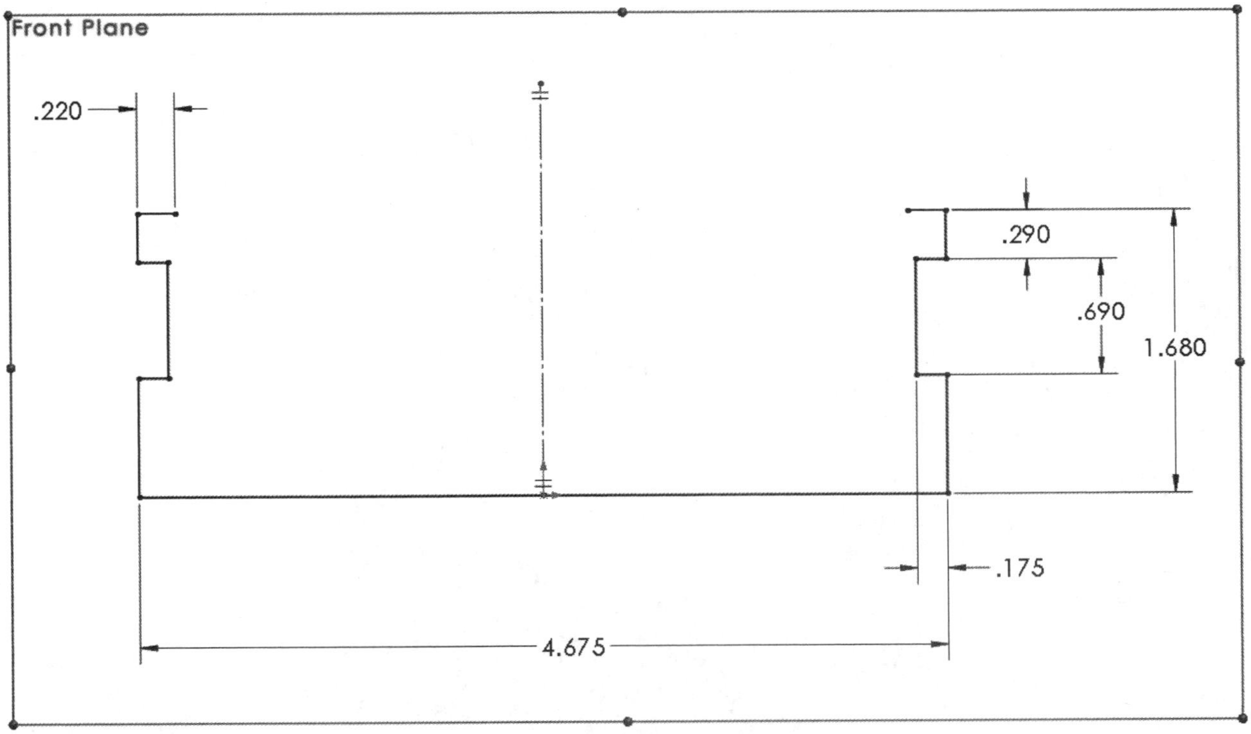

- Sketch the profile shown above, start with the vertical centerline .

- Use either the Mirror tool or the Symmetric relations to keep the sketch entities constrained about the centerline.

- Add the dimensions shown to fully define the sketch.

2. Creating the Base Flange :

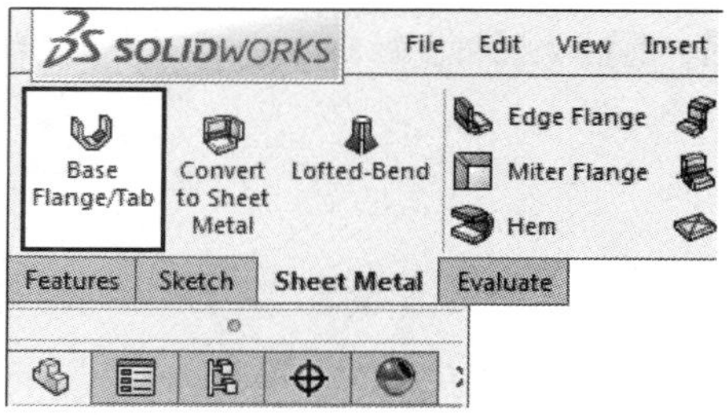

- If the Sheet Metal tab is not visible, right click one of the existing tabs and enable the Sheet-Metal checkbox.

- Switch to the new Sheet metal tab and click the **Base Flange** command.

> **Base Flange**
>
> A base flange is the first feature in a new sheet metal part. It is also considered as the parent feature of a sheet metal part.

- Set the following parameters:

  * Direction 1: **Mid Plane**

  * Depth: **7.280in**

  * Use Gauge Table: **Enabled**

  * Sample Table: **Steel** (Steel Air Bending)

  * Thickness: **16 Gauge**

  * Bend Radius: **.030in** (Override Radius enabled)

- Click **OK**.

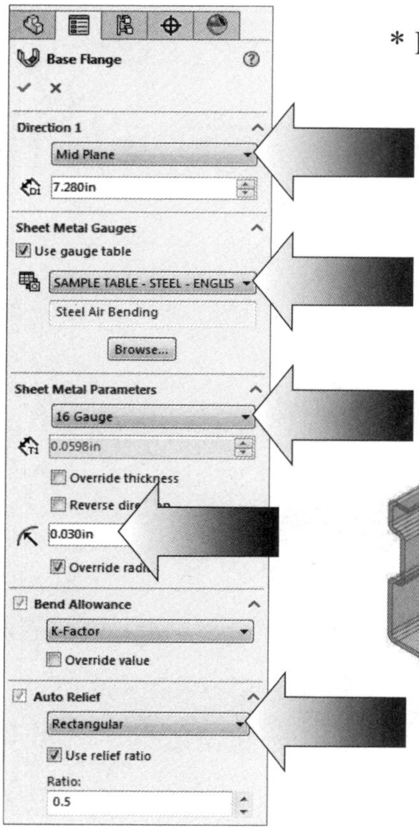

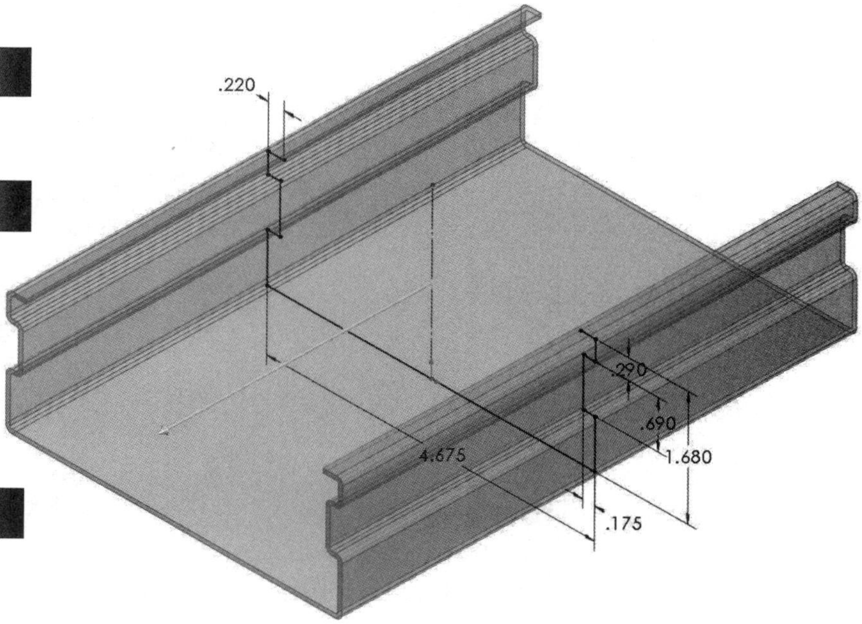

3. Creating a cut feature:

- Select the upper face as noted and open a new sketch.

- Sketch a Corner-Rectangle and mirror it in both directions (one direction at a time).

- Add the dimension and relation as indicated.

- Switch to the Sheet Metal tab and click **Extruded Cut**.

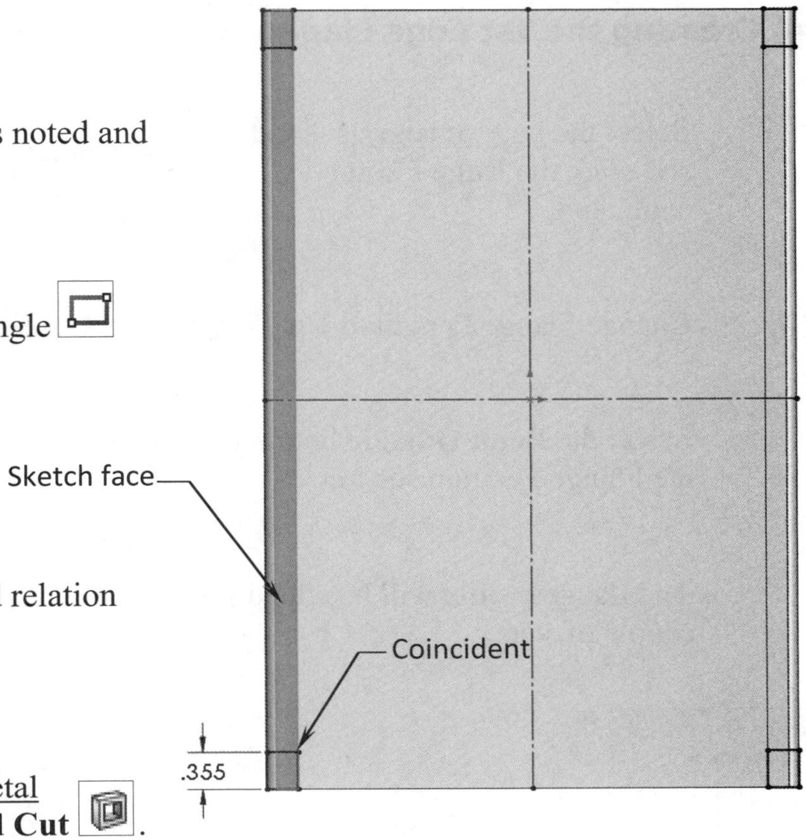

- Change Direction 1 to **Up To Vertex** and select the vertex as noted in the image below.

- Click **OK**.

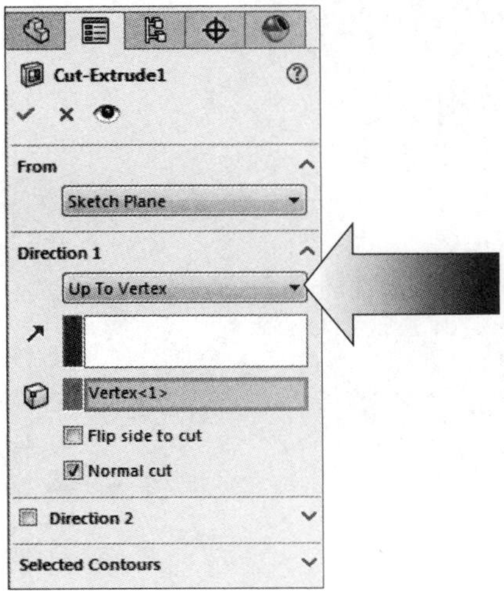

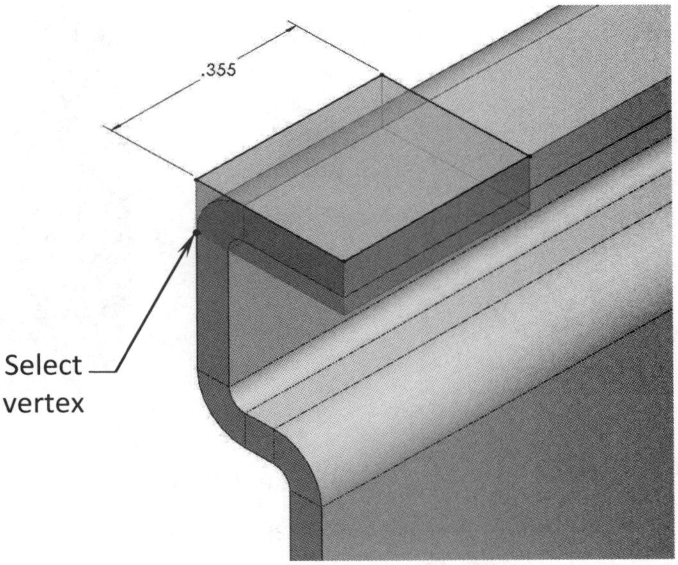

4. Creating the 1st Edge Flange:

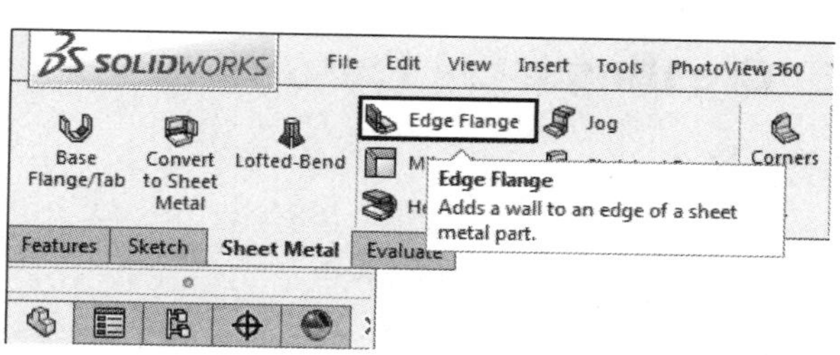

- Select the <u>bottom edge</u> as noted and click the **Edge Flange** command.

- Change Flange Length to **Up To Vertex** and select the <u>upper vertex</u> as indicated.

- Select the **Bend Outside** button (arrow) from the Flange Position section.

- The flange profile will be edited in the next couple of steps.

> ### Edge Flanges
>
> Edge Flanges are created from the linear or curved edges of the model, its thickness is automatically linked to the thickness of the sheet metal part.

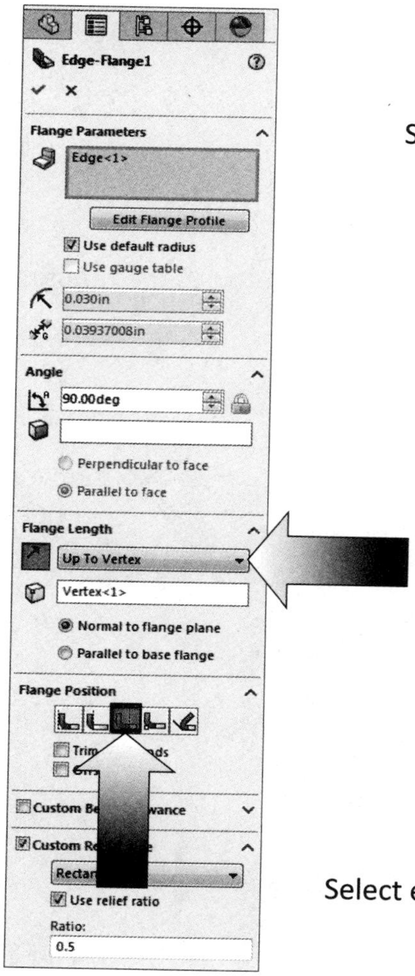

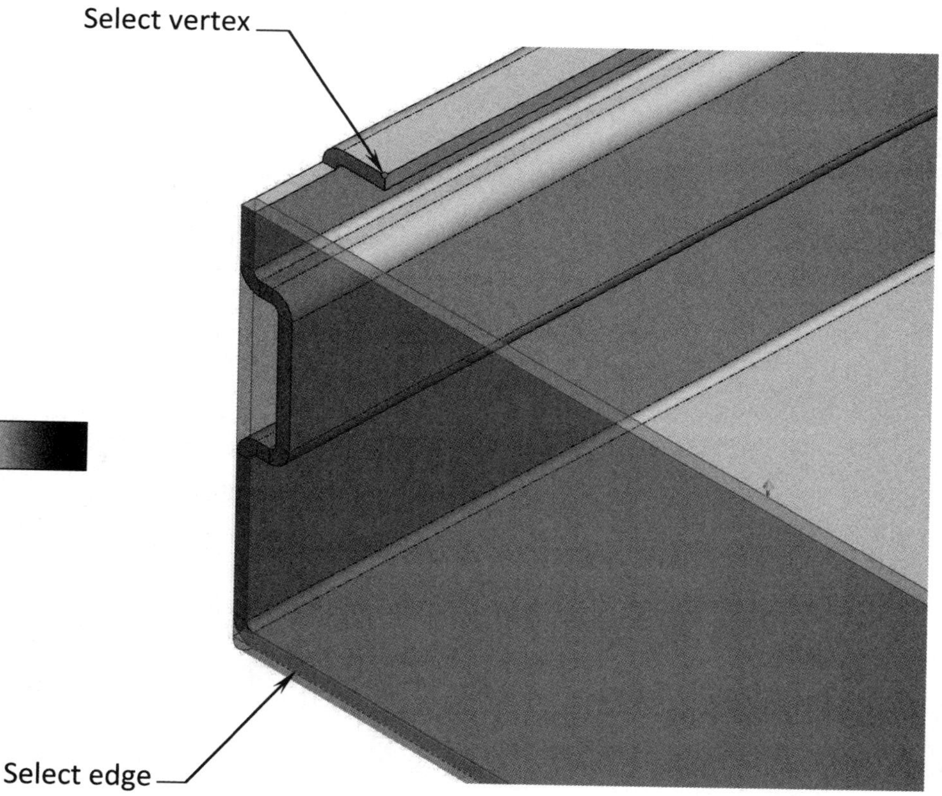

More...

- Click **Edit Flange Profile** to edit the sketch (arrow).

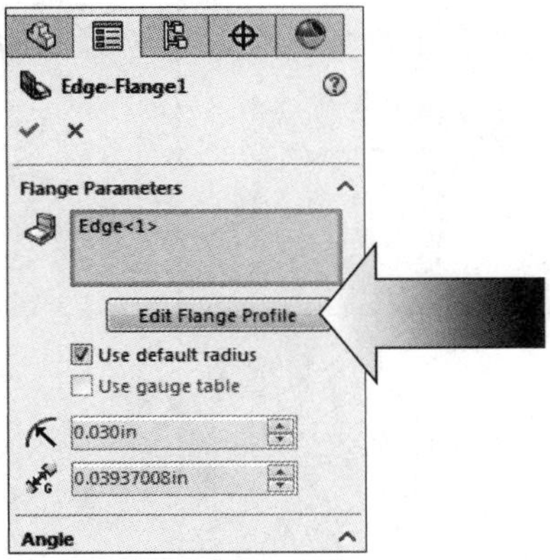

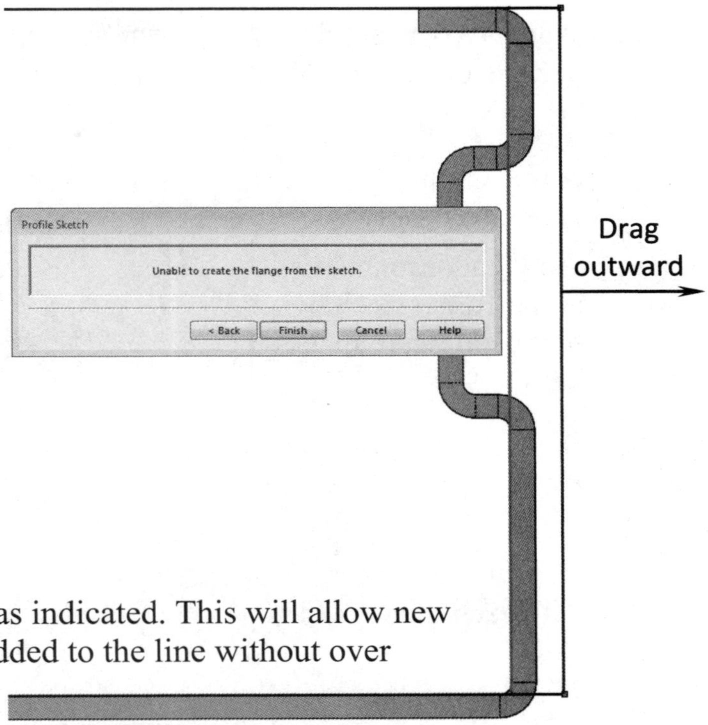

- Drag the vertical line outward as indicated. This will allow new relations or dimensions to be added to the line without over defining the sketch.

- Hold the **Control** key and select the 7 edges as indicated.

- Click the **Convert Entities** command.

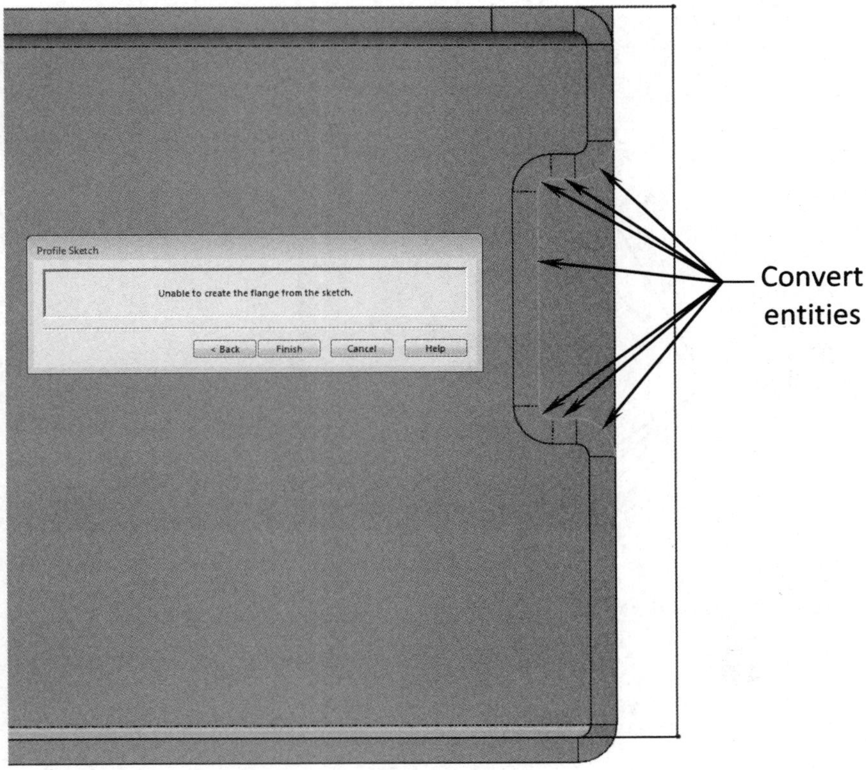

- The 7 selected edges are converted to 2D sketch entities.

- The next step is to join them into one continuous profile.

- Add a Collinear relation between the vertical line and the outer vertical edge of the model.

- Add 2 additional lines at the corner as shown in the enlarged images below.

- Repeat the same steps to ensure both corners are identical with each other.

- Extend or trim any of the sketch entities to form a continuous, closed profile. Add the dimensions and relations shown.

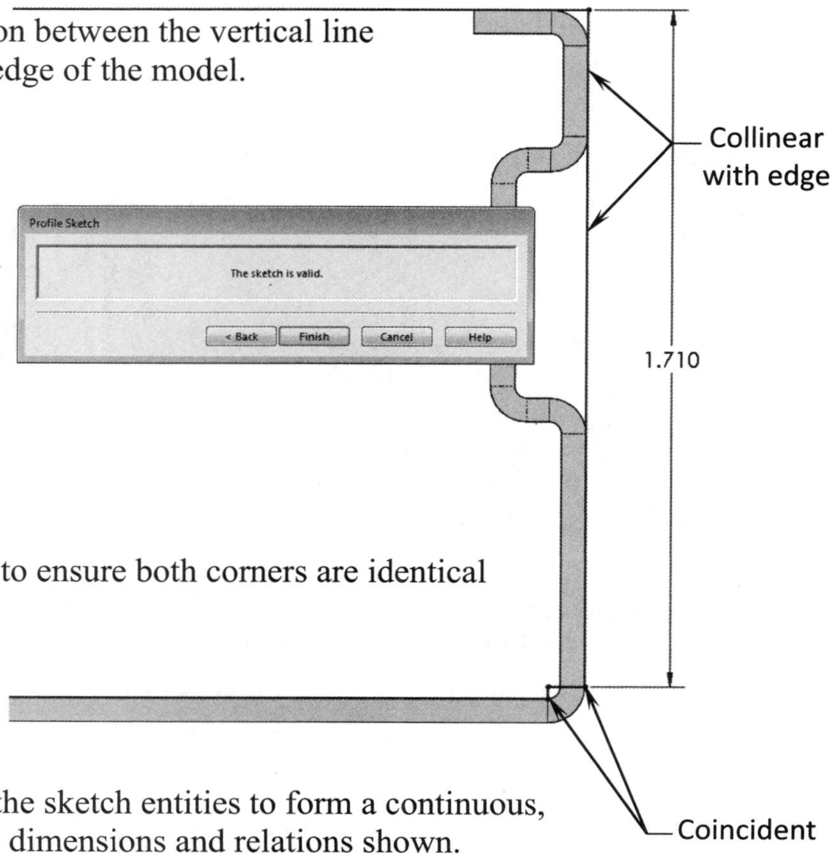

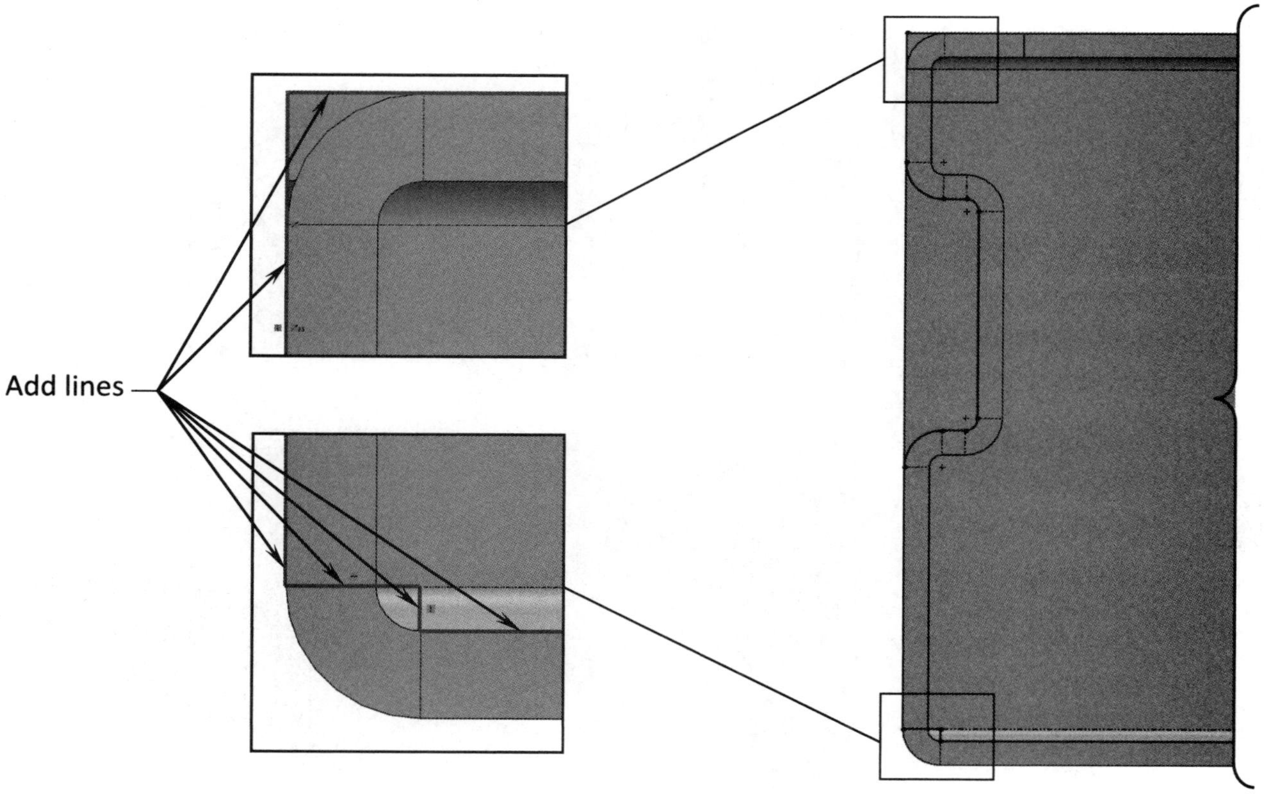

- Click the **Finish** button on the Profile Sketch dialog to exit the edit sketch mode.

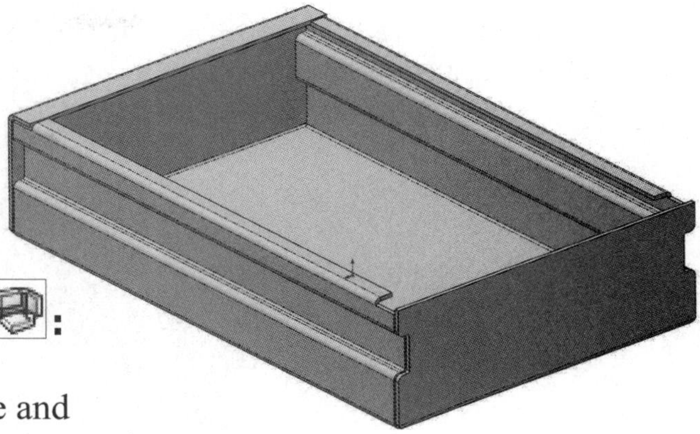

5. Creating the 2nd Edge Flange:

- Select the <u>outer edge</u> of the flange and click the **Edge Flange** command once again.

- Bring the cursor <u>inward</u> and enter **.410in** for Flange Length.

- Select the **Material Inside** button (arrow).

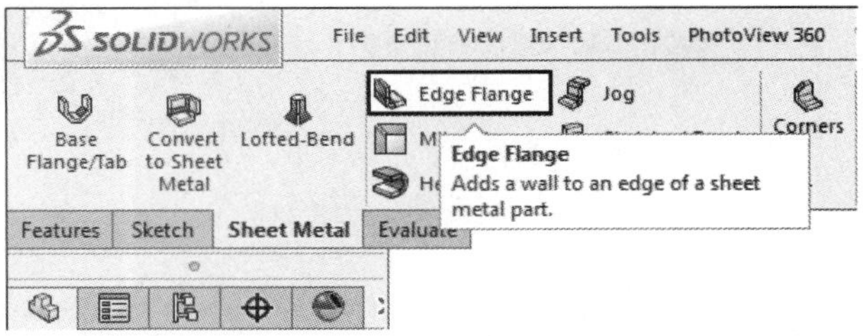

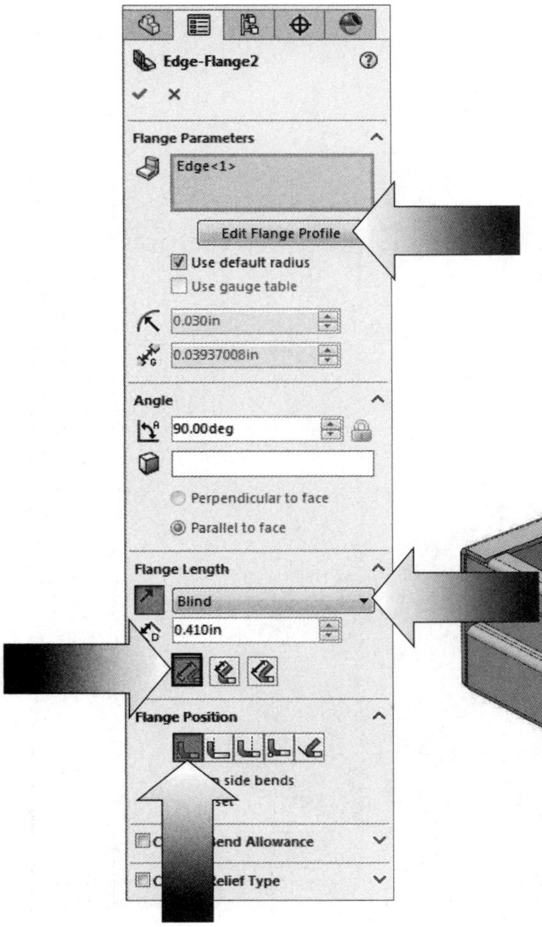

- Click the **Edit Flange Profile** button (arrow).

- The Flange Profile and length will be edited in the next couple of steps.

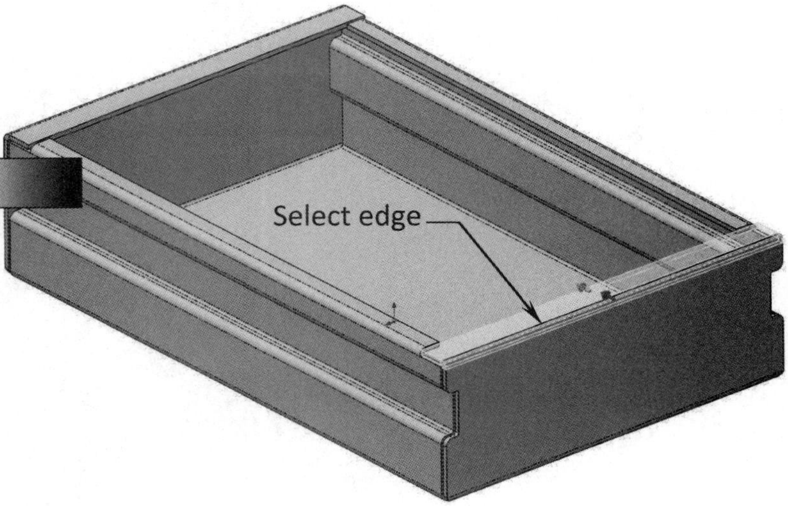

- Add the dimension **.410"** as shown.

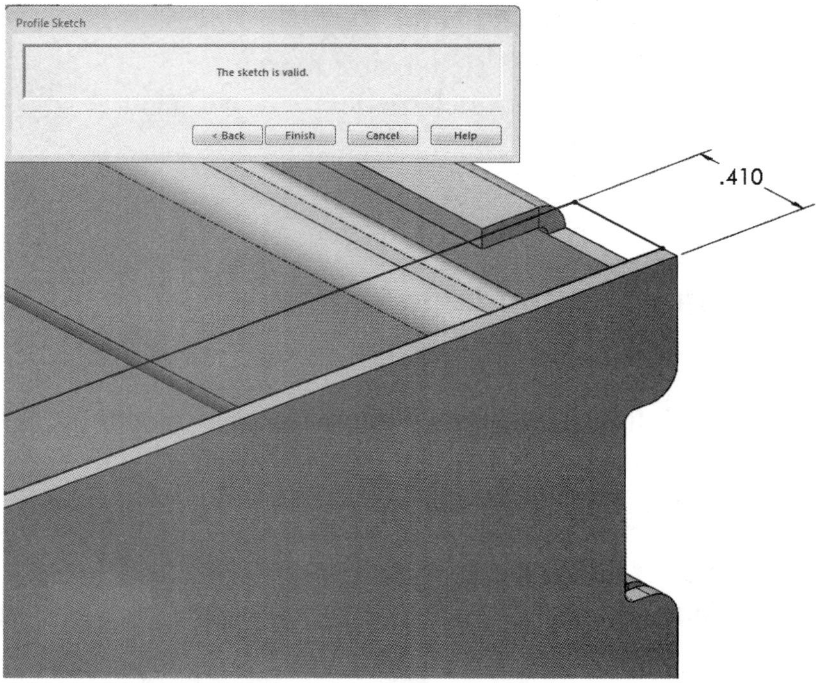

- The sketch should be fully defined at this point.

- Click the **Finish** button Finish to exit the edit mode.

- Examine the resulted flange and compare it with the image shown.

- It is good practice to save your work every once in a while. Save the first half of your work as: **SM Hard Drive Enclosure.sldprt**.

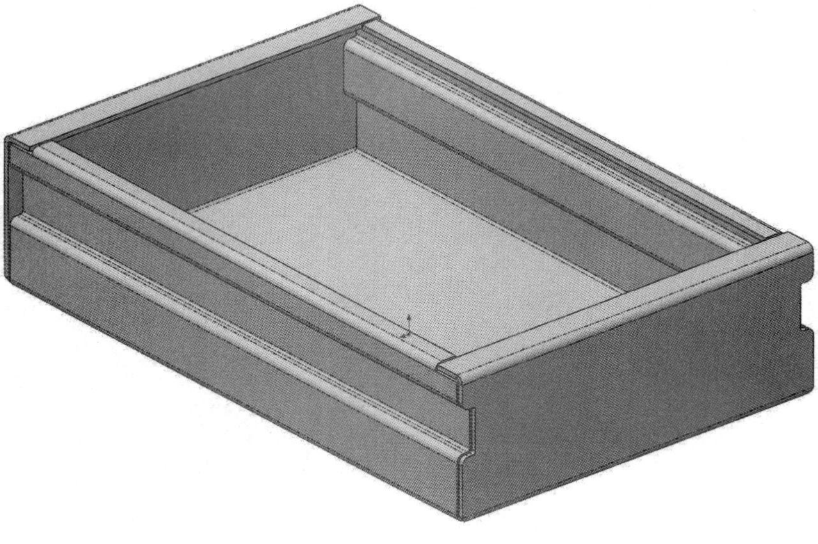

6. Copying and Pasting a sketch:

- Keep your model open while opening another document.

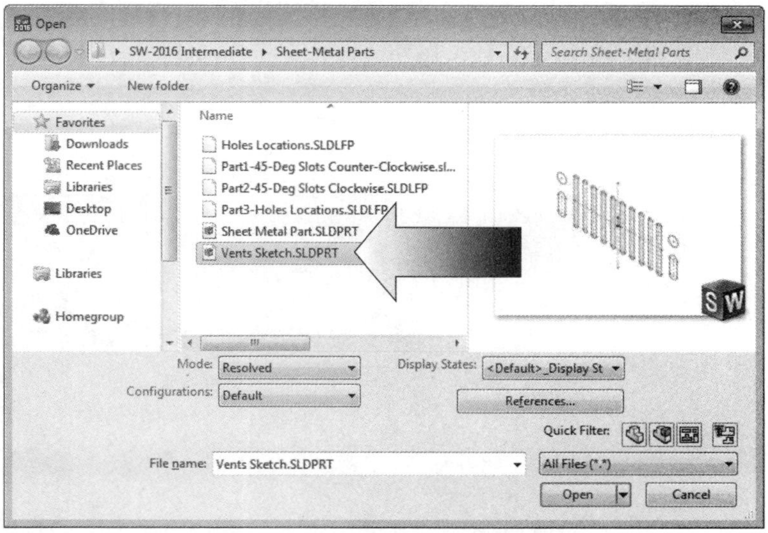

- Select **File / Open**.

- Browse to the training folder and open a document named: **Vents Sketch**.

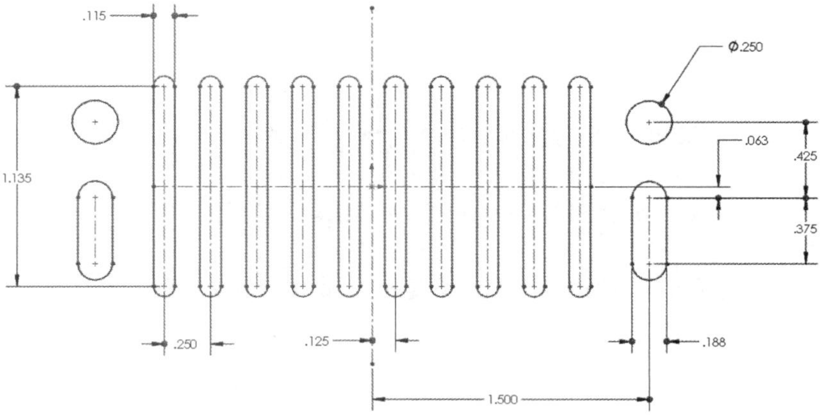

- Select the **Sketch1** from the Feature tree and press: **Ctrl + C**.

- Select the <u>face</u> as noted and press **Ctrl +V**.

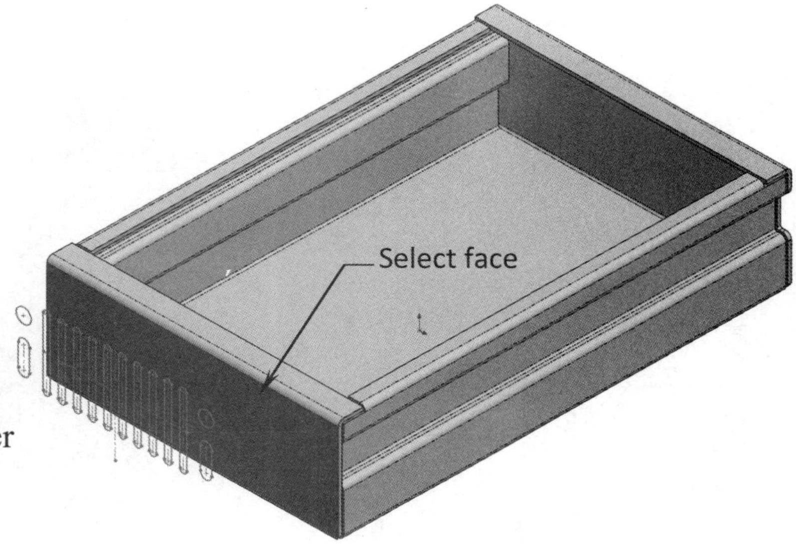

- A copy of the selected sketch appears on the front face of the model. The next step is to center it on the face.

- Select the new sketch and click: **Edit Sketch** .

- Add the **Midpoint** relation and dimension as indicated to fully position the sketch.

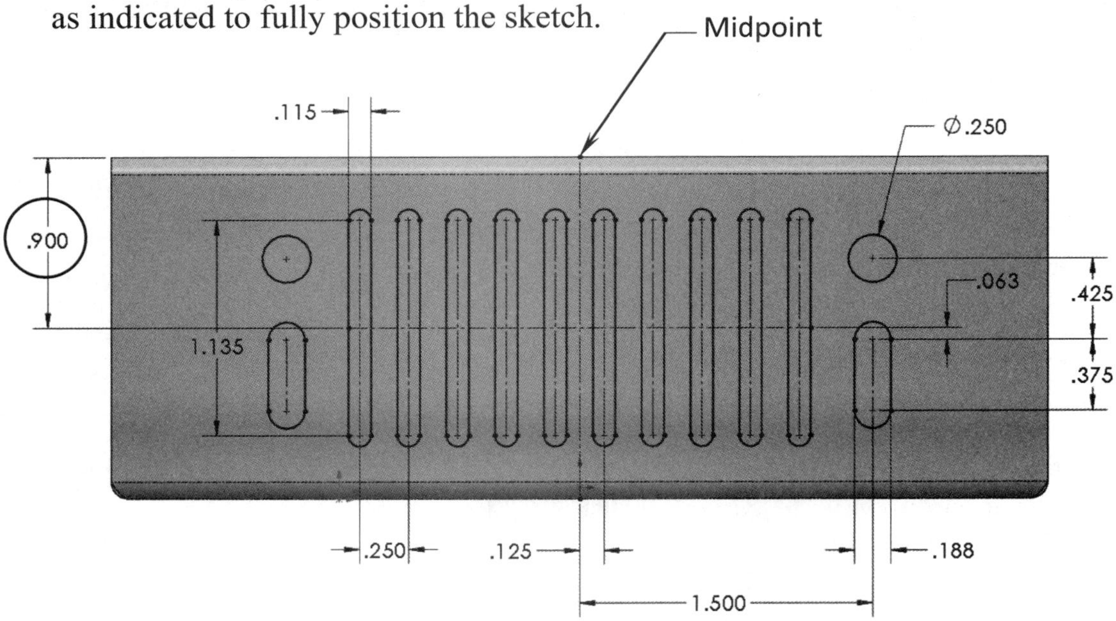

- Switch to the Sheet Metal tab and select **Extruded Cut** .

- Keep the Direction 1 at **Blind** (default).

- Enable the **Link To Thickness** check box.

- The **Normal Cut** check box is selected by default.

- Click **OK**.

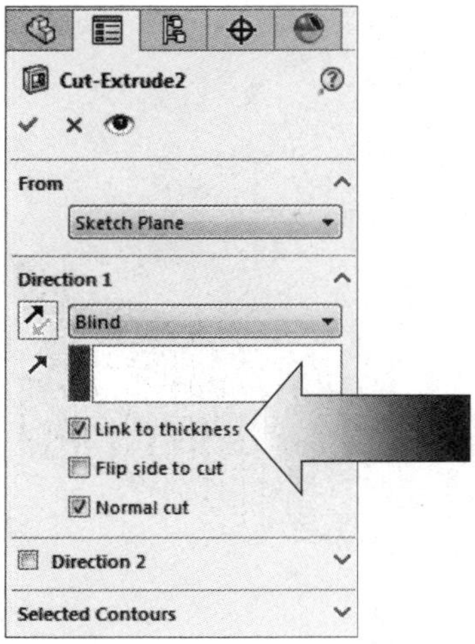

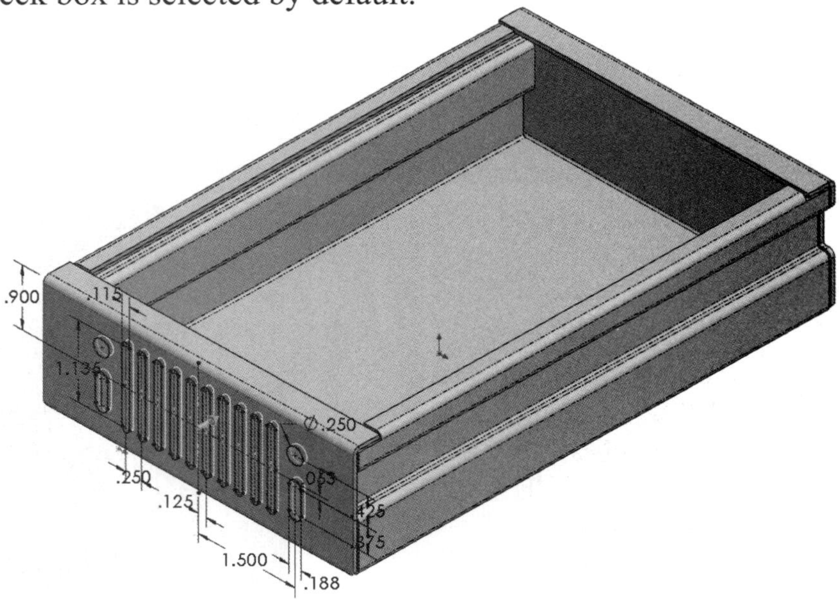

7. Creating more cuts:

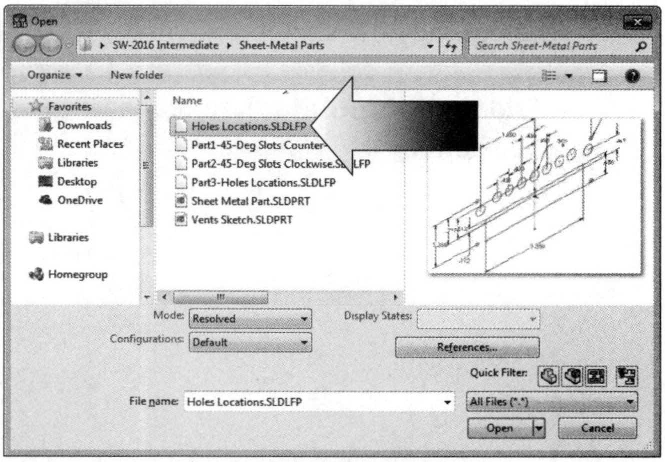

- The next cut feature will also be copied from an external sketch, similar to the last step.

- Select **File / Open**.

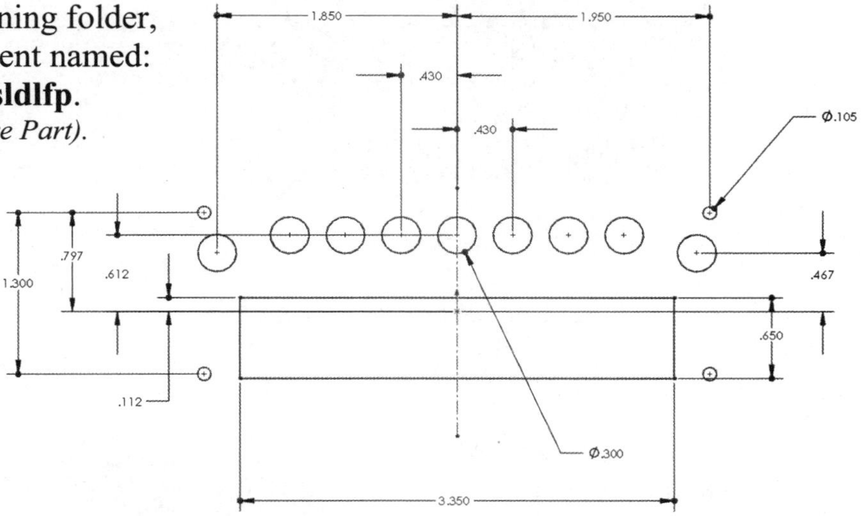

- Browse to the training folder, and open a document named: **Holes Locations.sldlfp**. *(Solid Library Feature Part).*

- Select the **Sketch1** from the Feature tree and press: **Ctrl + C**.

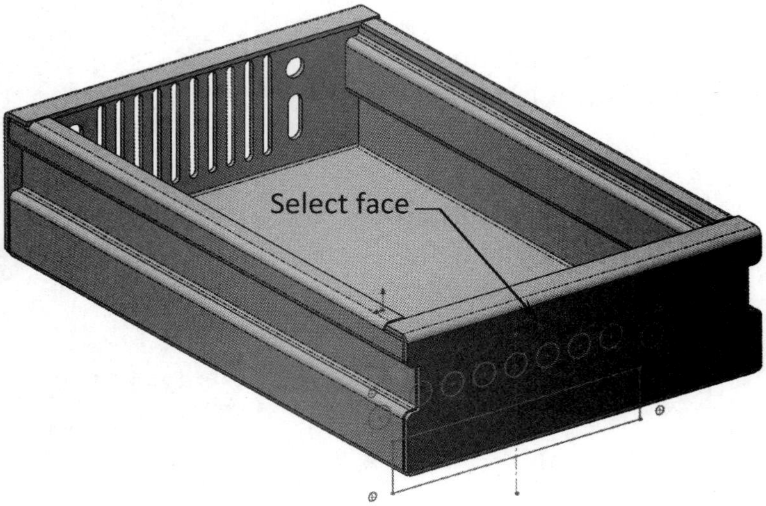

- Select the face as noted and press **Ctrl + V**.

- A copy of the selected sketch appears on the back face of the model. The next step is to center it on the face.

- Select the new sketch and click: **Edit Sketch** .

- Add the **Midpoint** relation and dimensions as indicated (circled) to fully position the sketch.

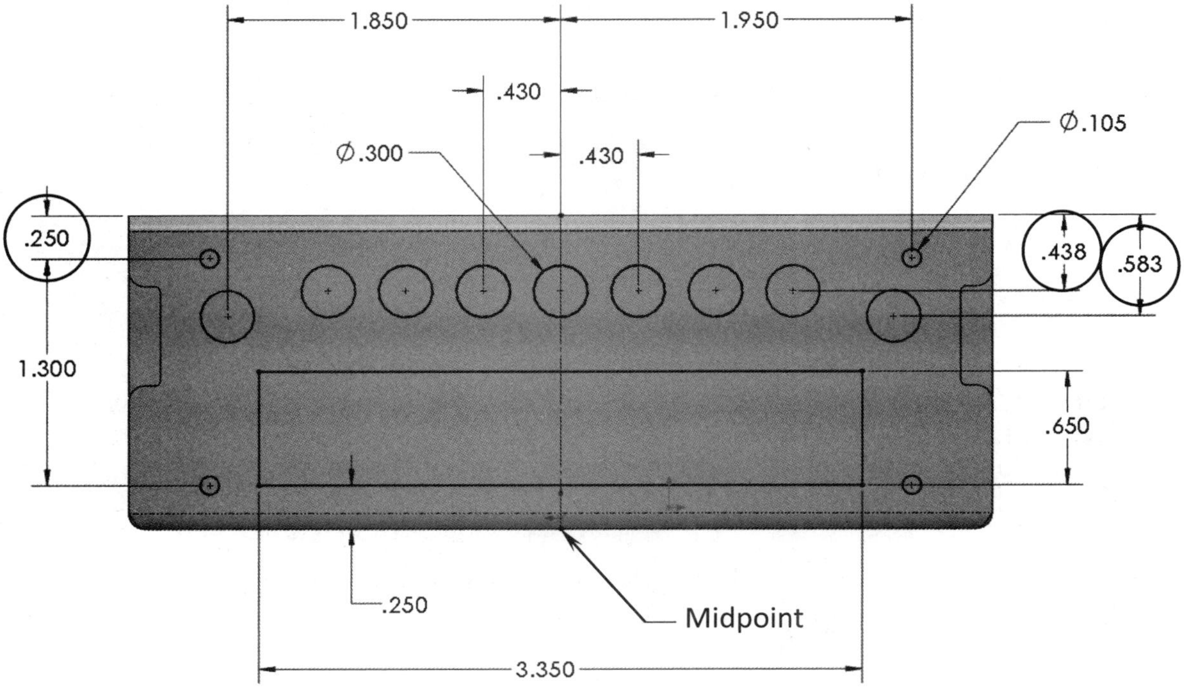

- Switch to the Sheet Metal tab and click: **Extruded Cut** .

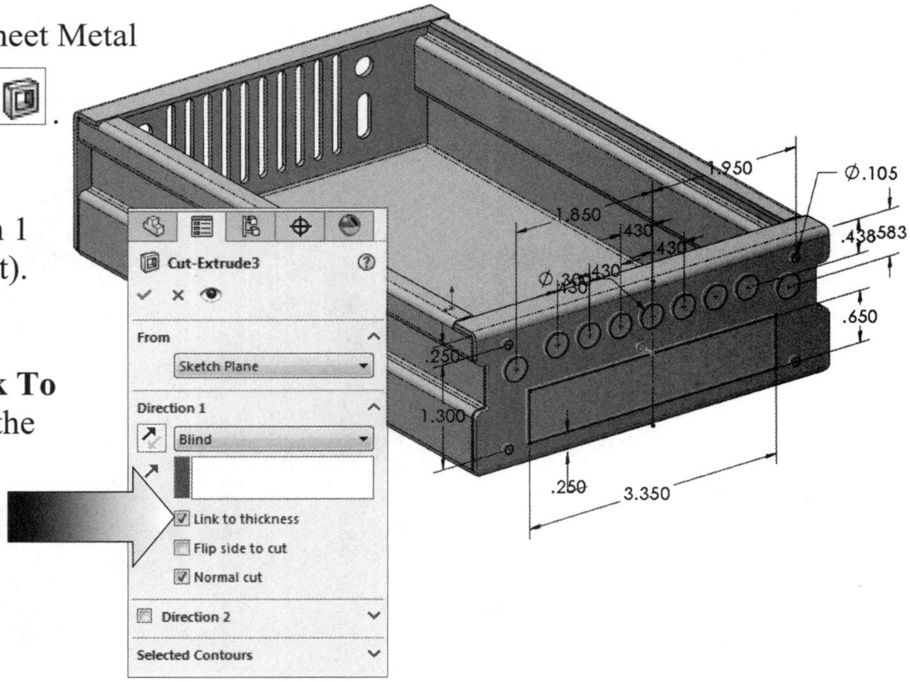

- Leave Direction 1 at **Blind** (default).

- Enable the **Link To Thickness** and the **Normal Cut** check boxes.

- Click **OK**.

8. Adding a Library Feature Cut :

- Any features created previously and saved as a Library Feature Part can be "re-used" by dragging and dropping from the file Explorer window.

- Select the **File Explorer** tab (arrow), browse to the training folder, expand the Sheet Metal Parts folder.

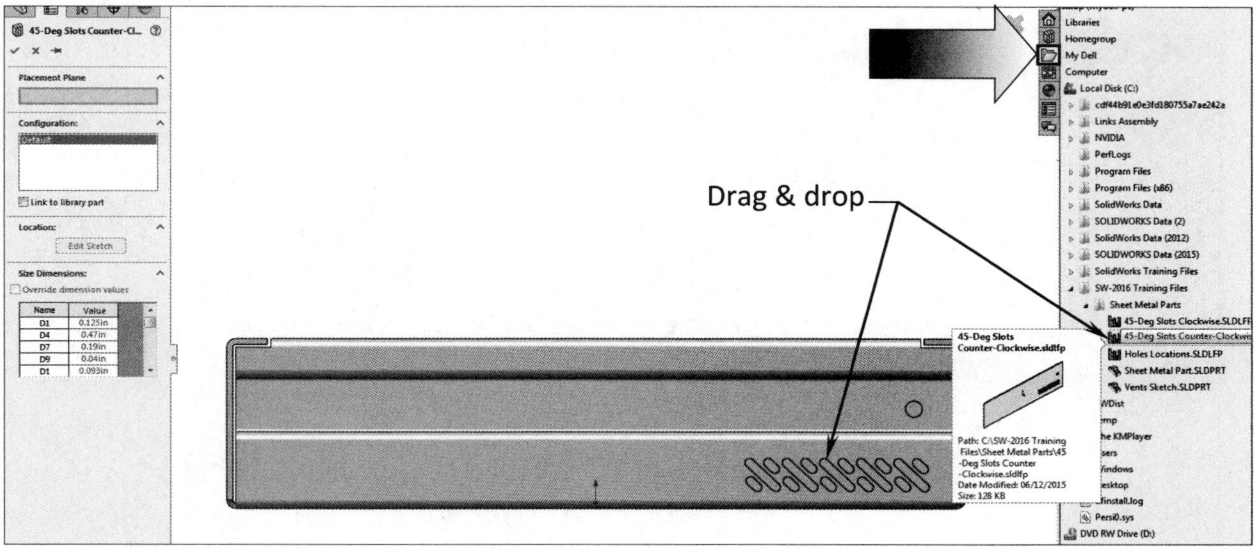

- Drag and drop the library feature named: **45-Deg Slots Counter-Clockwise** on the right side of the model as shown (Ctrl + 4 = Right side view).

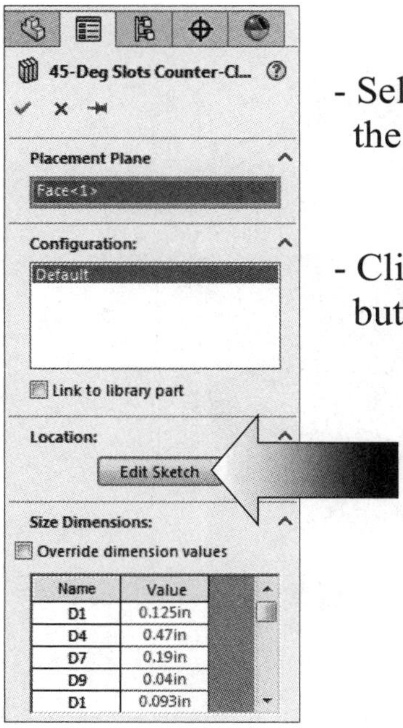

- Select the lower face as the **Placement Plane**.

- Click the **Edit Sketch** button to position the feature.

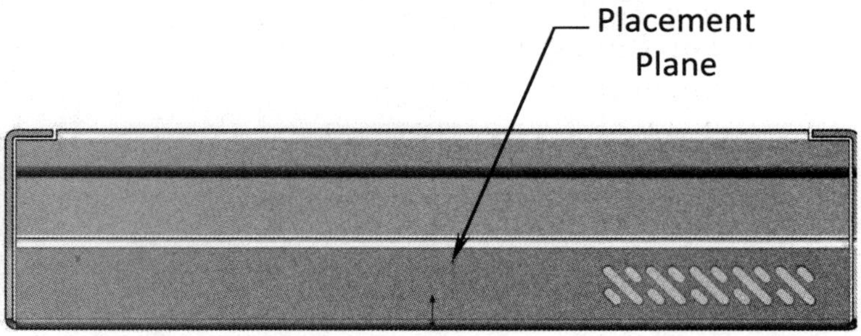

- Add the 2 locating dimensions (circled) to fully define the sketch.

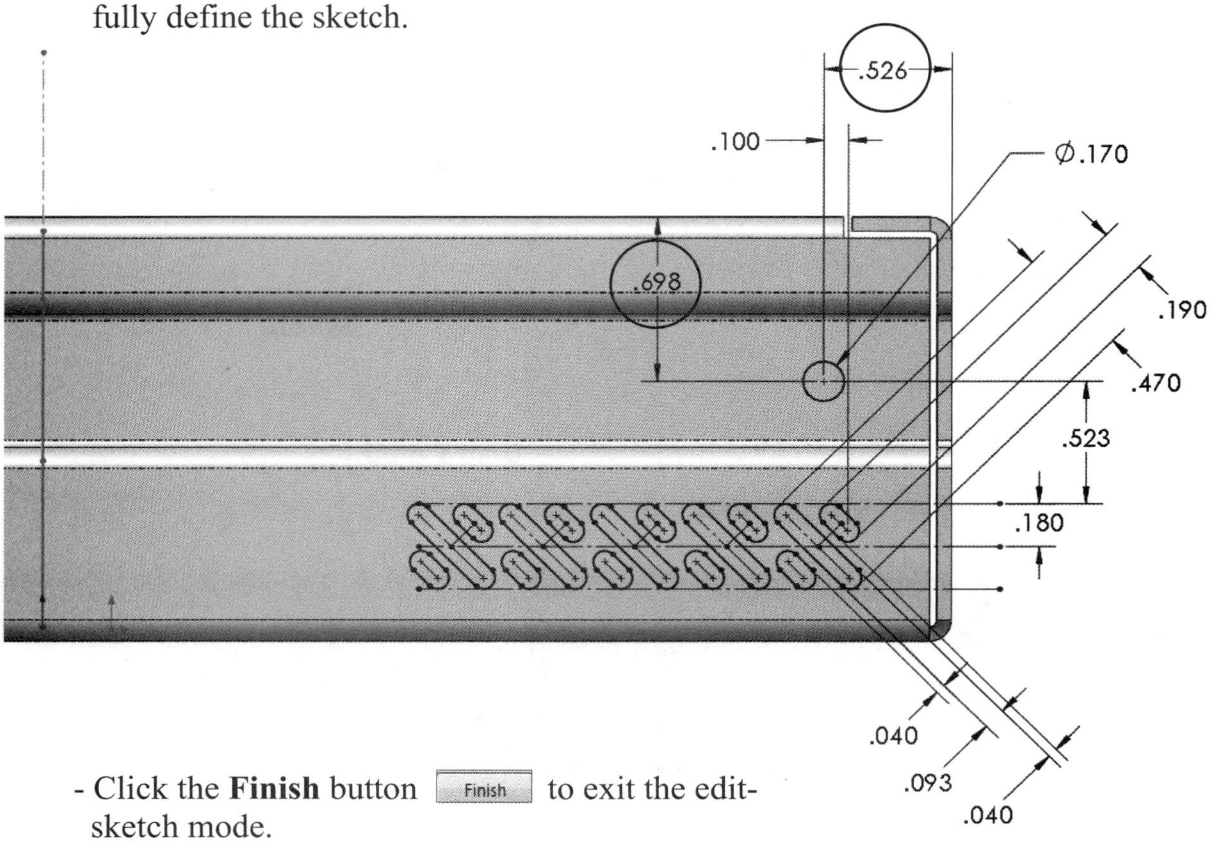

- Click the **Finish** button [Finish] to exit the edit-sketch mode.

- The cut feature will be mirrored to the opposite side in the next step.

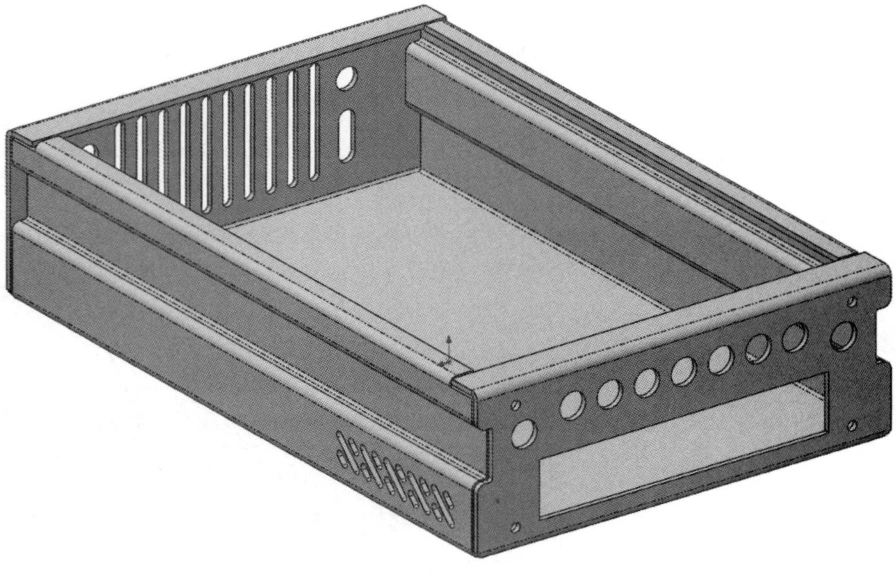

9. Mirroring a Feature:

- Once applied to the part, the library features can be copied, patterned, or mirrored just like any other features.

- Change to the Features tab and click the **Mirror** command 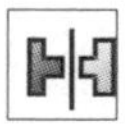.

- Select the **Right** plane from the FeatureManager tree for Mirror Face/Plane.

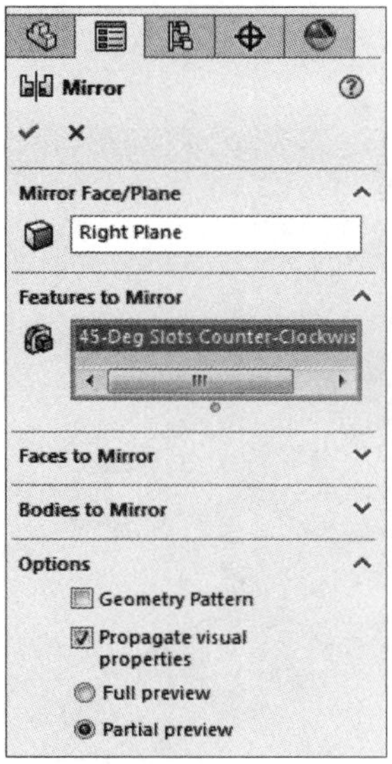

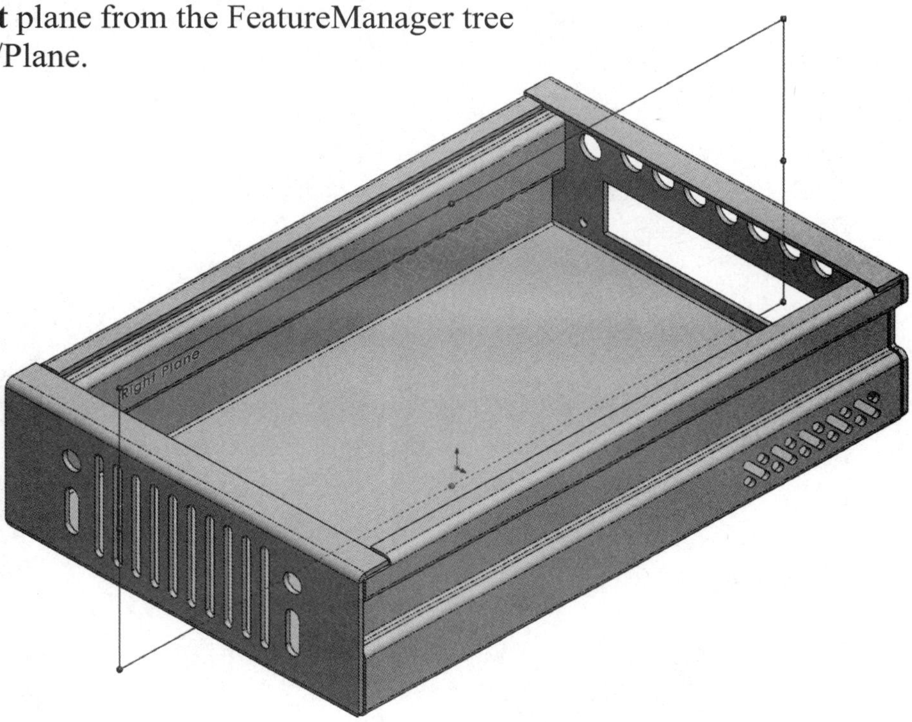

- Select the **45-Deg Slots** also from the FeatureManager tree for Features-to Mirror.

- The preview shows the selected feature is being mirrored to the opposite side.

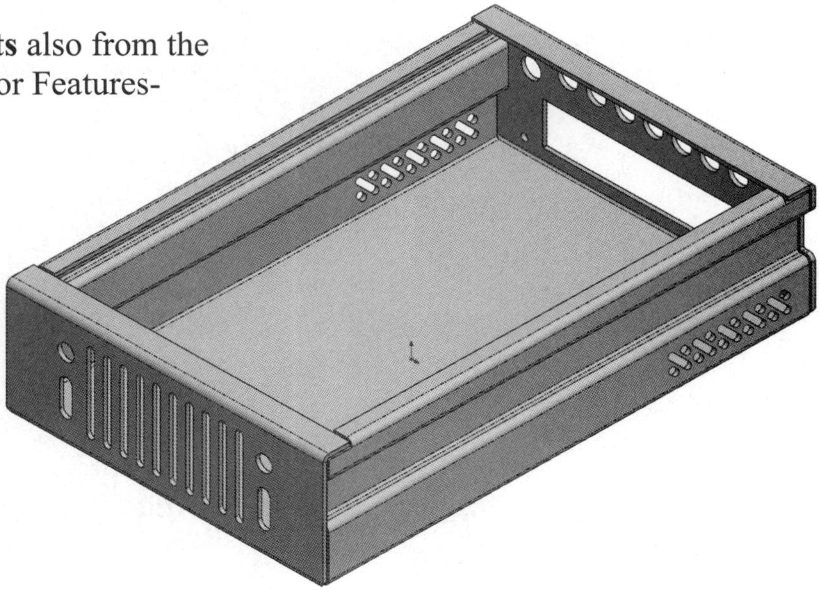

- Click **OK**.

10. Toggling the Flat Display:

- A flat pattern can now be "superimposed" on top of the fold pattern. This unique option allows the user to preview the flat pattern while comparing the features between the flat and fold patterns.

- Right click on the sheet metal part and select: **Toggle Flat Display**.

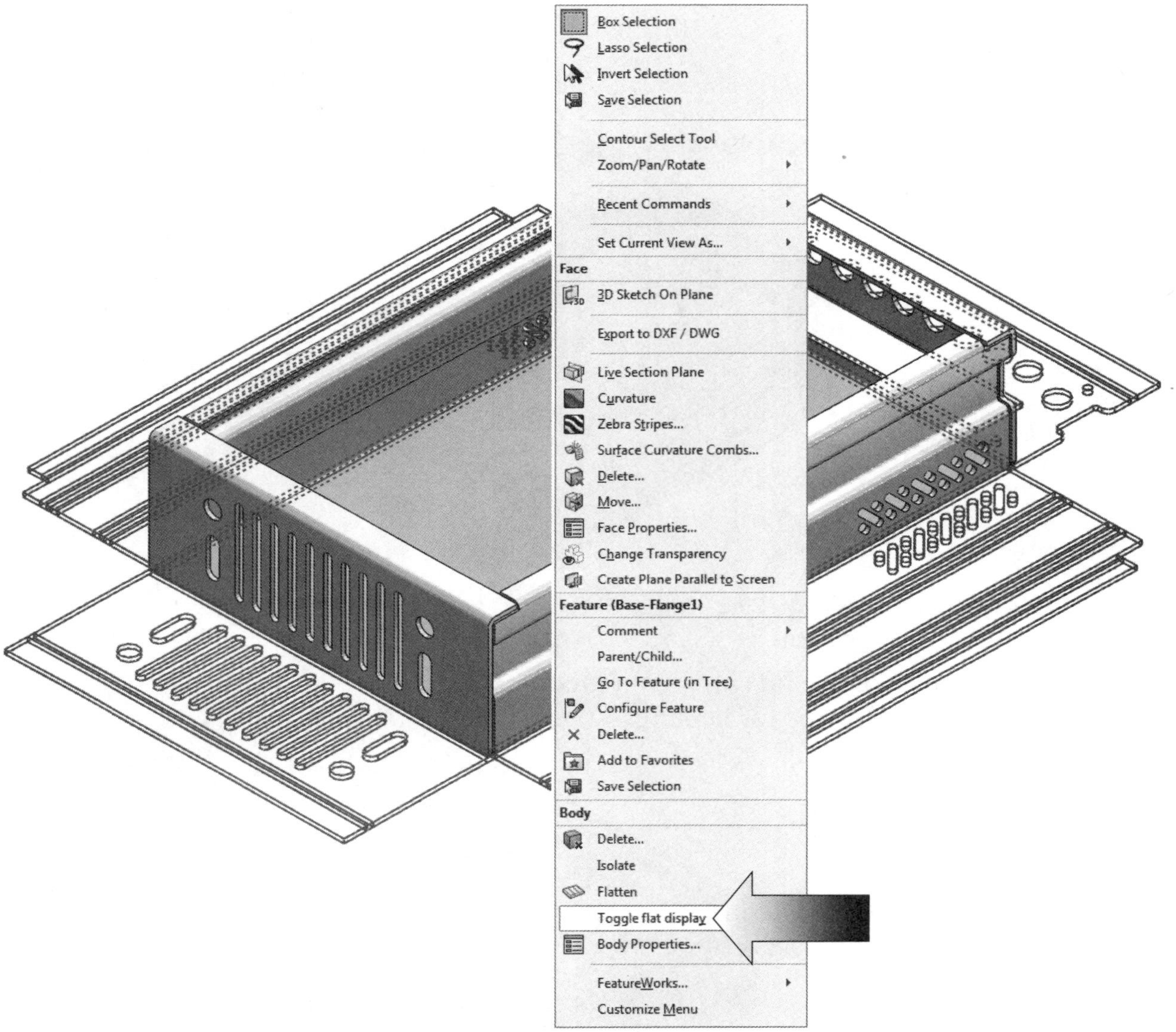

- The flat pattern is displayed over the folded part, in the preset color (blue, green, or orange).

11. Creating the Flat Pattern:

- An actual Flat pattern can be created at anytime. All features within the sheet metal part will be flattened and a bounding box is added to show the overall size of the flat sheet metal.

- Change to the Sheet Metal tab and click the **Flatten** command  .

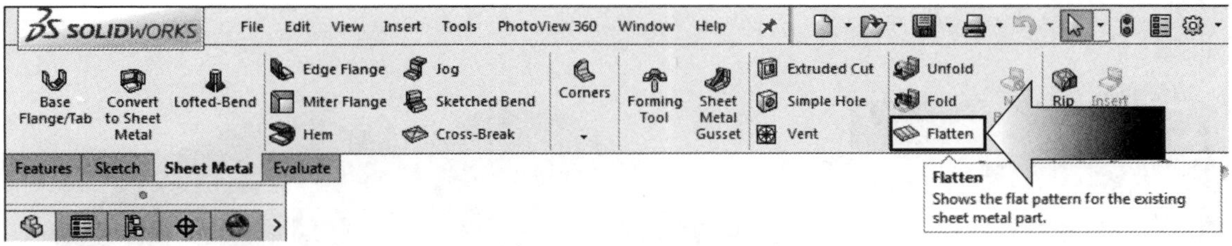

- The sheet metal part is flattened and all of its features are unfolded with it.

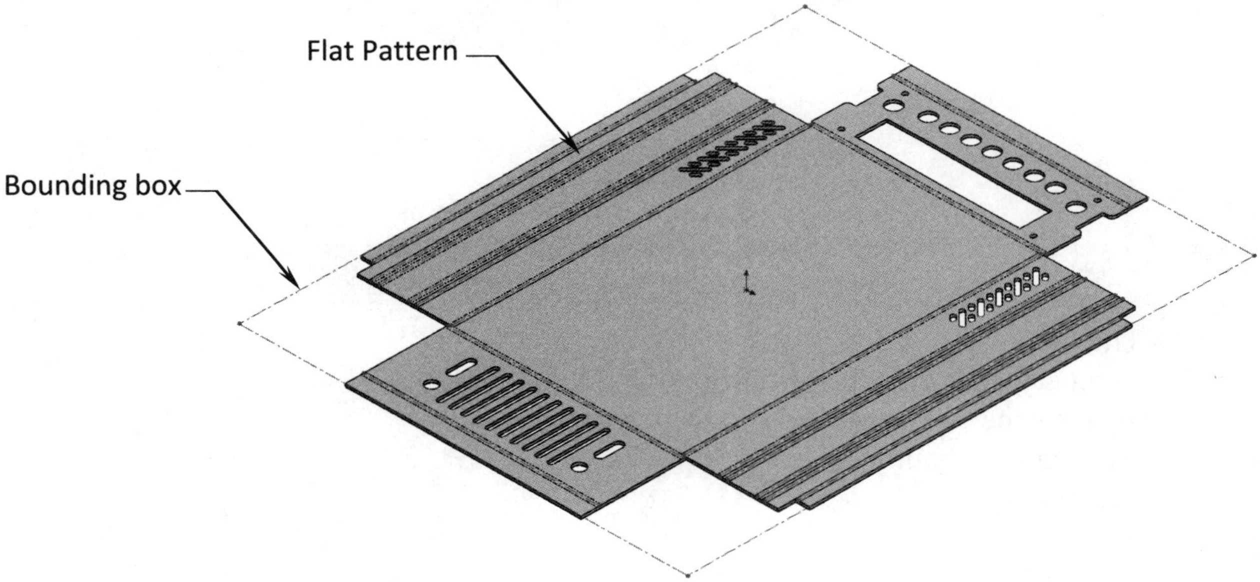

- A "dotted box" is added around the part to show the bounding box area of the flat sheet. Further information like thickness, bend allowance, bend radius, etc. can be retrieved by accessing the properties of the sheet.

12. Accessing the Sheet Properties:

- Expand the **Cut List** from the FeatureManager tree and right-click on the **Sheet** item and select **Properties** (arrow).

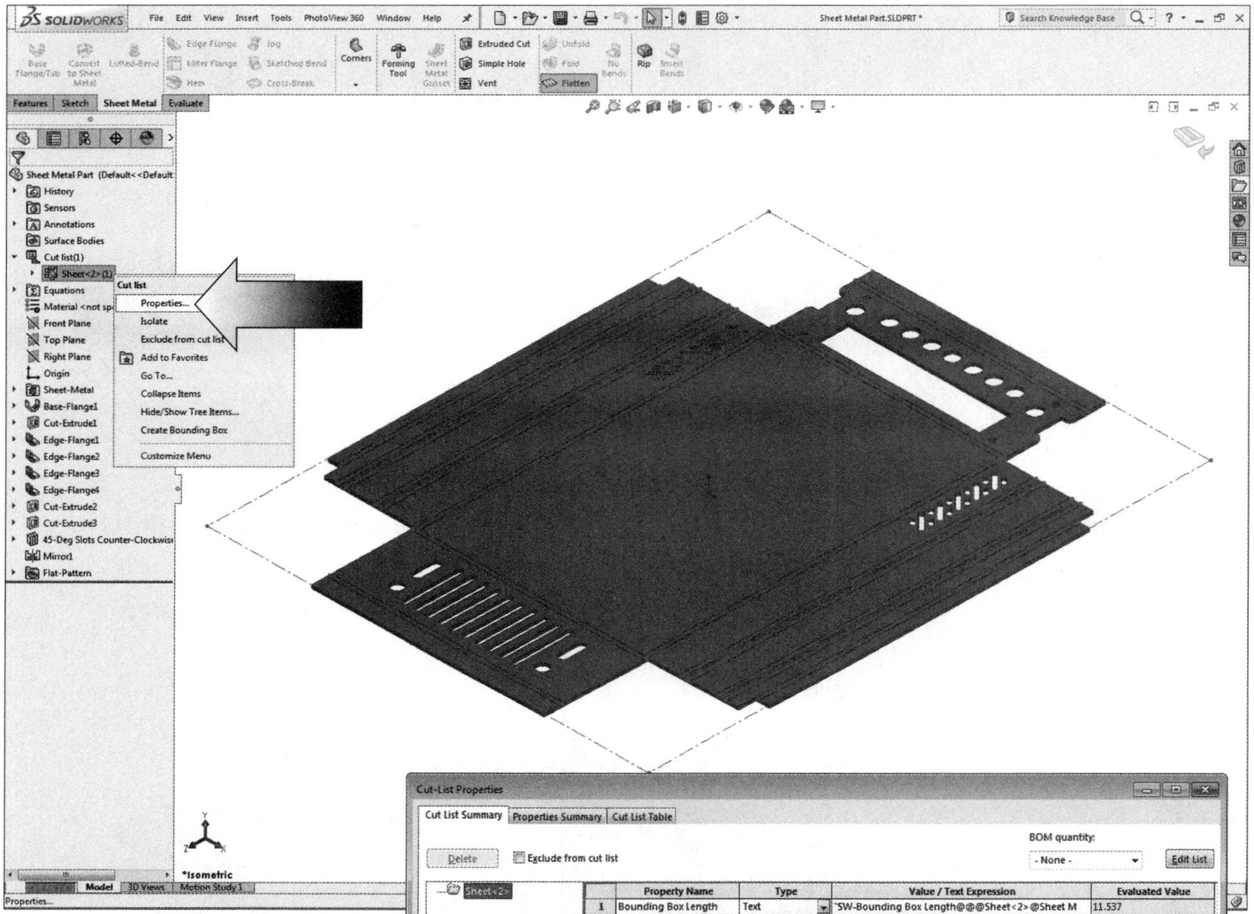

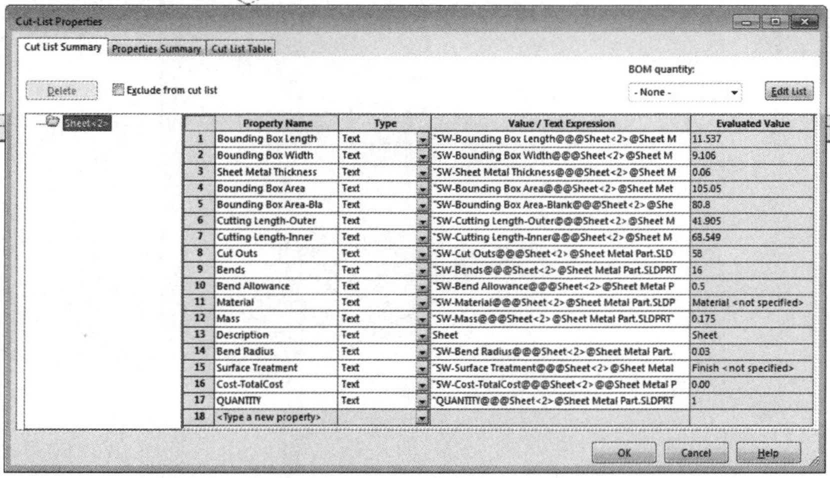

- The Cut List summary dialog displays the information about the sheet metal part.

13. Saving your work:

- Save your work as **SM Hard Drive Enclosure.sldprt** and replace the one saved earlier.

Glossary

Alloys:

An Alloy is a mixture of two or more metals (and sometimes a non-metal). The mixture is made by heating and melting the substances together.
Example of alloys are Bronze (Copper and Tin), Brass (Copper and Zinc), and Steel (Iron and Carbon).

Gravity and Mass:

Gravity is the force that pulls everything on earth toward the ground and makes things feel heavy. Gravity makes all falling bodies accelerate at a constant 32ft. per second (9.8 m/s). In the earth's atmosphere, air resistance slows acceleration. Only on airless Moon would a feather and a metal block fall to the ground together.
The mass of an object is the amount of material it contains.
A body with greater mass has more inertia; it needs a greater force to accelerate.
Weight depends on the force of gravity, but mass does not.

When an object spins around another (for example, a satellite orbiting the earth) it is pushed outward. Two forces are at work here: Centrifugal (pushing outward) and Centripetal (pulling inward). If you whirl a ball around you on a string, you pull it inward (Centripetal force). The ball seems to pull outward (Centrifugal force) and if released will fly off in a straight line.

Heat:

Heat is a form of energy and can move from one substance to another in one of three ways: by Convection, by Radiation, and by Conduction.

- Convection takes place only in liquids like water (for example, water in a kettle) and gases (for example, air warmed by a heat source such as a fire or radiator). When liquid or gas is heated, it expands and becomes less dense. Warm air above the radiator rises and cool air moves in to take its place, creating a convection current.

- Radiation is movement of heat through the air. Heat forms match set molecules of air moving and rays of heat spread out around the heat source.

- Conduction occurs in solids such as metals. The handle of a metal spoon left in boiling liquid warms up as molecules at the heated end move faster and collide with their neighbors, setting them moving. The heat travels through the metal, which is a good conductor of heat.

Inertia:

A body with a large mass is harder to start and also to stop. A heavy truck traveling at 50mph needs more power brakes to stop its motion than a smaller car traveling at the same speed.
Inertia is the tendency of an object either to stay still or to move steadily in a straight line, unless another force (such as a brick wall stopping the vehicle) makes it behave differently.

Joules:

The Joules is the SI unit of work or energy.
One Joule of work is done when a force of one Newton moves through a distance of one meter. The Joule is named after the English scientist James Joule (1818-1889).

Materials:

- Stainless steel is an alloy of steel with chromium or nickel.

- Steel is made by the basic oxygen process. The raw material is about three parts melted iron and one part scrap steel. Blowing oxygen into the melted iron raises the temperature and gets rid of impurities.

- All plastics are chemical compounds called polymers.

- Glass is made by mixing and heating sand, limestone, and soda ash. When these ingredients melt they turn into glass, which is hardened when it cools. Glass is in fact not a solid but a "supercooled" liquid, it can be shaped by blowing, pressing, drawing, casting into molds, rolling, and floating across molten tin, to make large sheets.

- Ceramic objects, such as pottery and porcelain, electrical insulators, bricks, and roof tiles are all made from clay. The clay is shaped or molded when wet and soft, and heated in a kiln until it hardens.

Machine Tools:

Are powered tools used for shaping metal or other materials, by drilling holes, chiseling, grinding, pressing or cutting. Often the material (the work piece) is moved while the tool stays still (lathe), or vice versa, the work piece stays while the tool moves (mill).
Most common machine tools are: Mill, Lathe, Saw, Broach, Punch press, Grind, Bore and Stamp break.

CNC

Computer Numerical Control is the automation of machine tools that are operated by precisely programmed commands encoded on a storage medium, as opposed to controlled manually via hand wheels or levers, or mechanically automated via cams alone. Most CNC today is computer numerical control in which computers play an integral part of the control.

3D Printing

All methods work by working in layers, adding material, etc. different to other techniques, which are subtractive. Support is needed because almost all methods could support multi material printing, but it is currently only available in certain top tier machines.

A method of turning digital shapes into physical objects. Due to its nature, it allows us to accurately control the shape of the product. The drawback is size restraints and materials are often not durable.

While FDM doesn't seem like the best method for instrument manufacturing, it is one of the cheapest and most universally available methods.

EDM
Electric Discharge Machining.

FDM
Fused Deposition Modeling.

SLA
Stereo Lithography.

SLS
Selective Laser Sintering.

SLM
Selective Laser Melting.

J-P
Jetted Photopolymer (or Polyjet)

Newton's Law:

1. Every object remains stopped or goes on moving at a steady rate in a straight line unless acted upon by another force. This is the inertia principle.
2. The amount of force needed to make an object change its speed depends on the mass of the object and the amount of the acceleration or deceleration required.
3. To every action there is an equal and opposite reaction. When a body is pushed on way by a force, another force pushes back with equal strength.

Polymers:

A polymer is made of one or more large molecules formed from thousands of smaller molecules. Rubber and Wood are natural polymers. Plastics are synthetic (artificially made) polymers.

Speed and Velocity:

- Speed is the rate at which a moving object changes position (how far it moves in a fixed time).
- Velocity is speed in a particular direction.
- If either speed or direction is changed, velocity also changed.

Absorbed
A feature, sketch, or annotation that is contained in another item (usually a feature) in the FeatureManager design tree. Examples are the profile sketch and profile path in a base-sweep, or a cosmetic thread annotation in a hole.

Align
Tools that assist in lining up annotations and dimensions (left, right, top, bottom, and so on). For aligning parts in an assembly.

Alternate position view
A drawing view in which one or more views are superimposed in phantom lines on the original view. Alternate position views are often used to show range of motion of an assembly.

Anchor point
The end of a leader that attaches to the note, block, or other annotation. Sheet formats contain anchor points for a bill of materials, a hole table, a revision table, and a weldment cut list.

Annotation
A text note or a symbol that adds specific design intent to a part, assembly, or drawing. Specific types of annotations include note, hole callout, surface finish symbol, datum feature symbol, datum target, geometric tolerance symbol, weld symbol, balloon, and stacked balloon. Annotations that apply only to drawings include center mark, annotation centerline, area hatch, and block.

Appearance callouts
Callouts that display the colors and textures of the face, feature, body, and part under the entity selected and are a shortcut to editing colors and textures.

Area hatch
A crosshatch pattern or fill applied to a selected face or to a closed sketch in a drawing.

Assembly
A document in which parts, features, and other assemblies (sub-assemblies) are mated together. The parts and sub-assemblies exist in documents separate from the assembly. For example, in an assembly, a piston can be mated to other parts, such as a connecting rod or cylinder. This new assembly can then be used as a sub-assembly in an assembly of an engine. The extension for a SOLIDWORKS assembly file name is .SLDASM.

Attachment point
The end of a leader that attaches to the model (to an edge, vertex, or face, for example) or to a drawing sheet.

Axis
A straight line that can be used to create model geometry, features, or patterns. An axis can be made in a number of different ways, including using the intersection of two planes.

Balloon
Labels parts in an assembly, typically including item numbers and quantity. In drawings, the item numbers are related to rows in a bill of materials.

Base
The first solid feature of a part.

Baseline dimensions
Sets of dimensions measured from the same edge or vertex in a drawing.

Bend
A feature in a sheet metal part. A bend generated from a filleted corner, cylindrical face, or conical face is a round bend; a bend generated from sketched straight lines is a sharp bends.

Bill of materials
A table inserted into a drawing to keep a record of the parts used in an assembly.

Block
A user-defined annotation that you can use in parts, assemblies, and drawings. A block can contain text, sketch entities (except points), and area hatch, and it can be saved in a file for later use as, for example, a custom callout or a company logo.

Bottom-up assembly
An assembly modeling technique where you create parts and then insert them into an assembly.

Broken-out section
A drawing view that exposes inner details of a drawing view by removing material from a closed profile, usually a spline.

Cavity
The mold half that holds the cavity feature of the design part.

Center mark
A cross that marks the center of a circle or arc.

Centerline
A centerline marks, in phantom font, an axis of symmetry in a sketch or drawing.

Chamfer
Bevels a selected edge or vertex. You can apply chamfers to both sketches and features.

Child
A dependent feature related to a previously-built feature. For example, a chamfer on the edge of a hole is a child of the parent hole.

Click-release
As you sketch, if you click and then release the pointer, you are in click-release mode. Move the pointer and click again to define the next point in the sketch sequence.

Click-drag
As you sketch, if you click and drag the pointer, you are in click-drag mode. When you release the pointer, the sketch entity is complete.

Closed profile
Also called a closed contour, it is a sketch or sketch entity with no exposed endpoints; for example, a circle or polygon.

Collapse
The opposite of explode. The collapse action returns an exploded assembly's parts to their normal positions.

Collision Detection
An assembly function that detects collisions between components when components move or rotate. A collision occurs when an entity on one component coincides with any entity on another component.

Component
Any part or sub-assembly within an assembly

Configuration
A variation of a part or assembly within a single document. Variations can include different dimensions, features, and properties. For example, a single part such as a bolt can contain different configurations that vary the diameter and length.

ConfigurationManager
Located on the left side of the SOLIDWORKS window, it is a means to create, select, and view the configurations of parts and assemblies.

Constraint
The relations between sketch entities, or between sketch entities and planes, axes, edges, or vertices.

Construction geometry
The characteristic of a sketch entity that the entity is used in creating other geometry but is not itself used in creating features.

Coordinate system
A system of planes used to assign Cartesian coordinates to features, parts, and assemblies. Part and assembly documents contain default coordinate systems; other coordinate systems can be defined with reference geometry. Coordinate systems can be used with measurement tools and for exporting documents to other file formats.

Cosmetic thread
An annotation that represents threads.

Crosshatch
A pattern (or fill) applied to drawing views such as section views and broken-out sections.

Curvature
Curvature is equal to the inverse of the radius of the curve. The curvature can be displayed in different colors according to the local radius (usually of a surface).

Cut
A feature that removes material from a part by such actions as extrude, revolve, loft, sweep, thicken, cavity, and so on.

Dangling
A dimension, relation, or drawing section view that is unresolved. For example, if a piece of geometry is dimensioned, and that geometry is later deleted, the dimension becomes dangling.

Degrees of freedom
Geometry that is not defined by dimensions or relations is free to move. In 2D sketches, there are three degrees of freedom: movement along the X and Y axes, and rotation about the Z axis (the axis normal to the sketch plane). In 3D sketches and in assemblies, there are six degrees of freedom: movement along the X, Y, and Z axes, and rotation about the X, Y, and Z axes.

Derived part
A derived part is a new base, mirror, or component part created directly from an existing part and linked to the original part such that changes to the original part are reflected in the derived part.

Derived sketch
A copy of a sketch, in either the same part or the same assembly that is connected to the original sketch. Changes in the original sketch are reflected in the derived sketch.

Design Library
Located in the Task Pane, the Design Library provides a central location for reusable elements such as parts, assemblies, and so on.

Design table
An Excel spreadsheet that is used to create multiple configurations in a part or assembly document.

Detached drawing
A drawing format that allows opening and working in a drawing without loading the corresponding models into memory. The models are loaded on an as-needed basis.

Detail view
A portion of a larger view, usually at a larger scale than the original view.

Dimension line
A linear dimension line references the dimension text to extension lines indicating the entity being measured. An angular dimension line references the dimension text directly to the measured object.

DimXpertManager
Located on the left side of the SOLIDWORKS window, it is a means to manage dimensions and tolerances created using DimXpert for parts according to the requirements of the ASME Y.14.41-2003 standard.

DisplayManager
The DisplayManager lists the appearances, decals, lights, scene, and cameras applied to the current model. From the DisplayManager, you can view applied content, and add, edit, or delete items. When PhotoView 360 is added in, the DisplayManager also provides access to PhotoView options.

Document
A file containing a part, assembly, or drawing.

Draft
The degree of taper or angle of a face, usually applied to molds or castings.

Drawing
A 2D representation of a 3D part or assembly. The extension for a SOLIDWORKS drawing file name is .SLDDRW.

Drawing sheet
A page in a drawing document.

Driven dimension
Measurements of the model, but they do not drive the model and their values cannot be changed.

Driving dimension
Also referred to as a model dimension, it sets the value for a sketch entity. It can also control distance, thickness, and feature parameters.

Edge
A single outside boundary of a feature.

Edge flange
A sheet metal feature that combines a bend and a tab in a single operation.

Equation
Creates a mathematical relation between sketch dimensions, using dimension names as variables, or between feature parameters, such as the depth of an extruded feature or the instance count in a pattern.

Exploded view
Shows an assembly with its components separated from one another, usually to show how to assemble the mechanism.

Export
Save a SOLIDWORKS document in another format for use in other CAD/CAM, rapid prototyping, web, or graphics software applications.

Extension line
The line extending from the model indicating the point from which a dimension is measured.

Extrude
A feature that linearly projects a sketch to either add material to a part (in a base or boss) or remove material from a part (in a cut or hole).

Face
A selectable area (planar or otherwise) of a model or surface with boundaries that help define the shape of the model or surface. For example, a rectangular solid has six faces.

Fasteners
A SOLIDWORKS Toolbox library that adds fasteners automatically to holes in an assembly.

Feature
An individual shape that, combined with other features, makes up a part or assembly. Some features, such as bosses and cuts, originate as sketches. Other features, such as shells and fillets, modify a feature's geometry. However, not all features have associated geometry. Features are always listed in the FeatureManager design tree.

FeatureManager design tree
Located on the left side of the SOLIDWORKS window, it provides an outline view of the active part, assembly, or drawing.

Fill
A solid area hatch or crosshatch. Fill also applies to patches on surfaces.

Fillet
An internal rounding of a corner or edge in a sketch, or an edge on a surface or solid.

Forming tool
Dies that bend, stretch, or otherwise form sheet metal to create such form features as louvers, lances, flanges, and ribs.

Fully defined
A sketch where all lines and curves in the sketch, and their positions, are described by dimensions or relations, or both, and cannot be moved. Fully defined sketch entities are shown in black.

Geometric tolerance
A set of standard symbols that specify the geometric characteristics and dimensional requirements of a feature.

Graphics area
The area in the SOLIDWORKS window where the part, assembly, or drawing appears.

Guide curve
A 2D or 3D curve used to guide a sweep or loft.

Handle
An arrow, square, or circle that you can drag to adjust the size or position of an entity (a feature, dimension, or sketch entity, for example).

Helix
A curve defined by pitch, revolutions, and height. A helix can be used, for example, as a path for a swept feature cutting threads in a bolt.

Hem
A sheet metal feature that folds back at the edge of a part. A hem can be open, closed, double, or tear-drop.

HLR
(Hidden lines removed) a view mode in which all edges of the model that are not visible from the current view angle are removed from the display.

HLV
(Hidden lines visible) A view mode in which all edges of the model that are not visible from the current view angle are shown gray or dashed.

Import
Open files from other CAD software applications into a SOLIDWORKS document.

In-context feature
A feature with an external reference to the geometry of another component; the in-context feature changes automatically if the geometry of the referenced model or feature changes.

Inference
The system automatically creates (infers) relations between dragged entities (sketched entities, annotations, and components) and other entities and geometry. This is useful when positioning entities relative to one another.

Instance
An item in a pattern or a component in an assembly that occurs more than once. Blocks are inserted into drawings as instances of block definitions.

Interference detection
A tool that displays any interference between selected components in an assembly.

Jog
A sheet metal feature that adds material to a part by creating two bends from a sketched line.

Knit
A tool that combines two or more faces or surfaces into one. The edges of the surfaces must be adjacent and not overlapping, but they cannot ever be planar. There is no difference in the appearance of the face or the surface after knitting.

Layout sketch
A sketch that contains important sketch entities, dimensions, and relations. You reference the entities in the layout sketch when creating new sketches, building new geometry, or positioning components in an assembly. This allows for easier updating of your model because changes you make to the layout sketch propagate to the entire model.

Leader
A solid line from an annotation (note, dimension, and so on) to the referenced feature.

Library feature
A frequently used feature, or combination of features, that is created once and then saved for future use.

Lightweight
A part in an assembly or a drawing has only a subset of its model data loaded into memory. The remaining model data is loaded on an as-needed basis. This improves performance of large and complex assemblies.

Line
A straight sketch entity with two endpoints. A line can be created by projecting an external entity such as an edge, plane, axis, or sketch curve into the sketch.

Loft
A base, boss, cut, or surface feature created by transitions between profiles.

Lofted bend
A sheet metal feature that produces a roll form or a transitional shape from two open profile sketches. Lofted bends often create funnels and chutes.

Mass properties
A tool that evaluates the characteristics of a part or an assembly such as volume, surface area, centroid, and so on.

Mate
A geometric relationship, such as coincident, perpendicular, tangent, and so on, between parts in an assembly.

Mate reference
Specifies one or more entities of a component to use for automatic mating. When you drag a component with a mate reference into an assembly, the software tries to find other combinations of the same mate reference name and mate type.

Mates folder
A collection of mates that are solved together. The order in which the mates appear within the Mates folder does not matter.

Mirror
(a) A mirror feature is a copy of a selected feature, mirrored about a plane or planar face.
(b) A mirror sketch entity is a copy of a selected sketch entity that is mirrored about a centerline.

Miter flange
A sheet metal feature that joins multiple edge flanges together and miters the corner.

Model
3D solid geometry in a part or assembly document. If a part or assembly document contains multiple configurations, each configuration is a separate model.

Model dimension
A dimension specified in a sketch or a feature in a part or assembly document that defines some entity in a 3D model.

Model item
A characteristic or dimension of feature geometry that can be used in detailing drawings.

Model view
A drawing view of a part or assembly.

Mold
A set of manufacturing tooling used to shape molten plastic or other material into a designed part. You design the mold using a sequence of integrated tools that result in cavity and core blocks that are derived parts of the part to be molded.

Motion Study
Motion Studies are graphical simulations of motion and visual properties with assembly models. Analogous to a configuration, they do not actually change the original assembly model or its properties. They display the model as it changes based on simulation elements you add.

Multibody part
A part with separate solid bodies within the same part document. Unlike the components in an assembly, multibody parts are not dynamic.

Native format
DXF and DWG files remain in their original format (are not converted into SOLIDWORKS format) when viewed in SOLIDWORKS drawing sheets (view only).

Open profile
Also called an open contour, it is a sketch or sketch entity with endpoints exposed. For example, a U-shaped profile is open.

Ordinate dimensions
A chain of dimensions measured from a zero ordinate in a drawing or sketch.

Origin
The model origin appears as three gray arrows and represents the (0,0,0) coordinate of the model. When a sketch is active, a sketch origin appears in red and represents the (0,0,0) coordinate of the sketch. Dimensions and relations can be added to the model origin, but not to a sketch origin.

Out-of-context feature
A feature with an external reference to the geometry of another component that is not open.

Over defined
A sketch is over defined when dimensions or relations are either in conflict or redundant.

Parameter
A value used to define a sketch or feature (often a dimension).

Parent
An existing feature upon which other features depend. For example, in a block with a hole, the block is the parent to the child hole feature.

Part
A single 3D object made up of features. A part can become a component in an assembly, and it can be represented in 2D in a drawing. Examples of parts are bolt, pin, plate, and so on. The extension for a SOLIDWORKS part file name is .SLDPRT.

Path
A sketch, edge, or curve used in creating a sweep or loft.

Pattern
A pattern repeats selected sketch entities, features, or components in an array, which can be linear, circular, or sketch-driven. If the seed entity is changed, the other instances in the pattern update.

Physical Dynamics
An assembly tool that displays the motion of assembly components in a realistic way. When you drag a component, the component applies a force to other components it touches. Components move only within their degrees of freedom.

Pierce relation
Makes a sketch point coincident to the location at which an axis, edge, line, or spline pierces the sketch plane.

Planar
Entities that can lie on one plane. For example, a circle is planar, but a helix is not.

Plane
Flat construction geometry. Planes can be used for a 2D sketch, section view of a model, a neutral plane in a draft feature, and others.

Point
A singular location in a sketch, or a projection into a sketch at a single location of an external entity (origin, vertex, axis, or point in an external sketch).

Predefined view
A drawing view in which the view position, orientation, and so on can be specified before a model is inserted. You can save drawing documents with predefined views as templates.

Profile
A sketch entity used to create a feature (such as a loft) or a drawing view (such as a detail view). A profile can be open (such as a U shape or open spline) or closed (such as a circle or closed spline).

Projected dimension
If you dimension entities in an isometric view, projected dimensions are the flat dimensions in 2D.

Projected view
A drawing view projected orthogonally from an existing view.

PropertyManager
Located on the left side of the SOLIDWORKS window, it is used for dynamic editing of sketch entities and most features.

RealView graphics
A hardware (graphics card) support of advanced shading in real time; the rendering applies to the model and is retained as you move or rotate a part.

Rebuild
Tool that updates (or regenerates) the document with any changes made since the last time the model was rebuilt. Rebuild is typically used after changing a model dimension.

Reference dimension
A dimension in a drawing that shows the measurement of an item, but cannot drive the model and its value cannot be modified. When model dimensions change, reference dimensions update.

Reference geometry
Includes planes, axes, coordinate systems, and 3D curves. Reference geometry is used to assist in creating features such lofts, sweeps, drafts, chamfers, and patterns.

Relation
A geometric constraint between sketch entities or between a sketch entity and a plane, axis, edge, or vertex. Relations can be added automatically or manually.

Relative view
A relative (or relative to model) drawing view is created relative to planar surfaces in a part or assembly.

Reload
Refreshes shared documents. For example, if you open a part file for read-only access while another user makes changes to the same part, you can reload the new version, including the changes.

Reorder
Reordering (changing the order of) items is possible in the FeatureManager design tree. In parts, you can change the order in which features are solved. In assemblies, you can control the order in which components appear in a bill of materials.

Replace
Substitutes one or more open instances of a component in an assembly with a different component.

Resolved
A state of an assembly component (in an assembly or drawing document) in which it is fully loaded in memory. All the component's model data is available, so its entities can be selected, referenced, edited, and used in mates, and so on.

Revolve
A feature that creates a base or boss, a revolved cut, or revolved surface by revolving one or more sketched profiles around a centerline.

Rip
A sheet metal feature that removes material at an edge to allow a bend.

Rollback
Suppresses all items below the rollback bar.

Section
Another term for profile in sweeps.

Section line
A line or centerline sketched in a drawing view to create a section view.

Section scope
Specifies the components to be left uncut when you create an assembly drawing section view.

Section view
A section view (or section cut) is (1) a part or assembly view cut by a plane, or (2) a drawing view created by cutting another drawing view with a section line.

Seed
A sketch or an entity (a feature, face, or body) that is the basis for a pattern. If you edit the seed, the other entities in the pattern are updated.

Shaded
Displays a model as a colored solid.

Shared values
Also called linked values, these are named variables that you assign to set the value of two or more dimensions to be equal.

Sheet format
Includes page size and orientation, standard text, borders, title blocks, and so on. Sheet formats can be customized and saved for future use. Each sheet of a drawing document can have a different format.

Shell
A feature that hollows out a part, leaving open the selected faces and thin walls on the remaining faces. A hollow part is created when no faces are selected to be open.

Sketch
A collection of lines and other 2D objects on a plane or face that forms the basis for a feature such as a base or a boss. A 3D sketch is non-planar and can be used to guide a sweep or loft, for example.

Smart Fasteners
Automatically adds fasteners (bolts and screws) to an assembly using the SOLIDWORKS Toolbox library of fasteners.

SmartMates
An assembly mating relation that is created automatically.

Solid sweep
A cut sweep created by moving a tool body along a path to cut out 3D material from a model.

Spiral
A flat or 2D helix, defined by a circle, pitch, and number of revolutions.

Spline
A sketched 2D or 3D curve defined by a set of control points.

Split line
Projects a sketched curve onto a selected model face, dividing the face into multiple faces so that each can be selected individually. A split line can be used to create draft features, to create face blend fillets, and to radiate surfaces to cut molds.

Stacked balloon
A set of balloons with only one leader. The balloons can be stacked vertically (up or down) or horizontally (left or right).

Standard 3 views
The three orthographic views (front, right, and top) that are often the basis of a drawing.

StereoLithography
The process of creating rapid prototype parts using a faceted mesh representation in STL files.

Sub-assembly
An assembly document that is part of a larger assembly. For example, the steering mechanism of a car is a sub-assembly of the car.

Suppress
Removes an entity from the display and from any calculations in which it is involved. You can suppress features, assembly components, and so on. Suppressing an entity does not delete the entity; you can unsuppress the entity to restore it.

Surface
A zero-thickness planar or 3D entity with edge boundaries. Surfaces are often used to create solid features. Reference surfaces can be used to modify solid features.

Sweep
Creates a base, boss, cut, or surface feature by moving a profile (section) along a path. For cut-sweeps, you can create solid sweeps by moving a tool body along a path.

Tangent arc
An arc that is tangent to another entity, such as a line.

Tangent edge
The transition edge between rounded or filleted faces in hidden lines visible or hidden lines removed modes in drawings.

Task Pane
Located on the right-side of the SOLIDWORKS window, the Task Pane contains SOLIDWORKS Resources, the Design Library, and the File Explorer.

Template
A document (part, assembly, or drawing) that forms the basis of a new document. It can include user-defined parameters, annotations, predefined views, geometry, and so on.

Temporary axis
An axis created implicitly for every conical or cylindrical face in a model.

Thin feature
An extruded or revolved feature with constant wall thickness. Sheet metal parts are typically created from thin features.

TolAnalyst
A tolerance analysis application that determines the effects that dimensions and tolerances have on parts and assemblies.

Top-down design
An assembly modeling technique where you create parts in the context of an assembly by referencing the geometry of other components. Changes to the referenced components propagate to the parts that you create in context.

Triad
Three axes with arrows defining the X, Y, and Z directions. A reference triad appears in part and assembly documents to assist in orienting the viewing of models. Triads also assist when moving or rotating components in assemblies.

Under defined
A sketch is under defined when there are not enough dimensions and relations to prevent entities from moving or changing size.

Vertex
A point at which two or more lines or edges intersect. Vertices can be selected for sketching, dimensioning, and many other operations.

Viewports
Windows that display views of models. You can specify one, two, or four viewports. Viewports with orthogonal views can be linked, which links orientation and rotation.

Virtual sharp
A sketch point at the intersection of two entities after the intersection itself has been removed by a feature such as a fillet or chamfer. Dimensions and relations to the virtual sharp are retained even though the actual intersection no longer exists.

Weldment
A multibody part with structural members.

Weldment cut list
A table that tabulates the bodies in a weldment along with descriptions and lengths.

Wireframe
A view mode in which all edges of the part or assembly are displayed.

Zebra stripes
Simulate the reflection of long strips of light on a very shiny surface. They allow you to see small changes in a surface that may be hard to see with a standard display.

Zoom
To simulate movement toward or away from a part or an assembly.

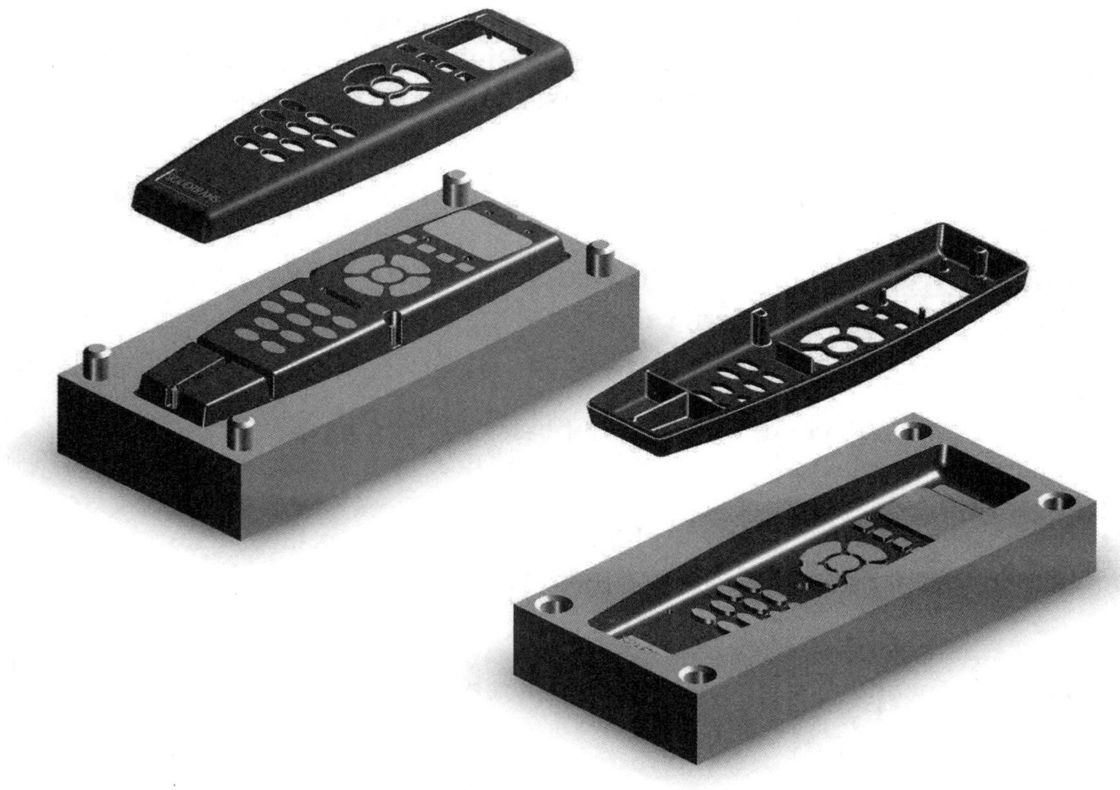

Learn Mold-Tooling Designs with SOLIDWORKS Advanced Techniques Textbook

Index

2

2D CAD, 16-1
2D sketch, 5-1, 17-7

3

3D curve, 7-1
3D drawing, 16-28
3D sketch, 5-1, 6-3, 8-16
3-point-arc, 8-14

A

add parenthesis, 16-14
add symbol, 16-15
advanced mates, 11-1
advanced shading, 7-5
align with other geometry, 9-11
alignment, 9-10, 12-10, 15-12, 16-5, 16-13
alt, 1-9, 1-12, 12-10
alt key, 12-5, 12-6, 12-7
aluminum, 15-5, 15-15, 15-16, 16-8
angle, 2-7, 5-3, 5-4, 6-9, 7-20, 11-4, 13-6, 15-22, 15-23
angularity, 15-22
animate collapse, 13-16
animation, 11-11, 13-15, 13-16
animation controller, 13-16
annotation, 15-6, 15-11, 16-10, 16-16, 16-25
ANSI, 1-2, 1-4, 2-4, 15-3, 15-4, 15-22, 16-3, 17-3
anti-aligned, 4-15
appearance, 8-22
apply, 2-16, 3-14, 9-10, 9-11, 9-13
arc length, 6-9
area hatch/fills, 16-8
ASME, 15-22, 16-18
assemblies, 2-4, 6-4, 10-3, 10-10, 11-3, 11-10, 12-6
assembly, 4-4, 11-1, 11-3, 11-6, 11-8, 11-10, 11-11, 11-12, 12-1, 12-3, 12-4, 12-6, 12-12, 12-13, 13-3, 13-4, 13-14, 14-2, 14-9, 14-11, 15-5, 16-4
assembly drawing, 15-1
assembly Motions, 11-1, 11-3
auto balloon, 15-11
auto create, 10-11
auto start projected view, 16-4

B

balloons, 15-11, 15-12
base flange, 17-4
basic, 16-23, 16-24
basic dimension, 15-22
bend angle, 6-9
bend outside, 17-6
bilateral, 16-23
bill of materials, 15-5, 15-6
blind, 2-7, 2-8, 3-6, 3-9, 3-12, 5-3, 7-16, 7-20, 9-5, 13-6, 17-12, 17-14
bodies to mirror, 4-11
body, 3-3, 3-4, 3-6, 4-4, 4-5, 4-8, 4-10, 4-11, 4-13, 4-14, 4-15, 6-3, 6-10, 7-3, 7-6, 7-8, 7-10, 7-13, 8-3, 8-5, 8-11, 8-14, 8-18, 8-21, 10-12, 12-10
bolt circle, 5-5
bom, 15-6, 15-7, 15-8
bom-standard, 15-6
boss/base, 2-7, 2-8, 3-9, 3-12, 5-3, 7-3, 7-16, 7-19, 7-20, 8-3, 8-7, 8-10, 8-11, 8-17, 9-3, 13-6, 13-10
boundaries, 8-1
boundary, 8-1, 8-3, 8-5, 8-6, 8-10, 8-11, 8-11, 8-24, 9-10, 9-11
boundary boss/base, 8-5

boundary surface, 9-10, 9-11
bounding box, 5-12, 17-19
bounding box area, 17-19
box Selection, 4-5
Break Alignment, 15-12, 16-6
browse, 4-3, 6-3, 6-8, 7-3, 8-3, 9-3, 11-3, 11-12, 12-3, 13-3, 14-4, 14-9, 15-5, 16-3, 17-11, 17-13

C

cancel, 8-9
center axis, 11-11
center of mass, 2-16
center rectangle, 3-4
centerline, 2-7, 2-9, 5-1, 5-3, 7-15, 8-15, 16-16, 16-17, 17-3
centerline parameter, 8-6, 8-7
chamfer, 5-4
circle, 1-8, 1-10, 1-11, 5-4, 5-5, 16-9
circular pattern, 2-11, 2-13
circular sketch pattern, 5-5
circularity, 15-22
click-click, 2-5
coincident, 4-9, 4-14, 4-16, 5-5, 12-4, 12-5, 12-6, 12-8
collapse, 3-15, 4-6, 4-12, 12-1, 13-16, 14-11
collinear, 17-7
collision detection, 3-1
color, 2-6, 2-10, 8-22, 8-23, 9-18, 15-10, 16-11, 17-18
column, 1-8, 1-11, 10-2, 10-4, 10-12, 15-8, 15-9
command, 6-10, 7-19, 16-17,13, 3-7, 5-7, 8-12
common points, 8-3, 8-5
concentric, 4-8, 4-14, 4-15, 11-5, 11-6, 12-4, 12-5, 12-6, 12-7, 12-8
concentricity, 15-22
configuration, 3-15, 4-6, 4-16, 10-4, 10-6, 10-7, 10-8, 10-9, 10-10, 10-12, 10-13, 10-14, 12-1, 12-10
ConfigurationManager, 3-15, 4-6, 4-12, 4-13, 4-16, 10-6, 10-11, 10-13, 12-1, 13-15
configure component, 10-1
configure dimension, 10-1
configure features, 10-1
configure material, 10-1
connector, 8-2
constant pitch, 7-17
constant radius Size, 7-9, 7-12, 9-14
constant size fillet, 2-14, 8-18, 8-21
constrained, 2-10, 4-16, 5-5, 7-1, 17-3
constraints, 3-7, 4-8, 9-10
context, 13-3, 13-14
control, 2-9, 3-8, 3-9, 3-11, 3-12, 4-5, 5-8, 5-9, 5-10, 8-6, 8-7, 8-11, 8-12, 8-14, 8-16, 9-10, 9-11, 11-11, 11-14, 12-10, 12-11, 12-12, 13-5, 16-20, 17-7, 17-11, 17-13, 17-15
control frame, 15-25, 16-19, 16-20, 16-21, 16-22
convert entities, 7-17, 7-20, 8-16, 13-5, 13-6, 13-9
copy, 1-14, 3-7, 4-7, 12-1
corner rectangle, 2-12
countersink, 16-15
crosshatch pattern, 15-1
curves, 7-3, 7-4, 7-5, 7-7, 7-17, 8-4, 8-13, 8-17, 8-22
custom property, 15-9
customize, 1-7, 1-11, 1-12, 3-7, 5-7
cut list, 17-20
cut thread, 5-8, 5-10
cut-with-surface, 7-10, 7-13
cylindricity, 15-22

D

datum target, 15-22
datum, 15-22
datums, 16-16
decimals, 1-4, 1-5, 16-23

default, 3-15, 4-6, 4-16, 10-4, 10-9, 10-10, 12-1, 12-10, 12-11, 13-16, 16-6
deform, 6-3
degrees, 4-15, 11-1, 12-6, 16-15
degrees of freedom, 11-1
delete, 1-12, 15-11
depth, 16-12, 17-4
design table, 10-3
detail view, 16-9
detail views, 15-1
detailing, 15-27
dialog Box, 10-4
dimension, 1-4, 1-9, 1-11, 2-5, 2-6, 2-7, 2-10, 2-12, 3-4, 3-5, 7-5, 7-7, 7-15, 7-18, 8-11, 8-14, 10-3, 11-4, 13-12, 14-10, 14-13, 15-22, 16-10, 16-11, 16-12, 16-15, 16-24, 17-7, 17-14, 17-16
DimXpertManager, 4-12
display mode, 13-16
display selection, 8-23
document, 1-3, 1-12, 4-3, 4-12, 5-3, 7-3, 8-1, 9-3, 9-9, 10-1, 11-3, 11-11, 11-12, 12-1, 12-3, 13-3, 13-4, 14-4, 14-7, 14-9, 14-14, 15-3, 15-5, 15-15, 17-11, 17-13
document properties, 1-1, 1-2, 1-3, 2-3
document templates, 1-1
draft, 13-6, 14-6
draft on/off, 13-6
drafting, 1-3, 15-4, 17-3
drafting standard, 2-3, 15-4
drag, 1-12, 3-7, 4-12, 5-7, 11-6, 12-4, 12-5, 12-6, 12-7, 12-10, 12-11, 12-12, 13-15, 15-12, 16-28
dragged, 1-12, 12-5, 15-5
drawing, 2-3, 15-3, 15-5, 15-10, 15-15, 16-3, 16-6, 16-10, 16-26, 16-28
drawing paper color, 15-10
drawing views, 16-4, 16-5, 16-6, 16-10
drop, 1-7, 1-12, 2-11, 3-7, 4-10, 5-4, 5-7, 7-5, 7-17, 8-15, 8-16, 11-12, 12-5, 12-6, 12-7, 12-10, 12-11, 13-5, 15-4, 15-5, 15-6, 15-10, 15-12, 15-14, 15-15, 16-4, 16-9, 16-21, 17-15
dropped, 1-12, 12-5, 15-5
dynamic clearance, 3-1

E

edge display, 8-23, 9-18
edge flange, 17-6, 17-9
edges, 2-11, 2-13, 2-14, 2-15, 5-4, 7-14, 8-4, 8-16, 8-17, 8-18, 8-19, 8-20, 8-24, 9-1, 9-9, 9-10, 13-11, 14-5, 16-6, 16-7, 16-28, 17-7
edit component, 13-5, 13-12, 14-4, 14-7, 14-9, 14-11, 14-12, 14-13
edit document units, 15-4, 17-3
edit feature, 4-16
edit flange profile, 17-7, 17-9
edit material, 2-15
edit sheet, 15-14
eDrawings, 11-11
ellipse, 7-3, 7-7, 8-7
enclosures, 16-29
end condition, 5-8, 5-9
endpoints, 2-4, 9-1
entire model, 16-10
equal spacing, 2-11, 2-13
exit, 8-9, 8-10, 8-16, 8-17, 14-11
exploded view, 3-13, 3-15, 4-4, 4-16, 11-11, 11-13, 11-14, 13-14, 13-15
external references, 13-3, 13-14
extrude cut, 2-10
extruded, 2-10, 2-13, 3-6, 3-9, 3-12, 5-6, 8-11, 9-4, 9-5, 9-6, 13-6, 13-10, 17-5, 17-12, 17-14
extruded surface, 9-4, 9-5

F

face, 2-14, 3-7, 3-10, 3-11, 4-8, 4-9, 4-11, 4-14, 5-4, 5-7, 5-8, 5-9, 7-5, 7-6, 7-7, 7-8, 7-16, 7-17, 7-19, 7-20, 8-9, 8-10, 8-18, 8-19, 8-20, 8-21, 8-22, 9-10, 9-12, 9-14, 11-8, 12-4, 12-5, 12-7, 12-11, 12-12, 12-13, 13-7, 13-8, 14-9, 14-10, 14-12,

14-13, 17-5, 17-11, 17-13, 17-14, 17-15, 17-17
face fillet, 7-6, 8-21, 9-14
fasteners, 12-13
fastening feature, 14-4, 14-9
feature control frame, 15-25
feature recognition, 4-3
FeatureManager, 1-10, 2-15, 3-1, 3-3, 4-6, 4-7, 4-11, 4-12, 9-4, 10-6, 11-12, 12-9, 14-5, 15-11, 17-17, 17-20
features, 1-14, 2-4, 2-7, 2-10, 2-13, 2-14, 3-6, 3-7, 3-9, 3-10, 3-12, 4-10, 4-11, 5-3, 5-6, 5-7, 5-9, 6-4, 6-5, 6-9, 6-10, 7-3, 7-5, 7-7, 7-14, 7-16, 7-17, 7-19, 7-20, 8-3, 8-5, 8-11, 8-17, 8-18, 8-22, 9-3, 9-14, 10-3, 10-12, 11-1, 13-6, 13-7, 13-10, 17-17
file explorer, 17-15
filled surface, 9-12, 9-13
fillet, 2-14, 5-4, 7-6, 7-9, 7-12, 7-14, 8-18, 8-21, 9-14, 13-7, 13-11
fixture, 9-1, 12-2, 12-3
flat display, 17-18
flat head screw, 11-12
flat pattern, 17-19
flatness, 15-23, 16-18
flex bending, 6-1, 6-3, 6-6, 6-7, 6-8, 7-1
flex examples, 6-6
flex features, 6-1, 6-3
flex stretching, 6-1, 6-6
flex tapering, 6-1, 6-7
flex twisting, 6-1, 6-6
flexible, 11-3, 11-10
flip direction, 16-8
flip mate alignment, 12-11, 12-12
flip offset, 7-17
for construction, 5-4
form examples, 15-17
formula bar, 10-12
Free, 11-4
free state, 15-23
front plane, 1-10, 2-4, 3-3, 3-10, 7-5, 7-7, 7-9, 7-11, 7-15, 17-3
full preview, 7-10
fully define, 2-7, 2-12, 3-5, 5-5, 7-5, 7-7, 7-16, 7-18, 8-12, 8-14, 8-16, 12-8, 17-3, 17-16

G

Gap, 14-6
GD&T, 5-6, 15-18, 16-19
gear mate, 11-9, 11-7
general notes, 16-25
geometric dimensioning & tolerancing, 15-18, 15-21
geometric tolerance, 16-18, 16-20, 16-21
geometry, 5-4, 8-16, 9-1, 13-3, 16-28
guide curve, 7-1, 8-10

H

hard edge, 6-4
hatch pattern, 16-8
heads-up, 5-11, 9-17, 13-11
helix, 7-17, 7-19
helix/spiral, 7-17
hide, 6-10, 7-8, 7-11, 7-13, 13-4, 13-8
hide/show, 6-10
high quality, 8-5
hold line, 7-6
hole callouts, 16-10
hole wizard, 16-10
holes, 5-4, 5-5, 11-12, 11-13, 12-8, 16-13
horizontal, 2-5, 2-7, 2-8, 2-9, 3-4, 4-17, 5-3, 7-5, 8-9, 8-11, 16-5, 16-6, 16-16, 16-17
hotkey, 1-8, 1-9, 5-9

I

image quality, 1-3, 1-6
in context, 16-29
inch die, 5-8, 5-10
inferencing, 2-4

insert, 3-6, 3-13, 4-4, 4-7, 4-13, 4-15, 5-7, 5-9, 6-4, 6-5, 6-9, 8-15, 10-11, 13-5, 14-4, 14-9, 14-12, 15-8, 16-13, 16-14, 16-15
insert component, 13-5
instances, 2-11, 2-13, 3-9, 3-12, 5-5, 11-13, 11-14
intersection zone, 5-12
intersections, 2-4
isometric view, 5-9, 15-1, 15-12, 15-13
isometric view, 3-9, 3-12, 8-6, 16-5

K

keep selections, 9-6, 9-7, 9-8
keyboard, 1-7, 1-11, 1-12
keyboard shortcuts, 1-7
knit surface, 7-9, 7-12

L

least material condition, 15-23
library feature, 17-13, 17-15
limit, 11-7, 16-23, 16-24
limit mates, 11-7
limit angle, 11-7
line, 1-8, 1-10, 2-5, 2-8, 7-3, 7-5, 7-6, 7-7, 7-15, 8-7, 8-12, 8-13, 8-22, 16-7
linear, 3-9, 3-12, 11-1, 12-4
linear pattern, 3-9, 3-12
link to thickness, 17-13
lip & groove, 14-1, 14-2
location examples, 15-20
loft, 8-1, 8-3, 8-10, 8-11, 8-24, 9-9
loft profile, 8-17
lofted boss/base, 8-3
loft-profiles, 8-4

M

make drawing, 16-3
manipulating, 6-3
marked for drawing, 16-10
mass, 2-16
mass properties, 2-16
mate alignment, 12-2
material, 2-15, 9-16, 10-12, 14-5, 16-8, 16-19, 16-26, 17-9
material inside, 9-16, 17-9
mates, 4-1, 4-15, 11-1, 11-3, 11-5, 11-8, 11-9, 12-2, 12-4, 12-5, 12-6, 12-8, 13-5
mating face, 14-13
maximum material condition, 15-23
mechanical mates, 11-2
mechanical mates, 11-9
merge entities, 7-9, 7-12, 9-16
merge result, 3-9, 8-12, 8-13
merge solids, 4-11
Microsoft Excel, 10-10, 10-11
mid Plane, 4-10, 8-11, 8-12, 9-4, 9-5, 17-4
midpoint, 2-4, 17-12, 17-14
mirror, 2-9, 3-10, 4-11, 7-18, 8-17, 8-18, 17-3, 17-17
mirror body, 4-11
mirror Entities, 2-9
mirror plane, 4-10
mirroring, 2-9, 3-10, 17-17
model dimensions, 16-10
model item, 16-10, 16-12, 16-13
modify, 10-1
modify sketch, 1-13
more symbols, 16-15
mounting boss, 14-8, 14-9, 14-12
mounting bosses, 14-8, 14-11, 14-14
move component, 3-1
move, 1-14, 4-7
move/copy, 1-14, 3-6, 3-7
multibody parts, 3-1, 3-16
mutual, 9-7

N

natural, 9-6, 9-7, 9-8
neutral plane, 6-9

new column, 15-8
new sketch, 1-10, 2-4, 2-7, 2-8, 2-12, 3-8, 5-4, 7-5, 7-7, 7-15, 7-17, 7-18, 7-19, 7-20, 8-9, 8-11, 8-12, 8-14, 8-15, 13-5, 13-8, 13-9, 17-3, 17-5, 17-12, 17-14
normal cut, 17-12, 17-14
nose, 8-9, 8-10, 8-11, 8-11
note, 7-4, 7-14, 11-4, 16-16, 16-25
novice, 2-3

O

offset, 5-8, 5-9, 7-8, 7-16, 7-17, 13-10
offset entities, 13-9
offset surface, 7-8, 7-11
optimize surface, 9-13, 9-14
orientation examples, 15-19
origin, 2-5, 3-4, 6-9, 7-15, 13-4

P

parallel mates, 11-7
paralellism, 15-23
parameters, 7-6, 7-10, 7-17, 10-2, 14-5, 14-9
parametric models, 13-1
parent, 2-4, 2-7, 12-6, 13-1
parent sketch, 2-4
part, 1-3, 1-6, 1-7, 2-3, 3-3, 4-7, 4-8, 4-13, 4-14, 4-15, 4-16, 6-3, 6-8, 8-24, 9-18, 13-4, 13-5, 13-16, 14-9, 15-5, 15-9, 16-3, 16-26, 17-3, 17-13, 17-15
part document, 1-3, 1-6, 1-7, 2-3, 2-4, 3-3, 4-3, 4-7, 4-13, 5-3, 6-3, 6-8, 7-3, 8-3, 9-3, 10-3, 13-3, 16-3, 17-3
part template, 1-6
partial section, 16-7, 16-8, 16-13
partno, 15-10
patches, 9-1, 9-3
path, 5-7, 7-1, 7-4, 8-7
pattern driven component, 11-12
pencil, 1-10, 2-4, 3-3
per standard, 16-10
percent, 11-4
perpendicular, 16-19
perpendicularity, 15-23
phantom line, 16-6
physical, 2-15
pierce, 7-18, 8-16
pin boss, 14-10, 14-12
pitch and revolution, 7-17
planar face, 4-9, 7-19
plane, 3-10, 4-10, 4-11, 7-16, 8-15, 8-18, 17-15, 17-17
position, 6-5, 14-9, 14-10, 14-12, 15-22, 16-18, 16-21, 16-22, 17-6
preview sections, 7-4
principal, 2-16
profile, 2-7, 3-4, 5-7, 7-1, 7-4, 7-15, 7-18, 8-7, 8-11, 8-12, 8-14, 8-15, 8-16, 8-17, 15-23, 16-24, 17-3, 17-6, 17-7, 17-8
profile examples, 15-19
profile of any line, 15-23
profile of any surface, 15-23
projected tolerance zone, 15-24
projected view, 16-5, 16-14
projection, 7-5, 7-7, 8-13, 8-22, 15-3, 16-4
PropertyManagers, 16-15
pull down menu, 8-13, 16-3

Q

quick snap, 2-1

R

radial explode, 11-11, 12-1
radial step, 11-13, 11-14
ratio, 11-9
RealView Graphics, 2-16, 7-4, 7-5, 10-14, 14-2
rebuild, 13-13
recessed, 7-14
reciprocate, 13-16
rectangle, 1-9, 1-11, 3-4, 3-8, 3-11, 17-5

reference dimension, 2-6
reference geometry, 4-10, 7-16, 8-15
regardless of feature size, 15-23, 15-24
relations, 2-4, 2-7, 2-10, 2-12, 5-5, 8-11, 8-12, 8-16, 17-3, 17-7, 17-8
remove, 8-23, 9-18, 13-7, 13-16
rename, 10-9
reverse, 2-10, 5-8, 5-9, 7-8, 7-11, 7-18, 8-22, 11-9, 13-6, 13-10
revolved, 2-8, 5-1, 5-3, 7-16, 7-20
revolved cut, 5-1
revolving, 2-7, 2-8, 7-16, 7-20
right plane, 5-11, 7-18, 8-12, 8-14, 8-15, 8-18, 14-6, 14-14, 17-17
right-hand thread, 5-8, 5-10
rigid, 11-3
rings, 6-4, 6-5
rotational motion, 11-1
row height, 15-7
ruled surface, 7-8
runout, 15-23
runout examples, 15-20

S

save table, 10-4, 10-6, 10-7, 10-8
scene reflections, 7-5
search, 1-8, 1-9
section view, 9-17, 9-18, 13-11, 14-6, 14-14, 15-1, 16-8, 16-13
select tangency, 13-5, 13-8, 13-11
selection, 4-5, 8-13, 9-18, 11-4, 12-4, 13-16, 14-5
SelectionManager, 8-4, 8-5
self-shadowing, 7-5
shaded with edges, 8-23
sheet format, 15-3, 15-13, 15-14, 15-16, 16-4, 16-26, 17-4, 17-5, 17-12, 17-14, 17-15, 17-19, 17-20
sheet metal, 16-29
shell, 7-14, 7-15, 13-7
shift, 1-9, 5-9, 7-15
show component, 13-11
sketch, 1-13, 2-3, 2-4, 2-5, 2-6, 2-7, 2-12, 3-5, 3-8, 3-11, 5-4, 5-5, 7-5, 7-6, 7-7, 7-15, 7-18, 8-11, 8-12, 8-13, 8-15, 8-16, 8-17, 8-22, 9-3, 16-7, 16-9, 17-3, 17-5, 17-9, 17-11, 17-12, 17-14, 17-15
sketch entities, 2-4, 2-9, 2-10, 6-3, 8-11, 13-9, 17-3, 17-8
sketch snap, 2-1
smart dimension, 2-5, 2-10, 16-11
smart mate symbols, 12-6
smart mates, 12-1
snap hook, 14-8
socket head cap screw, 11-13
solar, 8-21, 8-22
solid bodies, 3-1,40, 4-6, 4-7, 4-11, 7-8
solid feature, 8-1, 8-3
solid library feature part, 17-13
spacing, 3-12, 5-5, 6-10, 14-6
split line, 7-5, 7-6, 7-7, 8-13, 8-21
stainless steel, 2-15
standard mates, 11-1
standard sheet size, 15-3
standard trim, 9-6
standards, 1-4, 15-3, 15-4, 15-24
status, 2-4, 12-9
status of the sketch, 2-10
steel, 2-15, 17-4
straightness, 15-24
straight slot, 3-5
sub assembly, 11-10
support, 7-5, 8-7, 8-19
suppress, 10-6
suppression state, 10-4
surface feature, 8-1, 8-3
surface finish, 16-15
surfaces, 7-8, 7-10, 9-1, 9-3, 9-6, 9-8, 9-10, 9-11, 9-12, 9-13, 9-15
sweep, 7-1, 7-3, 7-19, 9-3
sweep boss/base, 7-1, 7-19
swept cut, 7-1
swept surface, 7-1, 9-3
symbols description, 15-22
symmetric, 2-9, 7-18, 16-22, 16-23, 17-3

symmetry, 15-24
system options, 2-3

T

table, 10-3, 10-4, 10-6, 10-7, 10-8, 10-10, 10-11, 10-12, 10-13, 15-6
tail, 8-11, 8-12, 8-19
tangent, 2-8, 2-9, 2-14, 7-16, 8-23, 8-24, 9-10, 9-11, 9-13, 9-18, 13-16, 16-7
tangent arc, 2-8
tangent edges remove, 8-23, 13-16
tangent edges with font, 16-7
tangent to face, 9-10
tangent weight, 9-10, 9-11
taper to vector, 7-8
temporary axis, 6-10
thicken, 9-16
thin feature, 5-1
third angle, 15-3, 16-4
threads, 5-7, 5-8, 5-9, 5-11, 7-15, 7-16, 7-19
through all, 2-10, 2-13
through all both, 2-13
title block, 15-13, 16-26
toggle flat display, 17-18
toggled, 4-4
tool buttons, 1-12
toolbar, 1-12, 1-13, 1-14, 2-5, 5-7, 5-11, 9-17, 11-13, 12-5, 12-11, 12-12, 13-11, 13-16
tools, 1-3, 1-12, 2-3, 3-7, 5-7, 9-18, 12-4
top down assembly, 13-1, 14-2, 14-8
top plane, 2-7, 2-12, 5-11, 8-11, 13-5, 13-12, 14-12
topology, 9-1
training Files, 4-3, 6-3, 6-8, 7-3, 9-3, 11-3, 11-12, 12-3
transitioning, 2-8
transitions, 8-3
translate/rotate, 3-7
triad, 2-16, 3-13, 6-5, 6-9, 6-3, 6-8, 13-15
trim, 6-4, 6-5, 6-9, 8-9, 9-1, 17-8
trim planes, 6-4
trim surface, 9-6, 9-7
trimmed surface, 9-5, 9-6, 9-7
true position, 15-24, 16-20, 16-21
twisting, 8-2, 8-4, 8-5, 9-10, 9-12
type of split, 7-5, 8-13

U

unit, 1-5
unsuppressed, 10-4
up to surface, 5-8
up to vertex, 17-5, 17-6
up to next, 5-6
use document font, 15-7

V

vents, 14-8, 17-11
vertical, 2-5, 2-8, 3-4, 3-5, 3-8, 3-11, 7-7, 7-15, 8-12, 8-15, 13-15, 16-5, 16-7, 16-16, 16-18, 17-3, 17-7, 17-8
vertices, 9-1, 12-4
view alignment, 16-13
view layout, 16-7
view palette, 15-5, 15-12, 16-4
virtual sharp, 1-5
visual, 2-15

W

wall thickness, 7-15, 9-18
weld symbols, 16-15
welding, 9-1
width mate, 11-4
wing, 8-6, 8-7, 8-18, 8-19, 8-23, 11-4, 11-6
wireframe, 1-6, 5-8, 5-10, 12-4

X

x, 10-13, 15-14, 15-15

Y

y145-2009, 15-25

Z

zonal section view, 5-11

SOLIDWORKS Quick-Guide

Quick Reference Guide To SOLIDWORKS Command Icons & Toolbars

The STANDARD Toolbar

- Creates a new document.
- Opens an existing document.
- Saves an active document.
- Make Drawing from Part/Assembly
- Make Assembly from Part/Assembly
- Prints the active document.
- Print preview
- Cuts the selection & puts it on the clipboard.
- Copies the selection & puts it on the clipboard.
- Inserts the clipboard contents.
- Deletes the selection.
- Reverses the last action.
- Rebuilds the part / assembly / drawing.
- Redo the last action that was undone.
- Saves all documents.
- Edits material.
- Closes an existing document
- Shows or hides the Selection Filter toolbar.
- Shows or hides the Web toolbar.
- Properties.
- File properties

The STANDARD Toolbar (Cont.)

- Loads or unloads the 3D instant website add-in
- Select tool.
- Select the entire document.
- Checks read-only files.
- Options.
- Help
- Full screen view.
- OK.
- Cancel.
- Magnified selection.

The SKETCH TOOLS Toolbar

- Select
- Sketch
- 3D Sketch
- Sketches a rectangle from the center.
- Sketches a centerpoint arc slot.
- Sketches a 3-point arc slot.
- Sketches a straight slot.
- Sketches a centerpoint straight slot.
- Sketches a 3-point arc.
- Creates sketched ellipses.

SOLIDWORKS Quick-Guide

Standard & Sketch toolbar

The SKETCH TOOLS Toolbar

- 3D sketch on plane.
- Sets up Grid parameters.
- Creates a sketch on a selected plane or face.
- Equation driven curve
- Modifies a sketch.
- Copies sketch entities.
- Scales sketch entities.
- Rotates sketch entities.
- Sketches 3 point rectangle from the center.
- Sketches 3 point corner rectangle.
- Sketches a line.
- Creates a center point arc: center, start, end.
- Creates an arc tangent to a line.
- Sketches splines on a surface or face.
- Sketches a circle.
- Sketches a circle by its perimeter.
- Makes a path of sketch entities.
- Mirrors entities dynamically about a
- Insert a plane into the 3D sketch.
- Instant 2D.
- Sketch numeric input.
- Detaches segment on drag.
- Sketch picture

The SKETCH TOOLS Toolbar (Cont.)

- Partial ellipses.
- Adds a Parabola.
- Adds a spline.
- Sketches a polygon.
- Sketches a corner rectangle.
- Sketches a parallelogram.
- Creates points.
- Creates sketched centerlines.
- Adds text to sketch.
- Converts selected model edges or sketch entities to sketch segments.
- Creates a sketch along the intersection of multiple bodies.
- Converts face curves on the selected face into 3D sketch entities.
- Mirrors selected segments about a centerline.
- Fillets the corner of two lines.
- Creates a chamfer between two sketch entities.
- Creates a sketch curve by offsetting model edges or sketch entities at a specified distance.
- Trims a sketch segment.
- Extends a sketch segment.
- Splits a sketch segment.
- Construction Geometry.
- Creates linear steps and repeat of sketch entities.
- Creates circular steps and repeat of sketch entities.

Quick Reference Guide To SOLIDWORKS Command Icons & Toolbars

The SHEET METAL

- Add a bend from a selected sketch in a Sheet Metal part.
- Shows flat pattern for this sheet metal part.
- Shows part without inserting any bends.
- Inserts a rip feature to a sheet metal part.
- Create a Sheet Metal part or add material to existing Sheet Metal part
- Inserts a Sheet Metal Miter Flange feature.
- Folds selected bends.
- Unfolds selected bends.
- Inserts bends using a sketch line.
- Inserts a flange by pulling an edge.
- Inserts a sheet metal corner feature.
- Inserts a Hem feature by selecting edges.
- Breaks a corner by filleting/chamfering it.
- Inserts a Jog feature using a sketch line.
- Inserts a lofted bend feature using 2 sketches.
- Creates inverse dent on a sheet metal part.
- Trims out material from a corner, in a sheet metal
- Inserts a fillet weld bead.
- Converts a solid/surface into a sheet metal part.
- Adds a Cross Break feature into a selected face.
- Sweeps an open profile along an open/closed path.
- Adds a gusset/rib across a bend
- Corner relief
- Welds the selected corner

The SURFACES Toolbar

- Creates mid surfaces between offset face pairs.
- Patches surface holes and external edges.
- Creates an extruded surface.
- Creates a revolved surface.
- Creates a swept surface.
- Creates a lofted surface.
- Creates an offset surface.
- Radiates a surface originating from a curve, parallel to a plane.
- Knits surfaces together.
- Creates a planar surface from a sketch or A set of edges.
- Creates a surface by importing data from a file.
- Extends a surface.
- Trims a surface.
- Surface flatten
- Deletes Face(s).
- Replaces Face with Surface.
- Patches surface holes and external edges by extending the surfaces.
- Creates parting surfaces between core & cavity surfaces.
- Inserts ruled surfaces from edges.

The WELDMENTS Toolbar

- Creates a weldment feature.
- Creates a structure member feature.
- Adds a gusset feature between 2 planar adjoining faces.
- Creates an end cap feature.
- Adds a fillet weld bead feature.
- Trims or extends structure members.
- Weld bead.

The DIMENSIONS/RELATIONS Toolbar

- Inserts dimension between two lines.
- Creates a horizontal dimension between selected entities.
- Creates a vertical dimension between selected entities.
- Creates a reference dimension between selected entities.
- Creates a set of ordinate dimensions.
- Creates a set of Horizontal ordinate dimensions.
- Creates a set of Vertical ordinate dimensions.
- Creates a chamfer dimension.
- Adds a geometric relation.
- Automatically Adds Dimensions to the current sketch.
- Displays and deletes geometric relations.
- Fully defines a sketch.
- Scans a sketch for elements of equal length or radius.
- Angular Running dimension
- Display / Delete dimension.
- Isolate changed dimension.
- Path length dimension.

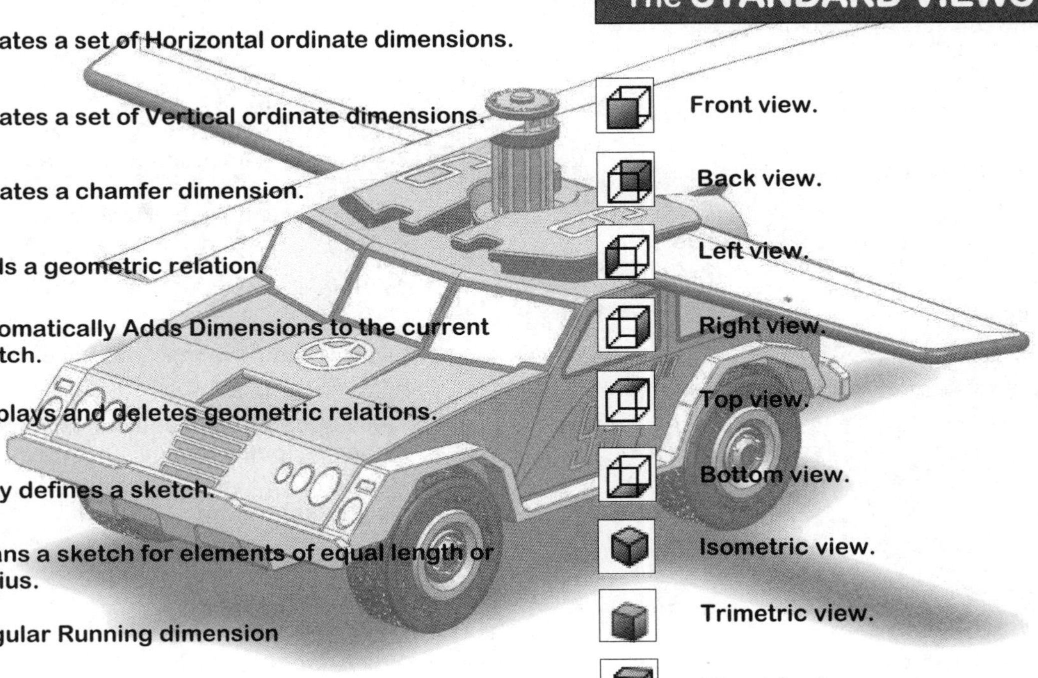

The BLOCK Toolbar

- Makes a new block.
- Edits the selected block.
- Inserts a new block to a sketch or drawing.
- Adds/Removes sketch entities to/from blocks.
- Updates parent sketches effected by this block.
- Saves the block to a file.
- Explodes the selected block.
- Inserts a belt.

The STANDARD VIEWS

- Front view.
- Back view.
- Left view.
- Right view.
- Top view.
- Bottom view.
- Isometric view.
- Trimetric view.
- Dimetric view.
- Normal to view.
- Links all views in the viewport together.
- Displays viewport with front & right views
- Displays a 4 view viewport with 1st or 3rd Angle of projection.
- Displays viewport with front & top
- Displays viewport with a single
- View selector.
- New view.

The **FEATURES** Toolbar

- Creates a boss feature by extruding a sketched profile.
- Creates a revolved feature based on profile and angle parameter.
- Creates a cut feature by extruding a sketched profile.
- Creates a cut feature by revolving a sketched profile.
- Thread
- Creates a cut by sweeping a closed profile along an open or closed path.
- Loft cut
- Creates a cut by thickening one or more adjacent surfaces.
- Adds a deformed surface by push or pull on
- Creates a lofted feature between two or more profiles.
- Creates a solid feature by thickening one or more adjacent surfaces.
- Creates a filled feature.
- Chamfers an edge or a chain of tangent edges.
- Inserts a rib feature.
- Combine.
- Creates a shell feature.
- Applies draft to a selected surface.
- Creates a cylindrical hole.
- Inserts a hole with a pre-defined cross section.
- Puts a dome surface on a face.
- Model break view.
- Applies global deformation to solid or surface bodies.
- Wraps closed sketch contour(s) onto a face.
- Curve Driven pattern.
- Suppresses the selected feature or component.
- Un-suppresses the selected feature or component.
- Flexes solid and surface bodies
- Intersect
- Variable Patterns
- Live Section Plane
- Mirrors.
- Scale.
- Creates a Sketch Driven pattern.
- Creates a Table Driven Pattern.
- Inserts a split Feature.
- Hole series.
- Joins bodies from one or more parts into a single part in the context of an assembly.
- Deletes a solid or a surface.
- Instant 3D
- Inserts a part from file into the active part document.
- Moves/Copies solid and surface bodies or moves graphics bodies.
- Merges short edges on faces
- Pushes solid / surface model by another solid / surface model
- Moves face(s) of a solid
- FeatureWorks Options.
- Linear Pattern.
- Fill Pattern.
- Cuts a solid model with a surface.
- Boundary Boss/Base
- Boundary Cut
- Circular Pattern
- Recognize Features
- Grid System

The MOLD TOOLS Toolbar

- Extracts core(s) from existing tooling split
- Constructs a surface patch
- Moves face(s) of a solid
- Creates offset surfaces.
- Inserts cavity into a base part.
- Scales a model by a specified factor.
- Applies draft to a selected surface.
- Inserts a split line feature.
- Creates parting lines to separate core & cavity surfaces
- Finds & creates mold shut-off surfaces
- Creates a planar surface from a sketch or a set of edges.
- Knits surfaces together.
- Inserts ruled surfaces from edges.
- Creates parting surfaces between core & cavity surfaces
- Creates multiple bodies from a single body.
- Inserts a tooling split feature.
- Creates parting surfaces between the core & cavity.
- Inserts surface body folders for mold operation.

The SELECTION FILTERS

- Turns selection filters on and off.
- Clears all filters.
- Selects all filters.
- Inverts current selection.

The SELECTION FILTERS cont.

- Allows selection of edges only.
- Allows selection filter for vertices only.
- Allows selection of faces only.
- Adds filter for Surface Bodies.
- Adds filter for Solid Bodies.
- Adds filter for Axes.
- Adds filter for Planes.
- Adds filter for Sketch Points.
- Allows selection for sketch only.
- Adds filter for Sketch Segments.
- Adds filter for Midpoints.
- Adds filter for Center Marks.
- Adds filter for Centerline.
- Adds filter for Dimensions and Hole Callouts.
- Adds filter for Surface Finish Symbols.
- Adds filter for Geometric Tolerances.
- Adds filter for Notes / Balloons.
- Adds filter for Weld Symbols.
- Adds filter for Weld beads.
- Adds filter for Datum Targets.
- Adds filter for Datum feature only.
- Adds filter for blocks.
- Adds filter for Cosmetic Threads.

Adds filter for Dowel pin symbols.

Adds filter for connection points.

Adds filter for routing points.

The SOLIDWORKS Add-Ins Toolbar

Loads/unloads CircuitWorks add-in.

Loads/unloads the Design Checker add-in.

Loads/unloads the PhotoView 360 add-in.

Loads/unloads the Scan-to-3D add-in.

Loads/unloads the SOLIDWORKS Motions add-in.

Loads/unloads the SOLIDWORKS Routing add-in.

Loads/unloads the SOLIDWORKS Simulation add-in.

Loads/unloads the SOLIDWORKS Toolbox add-in.

Loads/unloads the SOLIDWORKS TolAnalysis add-in.

Loads/unloads the SOLIDWORKS Flow Simulation add-in.

Loads/unloads the SOLIDWORKS Plastics add-in.

Loads/unloads the SOLIDWORKS MBD SNL license.

The FASTENING FEATURES

Creates a parameterized mounting boss.

Creates a parameterized snap hook.

Creates a groove to mate with a hook feature.

Uses sketch elements to create a vent for air flow.

Creates a lip/groove feature.

The SCREEN CAPTURE Toolbar

Copies the current graphics window to the clipboard.

Records the current graphics window to an AVI file.

Stops recording the current graphics window to an AVI file.

The EXPLODE LINE SKETCH

Adds a route line that connect entities.

Adds a jog to the route lines.

The LINE FORMAT Toolbar

Changes layer properties.

Changes the current document layer.

Changes line color.

Changes line thickness.

Changes line style.

Hides / Shows a hidden edge.

Changes line display mode.

Did you know??

* Ctrl+Q will force a rebuild on all features of a part.

* Ctrl+B will rebuild the feature being worked on and its dependants.

The 2D-To-3D Toolbar

Makes a Front sketch from the selected entities.

Makes a Top sketch from the selected entities.

Makes a Right sketch from the selected entities.

Makes a Left sketch from the selected entities.

Makes a Bottom sketch from the selected entities.

Makes a Back sketch from the selected entities.

Makes an Auxiliary sketch from the selected entities.

Creates a new sketch from the selected entities.

Repairs the selected sketch.

Aligns a sketch to the selected point.

Creates an extrusion from the selected sketch segments, starting at the selected sketch point.

Creates a cut from the selected sketch segments, optionally starting at the selected sketch point.

The ALIGN Toolbar

Aligns the left side of the selected annotations with the leftmost annotation.

Aligns the right side of the selected annotations with the rightmost annotation.

Aligns the top side of the selected annotations with the topmost annotation.

Aligns the bottom side of the selected annotations with the lowermost annotation.

Evenly spaces the selected annotations horizontally.

Evenly spaces the selected annotations vertically.

Centrally aligns the selected annotations horizontally.

Centrally aligns the selected annotations vertically.

Compacts the selected annotations horizontally.

Compacts the selected annotations vertically.

Creates a group from the selected items

Deletes the grouping between these items

Aligns & groups selected dimensions along a line or an arc

Aligns & groups dimensions at a uniform distances

Evenly spaces selected dimensions.

Aligns collinear selected dimensions.

Aligns stagger selected dimensions.

The SOLIDWORKD MBD Toolbar

Captures 3D view.

Manages 3D PDF templates

Creates shareable 3D PDF presentations

Toggles dynamic annotation views.

The MACRO Toolbar

Runs a Macro.

Stops Macro recorder.

Records (or pauses recording of) actions to create a Macro.

Launches the Macro Editor and begins editing a new macro.

Opens a Macro file for editing.

Creates a custom macro.

The SMARTMATES icons

Concentric & Coincident 2 circular edges

Concentric 2 cylindrical faces

Coincident 2 linear edges

Coincident 2 planar faces

Coincident 2 vertices

Coincident 2 origins or coordinate systems

The TABLE Toolbar

- Adds a hole table of selected holes from a specified origin datum.
- Adds a Bill of Materials.
- Adds a revision table.
- Displays a Design table in a drawing.
- Adds a weldments cuts list table.
- Adds a Excel based of Bill of Materials
- Adds a weldment cut list table

The REFERENCE GEOMETRY

- Adds a reference plane
- Creates an axis.
- Creates a coordinate system.
- Adds the center of mass.
- Specifies entities to use as references using SmartMates.

The SPLINE TOOLS Toolbar

- Inserts a point to a spline.
- Displays all points where the concavity of selected spline changes.
- Displays minimum radius of selected spline.
- Displays curvature combs of selected spline.
- Reduces numbers of points in a selected spline.
- Adds a tangency control.
- Adds a curvature control.
- Adds a spline based on selected sketch entities & edges.
- Displays the spline control polygon.

The ANNOTATIONS Toolbar

- Inserts a note.
- Inserts a surface finish symbol.
- Inserts a new geometric tolerancing symbol.
- Attaches a balloon to the selected edge or face.
- Adds balloons for all components in selected view.
- Inserts a stacked balloon.
- Attaches a datum feature symbol to a selected edge / detail.
- Inserts a weld symbol on the selected edge / face / vertex.
- Inserts a datum target symbol and / or point attached to a selected edge / line.
- Selects and inserts block.
- Inserts annotations & reference geometry from the part / assembly into the selected.
- Adds center marks to circles on model.
- Inserts a Centerline.
- Inserts a hole callout.
- Adds a cosmetic thread to the selected cylindrical feature.
- Inserts a Multi-Jog leader.
- Selects a circular edge or and arc for Dowel pin symbol insertion.
- Adds a view location symbol.
- Inserts latest version symbol.
- Adds a cross hatch patterns or solid fill.
- Adds a weld bead caterpillar on an edge.
- Adds a weld symbol on a selected entity.
- Inserts a revision cloud.
- Inserts a magnetic line.
- Hides/shows annotation.

The DRAWINGS Toolbar

- Updates the selected view to the model's current stage.
- Creates a detail view.
- Creates a section view.
- Inserts an Alternate Position view.
- Unfolds a new view from an existing view.
- Generates a standard 3-view drawing (1st or 3rd angle).
- Inserts an auxiliary view of an inclined surface.
- Adds an Orthogonal or Named view based on an existing part or assembly.
- Adds a Relative view by two orthogonal faces or planes.
- Adds a Predefined orthogonal projected or Named view with a model.
- Adds an empty view.
- Adds vertical break lines to selected view.
- Crops a view.
- Creates a Broken-out section.

The QUICK SNAP Toolbar

- Snap to points.
- Snap to center points.
- Snap to midpoints.
- Snap to quadrant points.
- Snap to intersection of 2 curves.
- Snap to nearest curve.
- Snap tangent to curve.
- Snap perpendicular to curve.
- Snap parallel to line.
- Snap horizontally / vertically to points.
- Snap horizontally / vertically.
- Snap to discrete line lengths.
- Snap to angle.

The LAYOUT Toolbar

- Creates the assembly layout sketch.
- Sketches a line.
- Sketches a corner rectangle.
- Sketches a circle.
- Sketches a 3 point arc.
- Rounds a corner.
- Trims or extends a sketch.
- Adds sketch entities by offsetting faces, Edges curves.
- Mirrors selected entities about a centerline.
- Adds a relation.
- Creates a dimension.
- Displays / Deletes geometric relations.
- Makes a new block.
- Edits the selected block.
- Inserts a new block to the sketch or drawing.
- Adds / Removes sketch entities to / from a block.
- Saves the block to a file.
- Explodes the selected block.
- Creates a new part from a layout sketch block.
- Positions 2 components relative to one another.

The CURVES Toolbar

- Projects sketch onto selected surface.
- Inserts a split line feature.
- Creates a composite curve from selected edges, curves and sketches.
- Creates a curve through free points.
- Creates a 3D curve through reference points.
- Helical curve defined by a base sketch and shape parameters.

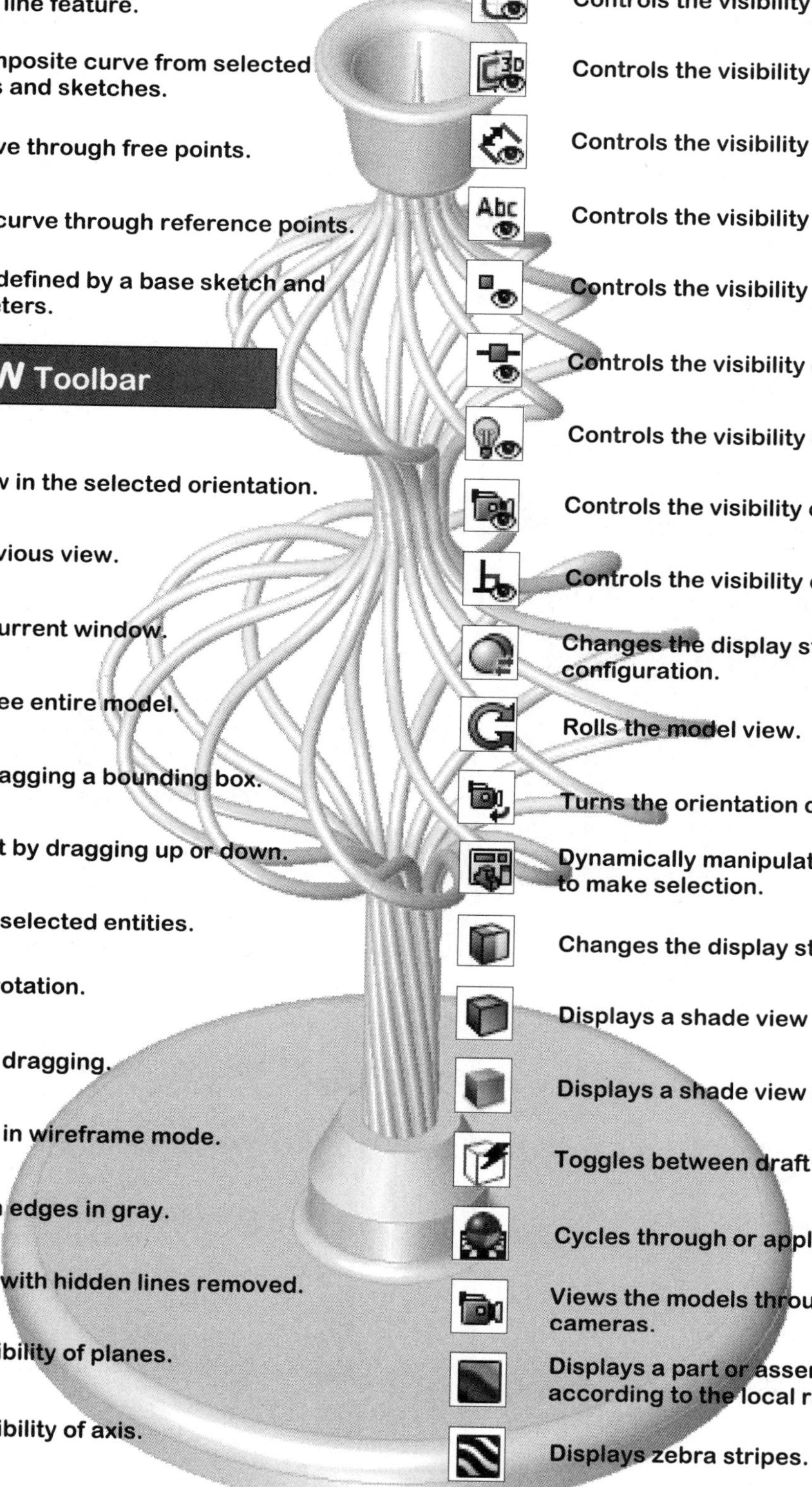

The VIEW Toolbar

- Displays a view in the selected orientation.
- Reverts to previous view.
- Redraws the current window.
- Zooms out to see entire model.
- Zooms in by dragging a bounding box.
- Zooms in or out by dragging up or down.
- Zooms to fit all selected entities.
- Dynamic view rotation.
- Scrolls view by dragging.
- Displays image in wireframe mode.
- Displays hidden edges in gray.
- Displays image with hidden lines removed.
- Controls the visibility of planes.
- Controls the visibility of axis.
- Controls the visibility of parting lines.
- Controls the visibility of temporary axis.
- Controls the visibility of origins.
- Controls the visibility of coordinate systems.
- Controls the visibility of reference curves.
- Controls the visibility of sketches.
- Controls the visibility of 3D sketch planes.
- Controls the visibility of 3D sketch
- Controls the visibility of all annotations.
- Controls the visibility of reference points.
- Controls the visibility of routing points.
- Controls the visibility of lights.
- Controls the visibility of cameras.
- Controls the visibility of sketch relations.
- Changes the display state for the current configuration.
- Rolls the model view.
- Turns the orientation of the model view.
- Dynamically manipulate the model view in 3D to make selection.
- Changes the display style for the active view.
- Displays a shade view of the model with its edges.
- Displays a shade view of the model.
- Toggles between draft quality & high quality HLV.
- Cycles through or applies a specific scene.
- Views the models through one of the model's cameras.
- Displays a part or assembly w/different colors according to the local radius of curvature.
- Displays zebra stripes.
- Displays a model with hardware accelerated shades.
- Applies a cartoon affect to model edges & faces
- Views simulations symbols

The TOOLS Toolbar

- Calculates the distance between selected items.
- Adds or edits equation.
- Calculates the mass properties of the model.
- Checks the model for geometry errors.
- Inserts or edits a Design Table.
- Evaluates section properties for faces and sketches that lie in parallel planes.
- Reports Statistics for this Part/Assembly.
- Deviation Analysis.
- Runs the SimulationXpress analysis wizard Powered by SOLIDWORKS Simulation.
- Checks the spelling.
- Import diagnostics.
- Runs the DFMXpress analysis wizard.
- Runs the SOLIDWORKSFloXpress analysis wizard.

The ASSEMBLY Toolbar

- Creates a new part & inserts it into the assembly.
- Adds an existing part or sub-assembly to the assembly.
- Creates a new assembly & inserts it into the assembly.
- Turns on/off large assembly mode for this document.
- Hides / shows model(s) associated with the selected model(s).
- Toggles the transparency of components.
- Changes the selected components to suppressed or resolved.
- Inserts a belt.
- Toggles between editing part and assembly.
- Smart Fasteners.
- Positions two components relative to one another.
- External references will not be created.
- Moves a component.
- Rotates an un-mated component around its center point.
- Replaces selected components.
- Replaces mate entities of mates of the selected components on the selected Mates group.
- Creates a New Exploded view.
- Creates or edits explode line sketch.
- Interference detection.
- Shows or Hides the Simulation toolbar.
- Patterns components in one or two linear directions.
- Patterns components around an axis.
- Sets the transparency of the components other than the one being edited
- Sketch driven component pattern.
- Pattern driven component pattern.
- Curve driven component pattern
- Chain driven component pattern
- SmartMates by dragging & dropping components
- Checks assembly hole alignments.
- Mirrors subassemblies and parts.

To add or remove an icon
to or from the toolbar, first select:
Tools/Customize/Commands
Next, select a **Category**, click a button to see its description and then drag/drop the command icon into any toolbar.

SOLIDWORKS Quick-Guide©

Standard Keyboard Shortcuts

Rotate the model

* Horizontally or Vertically: ______ Arrow keys
* Horizontally or Vertically 90°: ______ Shift + Arrow keys
* Clockwise or Counterclockwise: ______ Alt + left or right Arrow
* Pan the model: ______ Ctrl + Arrow keys
* Zoom in: ______ Z (shift + Z or capital Z)
* Zoom out: ______ z (lower case z)
* Zoom to fit: ______ F
* Previous view: ______ Ctrl+Shift+Z

View Orientation

* View Orientation Menu: ______ Space bar
* Front: ______ Ctrl+1
* Back: ______ Ctrl+2
* Left: ______ Ctrl+3
* Right: ______ Ctrl+4
* Top: ______ Ctrl+5
* Bottom: ______ Ctrl+6
* Isometric: ______ Ctrl+7

Selection Filter & Misc.

* Filter Edges: ______ e
* Filter Vertices: ______ v
* Filter Faces: ______ x
* Toggle Selection filter toolbar: ______ F5
* Toggle Selection Filter toolbar (on/off): ______ F6
* New SOLIDWORKS document: ______ F1
* Open Document: ______ Ctrl+O
* Open from Web folder: ______ Ctrl+W
* Save: ______ Ctrl+S
* Print: ______ Ctrl+P
* Magnifying Glass Zoom ______ g
* Switch between the SOLIDWORKS documents ______ Ctrl + Tab

SOLIDWORKS Quick-Guide

SOLIDWORKS Keyboard Shortcuts

SOLIDWORKS Quick-Guide©

Sample Customized Keyboard Shortcuts

SOLIDWORKS Sample Customized **Hot Keys**

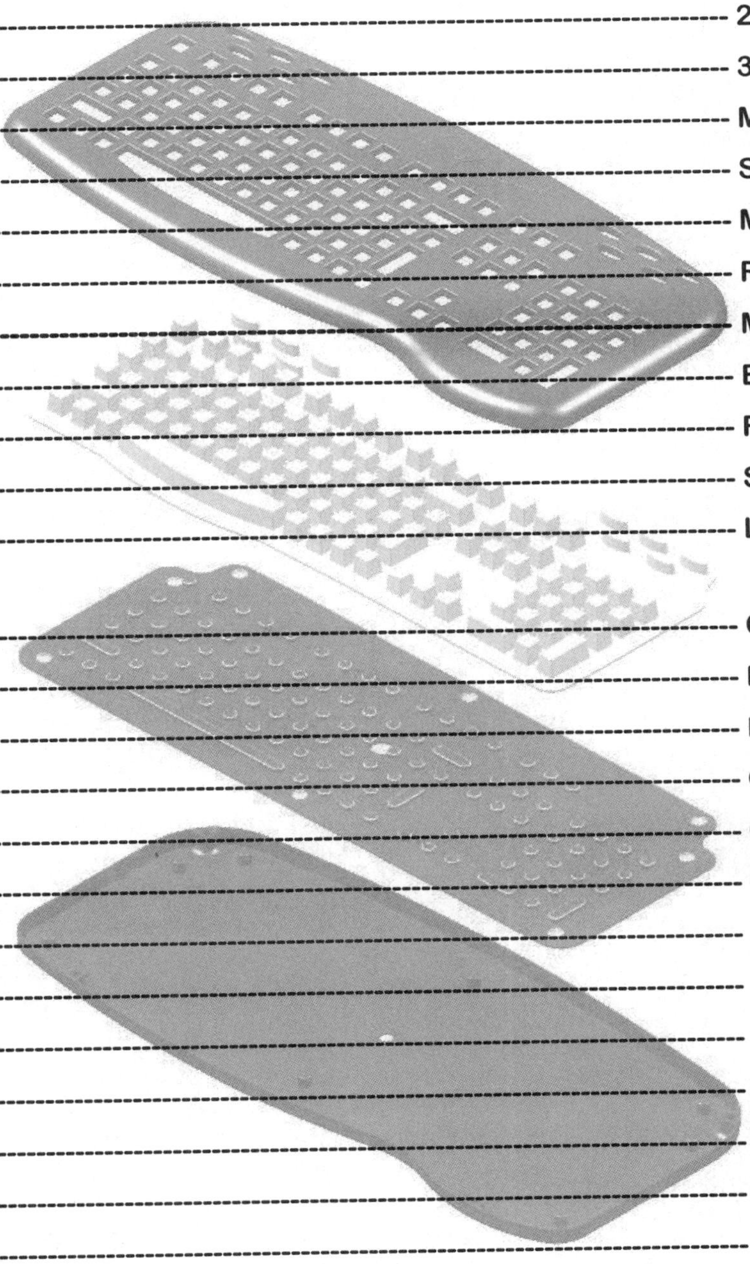

Function Keys

F1	SW-Help
F2	2D Sketch
F3	3D Sketch
F4	Modify
F5	Selection Filters
F6	Move (2D Sketch)
F7	Rotate (2D Sketch)
F8	Measure
F9	Extrude
F10	Revolve
F11	Sweep
F12	Loft

Sketch

C	Circle
P	Polygon
E	Ellipse
O	Offset Entities
Alt + C	Convert Entities
M	Mirror
Alt + M	Dynamic Mirror
Alt + F	Sketch Fillet
T	Trim
Alt + X	Extend
D	Smart Dimension
Alt + R	Add Relation
Alt + P	Plane
Control + F	Fully Define Sketch
Control + Q	Exit Sketch

SOLIDWORKS Quick-Guide by Paul Tran – Sr. Certified SOLIDWORKS Instructor